SILVER BURDETT
EARTH SCIENCE

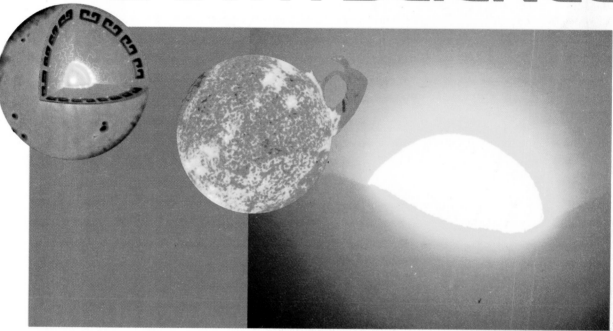

Series Authors

Peter Alexander, Ph.D.
Professor of Biology and Computer Science
St. Peter's College
Jersey City, New Jersey

Marilyn Fiegel, Ed.D.
Science Coordinator
West Seneca High School
West Seneca, New York

Steven K. Foehr
Teacher of Science
Wickford Middle School
North Kingston, Rhode Island

Anne F. Harris
Environmental Scientist
Black and Veatch, Engineers/Architects
Kansas City, Missouri

Joseph G. Krajkovich, Ed.D.
Supervisor of Science
Edison Twp. Board of Education
Edison, New Jersey

Kenneth W. May
Chairperson, Science Department
Camden Central School
Camden, New York

Nicholas Tzimopoulos, Ph.D.
Director of Science
Sleepy Hollow High School
North Tarrytown, New York

Rita K. Voltmer, Ph.D.
Assistant Professor of Science Education
Miami University
Oxford, Ohio

SILVER BURDETT COMPANY   MORRISTOWN, NJ
Atlanta, GA • Cincinnati, OH • Dallas, TX • Northfield, IL • San Carlos, CA • Agincourt, Ontario

Content Reviewers

Edmund Bertschinger, Ph.D.
Department of Astronomy
University of California
Berkeley, California

John E. Callahan, Ph.D.
Geology Department
Appalachian State University
Boone, North Carolina

Herndon G. Dowling, Ph.D.
Professor of Biology
New York University
New York, New York

W. Michael Mogil
Science Consultant
Burtonsville, Maryland

John V. Thiruvathukal, Ph.D.
Associate Professor of Geoscience
Physics-Geoscience Department
Montclair State College
Upper Montclair, New Jersey

Teacher Reviewers

Donald L. Birdd, Ph.D.
Science Educator
Geosciences, Physics and
Interdisciplinary Sciences
State University College at Buffalo
Buffalo, New York

William E. Buenting
Chairperson, Science Department
Park Junior High School
Antioch, California

Judith Camosso
American Overseas School of Rome
Rome, Italy

Genoveva Cantu
Maestra de Ciencias y Matematicas
Escuela Intermedia Washington
Yakima, Washington

Teresa T. Chavez
Madison Middle School
Albuquerque, New Mexico

C.W. Chism
Chairperson, Science Department
Madison Consolidated
Junior High School
Madison, Indiana

Toni Lynne DeVore
Chairperson, Science
Washington Junior High School
Parkersburg, West Virginia

Michael S. Goodrich
Earth Science Teacher
Lake Oswego High School
Lake Oswego, Oregon

Cheryl Hollingshead
Chairperson,
Junior High Science Department
Lake Hamilton Junior High School
Pearcy, Arkansas

John Kominski
Assistant Director of Science
New York City Board of Education
New York, New York

William E. Martin
Chairperson, Science Department
Mundy's Mill Junior High School
Jonesboro, Georgia

Mary Nalbandian
Director of Science
Chicago Public Schools
Chicago, Illinois

Harry F. Pomeroy, Jr.
Chairperson, Science Department
Yucca Junior High School
Clovis, New Mexico

Louis G. Salvio
Chairperson, Science Department
William H. Hall High School
West Hartford, Connecticut

Martin Jay Steinbaum, Ph.D.
Executive Director, Planetarium
Space Science Instructor of the
City School District of New Rochelle
New Rochelle, New York

Ovid K. Wong, Ph.D.
Science Curriculum Specialist
School District #65
Evanston, Illinois

About the Cover
The front cover shows the sun on the horizon. Images of the sun, showing its surface and its internal structure, are shown on the back cover. See Chapter 4, sections 4-3 and 4-4, for more information on the nature of the sun.

Contents

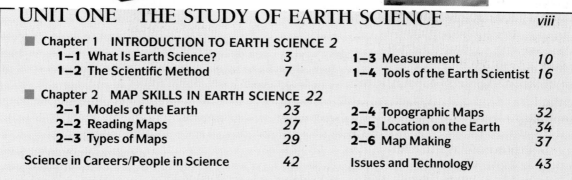

Activities

THE STUDY OF EARTH SCIENCE

What causes earthquakes and volcanoes? Why do hurricanes and tornadoes form? What is the earth made of? How did the earth and the other planets get here? What are black holes? Why did the dinosaurs die out? These and hundreds of other questions are what earth science is all about. In this unit you will study the skills needed to be an earth scientist. ■

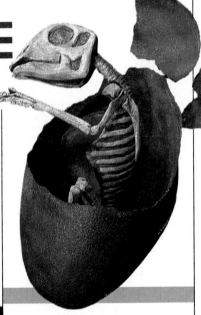

▲ Fossil of a baby dinosaur, from the late Cretaceous period, hatching from an egg.

▲ Two tectonic plates are separating at the Mid-Atlantic Ridge, causing this volcano. As the volcano rose out of the sea it formed the island Surtsey, off the Iceland coast, in 1963.

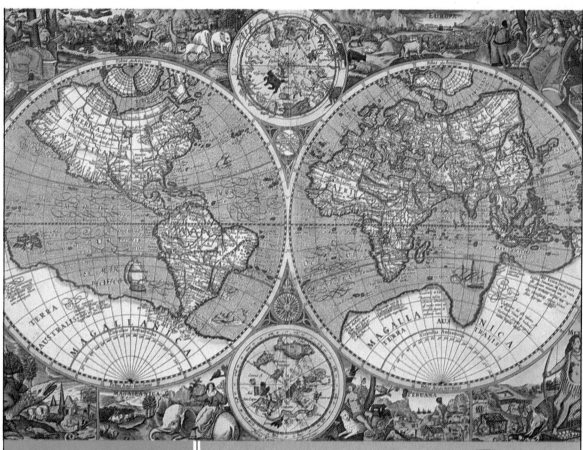

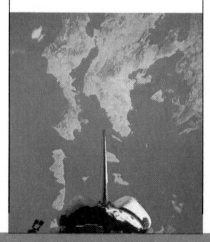

▼ *A camera attached to the nose of the space shuttle photographed the Mediterranean Sea* (below).

▲ *Pieter van der Keere's 1607 map of the world.*

▶ *Gerhardus Mercator 512–94) was a famous map and globe maker* (right).

▼ *The globe he made in 1541*

INTRODUCTION TO EARTH SCIENCE

This photoghaph, taken by the Voyager 2 spacecraft, shows the view an astronaut might have as he or she approached the planet Uranus. A section of one of the moons of Uranus, Miranda, is in front of the planet. Uranus is surrounded by dark rings, which have been drawn in on the photograph. Investigating other world's is part of the work of earth scientists.

- *What color is the atmosphere of Uranus?*
- *What gases might make up the atmosphere?*
- *What is the ring system made of?*
- *How did the surface of Miranda become cratered?*

1-1 WHAT IS EARTH SCIENCE?

Many scientists think that the amount of carbon dioxide gas in the air is increasing. They believe that such an increase will cause the air temperature of the earth to rise. Carbon dioxide causes air around the earth to act like the glass panels in a greenhouse. This gas, which makes up less than 0.1 percent of air, allows sunlight to pass through the air to the earth. But it blocks heat from passing from the earth into space. The increasing temperature resulting from increasing carbon dioxide in the air is called the *greenhouse effect.* What changes, do you predict, will occur if the air temperature around the earth increases?

The idea that the earth's air temperature is increasing is part of science. **Science** is a way of obtaining knowledge about nature. The earth, space, living things, and nonliving things are all part of nature. *Scientists,* people who study nature, obtain knowledge about nature by making observations and experimenting.

Earth science is the branch of science that studies the earth and space. Did you know that a star has a life cycle, like a plant or an animal? Did you know that the continents move? Even the rocks that make up the con-

> After completing this section, you will be able to
>
> - **define** the term *science.*
> - **define** the term *earth science.*
> - **define** *technology* and give two examples of it.
> - **identify** the branches of earth science.
>
> The key terms in this section are
> earth science   technology
> science

scientia (knowledge)

tinents change as they age. The earth's climate, too, changes through time. Such changes continue today, and the study of such changes belongs to earth science.

Knowledge from earth science is useful in many ways. For example, earth scientists are learning how to predict dangerous natural events, such as earthquakes, storms, and tidal waves. Knowledge of the earth's structure helps people locate minerals and energy sources. An understanding of droughts and floods may lead to methods of preventing them or making them less harmful. Also, an understanding of the earth's past is helpful in predicting the earth's future.

Often, knowledge from earth science is used to make life better or easier for people. The use of knowledge from science in an attempt to improve the quality of human life is called **technology** (tehk NAHL uh jee). There are many examples of technology in earth science.

techne (art)
-logy (study of)

Figure 1-1

Events in nature that earth scientists study include volcanic eruptions (*left, and top right*), storms (*top center*), and earthquakes (*bottom*).

Figure 1-2

A satellite photograph of a landscape in Alaska clearly shows mountains and glaciers.

One example of technology results from studies by earth scientists of what causes raindrops to form. Based on these studies, scientists have searched for ways to produce rain over parts of the earth that receive almost none. One method of producing rain is called cloud seeding. A cloud is seeded by dropping small pieces of silver iodide or small pieces of frozen carbon dioxide into the air. These pieces aid the growth of raindrops. This method of producing rain has had some success. But some earth scientists are concerned that adding new chemicals to the air may affect living things. Others wonder if changing where rain falls will affect weather in other places. Permanent changes in climate would affect the environment.

Another example of technology is based on studies of gravity and the movement of the planets around the sun. From these studies, earth scientists have learned how to keep artificial satellites in orbit around the earth. Today, many such satellites orbit the earth. These satellites follow weather patterns, search for mineral deposits, locate fish in the oceans, and study drought areas. They are also used for communications around the earth. What kinds of information can be obtained from the satellite photograph shown in Figure 1-2?

Earth science is divided into different branches. *Geology* is the study of the composition, structure, and history of the earth. *Astronomy* (uh STRAHN uh mee) is the study of space and the heavenly bodies. *Meteorology* (mee-tee uh RAHL uh jee) is the study of the atmosphere. *Oceanography* is the study of the oceans. *Paleontology* (pay lee-ahn TAHL uh jee) is the study of ancient living things, based on fossil evidence. These five branches combined form the science called earth science. Figure 1-3 shows earth scientists involved in different kinds of investigations. Identify the major branch of earth science that each scientist shown is working in.

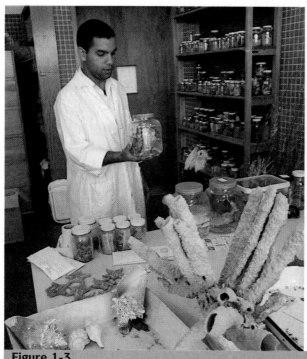

Figure 1-3

Earth scientists may be involved in studying life forms of the sea (*left*), effects of pollution on the earth's water (*top right*), and patterns of circulation in the atmosphere and oceans (*bottom right*).

REVIEW

1. What is science?
2. What is earth science?
3. How are technology and science related?
4. Which of the following branches of science belong to earth science: astronomy, biology, chemistry, geology, meteorology, neurology, oceanography, paleontology?

CHALLENGE Studies in oceanography and other sciences are allowing people to obtain minerals and energy resources from the sea. How might such technology benefit people? What possible drawbacks of such technology can you identify?

1-2 THE SCIENTIFIC METHOD

Scientists are problem solvers. They search for answers to questions about nature. Their list of unanswered questions is endless. For the earth scientist, the questions may range from How is the magnetic field of the earth produced? to What is the nature of objects at the outer edge of the universe? What kinds of questions might the scientist in Figure 1-4 ask?

Scientists try to understand nature. The **scientific method** describes the way that scientists gather information and test ideas about nature. The scientific method is not one set of steps to follow, like those in a recipe for a cake. It is a logical approach to solving a puzzle. Scientists bring their knowledge and experiences to the puzzles of nature. When you use your knowledge and experience in an attempt to solve a problem in a logical way, you are using the scientific method. The scientific method has four key processes.

Figure 1-4

A paleontologist reconstructing the fossil of a turtle.

You learned about a change that is taking place on the earth. This change is an increase in the amount of carbon dioxide in the air. Scientists discovered this change through observations, a process in the scientific method. An **observation** is an examination of some part of nature.

Observations often lead scientists to ask questions. One question an earth scientist would ask about the increasing level of carbon dioxide is, "What effect will this change have on the earth?" An earth scientist who is interested in this question would make more observations.

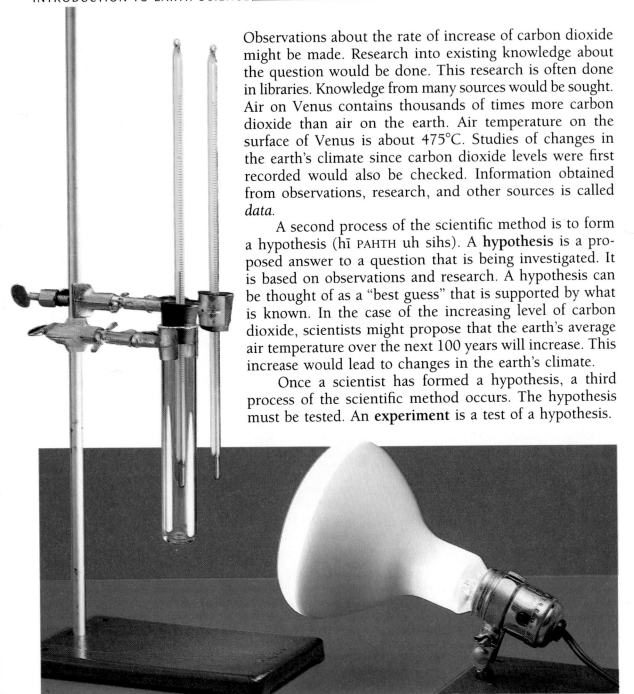

Observations about the rate of increase of carbon dioxide might be made. Research into existing knowledge about the question would be done. This research is often done in libraries. Knowledge from many sources would be sought. Air on Venus contains thousands of times more carbon dioxide than air on the earth. Air temperature on the surface of Venus is about 475°C. Studies of changes in the earth's climate since carbon dioxide levels were first recorded would also be checked. Information obtained from observations, research, and other sources is called *data*.

A second process of the scientific method is to form a hypothesis (hī PAHTH uh sihs). A **hypothesis** is a proposed answer to a question that is being investigated. It is based on observations and research. A hypothesis can be thought of as a "best guess" that is supported by what is known. In the case of the increasing level of carbon dioxide, scientists might propose that the earth's average air temperature over the next 100 years will increase. This increase would lead to changes in the earth's climate.

Once a scientist has formed a hypothesis, a third process of the scientific method occurs. The hypothesis must be tested. An **experiment** is a test of a hypothesis.

Figure 1-5

To determine the effect of carbon dioxide on air temperature, an experiment like this could be set up. Suppose the test tube contains air with a concentration of carbon dioxide twice that of the atmosphere. What should be added to this set up to act as a control?

In most cases, an experiment has two parts. One part, or group, is called the *control*, or *control group*. The other part, or group, is called the *experimental group*. The two groups differ in one way. A condition that makes the experimental group different from the control group is called a *variable*. When the experiment is done, the scientist can decide if the variable affects the experiment.

An earth scientist studying the effect of carbon dioxide on air temperature might build a structure to use in the experiment. Each condition—such as available water, the composition of the air, the composition of the soil, and the living things in the structure—would be regulated, or controlled. The experimental group would be the same as the control group, except that the carbon dioxide level would be higher in the experimental group. What would the variable be in this experiment? During the experiment, air temperature would be measured. Any other differences between the two groups would be recorded. Any difference in temperature between the experimental group and the control group should be caused by the increase in carbon dioxide. The level of carbon dioxide is the only condition that differs in the two groups.

Another process in the scientific method is to make a conclusion. A **conclusion** states whether or not the evidence supports the hypothesis. In our example, if the air temperature was higher in the experimental group, there is evidence that the amount of carbon dioxide in air affects air's temperature. It is very important that scientists publish their results. Other scientists will be working on the same problem. They must be able to learn about the results. Also, scientists repeat each other's work to check the accuracy.

The scientific method is not always followed in the exact order listed. For example, if the results of an experiment are different than expected, a scientist may design a new experiment based on the unexpected result. In this case, the scientist would not repeat the research.

Scientists accept a hypothesis only when it has been tested many times and when it is supported by the results. A hypothesis may become a theory (THEE uhr ee). A **theory** is a hypothesis that has been tested many times and that is supported by evidence. A theory may be used to help explain other events in nature. In our example, the melting of a polar ice cap might be explained as a result of the increasing level of carbon dioxide and warming of the air.

Figure 1-6

Publication of experimental results allows scientists to communicate their findings.

REVIEW

1. What is the scientific method?
2. Explain the processes of the scientific method.
3. How does a hypothesis differ from a theory?

CHALLENGE Design an experiment to determine whether a covered pot of water boils faster than an uncovered pot of water.

1-3 MEASUREMENT

Imagine that you and a friend are at a pool. The air is warm. When you test the water with your foot, it feels cold. You tell your friend that the water is cold today. Your friend remarks that the water was really colder last week, but it feels colder today because the air is warm. Without a thermometer and a record of the water temperature, can you say who is right? Scientists carefully measure and record the properties of the things they study. They measure properties such as temperature, time, and distance. Measurements help to ensure that observations and data are accurate. Measurements are recorded so that they can be used and referred to in the future.

Now imagine that you are on your way to a market to buy some hamburger for supper. On your way, you pass advertisements for sales at two different stores. The first store is selling hamburger for $2.09 per pound. The second store is selling hamburger for $5.29 per stone. Which store has the best price? What do you need to know to answer that question?

To use a system of measurement, you must know the values of the units used in the system. A system of measurement has standards. A *standard* is a unit that serves as a basis for making certain measurements. The pound is a standard of weight. If an object has a weight of 5 pounds, then its weight is five times the standard amount.

Figure 1-7

Measurements in science may be made on lava flowing from the earth, and on energy from stars.

OBJECTIVES

Measure various objects and distances, using early kinds of standards.
Recognize the limitations of such standards.

PROCEDURE

A. Standards are made by people. They were not discovered by scientists or made just for scientists. They were developed so that people could communicate ideas about size with each other. Using the drawings as guides, describe each of the following early standards in your own words: digit, palm, span, cubit, fathom, foot, and pace.

B. Using the early standards, measure the following objects and places and record your measurements on your paper.
1. Your palm in digits.
2. Your span in palms.
3. Your cubit in spans.
4. The length of a pen or pencil in digits.
5. The length and width of this science book in palms.
6. The length and width of your desk in spans.

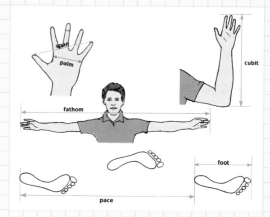

7. The width of the chalkboard in cubits.
8. The distance across 10 floor tiles in feet.
9. The distance across the room in paces.

RESULTS AND CONCLUSIONS

1. How do your measurements compare with those of your classmates?
2. Why is it important to standardize units so that everyone uses the same ones?

Standards are established and agreed to so that people can easily communicate ideas about size with each other. If you are told that a place is 20 miles away, you know that it is too far away for you to walk to that place easily. Hamburger on sale for $5.29 per stone may be a good buy. But the stone is not a familiar standard in this country. It does not tell you how much you are getting, because this country does not use that unit.

In the past, some standards were based on the lengths of people's hands, arms, and legs. These standards were convenient because measurements could be made quickly and a measurer was always close by. An item such as a piece of cloth or rope could be measured in yards. A yard was the distance between the nose and the tips of the fingers when the arm was outstretched. The distance between towns could be counted in paces. A pace is equal to a double step. What problems occur with a system of measurement based on such standards?

In France during the 1790s, a new system of measurement was introduced and then adopted into law. This sytem was called the metric system. A modern version of the metric system, called the International System of Mea-

Table 1-1 *Units of Measurement*

Measurement	Unit	Symbol
length	meter	m
mass	kilogram	kg
volume	liter	L
temperature	degree Celsius	°C
time	second	s

surement (SI), is used in science. What advantage is there in having scientists all over the world using the same system?

Four important units are the meter (m), kilogram (kg), liter (L), and second (s). These units can be made larger or smaller by multiplying or dividing them by 10 and multiples of 10. SI units use prefixes to describe how large or small a unit is. For example, *kilo-* means 1000. There are 1000 meters in a kilometer. Table 1-2 lists some common SI prefixes and their values. Generally, these prefixes are added to the unit names without changing the spelling of either the basic unit or the prefix. For example, 1/1000 of a liter is called a milliliter (milli- + liter). One thousand meters is called a kilometer. How many grams make up a kilogram? What fraction of a meter is a centimeter?

The **meter** (m) is the SI unit for measuring length or distance. A meter is slightly longer than a yard. Length is often measured with a meterstick. The numbers on a meterstick list centimeters (cm). The smallest spaces show

Table 1-2 *Prefixes For SI Units*

Prefix	Meaning	Symbol	Example
kilo-	one thousand	k	1 kilometer, or 1 km, is 1000 meters.
deci-	one tenth	d	1 decimeter, or 1 dm, is $\frac{1}{10}$ (0.1) of 1 meter.
centi-	one hundredth	c	1 centimeter, or 1 cm, is $\frac{1}{100}$ (.01) of 1 meter.
milli-	one thousandth	m	1 millimeter, or 1 mm, is $\frac{1}{1000}$ (.001) of 1 meter.
micro-	one millionth	μ	1 micrometer, or 1 μm, is $\frac{1}{1,000,000}$ (.000001) of 1 meter.

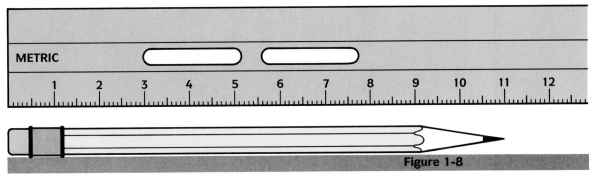

METRIC

Figure 1-8

Length can be measured in millimeters and centimeters.

millimeters (mm). There are 10 mm in 1 cm. In Figure 1-8, how long is the pencil?

The **kilogram** (kg) is the SI unit for measuring mass. **Mass** is a measure of the amount of matter in an object. Mass is different from weight. Weight is a measure of the force of gravity on something. Gravity is not constant from place to place. For example, the force of gravity is less on the moon than on the earth. Thus an object weighs less on the moon than on the earth. But the object's mass is the same in both places.

Mass is measured with a balance. A balance works like a seesaw. The material to be measured is placed on one pan. Objects of known mass are placed on the other pan until the pans balance. When the pans balance, the total mass of the known masses is equal to the mass of the material on the other pan.

ACTIVITY Measuring Length

OBJECTIVE
Measure various objects and distances in metric units.

MATERIALS
metric ruler, meterstick

PROCEDURE
A. Use a metric ruler to make the following measurements. Record the measurements.
   1. The width of your desk in centimeters.
   2. Your height in centimeters.
   3. The length of this book in millimeters.
   4. The length or width of the room in meters.
B. Using the measurements you made, make the following conversions.

1. What is the width of the desk in millimeters?
2. What is your height in meters?
3. What is the length of this book in centimeters?
4. What is the length or width of the room in centimeters?

RESULTS AND CONCLUSIONS
1. Why is it useful to have units of various sizes for measuring different-sized objects?
2. What metric unit would be useful for measuring distances between towns?

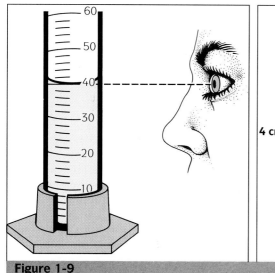

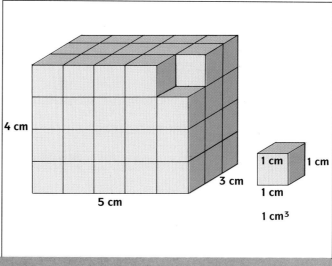

Figure 1-9

Note how to read the level of a fluid in a graduated cylinder (*left*). The volume of a regularly-shaped solid can be determined from its length, width, and height (*right*).

The **liter** (L) is a unit of volume. **Volume** is a measure of how much space something takes up. The volume of a liquid can be measured with a graduated cylinder, or graduate. Notice in Figure 1-9 that the surface of the liquid curves upward at the sides of the graduate. This curved surface is called a *meniscus* (muh NIHS kuhs). Read the mark that lines up with the bottom of the meniscus. What is the volume of the liquid in Figure 1-9?

The volume of a solid can be measured in two ways. If the solid has a regular shape, its dimensions can be used. The volume of a box, for example, can be measured by multiplying its three dimensions (volume = length × width × height). A box 3 cm by 5 cm by 4 cm has a volume of 60 cubic centimeters (cm^3), as shown in Figure 1-9. A volume of 1 cm^3 is equal to 1 mL. If a small solid object does not have a regular shape, its volume can be measured by placing it in a partially filled graduate. The amount of water the object displaces equals its volume.

SCIENCE PUZZLER

In SI, an accepted unit of volume is the cubic decimeter (dm^3). A decimeter is equal to one tenth of a meter. Recall that 1 cm^3 is equal to 1 mL. Using this information, show that 1L is equal to 1 dm^3.

Measuring Mass

OBJECTIVE
Measure the masses of various objects in metric units.

MATERIALS
balance and masses, forceps, variety of small objects

PROCEDURE
A. Examine the balance. Identify the parts by using the drawing as a guide.

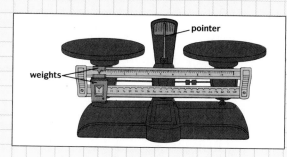

B. Notice the pointer and the scale in the center of the balance. The long line at the center of the scale is the zero point. When the pans are empty, the balance should be zeroed. The pointer should line up with the zero point. If the balance is not zeroed, use the adjustment knob to zero the balance.
C. Place one of the objects on the left pan. Add masses to the right pan until the balance is again zeroed. Your balance may have one or more small masses on the arm, or beam, to be used in determining the mass. Record the mass of the object.
D. Repeat step **C** for each object whose mass you are to determine.

RESULTS AND CONCLUSIONS
1. For each object whose mass you determined, give the mass in grams and in milligrams.
2. How would the results be affected if this activity were done on the moon?

The **degree Celsius** (°C) is a unit for measuring temperature. On a Celsius thermometer, water freezes at 0° and it boils at 100°. The temperature of a material is measured by placing a thermometer in the material for a period of time. The temperature is found by reading the number that lines up with the top of the liquid inside the thermometer. What is the temperature according to the thermometer shown in Figure 1-10? Normal room temperature is about 21°C, and normal body temperature is 37°C.

The **second** (s) is the SI unit for time. The existing system—of 60 seconds to a minute, 60 minutes to an hour, and 24 hours to a day—is already a universal system. In science, the prefix *milli-* is sometimes used with *second* in certain types of measurement.

REVIEW

1. Why is it important for scientists to make measurements?
2. What is the advantage of having standard units of measure?
3. Describe two ancient standards of measurement.
4. Identify the standard units of measurement used in science.

CHALLENGE How are the monetary systems of the United States and Canada similar to the metric system of measurement?

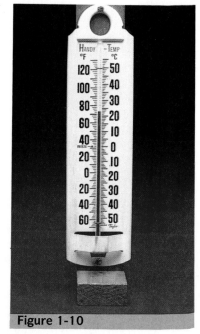

Figure 1-10

Temperature measurements can be made in degrees Celsius.

1-4 TOOLS OF THE EARTH SCIENTIST

After completing this section,
you will be able to

- **explain** why tools are useful in science.
- **describe** several tools used by earth scientists in their work.

As you sit outdoors on a pleasant day, your senses gather information. Your eyes gather light that tells you about the sizes, shapes, and colors of the things around you. They indicate how far away an object is and whether or not it is moving. Your ears detect sounds and your nose detects odors. You feel the warmth of the sun. Perhaps you feel the wind on your face. But are there things you cannot sense? Are there things you do not see? Are there sounds you do not hear?

Scientists use tools to observe things that their senses alone cannot detect. A microscope, for example, shows things that are too small for a person's eyes to see. High-speed cameras show things that happen too quickly to notice. Even a simple hammer can be used to find a fossil hidden inside a rock.

Earth scientists use microscopes for many reasons. Some scientists study crystals. Others study the fossils of spores, seeds, and tiny living things that once lived on the earth. Microscopes are also used to study tiny bits of rock and metal that strike the earth from space.

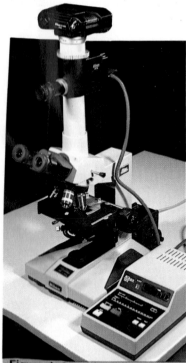
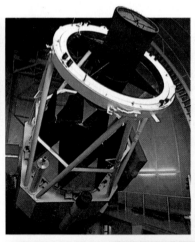

Figure 1-11

A microscope brings small items, such as pollen grains (*bottom*), into view. A telescope brings distant objects, such as another galaxy (top right), into view.

Supercomputers have enabled meteorologists to improve their forecasts. Like many other scientists, meteorologists use computers to make models of problems they want to solve. A weather model is made up of equations. Information about the atmosphere is turned into numbers and put into these equations.

In Massachusetts, the best meteorologists from many countries use the CRAY-MP, one of the fastest supercomputers. This machine can do over 100 million mathematical operations per second. Observations of the atmosphere from all over the world are continuously put into this computer's weather model. What results is a simulation of the weather over the globe up to 10 days in advance.

While supercomputers have increased the accuracy of general forecasts, forecasts concerning rapidly moving weather systems can be very inaccurate. By the time even a supercomputer has finished the calculations describing a short-term weather pattern, the weather may have changed.

Meteorologists may get help with a new type of computer now being developed. This new computer will use teamwork to reduce the computation time. Today's computers solve problems one computation at a time. The new type of computer will work on many computations at once. Twice as much data could be input about the atmosphere.

Telescopes are used by astronomers to study objects in the solar system and beyond. Telescopes collect light in a way that allows astronomers to observe objects that are not visible to the unaided eye. Telescopes also allow astronomers to look back in time. It takes time for light to travel. The light from even the closest stars left those stars years ago. Light reaching the earth from distant objects in space may be billions of years old. This light shows things as they were billions of years ago. Looking deep into space, therefore, is also looking into the distant past.

Some telescopes gather energy waves that are like light waves but that can't be seen. Radio telescopes gather radio waves produced by stars and galaxies. Some of these sources of radio waves are not visible through a light telescope. X-ray, infrared, and ultraviolet telescopes are also used to study space.

Satellites are used more and more today by earth scientists in their studies. Using satellite photographs, scientists make maps of the earth's surface that are more accurate than any made before. Satellite photographs are used to find minerals and fuels and to study weather. The Hubble space telescope, carried aboard a special satellite, can study objects in space from above the atmosphere. The atmosphere reduces the ability of telescopes on the earth to see objects in space clearly.

Start of Earthquake

Figure 1-12

A seismograph reading of the Mexico City earthquake (1985), and an example of the destruction the earthquake caused.

The seismograph (sīz muh graf) is an instrument that measures vibrations in the earth. Seismographs are used to measure the activity of earthquakes and volcanoes. These instruments are used to help predict when earthquakes or volcanic eruptions will occur. The Richter scale, which measures how severe the vibrations are, is based on seismograph readings. Each number on the scale indicates an increase in power of 10 times. For example, an earthquake that measures 3 is 10 times stronger than an earthquake that measures 2. Most earthquakes measure 4 or less on the Richter scale. An earthquake measuring 8, like the one in Mexico City in 1985, would be 10,000 times more powerful than one measuring 4.

Seismographs are located at many places around the earth. By using the readings from several seismographs, scientists can determine exactly where an earthquake occurred. Many earthquakes take place under the oceans. Seismograph data allow scientists to predict where waves produced by such earthquakes will strike land.

To study the oceans, some scientists use bathyscaphs (BATH uh skafs). A bathyscaph can protect scientists from extreme pressure that occur deep within the oceans. A bathyscaph supplies light and has artificial arms. With the help of this machine, oceanographers study the composition of deep water, the effects of high pressure, the deep ocean currents, the structure of the ocean floor, and life on the ocean floor.

Computers are important tools to earth scientists. Computers can analyze large amounts of data in a short time. This allows scientists to do experiments more quickly. Computers are used to predict the motion of weather systems. Computers are used with other equipment to map the ocean floor. Astronomers use computers for help in fixing their telescopes on a point in space.

These and other instruments allow scientists to go beyond their senses. In this book you will learn more about such instruments. You will find out what they can tell you about the earth and space.

REVIEW

1. Why do scientists use instruments?
2. Describe several instruments that an earth scientist might use.

CHALLENGE Many glaciers move so slowly that, over a few days, they do not appear to move at all. Describe how an earth scientist might use a camera to study the movement of glaciers.

Figure 1-13

Weather forecasts depend, in part, on computer analyses.

CHAPTER SUMMARY

The main ideas in this chapter are listed below. Read these statements before you answer the Chapter Review questions.

- Science is a way of obtaining knowledge about nature. (1-1)

- Earth science contains the fields of geology, astronomy, meteorology, oceanography, and paleontology. (1-1)

- The scientific method is the way a scientist gathers information and tests ideas. This method can be divided into four processes: observation, hypothesis, experiment, and conclusion. (1-2)

- A hypothesis may become a theory if it has been experimentally tested many times and the test results support it. Theories

may be used to help explain related events in nature. (1-2)

- SI, the system of measurement used in science, allows scientists worldwide to understand and use each other's data. (1-3)

- The meter, the kilogram, the liter, the degree Celsius, and the second are important units used in scientific measurements. (1-3)

- Scientists use many different tools to observe events that their senses alone cannot detect. (1-4)

The key terms in this chapter are listed below. Use each term in a sentence that shows the meaning of the term.

conclusion	hypothesis	meter	technology
degree Celsius	kilogram	observation	theory
earth science	liter	science	volume
experiment	mass	scientific method	

Chapter Review

VOCABULARY

Use the key terms from this chapter to complete the following sentences correctly.

1. An SI unit for measuring mass is the _____ .
2. A proposed answer to a question based on available information is a/an _____ .
3. A measure of the amount of space an object occupies is the object's _____ .
4. A way of obtaining knowledge about nature is called _____ .
5. Using knowledge from science in an attempt to improve the quality of human life is _____ .
6. Determining whether or not the evidence supports a hypothesis is part of the _____ .
7. A unit used in science for measuring volume is the _____ .
8. An examination of some part of nature is the process in the scientific method called _____ .
9. A unit used in science for measuring temperature is the _____ .
10. The major branch of science that studies the earth and space is _____ .

CONCEPTS

1. What does science study? (1-1)
2. What are the two major areas of study in earth science? (1-1)
3. Describe an example of technology from earth science. (1-1)
4. List the five branches of earth science. (1-1)
5. How does the scientific method differ from other methods of study? (1-2)
6. Give several examples of the kinds of observations that a scientist studying volcanoes might make. (1-2)
7. How does a hypothesis differ from a guess? (1-2)
8. Describe the two groups used in an experiment and explain the purpose of having two groups. (1-2)
9. Why is it important that an experiment's results be published? (1-2)
10. How does a hypothesis differ from a theory? (1-2)
11. Why is it important for scientists to measure and record their observations? (1-3)

12. Describe some standards of measurement used in the past. Why are such standards of limited value? (1-3)

13. List five common units used in scientific measurement today and describe what each one measures. (1-3)

14. If an object displaces 35 mL of water, what is the object's volume in cubic centimeters? (1-3)

15. In what unit would you measure the length of an eyelash? Explain why you chose that unit. (1-3)

16. An earth scientist determines that a certain rock sample has a mass of 1820 g. Express this mass in kilograms. (1-3)

17. Why do scientists use tools to aid their studies? (1-4)

18. What advantage do earth scientists have when they use microscopes and telescopes? Give examples of each. (1-4)

19. Describe two ways that satellites are useful in the study of earth science. (1-4)

20. How are computers useful in the study of earth science? (1-4)

APPLICATION/ CRITICAL THINKING

1. Where do you think the extra carbon dioxide in the air is coming from? What experiments or measurements would you like to make to learn more about the source of this carbon dioxide?

2. A scientific law is a description of some part of nature. For example, Boyle's law states that if the volume of a gas increases, the pressure decreases. Explain how a scientific law differs from a scientific theory.

3. A strong scientific theory is one that is consistent with theories in other, seemingly unrelated, branches of science. Explain what is meant by this statement.

EXTENSION

1. Prepare a report on technological spinoffs from the space program.

2. Record the masses or volumes of several household products. For those that are not expressed in metric units, convert the measurements to metric units.

3. Find out how the meter was originally defined and how it is defined today.

READINGS

Keerdoja, E. "Is the Earth Getting Hotter?" *Newsweek,* October 31, 1983, p. 90.

Raloff, J. "High Eyes Scout for Floods." *Science News,* June 11, 1983, p. 460.

Toon, Owen B., and Steve Olson. "The Warm Earth." *Science 85,* October 1985, p. 50.

G
Titepano
Masequetuc
Cautaking
Ricahokene
Croatamung
Moratuc
Etacrewac
Roanoac
Hatrask
Dasemunkepeuc
N
E
Tramaskecooc
A
Nausegoc
Paquiwac
Paquippe
Pomeiooc
P
Mentso
Aquascogoc
Seco
Secotan
A
Croatoan
Secotaoc
Wococon
Newasiwac

MAP SKILLS IN EARTH SCIENCE

Until about 600 years ago, people sailed mainly along coasts. There they could use natural landmarks, such as cliffs and harbors, to find their way. However, as people began to explore far from land, they drew maps so that they could find their way.

Just as sailors were mapping the world from ships centuries ago, scientists today are mapping the earth from spacecraft. The map shown on the left was drawn in 1587. It shows the Chesapeake Bay, on the Atlantic coast of North America, and the rivers flowing into it.

- *What features can be identified in the 1587 map?*
- *Why are land features absent from the 1587 map?*
- *In what ways would photographs taken from aircraft or satellites help make a more accurate map?*

2-1 MODELS OF THE EARTH

From the surface of the earth, you cannot tell that the earth is a ball-shaped planet. People probably began their search for a model of the earth long before civilization. Early civilizations created many models to help explain the different features of the earth. For example, the early Chinese made a model that showed their idea about why earthquakes took place. The model showed the earth on the back of a frog. It was thought that when the frog moved, an earthquake took place.

A **model** is a representation of an object. It can be a copy of an actual object, or it can represent something that cannot be seen. You probably have seen model airplanes and globes. All these are models because they are copies of real things. A representation of a real thing is called a *physical model*.

Physical models are often used to give an understanding of the real objects. For example, a model of a building may be made before the building is constructed. This gives people a good idea of what the building will look like when it is finished.

> *After completing this section, you will be able to*
>
> - **distinguish** between a physical model and a mental model.
> - **compare** a globe and a map.
> - **describe** two kinds of map projections.
>
> *The key terms in this section are*
> equal-area projection
> map
> map projection
> Mercator projection
> model

modus (measure)

In a physical model, relative size is an important factor. The parts of a model are in the same proportion as the parts of the object they represent. For example, notice in Figure 2-1 (*left*) that the wings of the model airplane are in the same proportion to the body as are the wings of a real airplane to the body.

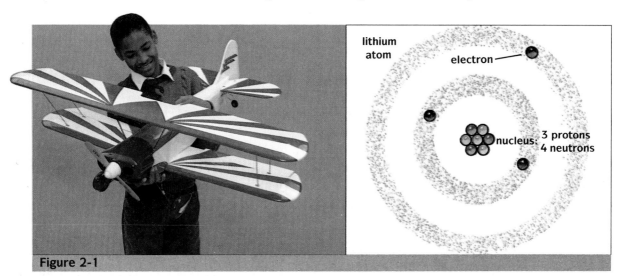

Figure 2-1

Physical model (*left*); mental model (*right*).

Another type of model is a mental model. A *mental model* is a representation of something that cannot be seen. Some objects, such as atoms, are too small to be seen. *Atoms* are tiny particles of matter that cannot be seen even with the most powerful microscope. Figure 2-1 (*right*) shows what scientists think an atom may look like.

One of the most common physical models used in earth science is a globe, shown in Figure 2-2. What type of model is a globe?

In some ways, a globe is the best model of the earth. It is round like the earth, and it shows all the continents and oceans. However, a globe is not always easy to use. For one thing, it cannot easily be carried around. A globe also does not show the earth's surface in detail. It does not show roads or the names of streets. Thus you could not use a globe to find your way if you were lost.

Figure 2-2

A globe is a model of the earth.

To show details on the earth's surface, maps are used. A **map** is a model of the earth's surface. A map can show the entire earth's surface or part of it. However, a map is not the same as a photograph of the earth's surface. This is because the earth's surface is curved. When the earth's curved surface is shown on the flat surface of a map, some areas of the earth are stretched out of their true size and shape in relation to other areas.

Imagine trying to flatten the whole peel, or skin, of an orange. As the orange peel is flattened, it will stretch and tear, changing in size and shape. In a similar way, a large area from a globe can be changed in shape and size when shown on a flat map.

What qualities should an accurate flat map of the earth have? One quality it should have is that direction should be shown accurately. Another quality is that the shapes of landmasses and bodies of water should be shown accurately. A third quality is that all areas should be shown in their proper size in relation to each other.

However, only a globe has all three of these qualities. The choice of which quality a map is to have depends on the use for which the map is made.

Mapmakers use several ways to present accurately the qualities that maps should have. A way of transferring the curved surface of the earth onto a flat map is called a **map projection.**

pro- (forward)
jacere (to throw)

One type of map projection that shows the true direction between any two points on a map is called a Mercator projection. A **Mercator projection** is a map projection that shows the earth's grid, or system of lines, as straight lines. Notice in Figure 2-3 that the vertical lines and horizontal lines cross at right angles.

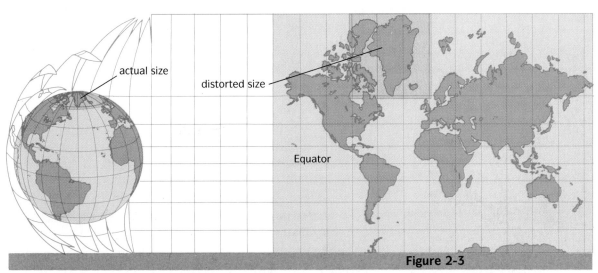

Figure 2-3

actual size

distorted size

Equator

A Mercator projection shows compass directions accurately.

The Mercator projection is very useful for navigation because it shows compass directions accurately. However, this type of map increases the size of polar areas greatly. Look at Figure 2-3. On the globe, Greenland is shown to be about one fourth the size of the United States. How does the size of Greenland compare to the size of the United States on the Mercator projection?

ACTIVITY   Maps from Round Objects

OBJECTIVE
Demonstrate why some features on maps are distorted.

MATERIALS
compass (for drawing a circle), pencil, baseball or softball, tracing paper (25 cm × 25 cm), scissors, tape, colored pencil

PROCEDURE

A. Using a ruler, set a compass to a radius of 12 cm. Then, using the compass, draw a circle 24 cm in diameter on tracing paper.
B. Cut the circle out of the tracing paper.
C. Cover a baseball carefully with the circle of tracing paper.
D. Use tape to hold the tracing paper in place if necessary.
E. Find the seams on the ball and trace them with a pencil.
F. Unwrap the paper and smooth it out.
G. Use a colored pencil to make your outline complete.

RESULTS AND CONCLUSIONS
1. What do you observe about the line on the paper?
2. How does the length of the line you have drawn compare with the length of the seam on the baseball?
3. How does the shape of the line you have drawn compare with the shape of the seam on the baseball?
4. What happens to the size and shape of areas on a globe when a map is made?

A much better projection for showing land and water areas of the earth accurately is the equal-area projection. An **equal-area projection** is a map projection that shows land and sea areas in their true shapes and relative sizes.

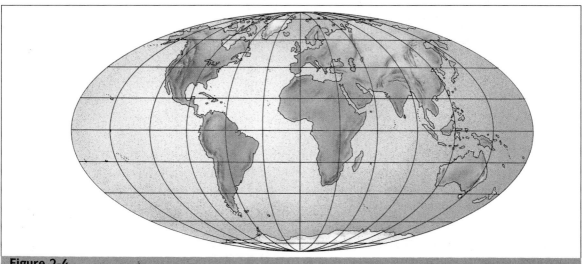

Figure 2-4

An equal-area projection shows the shapes and relative sizes of land and sea areas accurately.

REVIEW

1. What is the difference between a physical model and a mental model?
2. What advantages do maps have over globes?
3. Distinguish between a Mercator projection and an equal-area projection.

CHALLENGE Is there any kind of map projection that would not show any distortion? Explain your answer.

2-2 READING MAPS

You may have had more experience using maps than you think. You probably have seen the colorful type of display that shows the layout of a shopping mall. And during television weather reports, you probably have seen radar maps. These maps may seem completely different. Yet they have two basic things in common. They show locations and also characteristics at those locations. There are two very important things every map should have. Every map should have a *scale* and legend.

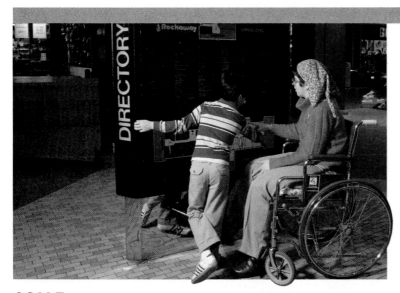

SCALE

As you learned, maps show what all or part of the earth's surface looks like. However, maps are smaller than the regions they show. To show the relationship between distance on a map and distance on the earth, a mapmaker draws a map to a scale. A **scale** is a proportion between a model and what it represents. For example, a model airplane may have a scale of 1 to 50. This means the model airplane is one fiftieth the size of a real airplane.

On a map, the scale might be expressed as 1 cm = 1 km. This means that 1 cm on the map represents 1 km on the earth. The scale on a map may be shown as a fraction, such as $\frac{1}{10,000}$, or as a ratio, 1 : 10,000, meaning that 1 is the distance on the map and 10,000 is the distance on the earth. The scale can also be shown as a bar scale. A *bar scale* is a line on a map that is divided into parts to show the units of distance on the earth.

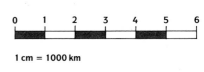

1 cm = 1000 km

LEGEND

Most maps use colors and symbols to show different kinds of information. By using colors and symbols, a map-maker can put much information on a map. To explain the symbols and colors, a legend, or key, is used. A **legend** is a list that explains the meaning of each symbol and color on a map. Without a legend, the user would not know the meaning of the special symbols, such as dots, squares, and lines, on the map. As you can see in Figure 2-7, some symbols look like the features they represent.

Most maps use color to show information. Color can be used on a map to show what the earth's surface is like. For example, blue is generally used to show rivers and bodies of water. Color can also be used to show differences in temperature or rainfall.

Figure 2-7

A legend shows the meaning of symbols on a map.

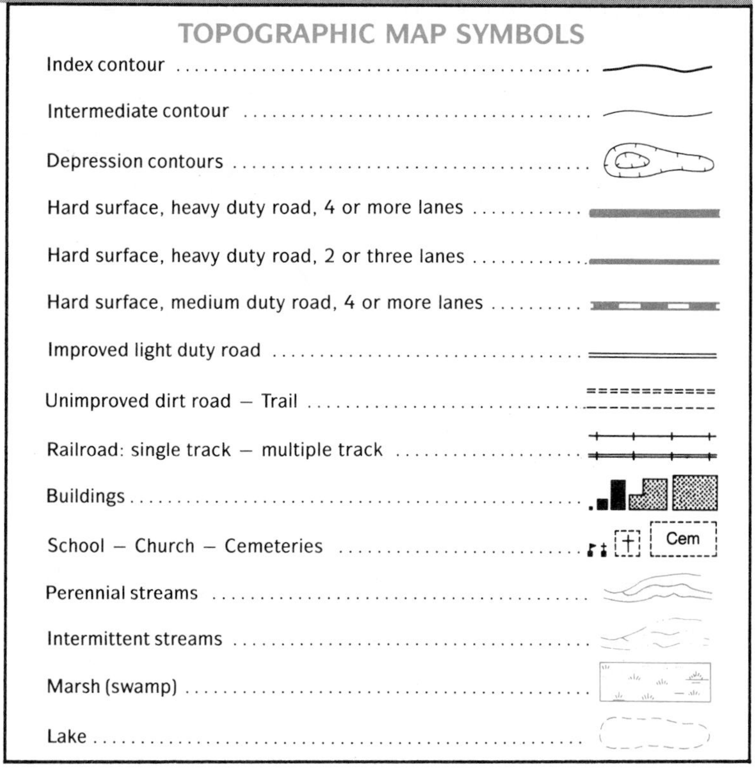

TOPOGRAPHIC MAP SYMBOLS

Index contour ....

Intermediate contour ....

Depression contours ....

Hard surface, heavy duty road, 4 or more lanes ....

Hard surface, heavy duty road, 2 or three lanes ....

Hard surface, medium duty road, 4 or more lanes ....

Improved light duty road ....

Unimproved dirt road — Trail ....

Railroad: single track — multiple track ....

Buildings ....

School — Church — Cemeteries ....

Perennial streams ....

Intermittent streams ....

Marsh (swamp) ....

Lake ....

REVIEW

1. How is a scale used on a map?

2. List several kinds of information a legend can show.

CHALLENGE The scale on a map reads 1:10,000. The distance measured between two points on the map is 20 cm. What is the distance between these two points on the earth's surface? 200,000

2-3 TYPES OF MAPS

Although there are many different types of maps, they can be classified into two groups: reference maps and special-purpose maps. A **special-purpose map** shows a particular feature of an area, such as rainfall, natural resources, or weather. A **reference map** shows the locations of features. Some common features are cities, highways, and rivers.

SPECIAL-PURPOSE MAPS

One of the most familiar special-purpose maps is a weather map. Weather maps are printed every day in many newspapers. Unlike land maps, which can be used for years, weather maps are made several times a day.

> *After completing this section, you will be able to*
>
> - **distinguish** between a reference map and a special-purpose map.
> - **describe** how a road map can be used to find the location of a place.
>
> *The key terms in this section are*
> chart
> reference map
> special-purpose map

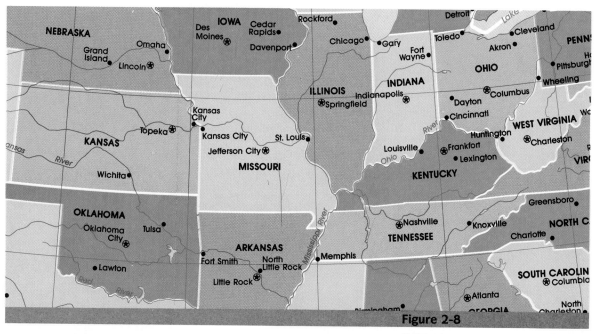

Figure 2-8

Political map.

The most common weather map you probably have seen is a surface weather map. Weather maps use symbols to represent weather observations, such as rain and snow. Measurements, such as temperature, are represented by numbers. Weather symbols are used in nearly all parts of the world, so scientists everywhere can understand weather data from other locations.

Another kind of special-purpose map is a *political map.* A political map uses different colors to show different countries. It also shows major cities. Notice in Figure 2-8 that the colors make it easier to compare the shapes and sizes of different states.

re- (back)
ferre (bring)

A special-purpose map that shows the features of the earth's surface is called a *physical map*. Colors or lines are used to show the height of land, or elevation. Symbols are used to show land features, such as swamps, trails, and streams. One of the most useful physical maps in earth science is a *topographic map*.

REFERENCE MAPS

One of the most common reference maps is a road map. A road map shows the locations of places, such as cities and towns. It also shows accurate distances between places. The general locations of places on a road map are given by letters and numbers in the map's list of place-names. The letters refer to those along the left or right margins of the map; they label horizontal rows. The numbers refer to those along the top or bottom margins; they

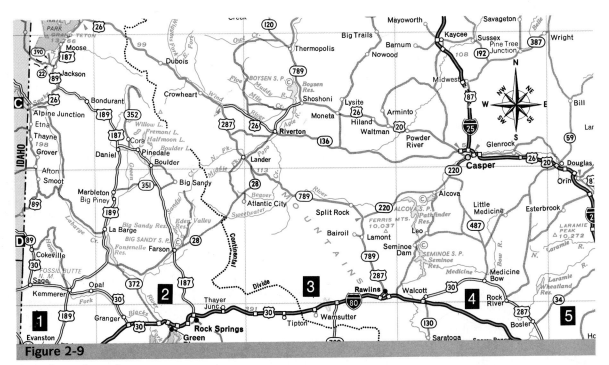

Figure 2-9

A road map is a reference map.

label vertical columns. The exact location of a place on a map can be found in the area where its lettered row and numbered column cross. For example, the letter-number key for Casper in the map shown in Figure 2-9 is "C-4." Find the location of Casper on the map.

Another kind of reference map is called a chart. A **chart** is a map used when flying or when traveling over water. Flight charts have many of the same features as road maps, such as cities and highways.

ACTIVITY   On the Road Again

OBJECTIVE
Read information on a road map.

MATERIALS
paper, pencil

PROCEDURE
Use the road map in Figure 2-9 to answer these questions.

1. What is the general location of Rock Springs?
2. In what direction is Casper from Rock Springs?
3. About how many kilometers is the drive from Rock Springs to Rawlins?
4. Which is wider, Route 80 or Route 287?
5. What are two interstate highways in Wyoming shown on the map?
6. What route would you travel from Rock Springs to Boulder?
7. If you were driving east on Route 80 from Rock Springs, would you turn north or south at Route 87 to reach Chugwater?
8. Compare the population of Rock Springs with the population of Casper.
9. What is the name of the mountains southwest of Casper?
10. On which part of the map would the roads be most hilly? Explain your answer.

RESULTS AND CONCLUSIONS
1. What map feature did you use to find distance?
2. List the main features shown on a road map.

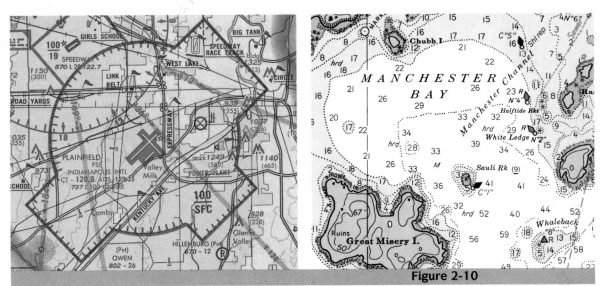

Figure 2-10

Flight chart (*left*); marine chart (*right*).

Marine charts show many kinds of features not shown on road maps or flight charts. Marine charts show the locations of landmarks and lighthouses as well as the depth of the ocean, and dangerous features, such as coral reefs.

REVIEW

1. What is the difference between a reference map and a special-purpose map? Give examples of each type of map.
2. Describe how a road map can be used to locate a place.

CHALLENGE   Explain why charts show areas out of shape.

2-4 TOPOGRAPHIC MAPS

After completing this section, you will be able to

- **describe** how contour lines show the shape of the land.
- **list** several features shown on a topographic map.

The key terms in this section are
contour interval
contour line
topographic map

A road map will show you the shortest route between two places. But you will notice that the roads and highways on a road map do not form straight lines. Instead, they curve and wind. Why aren't roads and highways built in straight lines?

To answer this question, you need to look at a map that shows surface features of the land. This type of map would show that the roads and highways wind around valleys and the steep parts of mountains. A map that shows surface features is called a topographic map.

Topographic maps are maps that use contour lines to show elevation and other surface land features. A **contour line** connects points on a map that are at the same elevation. The *elevation* of an area is the area's height above sea level. The difference in elevation between one contour line and the next is called the **contour interval**. For example, if each contour line differs from the contour line next to it by 200 m, the contour interval is 200 m.

Figure 2-11

A topographic map uses contour lines to show elevation.

Contour lines show changes in the height of the land. When contour lines are far apart, they show that the slope of the land is gentle. When they are close together, they show that the slope of the land is steep. Locate the steepest slope on the topographic map shown in Figure 2-11 (*right*).

Topographic maps often contain symbols for surface features. Some of these features are buildings, swamps, streams, and railroad tracks.

ACTIVITY **Making a Topographic Map**

OBJECTIVE

Make a topographic map using cutout contour shapes.

MATERIALS

scissors, ruler, paper, paste, colored pencils

PROCEDURE

A. Trace the contour shapes of Oxford Island on a sheet of paper and cut them out. Trace the dashes too. The outline of the largest shape represents 0 m of elevation. Each smaller shape represents 50 m more of elevation.
  1. What is another term for 0 m of elevation?
  2. Which shape represents the highest elevation?

B. Paste the largest shape on another sheet of paper.

C. Place the next-largest shape on top of the largest one. Paste this smaller shape on top of the larger shape, lining up the dashes on both pieces.

D. Repeat Step **C** until all the shapes have been pasted down.

E. Draw each contour line by tracing around each shape with a colored pencil. Label each contour line, starting with 0 m.

F. Draw a scale at the lower right side of your contour map sheet to show that 1 cm is equal to 160 km.
  3. About how wide is Oxford Island? About how long?

RESULTS AND CONCLUSIONS

1. What is the highest elevation represented on your map?
2. What is the contour interval of your map?
3. What part of your map has the most gentle slope?

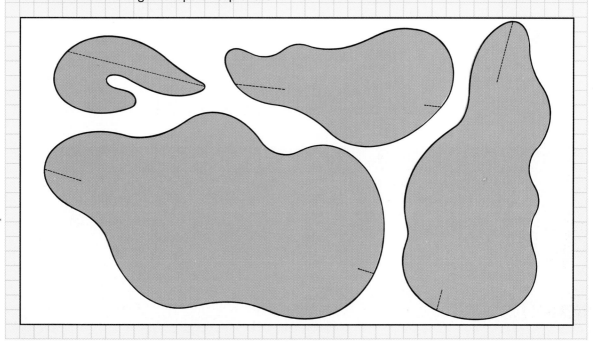

REVIEW

1. What do the contour lines on a topographic map show?
2. How would the contour lines appear for an area that has a steep slope?
3. List several features shown on a topographic map.

CHALLENGE Why doesn't the highest point on a hill have a contour line?

2-5 LOCATION ON THE EARTH

After completing this section, you will be able to

- **identify** the lines of latitude and the lines of longitude on a map or globe.
- **locate** a place on a map by using latitude and longitude.

The key terms in this section are

equator   longitude
latitude

You can find a place today by using its address. The address would probably include a house number, the name of a street or road, and the name of a city and state. However, thousands of years ago most places on the earth did not have a system of addresses. Maps only showed the names of nearby cities. Yet people traveled to places hundreds of kilometers away to get things they needed. How could you find a place that did not have an address?

LATITUDE

The earth is almost a perfect sphere. Like a ball, it does not have a top, bottom, or side that can be used as a "landmark" to find direction or location. However, the earth rotates, or turns on its axis. The *axis* is an imaginary line through the earth. The ends of the axis are called the *North Pole* and *South Pole*. They are used as fixed points, or reference points, on the earth. A *reference point* is a fixed place from which direction and location can be described. The earth's poles are used as reference points to describe four directions: north, south, east, and west.

A globe shows a line drawn halfway between the North and South poles. This line is called the equator. The **equator** is an imaginary line that circles the earth halfway between the North and South poles.

DO YOU KNOW?

Maps of the sea floor made with information taken from 800 km above the earth will prove to be a powerful new type of tool for geologists. These maps are produced from data gathered by a satellite called Seasat. One of the instruments aboard Seasat was a radar altimeter. This instrument uses radar waves to measure the floor of the ocean.

Using a computer, the data from Seasat has been used to produce images of the ocean bottom. More than 200 different shades of colors highlight the contours.

This method brings out features of the ocean bottom never seen in standard contour maps.

The new mapmaking technique will prove useful to many people other than

geologists. The Navy is interested in the locations of seamounts so that its submarines can avoid them. The technique may even be used to find oil and mineral deposits.

Distance north or south of the equator is called the **latitude**. Imaginary lines drawn around the earth, parallel to the equator, represent lines of latitude. Latitude is measured in degrees. As you can see in Figure 2-12, the location of the North Pole is at latitude 90 degrees north, or 90°N. This means that the North Pole is 90 degrees north of the equator. A place halfway between the North Pole and the equator is at latitude 45 degrees north, or 45°N. A place halfway between the equator and the South Pole is at latitude 45 degrees south, or 45°S. Why can the latitude never be greater than 90°?

latus (wide)

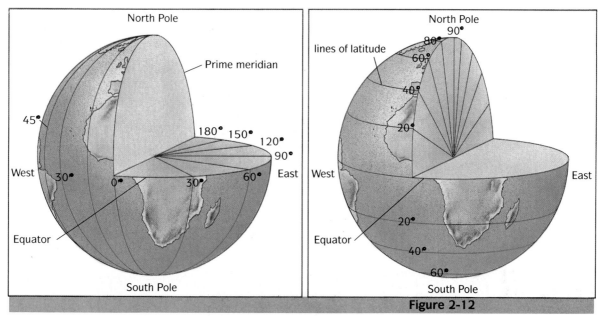

Figure 2-12

Lines of latitude (*right*); lines of longitude (*left*).

If you ran your finger along a line of latitude on a globe, you would see that many places have the same latitude. To tell more exactly where a place is, you must know its east or west location.

LONGITUDE

Location east or west on the earth can be found by using lines of longitude. The lines of longitude are imaginary lines that pass through the North Pole and the South Pole. The line of longitude called the *prime meridian* is labeled 0°. It runs through Greenwich (GREHN ihch), England. Distance east or west of the prime meridian is called **longitude**. Places east and west of the prime meridian are measured in degrees, up to 180 degrees. The location of a place 45 degrees west of the prime meridian is written as longitude 45 degrees west, or 45°W.

35

FINDING LOCATIONS

By using latitude and longitude, the location of any place on earth can be found. For example, New York City is located at about latitude 40°N and longitude 75°W. Figure 2-13 illustrates how to find New York City by using latitude and longitude. First find the line of latitude for 40°N. Then find the line of longitude for 75°W. New York City can be found where these two lines meet.

The grid system of latitude and longitude lines is not the only kind of grid system used on maps. For example, road maps have their own grid system. As you learned, road maps use a system of lettered and numbered lines to locate places of interest.

Figure 2-13

New York City is located at 40°N, 75°W.

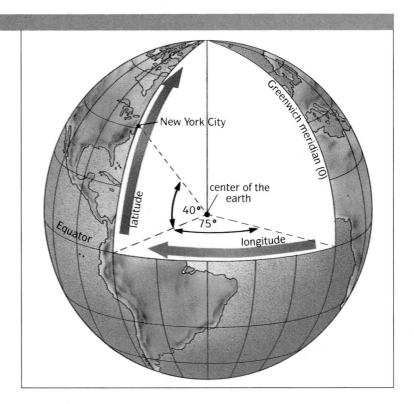

REVIEW

1. Describe the locations of the lines of latitude and lines of longitude on a map or globe.
2. A certain place has a location of latitude 30°N and longitude 65°E. Describe its location on the earth.

CHALLENGE Why can longitude never be greater than 180°?

2-6 MAPMAKING

The oldest known map was made about 2300 B.C. It is a small clay tablet with marks scratched into its surface. Many of today's maps are made by photographing the earth's surface from space.

The science of mapmaking is called **cartography** (kahr-TAHG ruh fee). Maps are made after making observations of and taking measurements of the earth's surface. For hundreds of years, maps were drawn by measuring distances, directions, and elevations of land features. The invention of the airplane allowed maps to be made from aerial photographs of the earth. This method made the mapping of large areas more accurate and easier than by just making measurements.

Today, aerial photographs are used in making nearly all the maps of large areas of the earth. Photographs are first taken of narrow sections of land. They are then put together, forming one large photograph called a *mosaic* (moh ZAY ihk). Two mosaics are shown in Figure 2-14.

After completing this section, you will be able to

- **compare** maps made by using aerial photographs with maps made from measurements on the earth.
- **list** two reasons why spacecraft are more useful than airplanes in photographing the earth.
- **distinguish** between a satellite image and a photograph.

The key terms in this section are
cartography   Landsat

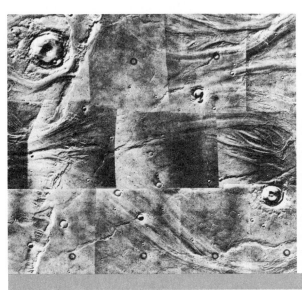

Figure 2-14

Maps can be made from mosaics.

About 20 years ago, astronauts orbiting the earth in spacecraft began taking photographs of the earth. *Cartographers,* or mapmakers, found that photographs taken from orbiting spacecraft can be more useful than photographs taken from airplanes. One reason is that spacecraft can travel at much higher altitudes than airplanes can. Thus spacecraft can photograph much larger areas of the earth than airplanes can. Large land features, such as entire mountain ranges, can be mapped accurately.

The photograph shows a color mosaic of the United States made from 569 images taken by Landsat. The colors shown are "false colors"—not the true colors that would be seen in an ordinary photograph of the United States. Make a legend that shows the meaning of the colors shown.

Another reason such photographs are more useful is that spacecraft can travel above the atmosphere, where there is no wind. This enables the spacecraft to take photographs without being blown around. Thus more accurate maps can be made from the photographs.

Some of the most valuable maps are made from photographs taken by the spacecraft called Landsat. **Landsat** is a satellite that photographs the resources of the earth. It uses special cameras called *sensors,* which measure heat. From the information collected by the sensors, special photographs called *satellite images* are taken.

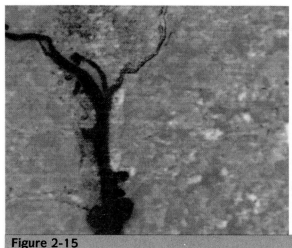 

Figure 2-15

A satellite image (*left*); a computer satellite image (*right*).

As you can see in Figure 2-15 (*left*), a satellite image does not look like an ordinary photograph. For one thing, it does not show the true colors of the earth. That is, green plant cover appears red, water appears black, and cities appear blue-gray. The true colors of materials on the earth do not appear because the information collected by the sensors is based on heat. Thus the satellite is able to collect information about materials that cannot be seen. For example, images can show the presence, underground, of water, oil, and minerals.

Computers can be used to improve the details shown on satellite images. A computer uses information collected by the sensors and produces an image that shows more features and details than an ordinary, or standard, satellite image. Compare the computer satellite image and the standard satellite image in Figure 2-15. What features can be identified in the computer satellite image that cannot be identified in the standard satellite image?

REVIEW

1. How have aerial photographs changed the way maps are made.
2. What are two reasons why spacecraft are more useful than airplanes in photographing the earth?
3. What is the difference between a satellite image and a photograph?

CHALLENGE Why does Landsat orbit around the North and South poles of the earth rather than around the equator?

CHAPTER SUMMARY

The main ideas in this chapter are listed below. Read these statements before you answer the Chapter Review questions.

- A globe and a map are models of the earth. (2-1)

- Maps contain information about the earth's surface. (2-2)

- Different maps are made for different purposes. (2-3)

- Topographic maps show the elevation and surface features of the land. (2-4)

- Any location on earth can be found by using latitude and longitude. (2-5)

- Today, satellites are used to make detailed maps of the earth's surface. (2-6)

The key terms in this chapter are listed below. Use each term in a sentence that shows the meaning of the term.

cartography	latitude	model
chart	legend	equal-area projection
contour interval	longitude	reference map
contour line	map	scale
equator	map projection	special-purpose map
Landsat	Mercator projection	topographic map

Chapter Review

Write the letter of the term that best matches the definition. Not all terms will be used.

1. Map that shows locations
2. Map that shows the elevation of land
3. A line connecting points of equal elevation
4. Model of part of the earth's surface
5. Map that shows earth's grid as straight lines
6. List that shows the meaning of symbols
7. Distance north or south of the equator
8. Map that shows a particular feature of the earth
9. Representation of an object
10. Relationship between distances

a. contour line
b. legend
c. latitude
d. longitude
e. map
f. Mercator projection
g. model
h. reference map
i. scale
j. special-purpose map
k. topographic map

Scientific Method!

Use the key terms from this chapter to complete the following sentences correctly.

1. The difference between one adjacent contour line and the next is called the _____ .
2. A map used when flying or when traveling on water is called a/an _____ .
3. A map that shows the earth's land and water areas in their true shape and relative size is called a/an _____ .
4. An imaginary line drawn halfway between the North and South poles is the _____ .
5. A model of the earth's surface is a/an _____ .

CONCEPTS

1. Give an example of a physical model and a mental model. (2-1)
2. If you were traveling somewhere, would you use a map or a globe? Why? (2-2)
3. On which type of map projection would the area of Central America change the least? (2-1)
4. How would a map scale affect the detail shown on a map? (2-2)
5. Give several examples of how symbols and colors are used to represent information on maps. (2-2)

6. Compare a road map with a weather map. (2-3)
7. What types of information can be found on a road map? (2-3)
8. Distinguish between a contour line and a contour interval. (2-4)
9. Compare the contour lines of a steep area with those of a level area. (2-4)
10. How are hills represented on a topographic map? (2-4)
11. List surface features shown on a topographic map. (2-4)
12. Distinguish between latitude and longitude. (2-5)
13. Name three reference points on the earth. (2-5)
14. Why are two sets of lines needed to locate the exact position of a place? (2-5)
15. What is the reference point for measuring latitude? Longitude? (2-5)
16. Explain how airplanes can be used to make maps. (2-6)
17. How have satellite images improved maps? (2-6)
18. Explain how computers are being used to improve satellite images. (2-6)

APPLICATION/ CRITICAL THINKING

1. How would a topographic map be helpful to a highway construction engineer?
2. Suppose you had a map of the Pacific Ocean. What two sets of lines would you need to locate an island?
3. Find several ways of determining which areas on a map are shown out of shape.
4. Look through your social studies or history book. What types of map projections are included?
5. Explain why contour lines can never cross.

EXTENSION

1. Use library resources or human resources in your community to find out what skills a cartographer must have.
2. Compare satellite photographs of land and water with aerial photographs or topographic maps.
3. Find the latitude and longitude of your city or town. Find out how a more precise location can be made by using *minutes*.
4. Find out more information about Landsat satellites that have been recording geologic, hydrologic, pollution, and land-use photographs.

READING

Madden, James F. The Wonderful World of Maps. Maplewood, N.J.: Hammond, Inc., 1982.

Science in Careers

How is a level house built on sloping ground? Why do some highways run straight for many kilometers and others wind and bend?

Before a house, highway, or other structure can be built, the shape, or contour, of the land must be measured. Measurements are made by people called surveyors.

Surveyors use a device called a theodolite to measure distances on land and elevation. The measurements can then be used to find the best route for a road or waterway. A surveyor's measurements are used to make sure a house being built is level. The lines on maps that separate properties, counties, and states also come from surveyors' measurements.

Surveyors work outdoors in groups or teams. Courses in mechanical drawing, mathematics, and geography are helpful for surveyors. You will need a high school diploma and will receive on-the-job training. ■

SURVEYOR

Before structures such as dams, roadways, shopping centers, and office buildings can be built, they must be planned and designed. In addition, these structures must be adapted to the ground on which they are to be built.

The civil engineer plans and designs structures and adapts them to the ground. For example, before the skyscrapers could be built, civil engineers had to design a special type of steel frame that would allow the structure to stand.

Civil engineers must have a knowledge of geology and chemistry as well as engineering. They usually work for engineering and construction companies large and small and the government.

To become a civil engineer you need a college degree in engineering. Mathematics courses are very important for work in this field. You will also benefit from courses in mechanical drawing. ■

CIVIL ENGINEER

People in Science

DR. E. MARGARET
BURBIDGE, ASTRONOMER

Astronomers are scientists who study objects in space. Until about 25 years ago, astronomers spent most of their time observing stars, galaxies, planets, and moons. But then a new kind of object was discovered.

Dr. E. Margaret Burbidge was studying objects that appeared to be stars. Like most stars, they gave off radiation in the form of light and radio waves.

Dr. Burbidge measured the distance and brightness of the objects. She found that they were some of the most distant objects in the universe. Although they appeared as mere points of light, they radiated a thousand times more light than an entire galaxy.

Astronomers gave them the name quasars, or quasi-stellar objects. Quasars are believed to be the cores of very disturbed galaxies. To date, over 1500 quasars have been located.

Many questions remain to be answered about quasars.

During the next few years, new technologies will help astronomers make more and better observations than ever before. ■

Issues and Technology

The earth is thought to be about 4.6 billion years old. But many of the machines we depend on today have only been invented within the last few hundred years. Figure 1 shows the history of the earth compressed into a single day. Notice that humans appear very late in that time. And the industrial revolution begins one thousandth of a second before the present, according to this scale. The technology that brought about the invention of televisions, jet airplanes, helicopters, nuclear power, computers, and satellites was developed in that last fraction of an instant.

Now, technology is part of everyday life. Cars and airplanes allow people to travel widely. Satellites let us talk with people thousands of miles away. Machines are used to make clothing, to print our books, and to assemble cars.

It would be hard to imagine life without the benefits that technology provides for us. However, just as technology can improve our lives, it can also have disadvantages.

Our cars, airplanes, and factories are polluting the air and water. We are using up many of the earth's material resources and energy resources at a very quick rate. Forests are cut to make our books, magazines, and cereal boxes. The earth's oil supplies are drained for our cars, buses, and other machines. And as the human population increases, more demands are placed on the earth's resources.

Food is one of the earth's most precious resources. There are millions of people in the world who do not have enough food. But you wouldn't know it by looking in a supermarket. People in the United States are probably

better fed than most people in the world. This is because our nation's farmers are very good at producing large amounts of food.

Only two out of every 100 Americans are farmers. These relatively few farmers feed the rest of the people of the United States. And they provide much of the food on the market around the world.

From the start of agriculture (about 10,000 years ago) until the early 1800s, farming methods did not change much. Almost all of the work was done by hand or with animals. Many people were needed to produce small amounts of food.

Technology is the key to the success of today's farmers. In the United States almost all of the work that used to be done by hand or with animals is done by machine. Machines break the ground for planting, plant the

**origin of universe —
10 billionth of a second
after midnight**

**stable atoms form —
4 seconds after midnight**

**stars and galaxies form —
5 AM**

**first life on earth —
6 PM**

**first invertebrates
in the sea — 8 PM**
Figure 1

**first vertebrates crawl
to land — 10:30 PM**

**dinosaurs roam the earth
11:35 – 11:56 PM**

**humans walk upright —
4 seconds to midnight**

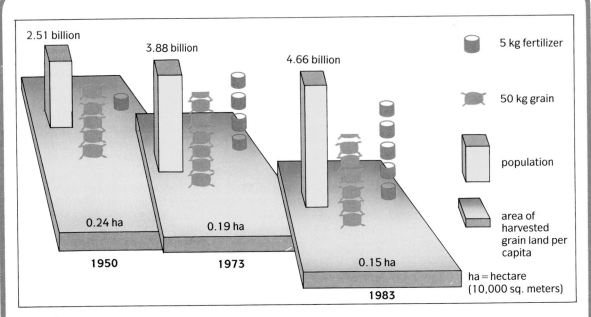

Figure 2

seeds, and control irrigation. They spread the chemical fertilizers that help plants grow bigger. They spread pesticides that kill insect pests. And machines harvest the crops.

Even foods themselves have been changed by technology. Thomas Jefferson would not recognize the corn on the cob we eat today. Scientists have created many new kinds of corn in the lab. They have done it by crossbreeding different kinds of plants. The corn we eat grows bigger and faster than did corn of 200 years ago. A piece of land that produced 10 bushels of corn at the beginning of the century can now produce over 100 bushels.

Each year the world's farms must feed 80 million more people. Technology helps farmers raise the additional food. But there are problems. The machines used on huge farms add to the pollution of our air and water. Fertilizers and pesticides are chemicals. They can be harmful

when they collect in soil and water. Fertilizers are washed off fields and into rivers, lakes, and underground water supplies. Perhaps half of the water pollution in the United States today results from fertilizer runoff.

Heavy farming is also wearing out the soil. It breaks down the soil's structure. So the soil erodes, turns to dust, and blows away. Much of the best topsoil in the United States has already been lost in this way.

Figure 2 will help you to understand one of the problems involved in the type of farming based on technology. The squares represent the amount of land used for growing grain for each person in the world in 1950, 1973, and 1983. The world's population is shown for those years. The barrels represent the amount of fertilizer per person used on the crops. The sacks represent the amount of grain harvested per person. Answer the following questions based on the drawing.

APPLYING CRITICAL THINKING SKILLS

1. Did the amount of land used to plant grain per person increase or decrease between 1950 and 1983?
2. How did the world's population change between 1950 and 1983?
3. How are the answers to questions 1 and 2 related?
4. Did the amount of food grown per equal land areas increase or did it decrease since 1950? Use the figure to explain your answer.
5. How much did the amount of fertilizer used per person go up between 1950 and 1983?
6. Fertilizer is made from petroleum. Predict what would happen to grain production if there was a shortage of petroleum.
7. What other problems could arise due to the fact that the fertilizer is made from petroleum? What can be done about these problems?

8. Why, do you think, was the amount of food per person less in 1983 than in 1973?
9. If the United States devoted less land to farming, soil erosion and the amounts of fertilizer used would be reduced. What effects would such action have on other nations?

You wake up on a school morning and turn off your alarm clock. You may shower, dress, and perhaps blow-dry your hair. It may be cold and dark outside, but your home is warm and bright. In the kitchen you have breakfast of toast, orange juice, and cereal. The TV plays in the background while you eat. When you finish your meal, you pick up your books and walk outside to wait for your school bus.

None of this seems strange. You wouldn't think twice about it. But thousands of people and tons of the earth's resources have made your morning possible.

Oil, coal, or gas may run the power plant that keeps your lights on and your electric appliances running. Your furnace uses electricity and probably some other fuel to produce heat. Fuel heats the water you use for your shower. Several metals are used in your alarm clock, hair dryer, and TV. Your house, food cartons, and books contain paper. There is gold in your school computer's microchips. Your bus in made from things like iron, aluminum, and silicon. It runs on gasoline.

All of the materials that go into making and running the things you use each day are resources.

They are cut from, dug from, or pumped out of the earth. Each one exists in a certain amount. And we are using many of them up.

Figure 3 shows how many years' supply of some important resources are left. Use Figure 3 to answer the following questions.

APPLYING CRITICAL THINKING SKILLS
1. For which substance is there the shortest supply?
2. Which substance will last longest?
3. Which substances *could* run out during our lifetime?
4. Name two reasons that some resources will run out faster than others.
5. Name some ways that we can make these resources last longer.

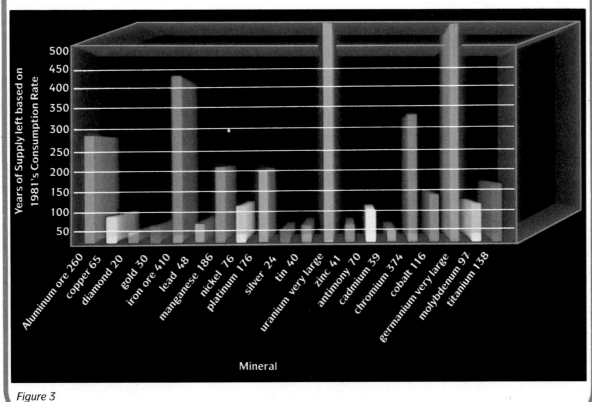

Figure 3

ASTRONOMY

*I*t was once thought that the entire universe — the moon, the sun, the planets and the stars — revolved around the earth. We now know that this is a rather small planet circling a medium-sized star on the outskirts of one of billions of galaxies. By using instruments on the earth, such as telescopes, and by sending space probes to explore the solar system, we are learning more about the universe. In this unit you will find out what is known, and unknown, about our universe. ■

▲ *The planet Uranus, made from images returned Jan. 17, 1986, by a camera on Voyager 2. The photographs were taken 9.1 million km away from the planet.*

▼ *Maria Mitchell (1818–1889), an American astronomer famous for her studies of sunspots.*

▲ The Armillary sphere is an old type of celestial globe used for determining positions of stars

▲ McDonald Observatory in West Texas (above). *The dome at left houses a 2-meter reflector and the dome at the right houses a 3-meter reflector.*

◀ *The "terrible" Halley's comet of 1680 is shown in this 17th Century woodcut* (left).

▲ Photograph of Halley's comet

THE EARTH IN SPACE

These 4-m-high stones rest on Salisbury Plain in England. The exact purpose of the monument they form is a mystery. Clues have been uncovered slowly. In the 1950s, scientists used carbon dating to estimate the age of the monument to be around 3500 years. In the 1960s, a scientist using a computer determined that the stones could have been used to predict the seasons. The monument was, in that scientist's opinion, a 98-m-diameter calendar.

- *Besides the seasons, what other events involving the earth, moon, and sun can be predicted to occur on a regular basis?*
- *Why do these events occur on a regular basis?*

3-1 WHERE IS THE EARTH LOCATED?

Can you describe the location of your home? You can easily name the street, town, state, and country in which you live. But your home also is located on the earth. Can you describe where the earth is located?

The earth is located in a solar system. Our solar system consists of the star we call the sun as well as the nine planets, more than 40 moons, and thousands of other smaller objects that circle the sun. The earth is the third planet from the sun.

Our solar system is located in a galaxy called the Milky Way galaxy. A galaxy consists of dust, gas, and billions of stars. The Milky Way galaxy contains over 100 billion stars. Our sun is an average-sized star located near the outer edge of the Milky Way galaxy.

Astronomers (uh STRAHN uh muhrz) have observed that many galaxies can be found in clusters. The Milky Way galaxy is located in a cluster of about 20 galaxies called the local group. The local group is just one of countless clusters in the universe.

It can be difficult to understand how far apart objects are in outer space. While a long trip on the earth might cover a few thousand kilometers, a trip across the solar

> After completing this section, you will be able to
>
> - **describe** where the earth is located in the universe.
> - **distinguish** between an astronomical unit and a light-year
>
> *The key terms in this section are*
> astronomical unit   light-year

Figure 3-1

The solar system. The distances between the planets are far greater than shown (*A*). Our solar system is a small part of the Milky Way galaxy (*B*).

Table 3-1 *Distances from Sun*

Planet	Distances from Sun in millions of km	in AU
Mercury	57.9	0.4
Venus	108.2	0.7
Earth	149.6	1.0
Mars	228.0	1.5
Jupiter	778.4	5.2
Saturn	1424.6	9.5
Uranus	2866.9	19.2
Neptune	4486.0	30.0
Pluto	5889.7	39.4

system would cover more than 12 *billion* km. To measure large distances such as this, the astronomical (as truh NAHM-uh kuhl) unit was created. An **astronomical unit** (AU) is a unit of length that is equal to the average distance from the sun to the earth. This distance is equal to about 150 million km. Table 3-1 shows the average distance from the sun to each planet. What is the average distance from the sun to Neptune? How much greater is this distance than the distance from the sun to the earth?

It can be even more difficult to understand distances to objects *beyond* our solar system. A trip to Proxima Centauri (PRAHK suh muh   sehn TAWR ī), the closest star to our sun, would cover almost 41 trillion km. The light-year was created to measure the vast distances to the stars and to the galaxies beyond the Milky Way. A **light-year** (ly) is a unit equal to the distance light can travel in one year. Light travels at almost 300,000 km/s. Therefore a light-year equals about 9.5 trillion km. The distance to the star that is nearest to the sun, Proxima Centauri, is 4.3 ly. The distance to the nearest galaxy, the Greater Magellanic Cloud, is about 160,000 ly.

REVIEW

1. Describe the location of the earth in the universe.
2. Distinguish between an astronomical unit and a light-year.

CHALLENGE How long would it take for light to travel across our solar system?

3-2 THE STRUCTURE OF THE EARTH

SHAPE AND SIZE OF THE EARTH

Through most of recorded history, people thought the earth was flat. It is easy to understand why. While traveling from one place to another, you do not sense the earth's curving surface. When you stand on the top of a mountain or a tall building, the earth's surface seems to stretch out endlessly in all directions.

Today we know that the earth is round. This was proved in 1522, when one of Magellan's ships circled the earth. Precise measurements have shown, however, that the earth is not a perfect sphere. The earth is slightly flattened at the poles and it bulges at the equator, as shown in Figure 3-2. The distance around the earth is about 40,000 km. The distance around the equator is greater than the distance around the poles.

> *After completing this section, you will be able to*
> - **describe** the shape and size of the earth.
> - **distinguish** between the atmosphere, hydrosphere, and lithosphere.
> - **explain** how the earth is like a magnet.
>
> *The key terms in this section are*
> atmosphere   magnetosphere
> hydrosphere   Van Allen belts
> lithosphere

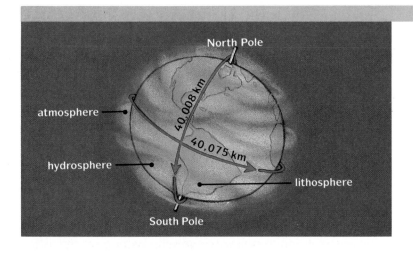

Figure 3-2

The earth is not a perfect sphere.

LAYERS OF THE EARTH

The earth can be organized into three layers or spheres. The **atmosphere** (AT muh sfihr) is the layer of air that surrounds the earth. The atmosphere extends more than 10,000 km from the earth's surface into space. However, most of the air is concentrated in the first 10 km above the earth. The **hydrosphere** (HĪ druh sfihr) is the layer of water that covers the earth. This layer includes water on the surface—such as rivers, lakes, and oceans—and water that is found beneath the ground. The **lithosphere** (LITH-uh sfihr) is the solid surface of the earth. It consists of the continents, the ocean floor, and all solid materials, such as rocks and minerals. You will learn more about each of these layers in later chapters.

atmo- (vapor)
sphaira (sphere)

hydro- (water)

litho- (stone)

51

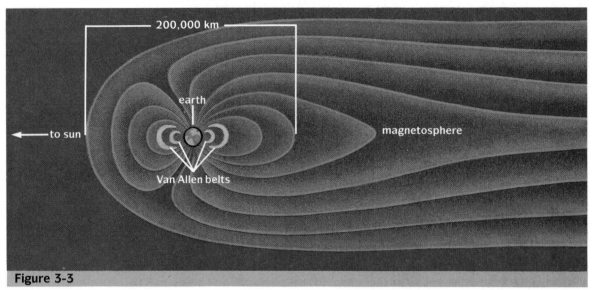

Figure 3-3

The Van Allen belts protect the earth from the sun's radiation.

THE EARTH'S MAGNETISM

The earth behaves as if it had a bar magnet inside of it. One pole of this imaginary magnet is located near the geographic North Pole. The other pole is located near the geographic South Pole. A free-hanging magnet is attracted to these magnetic poles. Because of this, a magnet can be used to indicate the directions of the poles.

An invisible magnetic field surrounds every magnet. Lines of force can be drawn to show the size and shape of the field. The **magnetosphere** (mag NEE tuh sfihr) is the magnetic field of the earth. The magnetosphere may extend millions of kilometers into space. Charged particles from the sun affect the magnetosphere and help give it its shape. The **Van Allen belts** are two doughnut-shaped regions of the magnetosphere in which charged particles are concentrated by the magnetosphere. One belt is found about 3000 km above the equator, and the other is about 16,000 km above the equator. You can see the locations of these belts in Figure 3-3. The Van Allen belts help to protect living things on earth by trapping radiation that would otherwise reach the surface.

REVIEW

1. Describe the shape of the earth.
2. Describe each of the three layers, or spheres, of the earth.
3. Why can magnets be used to find directions on the earth?
4. Describe the magnetosphere.

CHALLENGE Why doesn't a compass needle always point to the geographic North Pole?

3-3 THE EARTH'S MOVEMENTS

Sit perfectly still. How fast are you moving? You may think you are not moving at all. However, you are moving extremely fast because the earth is moving extremely fast. For one thing, the earth rotates, or spins, on an imaginary line called an axis, which extends through the earth's center. **Rotation** is the turning of an object on its axis. The earth's axis extends from the geographic North Pole to the geographic South Pole. Notice in Figure 3-4 that the earth's axis is tilted 23.5° from the vertical. The earth rotates on its axis once every 24 h. Since the distance around the earth is about 40,000 km, an object at the equator travels 40,000 km in 24 h, or about 1670 km/h!

After completing this section, you will be able to

- **distinguish** between *rotation* and *revolution*.
- **make** a drawing showing the movement of the earth around the sun.

The key terms in this section are
revolution   rotation

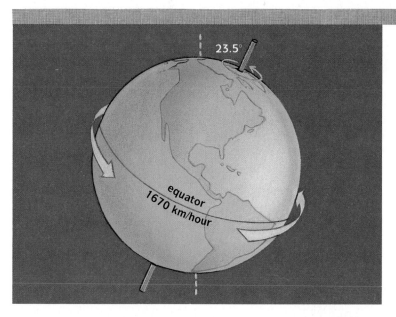

Figure 3-4

The earth is rotating on its axis. Would you be moving faster at the equator or at the poles?

While the earth is rotating, it is also revolving, or moving around the sun, at a tremendous rate. **Revolution** is the movement of an object along an orbit, or path, around another body, such as the sun. Figure 3-5 shows the earth's orbit around the sun. From above the North Pole the earth appears to revolve in a counterclockwise direction. It takes 365.24 days for the earth to revolve once. In that time the earth travels about 942 million km. To travel that distance in that amount of time, the earth must be moving at more than 107,000 km/h! Now think again about the question at the beginning of this section. How fast are you moving when you are sitting perfectly still?

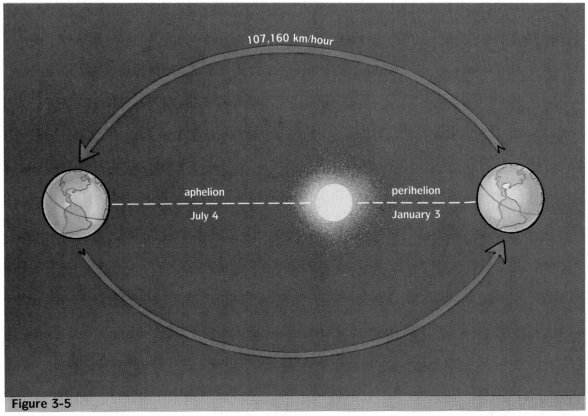

107,160 km/hour

aphelion
July 4

perihelion
January 3

Figure 3-5

The earth's orbit around the sun is elliptical.

peri (near)

helios (sun)

apo- (away)

The orbit that the earth follows around the sun is shaped like an ellipse, or a slightly flattened circle. The sun is not in the exact center of this orbit. For these reasons, the earth is not always the same distance from the sun. Notice in Figure 3-5 that the earth is closest to the sun at the point in its orbit called *perihelion* (pehr uh-HEE lee uhn). At perihelion, around January 3, the earth is about 147 million km away from the sun. At the point in its orbit called *aphelion* (uh FEE lee uhn), the earth is farthest from the sun. At aphelion, around July 4, the earth is about 152 million km away from the sun.

REVIEW

1. Describe the movements of the earth in space.
2. Distinguish between *rotation* and *revolution*.
3. Draw a diagram of the earth and sun. Show the directions of the earth's rotation and revolution.

CHALLENGE If you viewed the earth and sun from above the South Pole, in what direction would the earth appear to rotate? In what direction would it appear to revolve?

3-4 TIME ON THE EARTH

Since people began measuring time, the movements of objects in the sky have been used as points of reference. The movement of the sun, changes in the appearance of the moon, and changes in the positions of stars have all been used to measure time. Of these, the movement of the sun across the sky was the easiest to follow. Time can be determined by this movement of the sun by using a sundial, such as the one shown in Figure 3-6.

For thousands of years, noon in a particular place was the time the sun reached its highest point in the sky. When people began to travel farther from home, they became aware that noon occurs later as one moves farther west. Because of this difference in "local times," one city's clocks were set a little different from the next city's clocks. By the late 1800s travelers crossing the United States by train were encountering 53 different local times.

In 1883 an international system was set up to standardize time measurements. This system, which is still used today, is shown in Figure 3-7. According to the system, the earth is divided into 24 equal segments called **time zones**. The centers of bordering time zones are 15° of longitude apart. Clocks in a time zone are set to the local time at the center of the zone. The boundaries of the time zones vary according to local boundaries so that cities or towns are not split into different zones. The time zone to your east is one hour later than yours, and the time zone to your west is one hour earlier.

After completing this section, you will be able to

- **describe** how the movements of the earth can be used to determine time.
- **explain** why it was necessary to divide the earth into time zones.

The key terms in this section are
international   time zones
date line

Figure 3-6

A sundial tells time by the position of a shadow on a dial.

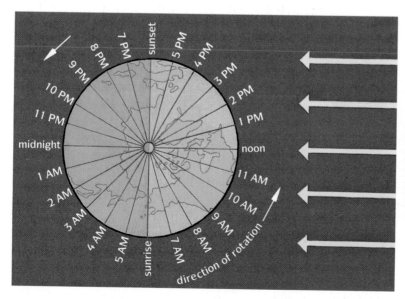

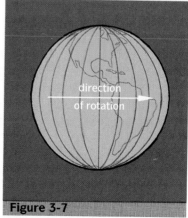

Figure 3-7

The earth is divided into 24 time zones. The lines in these figures mark the centers of time zones.

The time zones for North America are shown in Figure 3-8. When it is 2:00 P.M. in Atlanta, what time is it in Phoenix? What time is it in Juneau, Alaska? What time is it in Montreal? Imagine leaving home at 3:00 P.M., traveling west, and arriving in the next time zone one hour later. What time would it be there?

Suppose you go on a one-day trip around the world and a friend remains at home. You leave on Friday, November 20, at 9:00 A.M. You travel west, passing through all 24 time zones in 24 hours, and return home. Because you have set your watch back one hour at each time zone, it is still 9:00 A.M. on Friday, November 20, when you return, according to your watch. However, by your friend's watch, it is 9:00 A.M. on Saturday, November 21.

Figure 3-8

What time zone do you live in?

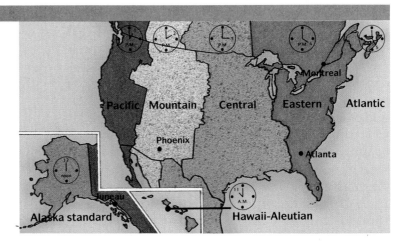

Figure 3-9

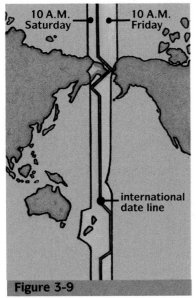

When people travel west from North America to Japan, they lose a day. They regain it when they return home.

The creation of the international date line eliminated problems such as this. The **international date line** is the place where one calendar day ends and the next begins. The international date line is an imaginary line located at 180° longitude. A traveler crossing the international date line finds that the time on a clock remains the same. However, the date changes when one crosses the line. When one goes west across the line, the date changes to the next day. When one goes east across the line, the date changes to the previous day.

In addition to being measured in days, time is also measured in years and months. A year is based on the time it takes for the earth to complete one revolution around the sun, or 365.24 days. An extra day is added to the calendar year during February of every fourth year to account for the extra .24 day per year. This fourth year is called a leap year.

OBJECTIVE

Observe the relationship between the apparent motion of the sun and time.

MATERIALS

compass, 30-cm-square piece of cardboard, small cube of clay (about 2 cm on a side), drinking straw, metric ruler

PROCEDURE

A. Draw a line along one edge of a 30-cm-square piece of cardboard as shown. The line should be 4 cm from the edge of the cardboard. Mark an X at the center of the line.

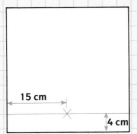

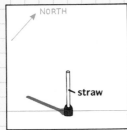

B. Firmly place a small cube of clay on the X. Stand a drinking straw upright in the clay.

C. Place your cardboard outside in direct sunlight. Turn the cardboard so that the straw's shadow falls across the middle of the cardboard. When you have done this, do not move the cardboard until you are told to do so.

D. Place a compass on your cardboard and draw an arrow that points north.

E. Mark the far end of the shadow and label the mark with the time.

F. Repeat step **E** every five minutes for 25 minutes. When you have finished, take your cardboard to your classroom and remove the straw and clay.

G. Measure the distance from the X to the first mark and to the last mark you made. Record these distances.

   1. Which distance is greater? Which shadow was longer?

   2. In what direction did the shadow move from the first mark to the last mark?

RESULTS AND CONCLUSIONS

1. In what direction does the sun appear to move across the sky?
2. How can shadows indicate direction?
3. How can shadows be used to indicate whether it is morning or afternoon?
4. How can shadows be used to tell time?

A lunar month is the time it takes for the moon to change from one full moon to the next. A lunar month is equal to 29.5 days. However, a calendar year is divided into 12 parts, which are called calendar months. A calendar month has 28, 30, or 31 days.

REVIEW

1. Describe how the movements of the earth can be used to determine time.
2. What is the purpose of having time zones?
3. What problem does the international date line solve?

CHALLENGE   A year is 365.24 days long. For three years our calendar year is 365 days long. Every fourth year an extra day is added to make up for the additional .24 days. However, adding a whole day every four years adds too much time. Calculate how many leap years will pass before one whole extra day has been added and a leap year must be skipped.

3-5 SEASONS

Another way that people measured time was by the change of seasons. The change of seasons is caused by the tilt of the earth's axis. As you can see in Figure 3-10, the earth's axis is tilted at an angle of 23.5°. As the earth revolves around the sun, its axis always points in the same direction. This causes each hemisphere to lean toward the sun during one part of the orbit and away from the sun during the opposite part of the orbit.

The tilt of the earth's axis affects how much energy a place on the earth receives from the sun. First, a place that receives the sun's rays directly receives more energy than a place that receives the rays at an angle. Second, a place that receives the sun's rays for a long period of time each day receives more energy than a place that receives the rays for a short period of time each day.

ACTIVITY   The Angle of Sunlight and the Seasons

OBJECTIVE
Determine the relationship between the angle at which sunlight strikes a surface and the concentration of solar energy received.

MATERIALS
overhead projector, clear overhead transparency, wax pencil, metric ruler, globe

PROCEDURE
A. Use a metric ruler and a wax pencil to make a grid on a clear overhead transparency. Each square in the grid should be 1 cm on each side. Place the grid on an overhead projector.
B. Project the grid onto a globe that is on the same level as the projector and about 1.5 m from it. The globe should be positioned so that its axis is vertical.

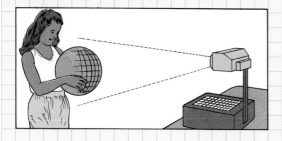

C. Find a grid shape that has been projected onto the globe at a place near 45° latitude and directly in front of the projector. Use the wax pencil to draw this shape directly on the globe. Repeat this with a shape directly below the first but at a place on the equator.
D. Use a metric ruler to measure the length and width of each grid shape you have drawn on the globe. Record the measurements.
E. Multiply the length of each grid shape by its width. This will give you the area of each shape. Record the area of each shape.

RESULTS AND CONCLUSIONS
1. Which shape was larger?
2. Suppose each square represented one unit of solar energy. Over which area would this energy be more concentrated—the area at 45° latitude or the area on the equator?
3. In which area would the energy strike more directly?
4. How is the angle at which the sun's rays strike an area related to the concentration of the solar energy in the area?

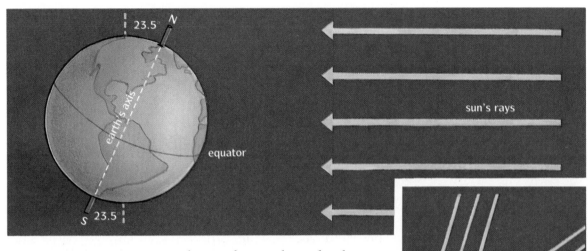

Figure 3-10

When the sun's rays strike a surface directly, the surface receives more energy than when the rays strike at an angle.

Summer occurs in a hemisphere when the hemisphere leans toward the sun. As shown in Figure 3-10, the sun's rays strike the hemisphere directly, or at a small angle, and for a long period of time each day. Winter occurs in a hemisphere when the hemisphere leans away from the sun. The sun's rays strike the hemisphere at a large angle and for a short period of time each day.

As the earth moves in its orbit around the sun, the seasons on the earth change. As you read about the changing seasons in the following paragraphs, refer to Figure 3-11. Notice how the tilt of the axis and the earth's position in its orbit determine the season.

At noon around March 21 the sun is directly overhead at the equator. Neither pole leans toward the sun. On this day the sun reaches the vernal equinox. The **vernal equinox** (VER nuhl   EE kwuh nahks) is a point in the sky through which the sun passes on the first day of spring in the Northern Hemisphere. As the earth continues in its orbit, the Northern Hemisphere leans more and more toward the sun. Each day at noon the sun is higher in the sky than on the previous day. The daylight hours increase, and the nights grow shorter.

The **summer solstice** (SUHM uhr   SAHL stihs) is a point in the sky through which the sun passes on the first day of summer in the Northern Hemisphere. The sun passes through the summer solstice around June 21, and is directly overhead at noon at the Tropic of Cancer. On this day the Northern Hemisphere has its longest period of daylight and its shortest night. As the earth continues its journey, the noon sun appears lower and lower in the sky. The period of daylight in the Northern Hemisphere grows shorter.

aequi (equal)
nox (night)

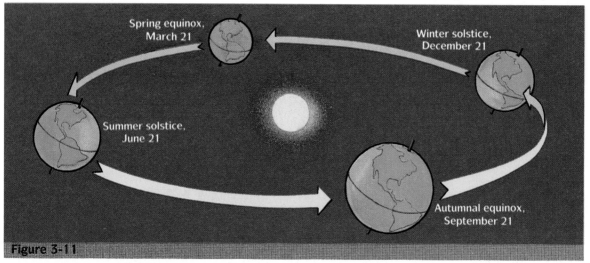

Figure 3-11

This diagram shows the earth's position at the start of every season.

The **autumnal equinox** (aw TUHM nuhl EE kwuh-nahks) is a point in the sky through which the sun passes on the first day of fall in the Northern Hemisphere. The sun passes through the autumnal equinox around September 23, and the noon sun again is directly overhead at the equator. As the earth continues to revolve, daylight hours in the Northern Hemisphere grow even shorter.

The **winter solstice** is a point in the sky through which the sun passes on the first day of winter in the Northern Hemisphere. The sun passes through the winter solstice around December 21, and the noon sun is directly overhead at the Tropic of Capricorn. On this day the Northern Hemisphere receives its shortest period of daylight and its longest night. As the earth continues to revolve, how will the period of daylight in the Northern Hemisphere change? How do the lengths of day and night in the Southern Hemisphere change from one equinox to the next?

REVIEW

1. Explain what causes the seasons in North America.
2. When it is summer in North America, what season is it in Australia?
3. In Figure 3-10, what season is occurring in the Northern Hemisphere?

CHALLENGE The longest day of the year in the Northern Hemisphere is around June 21, yet the warmest summer days do not occur until July or August. The shortest day of the year is around December 21, yet the coldest winter days do not occur until January or February. How can you explain these delays in hottest and coldest weather?

3-6 THE MOON

DESCRIPTION OF THE MOON

The brightest object in the night sky is the moon. The moon is our nearest neighbor in the solar system. The moon's diameter, 3476 km, is about one fourth of the earth's diameter, and its mass is about one eighteenth of the mass of the earth. This natural satellite follows an ellipse-shaped orbit around the earth at an average distance of 384,400 km.

The force of gravity on the moon is one sixth of that on the earth. This weak force is able to hold only a very thin atmosphere. A thicker atmosphere, such as that on the earth, helps to insulate a planet. Because of the lack of an insulating atmosphere on the moon, the temperature in the direct sunlight reaches 130°C, and in the shade, it can drop to −170°C.

Figure 3-12 shows a model of the structure of the moon. The model is based, in part, on evidence obtained by astronauts who visited the moon. Like the earth, the moon is thought to have layers. The *crust,* or top layer, is made up of rock material similar to that found on the earth. The same elements that make up the earth make up the moon. But the elements are found in different amounts on the moon than on the earth. Below the crust is a layer called the *mantle.* It is thought to be made of rock material. Beneath the mantle the moon probably has a small *core.* This core may contain some iron and perhaps other metals. However, the moon does not contain as high a percentage of iron as does the earth. This fact may explain why the moon is not as dense as the earth.

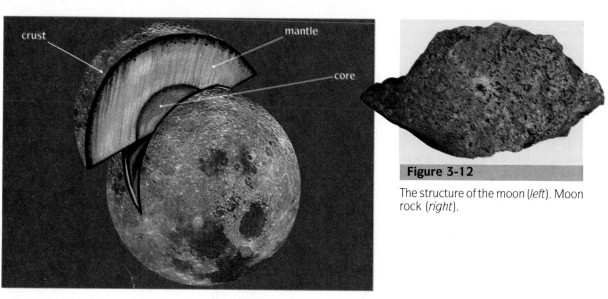

Figure 3-12

The structure of the moon (*left*). Moon rock (*right*).

The astronauts left many instruments on the moon. These instruments have helped scientists to study moonquakes and the magnetic properties of the moon. Some of the instruments have helped to more accurately measure the distance from the earth to the moon. From these instruments scientists have learned that quakes occur on the moon. The moon does not have a magnetic field, although it may once have had one. The lack of a magnetic field may be due to the small core and low amount of iron on the moon. Finally, measurements of the distance to the moon are now accurate to within several centimeters!

SURFACE FEATURES OF THE MOON

Although the early history of the moon is unclear, one theory about the moon's more recent history is generally accepted. After the moon formed, its surface was a hot liquid, hundreds of kilometers deep. Very light gases escaped the moon's gravity into space. In time the moon's surface began to cool and form a solid crust.

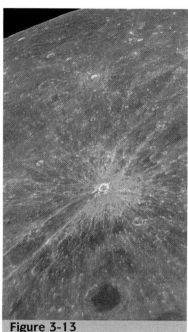

Figure 3-13

The moon has a variety of surface features.

OBJECTIVES

Sketch the surface of the moon.
Identify some of the features on the moon's surface.

MATERIALS

sheet of paper, pencil, binoculars, lunar map

PROCEDURE

A. Use a calendar to determine when the next full moon will occur.
B. On the night of the full moon, or the night before or the night after, go outdoors and observe the moon.
C. Make a sketch of the moon. Include as much detail as you can see. Label the sketch "Moon—Naked-Eye View."
D. Observe the moon with a pair of binoculars.
E. Make a sketch of the moon as it appears in the binoculars. Include as much detail as you can see. Label the sketch "Moon—Through Binoculars."
F. Using a map of the lunar surface, identify and label as many features as you can in each sketch.

RESULTS AND CONCLUSIONS

1. How do the sketches compare as to the amount of detail?
2. List the features that could be identified with the naked eye.
3. List the features that could be identified when using the binoculars.

EXTENSION

Observe the moon through a small telescope. Make a sketch of the moon. Identify the features in your sketch by using a lunar map. Compare this sketch with your other sketches.

The moon's gravity attracted rocks from space. These rocks formed craters as they crashed into the moon's surface. **Craters** are circular depressions on the moon's surface. Craters vary in size from small pits in boulders to the largest crater, which has a diameter of over 200 km.

Several types of craters can be seen on the moon. Some craters are surrounded by rays. These rays are the result of material that sprayed across the moon's surface when the crater was made. Molten rock from below the surface leaked out over the floors of some craters. This formed craters with flat bottoms. When molten material leaked over the floor of a huge crater, a mare (MAHR ee) was formed. A **mare** is a flat area on the moon's surface.

Today, small rocks still strike the moon. A soil made of broken rock and dust covers the surface. With little atmosphere to change the features, the landscape of the moon is much as it was after it first formed.

ORIGIN OF THE MOON

Throughout history, people have wondered about the origin of the moon. In recent times, three basic theories for the moon's origin have been developed. Each of the theories has supporting evidence as well as unanswered questions.

The *daughter theory* suggests that when the earth was still very hot and rapidly spinning, a piece of it tore off. According to this theory, the piece contained materials

that had floated to the top of the molten earth. The piece moved some distance away from the earth and then settled into an orbit as the earth's gravity pulled on it. The daughter theory is not supported by the scientists who feel that the earth could not have been spinning fast enough to throw off such a large amount of material.

The *capture theory* states that the moon formed in another part of the solar system and was caught by the gravity of the earth as it passed by. This idea would explain why the composition of the moon is a little different from that of the earth. This theory is not supported by the scientists who feel that the earth's gravity is not strong enough to catch a body as large as the moon.

The *sister theory* suggests that the moon and the earth formed at the same time in about the same area of the solar system. According to the sister theory, the earth and the moon started as collections of dust and gases that formed near each other. As the earth and the moon formed, each began to pull on the other, forming the earth-moon system known today. Since many scientists think the solar system formed from a collection of dust and gas, the sister theory is the most widely accepted theory for the origin of the moon.

There are still many questions to be answered about each of these theories. Possibly a new and different explanation will be created. Or maybe one of these three theories will prove to be accurate.

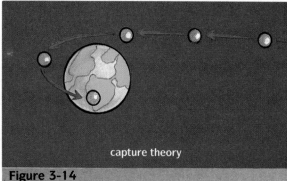

capture theory

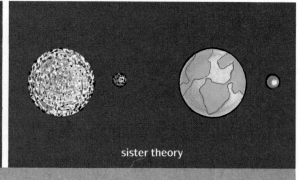

sister theory

Figure 3-14

Two of the theories of the moon's origin are the capture theory and the sister theory.

REVIEW

1. How does the moon compare to the earth in size, mass, temperature, and gravity?
2. Describe how craters on the moon formed.
3. How are the three scientific theories that describe the formation of the moon similar? How are they different?

CHALLENGE How much mass would you have on the moon?

3-7 THE EARTH AND THE MOON

MOTIONS OF THE EARTH AND MOON

The moon rotates once every 27.3 days, the same time as its period of revolution around the earth. Thus the same side of the moon always faces the earth. The moon circles the earth in an ellipse-shaped orbit. In its orbit it is closer to the earth at some points than at others. The astronauts who went to the moon left mirrors from which scientists on the earth can reflect laser light. Knowing exactly how fast light travels, the scientists measure how long it takes the light to reach the moon and reflect back. With this information they are able to measure the distance to the moon to within several centimeters at any place in its orbit. *Perigee* (PEHR uh jee) is the point at which the moon is closest to the earth, about 360,000 km. *Apogee* (AP uh jee) is the point at which the moon is farthest from earth, about 404,800 km.

After completing this section, you will be able to
- **describe** the moon's motion with respect to the earth.
- **illustrate** why the moon is seen in phases.
- **describe** what causes an eclipse.

The key terms in this section are
annular   phases
    eclipse   solar eclipse
lunar eclipse

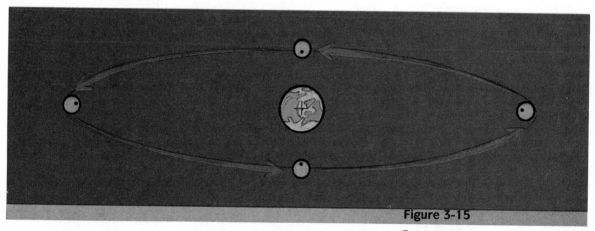

Figure 3-15

Because the moon rotates at the same speed that it revolves, the same side of the moon always faces the earth.

The earth and the moon revolve around a common center of gravity. This center of gravity is within the earth, since the earth has so much more mass than the moon. Thus the moon is thought of as orbiting, or revolving around, the earth.

PHASES OF THE MOON

The moon does not produce its own light, as a star does. The moon is seen from the earth because sunlight is reflected off its surface. The surface of the moon is only about as reflective as an asphalt roadway. However, the sun is a powerful source of light and the moon is not too far away from the earth, so the moon appears bright to us. In fact, on a clear night it is easy to find your way through a country area with only the light of a full moon.

The sun lights the half of the moon that is facing the sun. The shape the moon appears to have from the earth depends on how much of the side of the moon facing the earth is lit by the sun. The different shapes of the moon are called **phases**. As you read about the changing phases of the moon, locate the phases in Figure 3-16.

The *new moon* phase occurs when the moon is between the earth and the sun. At this time the dark side of the moon faces the earth. As the moon revolves, more of the lighted side becomes visible each evening. During this time the moon is said to be waxing, or growing.

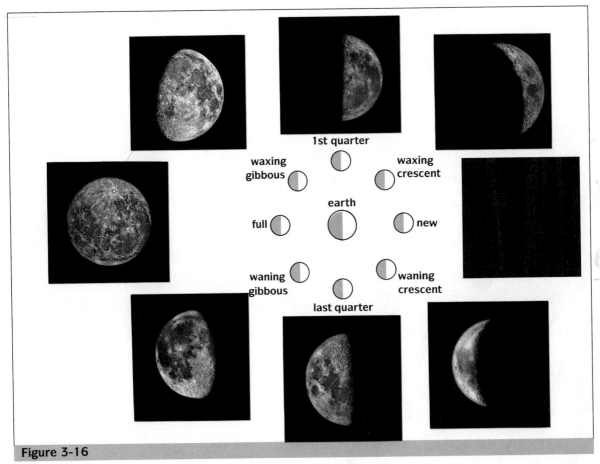

Figure 3-16

The phases of the moon.

The first visible phase is the *crescent* phase. After about one week, half of the lighted side is visible. This phase is called the *first-quarter* phase. The moon has now traveled one quarter of the way around the earth. Around the end of the second week, the moon enters the *full-moon* phase. How much of the lighted surface are we seeing at full moon? Between the first-quarter and full-moon phases is a *gibbous* phase.

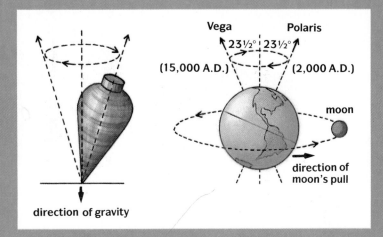
After the full-moon phase, the moon begins to wane, or grow smaller. By the end of about three weeks, the moon has gone through another *gibbous* phase and has reached the *last-quarter* phase. As in the first-quarter phase, only half of the sunlit side of the moon is now visible. During the final week of its revolution around the earth, the moon goes through another *crescent* phase. Then it becomes a new moon again.

ECLIPSES

All objects in the solar system cast shadows into space. The shadows cast by these objects have two parts. The part of the shadow directly behind an object is a cone-shaped area called the *umbra* (UHM bruh). Light is completely blocked in the umbra. A larger cone-shaped area called the *penumbra* (pih NUHM bruh) surrounds the umbra. Only some of the light is blocked in the penumbra.

umbra (shadow)

An eclipse occurs when one object passes through the shadow of another. A **lunar eclipse** occurs when the moon passes through the shadow of the earth. A **solar eclipse** occurs when the earth passes through the moon's shadow. A total eclipse occurs in a region when the umbra covers that region. A partial eclipse occurs in a region

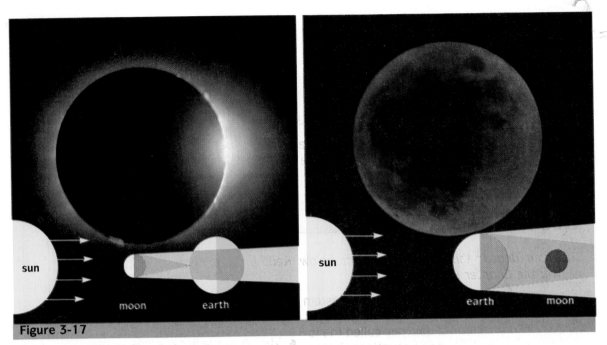

Figure 3-17

A total solar eclipse (*left*) and a lunar eclipse (*right*).

when the penumbra covers the region. If the moon is too far from the earth, as it is at apogee, its umbra will not reach the earth. Such an event is called an **annular eclipse**. During an annular eclipse, a ring of sunlight can be seen surrounding the moon.

Eclipses can only occur when the earth, moon, and sun form a straight line. Although this occurs twice each month, eclipses do not occur twice each month. Usually, the moon's shadow passes above or below the earth, or the moon passes above or below the earth's shadow. No more than seven eclipses—two lunar eclipses and five solar eclipses—can occur in a single year.

Total solar eclipses can occur only in a narrow region on the earth. This narrow region is never wider than 269 km. A total solar eclipse lasts no more than 7.5 minutes at any one place on the earth. This is because it takes no more than 7.5 minutes for a place on the earth to rotate through the umbra. The sky is dark during a total solar eclipse.

Unlike a solar eclipse, a lunar eclipse can be seen from everywhere on one side of the earth. A total lunar eclipse lasts more than 2 hours. However, even during a total lunar eclipse the moon can be seen from the earth. This is because the earth's atmosphere acts like a lens, bending certain colors of light, especially red light. For this reason, the moon has a reddish-copper glow during a total eclipse.

REVIEW

1. How does the moon move with respect to the earth?
2. Describe what causes a solar eclipse.
3. Draw a diagram to illustrate the positions of the earth, the sun, and the moon during the *new, first-quarter, full,* and *third-quarter* phases of the moon.
4. Why is it a rare event to see a total solar eclipse?

CHALLENGE How much of the moon's surface would be seen during a year if the moon did not rotate on its axis?

CHAPTER SUMMARY

The main ideas in this chapter are listed below. Read these statements before you answer the Chapter Review questions.

- The earth is the third planet in a solar system in the Milky Way galaxy. The Milky Way is located in a cluster of galaxies called the local group, which is one of countless clusters in the universe (3-1)

- Distances in the solar system are measured in astronomical units. Larger distances in space are measured in light-years. (3-1)

- The earth is sphere shaped. It consists of three layers—the atmosphere, the hydrosphere, and the lithosphere—and is surrounded by a magnetic field. (3-2)

- The earth rotates on its axis and revolves around the sun. (3-3)

- Time zones have been set up around the world to standardize time measurements. The center of each time zone is 15° longitude from the center of each bordering time zone. (3-4)

- Time on the earth is tied to movements of the earth, moon, and sun. (3-4)

- The tilt of the earth's axis causes the change of seasons. (3-5)

- The moon is about one fourth the size of the earth, has a force of gravity that is one sixth of that on the earth, and is not as dense as the earth. (3-6)

- Three basic theories about the origin of the moon are the daughter theory, the capture theory, and the sister theory. (3-6)

- As seen from the earth, the moon changes from a full moon to a new moon and back to a full moon each month. (3-7)

- Eclipses occur either when the earth passes through the moon's shadow or when the moon passes through the earth's shadow. (3-7)

The key terms in this chapter are listed below. Use each term in a sentence that shows the meaning of the term.

annular eclipse	light-year	rotation
astronomical unit	lithosphere	solar eclipse
atmosphere	lunar eclipse	summer solstice
autumnal equinox	magnetosphere	time zones
craters	mare	Van Allen belts
hydrosphere	phases	vernal equinox
international date line	revolution	winter solstice

Chapter Review

Use the key terms from this chapter to complete the following sentences correctly.

1. The regions surrounding the earth where charged particles are concentrated by the earth's magnetic field are called _____.

2. A large flat area on the moon is called a/an _____.

3. The _____ marks the first day of spring in the Northern Hemisphere.

4. A distance in the solar system is measured in a/an _____.

5. The earth is divided into 24 equal segments called _____.

6. A/an _____ occurs when the moon passes through the earth's shadow.

7. The turning of an object around its axis is _____.

8. The layer of water on the earth is called the _____.

9. Circular depressions on the moon's surface are called _____.

10. The movement of the earth around the sun is called _____.

CONCEPTS

1. Why are units of measurement such as the astronomical unit and the light-year useful when discussing distances in space? (3-1)

2. Why is it more practical to use the astronomical unit to measure distances in the solar system than it would be to use the light-year? (3-1)

3. Describe the structure of the earth. (3-2)

4. Distinguish between the atmosphere and the magnetosphere. (3-2)

5. What are the Van Allen belts? (3-2)

6. What are two ways the earth moves? (3-3)

7. Describe the movement of the earth around the sun. (3-3)

8. Distinguish between *perihelion* and *aphelion*. (3-3)

9. How is the movement of the sun across the sky used to tell time? (3-4)

10. Why are time zones necessary? (3-4)

11. Describe the international time zone system used today. (3-4)

12. What is the purpose of the international date line? (3-4)

13. Describe two factors that help determine how much energy a region on the earth receives from the sun. (3-5)

14. Distinguish betwen the vernal equinox and the autumnal equinox. (3-5)

15. What event occurs on the summer solstice? On the winter solstice? (3-5)

16. Compare the earth and the moon. (3-6)

17. Describe three theories for the origin of the moon. (3-6)

18. Describe the surface of the moon. (3-6)

19. Describe the motion of the moon around the earth. (3-7)

20. Distinguish between *perigee* and *apogee*. (3-7)

21. Describe what determines which phase of the moon can be seen from the earth. (3-7)

22. Distinguish between *umbra* and *penumbra*. (3-7)

23. What causes a lunar eclipse? (3-7)

1. How long would it take for light to travel the distance around the earth once?

2. Explain why seasons are so similar in the region between the Tropic of Cancer and the Tropic of Capricorn.

3. How would the weather and seasons on the earth be different if the earth's axis were not tilted?

4. Why doesn't summer in the Northern Hemisphere occur when the earth is closest to the sun?

5. Is the surface of the moon likely to change much in the next 100 years? In the next 500 years? Explain your answers.

1. Design an experiment to prove that the earth rotates. If you need help, find out about a pendulum designed by a French scientist named Jean Foucault (1819–1868).

2. Place a piece of thin cardboard over a bar magnet. Sprinkle some iron filings on the cardboard. Observe the magnet's magnetic field. How is it similar to the earth's magnetic field?

3. Find out why we see the planet Venus in phases.

Gallant, Ray. *Our Universe*. Washington, D.C.: National Geographic Society, 1980.

Moore, Patrick. *The Moon*. Chicago: Rand McNally & Co., 1981.

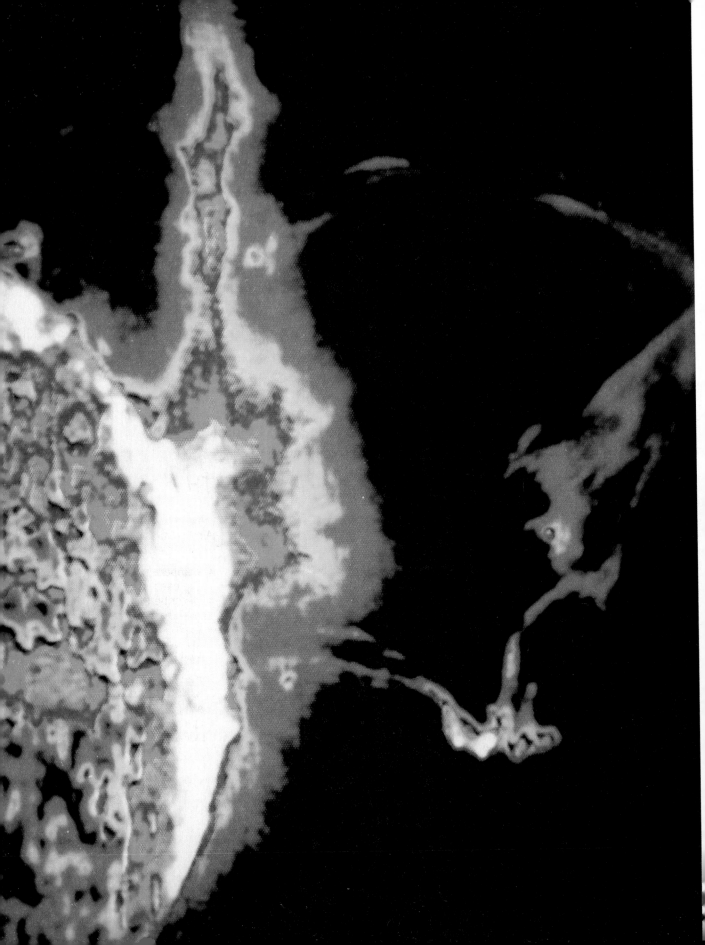

THE EARTH AND THE SUN

The photograph shows hot gases erupting from the sun. Each color represents a different temperature. The sun is a star composed mainly of hydrogen and helium gases. Deep inside it is powered by a nuclear furnace. The energy released by its furnace works its way slowly to the surface. There it is released outward into the solar system at the speed of light.

- *What do the colors show about the surface temperature of the sun?*
- *What does the photograph show about the size of eruptions on the sun?*
- *How does the loop of gas in the photograph show that there are strong forces around the sun?*

4-1 A CHANGING VIEW OF THE EARTH

You probably know that the sun rises in the east and sets in the west. If you observed the moon and the stars for an hour or more at night, you would see that they also move from east to west. It may seem that the earth is motionless. But the motions of the sun, moon, and stars in the sky have a great deal to do with the motion of the earth in space.

The first ideas to be recorded about the earth in space were those of the Sumerians, of the Middle East, about 5000 years ago. The Sumerians believed that the earth was flat and motionless and at the center of the universe. They also believed that the sky was a metal dome on which gods moved the sun, moon, stars, and planets.

Many discoveries about the earth and heavenly bodies were made by the ancient Greeks. For example, Aristotle (384–322 B.C.) observed the curved shadow of the earth on the moon during a lunar eclipse. From this observation he concluded that the earth was round.

Another Greek, Aristarchus (312–230 B.C.), used the size of the earth's shadow on the moon during a lunar eclipse as evidence that the sun was much larger than the

After completing this section, you will be able to

- **compare** two early models of the earth in space.
- **describe** Ptolemy's model of the universe
- **explain** how the telescope showed that the sun was the center of the solar system.

The key terms in this section are
earth-centered model
ellipse
epicycle
sun-centered model

Figure 4-1

Partial lunar eclipse.

earth. Aristarchus proposed that the sun was the center of the universe. He suggested that the earth and other planets revolved around the sun in circles.

Hundreds of years later, in the second century A.D., a Greek scientist named Ptolemy (TAHL uh mee) rejected the ideas of Aristarchus. In Ptolemy's model of the universe, the earth remained motionless at the center of the universe. All other bodies moved in circles around the earth. Ptolemy's model, with all objects moving around the earth, is called the **earth-centered model**.

Ptolemy observed that the sun, moon, and stars moved from east to west in the sky. He also observed that the planets sometimes moved from west to east. For example, Figure 4-2 shows the movement of the planet Mars among the stars for a one-year period. Notice the loop in the motion of Mars. Other planets show the same type of motion. To explain this reverse motion of the planets, Ptolemy placed the planets in small circles called epicycles. An **epicycle** is a small circle that is carried around in a larger circle. Ptolemy's model of the universe is shown in Figure 4-3. As you can see, the sun, moon, and planets are shown moving in small circles at the same time they are revolving around the earth. How do epicycles help explain the reverse motion of the planets?

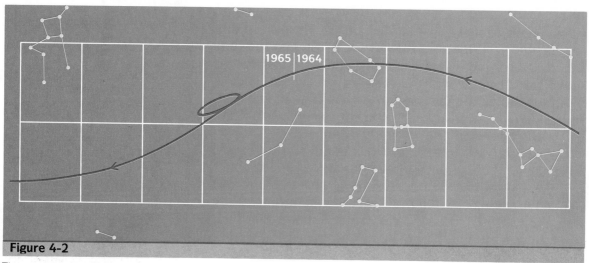

Figure 4-2

The apparent movement of Mars across the night sky in one year.

The earth-centered universe became the accepted view of the earth in space for the next 13 centuries. However, in the sixteenth century, an astronomer named Nicolaus Copernicus (1473–1543) proposed a new model of the universe. In Copernicus's model the earth was a planet, just like the other planets known at that time. His model

Figure 4-3

Ptolemy's model of the universe showed the planets circling the earth.

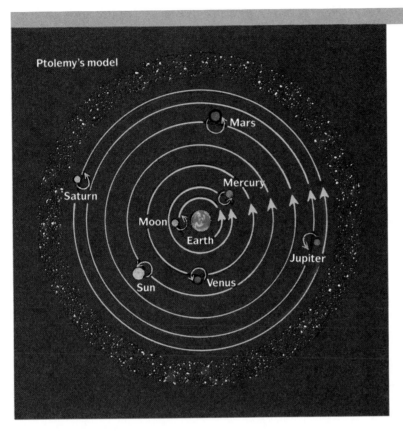

Ptolemy's model

SCIENCE PUZZLER

The stars in this photograph appear as partial circles in the sky. The photograph was made by pointing a camera at the night sky and leaving the shutter open for a period of time. The circular pattern of stars that formed in the picture was caused by the rotation of the earth. By looking at the pattern carefully, you will see that the stars form arcs, or parts of circles. Using the length of the arcs, what was the exposure time of the film, or amount of time the shutter of the camera was left open?

had the sun at the center and the known planets—Mercury, Venus, Earth, Mars, Jupiter, and Saturn—orbiting the sun. The model had the moon revolving around the earth. Copernicus explained that the motions of the sun and stars were caused by the earth rotating on its axis. Copernicus's model, with the planets moving around the sun, is called the **sun-centered model**.

A Danish astronomer, Tycho Brahe (1546–1601), did not believe in Copernicus's model. Instead, he believed that the earth was at the center of the universe. Without using a telescope, he made measurements that were the most accurate of his time. In 1600, Brahe was joined by a young assistant named Johannes Kepler (1571–1630). Kepler was very interested in Copernicus's sun-centered model of the universe. When Brahe died, Kepler used Brahe's data to show that the Copernicus model was better. Kepler's work showed that the planets moved around the sun. Kepler also showed that the orbits of the planets were not perfectly round. He said that the planets moved in orbits shaped like slightly flattened circles. A slightly flattened circle is called an **ellipse**.

The invention of the telescope in 1607 changed the science of astronomy. Telescopes allowed scientists to see stars and planets more clearly and to discover objects that no one knew existed. Galileo (1564–1642) is thought to have been the first scientist to turn a telescope toward the heavens. Galileo saw that the planet Jupiter had moons, which meant that all objects did not revolve around the earth. He also studied the planet Venus through his telescope. According to the earth-centered model, shown in Figure 4-4 (*left*), Venus should have always appeared as a crescent from the earth. But Galileo saw that Venus actually went through phases, as the moon did. Look at Figure 4-4 (*right*). This discovery meant that Venus moved in an orbit around the sun. It was evidence that the sun was the center of the solar system. The sun-centered model of the solar system eventually became the accepted model.

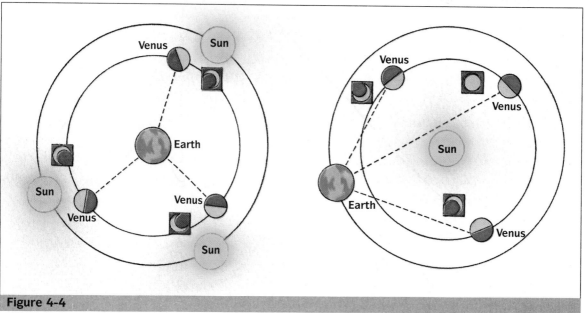

Figure 4-4

Galileo noticed that Venus, like the moon, went through phases. If Venus and the sun circled the earth, Venus should always have appeared to be a crescent.

REVIEW

1. Compare two models of the earth in space.
2. How did Ptolemy describe the motion of the sun, moon, and planets?
3. How did the telescope provide evidence for the sun-centered model of the solar system?

CHALLENGE One of Kepler's findings was that planets in orbits closer to the sun travel faster than planets in orbits farther away. How does this explain the west-to-east motion of some planets in the sky?

4-2 ORIGIN OF THE SOLAR SYSTEM

People have always wondered where the earth came from. One of the earliest stories dates about 3000 B.C. According to the story, the earth rose out of the sea. Any theory that explains how the earth formed should also explain how the solar system formed. The theory should explain certain characteristics of the solar system. First, the planets revolve around the sun in the same direction and in nearly the same plane. Second, the sun and most of the planets rotate in the same direction. Venus, Uranus, and Pluto rotate in the direction opposite to that of the sun and the other planets. Third, the planets differ in composition. The four planets closest to the sun are solid and contain heavy materials, such as metals. Excluding Pluto, the outer planets are made mostly of light gases— for example, hydrogen.

After completing this section, you will be able to

- **list** the characteristics that a theory for the origin of the system must explain.
- **describe** the collision hypothesis.
- **describe** the modern nebular hypothesis.

The key terms in this section are
collision hypothesis
nebular hypothesis
protoplanet

Figure 4-5

The great nebula in Orion.

A theory that explains characteristics of the solar system should also agree with observations. As you learned in Section 4-1, early telescopes were used to view objects in the sky. Some of the faint objects in the sky were found to be clouds of gas and dust called *nebulas*. Figure 4-5 shows a nebula in the constellation Orion. It is thought that stars are forming in this nebula. One hypothesis, proposed in the 1700s, said that the solar system formed

nebula (cloud)

77

from such a cloud. This hypothesis was called the nebular hypothesis. According to the **nebular hypothesis**, the solar system began to form as the cloud contracted, or came together. As the cloud contracted, it began to spin. The spinning motion of the cloud caused it to flatten into a disk. At the center of the disk, the gas and dust contracted into the sun. The remaining gas around the sun condensed into the planets and the other bodies of the solar system.

The nebular hypothesis explains many things about the solar system. For example, the spinning motion of the cloud explains why the planets revolve around the sun in the same direction. The flattening of the cloud explains why the planets revolve around the sun in nearly the same plane.

However, the nebular hypothesis does not explain everything. The hypothesis says that the planets and sun formed from the same material, yet the sun and planets have different compositions. The hypothesis does not explain how a cloud could condense into separate pieces.

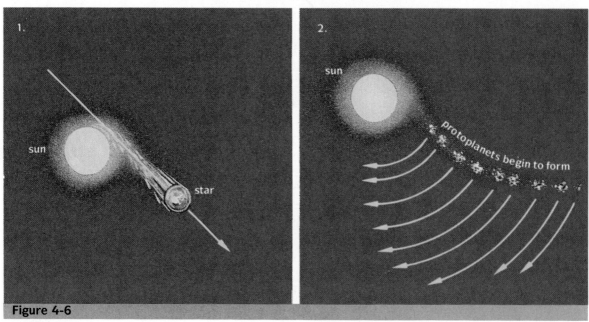

Figure 4-6

The collision hypothesis of the origin of the solar system.

Another hypothesis, proposed around 1900, said that while the sun was forming, a star passed close to it. As shown in Figure 4-6, the star pulled matter from the sun and scattered it across space. What force would pull the matter from the sun? Some of this matter condensed to form the bodies of the solar system. The idea that the planets were formed as a result of a star pulling matter from the sun is called the **collision hypothesis**.

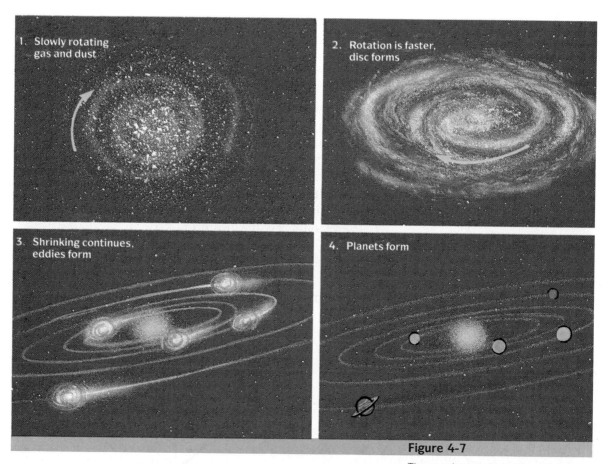

1. Slowly rotating gas and dust

2. Rotation is faster, disc forms

3. Shrinking continues, eddies form

4. Planets form

Figure 4-7

The modern nebular hypothesis of the origin of the solar system.

The collision hypothesis, like the nebular hypothesis, explains how the planets were placed along one plane. It also explains why the outer planets are larger, since the outer planets would travel along a longer orbit and collect more matter. However, there are two main arguments against this hypothesis. First, many scientists feel that a near collision between the sun and a star is a highly unlikely event because observations show that stars are so far apart. Second, if a star did pull matter from the sun, it is more likely that the gravity of the sun would simply pull the matter back into the sun.

A more recent hypothesis is based on the nebular hypothesis. This hypothesis is called the *modern nebular hypothesis*. It is the most widely accepted hypothesis today. Notice in Figure 4-7 that, like the first nebular hypothesis, it states that the solar system formed from a spinning cloud of gas and dust. As the cloud spun, small whirlpools formed within it. Most of the matter within the cloud was pulled by gravity to the center of the cloud. But matter also collected in the whirlpools. These whirlpools of matter

Telescopes on the earth view the universe through the atmosphere. The earth's atmosphere absorbs light waves coming from space. Therefore, the images received by telescopes on the earth are distorted. A new telescope, launched into space by a space shuttle, does not have this problem. At 500 km above the earth there is no distortion. This new telescope will help to clear up some mysteries about the universe.

The space telescope can detect objects that are 50 times fainter than those the earth telescopes detect. Imagine being able to read a license plate from 160 km away! Since the telescope will be serviced by space shuttle crews, it will remain active for at least 15 years.

The telescope will allow astronomers to study galaxies, supernovas, and other star systems in ways not possible until now.

In a way, a telescope is a time machine. The space telescope will show astronomers how galaxies looked billions of years ago. By comparing these young galaxies with older ones nearer the earth, astronomers may learn how galaxies form. The space telescope will provide clues to what it was like when the universe began.

proto (first)

which were the beginnings of the bodies of the solar system, are called **protoplanets**. Matter that collected in the center of the cloud became the sun when the pressure became high enough to cause it to radiate energy. The heat of the early sun drove off the lighter elements from the planets near the sun. For this reason, the planets near the sun became solid and rocklike. The planets farther away retained the lighter gases.

The modern nebular hypothesis is the most widely accepted hypothesis of the origin of the solar system. Look back at the list of characteristics that this hypothesis should explain. Which ones does it explain? Which characteristics would need further study?

REVIEW

1. Describe the characteristics that a hypothesis for the origin of the solar system must explain.
2. Compare the collision hypothesis with the modern nebular hypothesis.
3. Why does the modern nebular hypothesis seem to be a good explanation for the formation of the solar system?

CHALLENGE Which hypothesis for the origin of the moon in Chapter 3 best fits the modern nebular hypothesis?

4-3 THE SUN

The sun is a large sphere of very hot gases. It is so large that all the planets and moons of the solar system could easily fit inside of it. Over 100 earths could line up along the sun's diameter of 1,392,000 km. More than 1 million earths would be needed to fill its volume. The sun is less dense than the earth, but it is so much larger that it would still take about 333,000 earths to equal its mass. More than 99.8 percent of the matter in the solar system is present in the sun.

The sun contains at least 80 of the elements that are found on the earth. But by composition, the sun is about 92.1 percent hydrogen and 7.8 percent helium. The remaining 0.1 percent is a combination of the other elements. All of these elements exist in a form of matter called plasma. *Plasma* is matter in which atoms have lost their electrons because of very high temperatures.

The sun is believed to be made up of layers. Because the sun is gaseous, there are no definite boundaries between the layers. Instead, the layers blend into each other. Refer to Figure 4-8 as the layers of the sun are discussed.

The layer at the center of the sun is the **core**. As you can see in Figure 4-8, the core is small compared with the entire sun. But the core contains almost half of the sun's matter. According to Figure 4-8, what is the temperature of the core? The pressure here is about 200 billion times the pressure on the earth's surface.

> *After completing this section, you will be able to*
>
> - **compare** the diameter, mass, and volume of the sun and the earth.
> - **describe** the composition of the sun.
> - **explain** how the sun produces energy.
> - **diagram** the structure of the sun.
>
> *The key terms in this section are*
> chromosphere
> convection zone
> core
> corona
> photosphere
> radiation zone

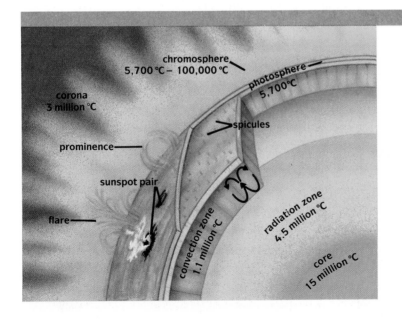

Figure 4-8

The structure of the sun.

As energy from the sun's core moves outward, it passes into the radiation zone. As you can see in Figure 4-8, the **radiation zone** is the thickest layer of the sun. In this layer, the temperature and pressure are less than in the core. Here the temperature is about 4.5 million °C.

Energy is transferred from the radiation zone to the sun's surface in the layer called the **convection zone**. The convection zone is cooler than the radiation zone. The temperature in this zone is about 1.1 million °C.

The **photosphere** is the visible surface of the sun. It produces mostly visible light. The temperature of the photosphere is about 5700°C. Notice in Figure 4-9 the granular surface of the photosphere. The bright areas are places where hot plasma from within is rising to the surface. These small bright areas that cover the photosphere are called *granules*. Granules are too small to be seen without a telescope, but they average 2000 km across.

Above the photosphere is the first layer of the sun's atmosphere, called the **chromosphere** (KROH muh sfir). The name *chromosphere,* meaning "colored sphere," is used because of the faint red light of this layer. The chromosphere is not usually visible, because the photosphere is so bright. It can be seen, however, during eclipses of the sun, when light from the photosphere is blocked by the moon. The tiny flames seen on the chromosphere in Figure 4-10 are called spicules. *Spicules* are pointed columns of gas extending upward from the chromosphere. They reach heights 1000 times greater than the earth's largest mountains. The temperature in the chromosphere rises from 5700°C at its bottom to 100,000°C at its top.

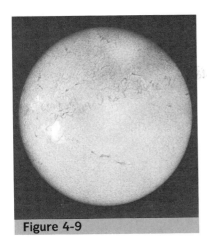

Figure 4-9

The surface of the sun has a granular appearance.

chroma (color)

Figure 4-10

During a total solar eclipse, the corona of the sun is visible. This is a computer-enhanced photograph.

The outer layer of the sun's atmosphere is called the **corona**. The corona is less dense than the chromosphere. The corona is not normally visible, but it can be seen as a halo around the sun during a solar eclipse. Identify the corona in Figure 4-10. Temperatures reaching almost 3 million °C have been measured in the corona.

corona (crown)

The sun produces a great amount of energy. For example, the sun produces enough energy in one second to supply the electricity needed by the United States for 50 million years. How does the sun produce its energy? One early idea was that the gas in the sun burned. However, it was found that an amount of coal equal to the sun's mass would burn out in less than 5000 years. Evidence from *fossils,* or the remains of once living things, shows that there has been life on the earth for millions of years. Other findings showed that a ball of gas equal to the sun's mass would burn out in only 1500 years.

A clue to how the sun produces energy came with the discovery that a small amount of mass could be changed into a large amount of energy. Another clue came with the discovery of a process called *fusion.* In fusion, small nuclei combine under high temperatures and pressures to form larger nuclei. In this process, a small amount of mass is changed into a large amount of energy.

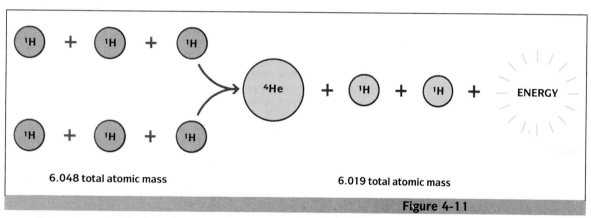

6.048 total atomic mass   6.019 total atomic mass

Figure 4-11

Scientists think that fusion takes place in the core of the sun. Here the temperature and pressure are high enough. In the core, hydrogen forms helium. The fusion process is shown in Figure 4-11. Six hydrogen nuclei join to form one helium nucleus and two hydrogen nuclei. Notice that the nuclei have less mass after the process. This missing mass has been changed into energy.

Scientists think that it takes about 10 million years for energy that is released in the core to reach the sun's surface. When the energy reaches the radiation zone, it is

Thermonuclear reactions occurring in the sun produce energy.

ACTIVITY   How Large Is the Sun?

OBJECTIVE
Measure the size of the sun.

MATERIALS
two 7.5 cm × 12.5 cm index cards, nail, meterstick, tape, metric scale

PROCEDURE

A. Use a nail to punch a round hole in the center of one index card.

B. Attach this first index card and another card to a meterstick with tape so that they stand 90 cm apart.

C. With your teacher's permission, move your meterstick to a place where it can be aimed at the sun. **Caution:** Never look directly at the sun. Aim the meterstick so that sunlight passes through the hole in the first card and shines on the second card, forming an image of the sun on the second card. The sun's image may be clearer if the second card is shaded.

D. Applying the rules of geometry, if you know the distance from the first index card to both the sun and its image, and the distance across one of the objects, then you can determine the distance across the other. The distance to the sun is 150 million km. The distance to the second card is 90 cm. Measure the distance across the sun's image on the second index card.

1. How far is it across the sun's image?

E. Using rules of geometry, when the cards are 90 cm apart and the sun is 150 million km away, the diameter of the sun is 1,666,660 times the distance across the sun's image on the second card. Multiply, 1,666,660 times your measurement in centimeters.

2. What is your estimate for the diameter of the sun?

RESULTS AND CONCLUSIONS

1. How close is your measurement to 1,392,000 km, an astronomer's measurement?

2. How does your measurement compare with the measurements your classmates obtained?

3. Why, do you think, were the measurements different?

4. How could you make your measurements more accurate?

---

passed from particle to particle. Each particle absorbs the energy and then releases it to the next particle. When the energy reaches the convection zone, hot gases carry it outward in *convection cells*. Hot gases rise by a process called convection. *Convection* is a process of transferring heat by moving material due to differences in temperature. Convection is the process that causes bubbles to rise in a pot of boiling water. As the energy nears the photosphere, or surface of the sun, much of it is changed into light.

REVIEW

1. How do the diameter, mass, and volume of the sun compare with those of the earth?
2. What is the composition of the sun?
3. How does the sun produce the energy that it radiates?
4. Diagram and label the structure of the sun.

CHALLENGE If you were going to build a scale model of the solar system and your scale was 1 m to 1 million km, how large would the sun and the earth be in your model? How far apart would they be in your model?

4-4 FEATURES OF THE SUN

Galileo used his telescope to project an image of the sun on a piece of paper. He saw dark areas in the image. He noticed that the images moved. He drew pictures of the dark areas each day, studying their changing shapes and positions. From their motion, Galileo determined that the sun spins on its axis once every 25 days. These dark areas are surface storms called **sunspots**.

Sunspots are found in pairs. Figure 4-12 illustrates a sunspot pair. Astronomers have found that sunspots are areas of strong magnetic fields. The magnetic field may be more than 2000 times stronger than the magnetic field of the earth. Sunspots are dark because they are cooler than the rest of the sun's surface, about 1500°C cooler.

Sunspots are irregularly shaped and vary in size from 15 km to 150,000 km across. As many as 10 earths could fit within a large sunspot. There are two regions to a sunspot. The dark central area called the *umbra* is surrounded by a lighter area called the *penumbra*. Sunspots can change in appearance as time passes, either by changing size or changing shape. Small sunspots last a few days to a week before they disappear. Larger ones can last several weeks and occasionally last months.

> *After completing this section, you will be able to*
>
> - **explain** how astronomers measured the rotation of the sun.
> - **describe** sunspots.
> - **relate** the sunspot cycle to climate on the earth.
> - **compare** solar flares and prominences.
>
> *The key terms in this section are*
> prominence   sunspots
> solar flare

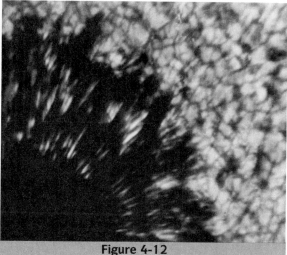

Figure 4-12

Sunspots generally appear in pairs.

Sunspots appear and disappear in cycles that average about 11 years. The cycle starts with few or no sunspots on the sun's surface. Then small spots occur about halfway between the sun's equator and each pole. As time goes on, the spots increase in number and size. Sunspots reach a maximum about five to six years into the cycle. Then

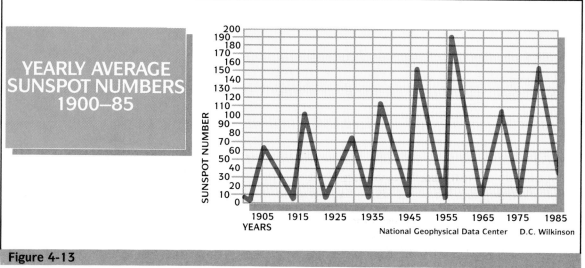

YEARLY AVERAGE SUNSPOT NUMBERS 1900—85

SUNSPOT NUMBER

200 190 180 170 160 150 140 130 120 110 100 90 80 70 60 50 40 30 20 10 0

1905 1915 1925 1935 1945 1955 1965 1975 1985
YEARS

National Geophysical Data Center   D.C. Wilkinson

Figure 4-13

The average number of sunspots per year from 1900 to 1985.

they appear less and less often for the next five to six years. Using Figure 4-13 determine when the next sunspot maximum will occur.

Sunspots near the sun's equator move faster than those closer to its poles. This is because the sun's surface is gaseous. Not all places on the surface rotate at the same speed. For example, at the equator the sun rotates once in 25 days, but at the poles it may take 34 days.

The sunspot cycle may have an influence on the earth's climate. For example, there is evidence that glaciers retreat, or melt back, during a sunspot maximum, and they advance during a minimum. This effect on glaciers indicates that sunspots may influence temperatures on the earth. Records show that during the late 1600s, sunspots had almost disappeared from the sun's surface. In that period, the earth's climate was colder than normal.

prominens (to stand out)

Magnetic fields seem to be responsible for forming solar prominences and flares. A **prominence** is a loop of plasma, or hot gas. It shoots from the photosphere but is held in the corona by a magnetic field. A prominence can reach more than 200,000 km into space. There may be as much matter in one prominence as there is in the entire earth. The temperature within a prominence can reach 10,000°C. Prominences are only visible during eclipses or with special instruments. These clouds of plasma can last from a few hours to several months.

A **solar flare** is a sudden, violent eruption of plasma from the chromosphere. The temperature within a flare may reach 100 million °C. Solar flares can cause power blackouts and stop radio communications.

ACTIVITY   Observing Sunspots

OBJECTIVE
Describe the pattern of sunspots on the sun's surface.

MATERIALS
binoculars, masking tape, 30 cm × 30 cm piece of cardboard, pencil, scissors, clipboard, sheet of plain white paper

PROCEDURE
A. Cover one lens on a pair of binoculars with tape so that light does not pass through the lens.
B. Carefully center the eyepieces of the binoculars on the cardboard. Trace around each eyepiece with a pencil. Put the binoculars aside and cut out the two circles that you traced. Fit the eyepieces of the binoculars through the holes in the cardboard.
C. Clip a sheet of white paper to the clipboard and place it in an area suggested by your teacher. Caution: Never look directly at the sun, especially with binoculars or a telescope, because permanent damage to your eyes will occur. Hold the binoculars about 25 cm above the paper with the eyepieces toward the paper. Move the binoculars toward and away from the paper so that an image of the sun is focused on the paper.
   1. Describe the image that you see.
   2. How does the image of the sun change as you move the binoculars toward and then away from the paper?
D. Focus the binoculars so that you make as large an image as you can make.
   3. Describe the image that you now see.
   4. Do sunspots appear on your image? If so, how many do you see, and where do they occur?

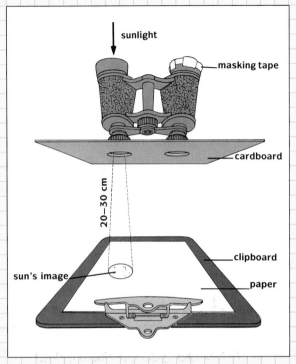

E. Hold the binoculars very still while your lab partner traces the image of the sun and the sunspots on your piece of paper.
   5. Where do the sunspots appear on the sun's surface?
   6. Describe the pattern of sunspots.
F. Repeat these procedures each day for several days. Compare the diagrams that you make.

RESULTS AND CONCLUSIONS
1. Are the sunspots together or apart?
2. How could sunspots be used to determine the rotation of the sun?

REVIEW

1. How did astronomers measure the rotation of the sun?
2. What are sunspots?
3. How does the sunspot cycle affect climate on the earth?
4. Compare solar prominences and solar flares.

CHALLENGE   If you could see a prominence in the corona, would it appear dark or bright, based on its estimated temperature? Why?

4-5 ENERGY FROM THE SUN

After completing this section,
you will be able to

- **distinguish** between the
  different types of solar
  radiation.
- **describe** the effects of the
  solar wind.
- **explain** how living things are
  protected from solar
  radiation and the solar wind.

The key terms in this section are
  aurora
  electromagnetic spectrum
  solar wind

All of the forms of energy given off by the sun are called *solar radiation*. Solar radiation moves through space at a speed of 300,000 km/s. At this speed, the sun's energy reaches the earth in about eight minutes.

At one time, it was thought that solar radiation moved through space the way sound moves through air. It was thought that there was some material in space through which solar radiation moved. However, that material was never found.

Today, it is known that solar radiation does not need a material in order to travel through space. Solar radiation travels in the form of electromagnetic waves. *Electromagnetic waves* are energy waves that move at the speed of light, 300,000 km/s, in a vacuum. The different kinds of electromagnetic waves, shown in Figure 4-14, make up the **electromagnetic spectrum**.

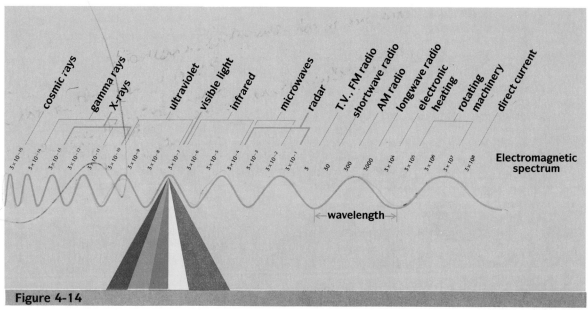

Figure 4-14

The electromagnetic spectrum.

The sun produces many kinds of electromagnetic waves. For example, sunlight is made mostly of electromagnetic waves called visible light. The warmth you feel in sunlight comes from waves called infrared rays. The tanning rays are waves called ultraviolet rays. As you can see in Figure 4-14, the waves you can sense in solar radiation are only part of the electromagnetic spectrum. What are the other kinds of waves in solar radiation?

The main difference between the types of solar radiation is their wavelengths. A *wavelength* is the distance between the top of one wave and the top of the next wave. In Figure 4-14, notice that each kind of wave has a different wavelength. Which waves have the shortest wavelength? Which waves have the longest wavelength?

Almost all of the solar radiation that reaches the earth's surface is in the form of visible light and infrared rays. These types of radiation are harmless to life. The sun also gives off some types of radiation that are harmful to life. These include gamma rays, X rays, and ultraviolet rays. However, the earth's atmosphere absorbs most of these harmful waves before they reach the surface. For example, a gas in the atmosphere called ozone absorbs ultraviolet rays. As a result, only small amounts of ultraviolet rays reach the earth's surface.

In addition to giving off radiation, the sun also gives off a steady stream of electrically charged particles called the **solar wind**. The solar wind moves at speeds from 300 km/s to 700 km/s and reaches beyond the orbit of Saturn.

ACTIVITY   What Colors Make Up Visible Light?

OBJECTIVE
Determine what colors make up white light.

MATERIALS
7.5 cm × 12.8 cm index card, scissors, sheet of plain white paper, book, tape, prism, light source

PROCEDURE
A. Fold an index card in half by bringing together the two sides that are 12.8 cm wide. With a pair of scissors, cut a thin slit, 5 cm long, out of the center of the fold, toward one of the 7.5 cm ends. Place the card on a table so that the section with the slit stands up and a beam of light shines through the slit.
B. Use tape to attach a sheet of white paper to a book cover. Stand the book up so that a beam of light shines on the piece of paper.
C. Carefully hold a prism along the slit of the card and adjust it so that the beam of light shines through it onto the paper.

1. What do you see on the paper?
2. List the colors that you see on the paper.
3. Where have you seen this array of colors before in your environment?
4. Does the light go straight through the prism? If not, then what happens to it?

D. A prism is able to bend light. As you have seen, different forms of radiation, such as the different colors of light, have different wavelengths. Each wavelength bends a different amount. Long wavelengths bend less than short wavelengths. Study the light going through the prism.

RESULTS AND CONCLUSIONS
1. Are there definite divisions between the colors or do they blend together?
2. Which color bends the least and has the longest wavelength?
3. Which color bends the most and has the shortest wavelength?
4. Based on this experiment, define white light. Define black.

Figure 4-15

The earth's magnetic field protects us from the solar wind except at the poles, where some of the particles penetrate the magnetic field and cause auroras.

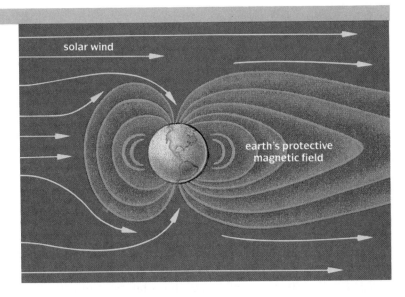

It is believed that many of the particles in the solar wind come from "holes" in the sun's corona. These are places where gas in the corona is missing.

Living things on the earth are protected from this stream of charged particles by the earth's magnetic field. The earth's magnetic field deflects many of the charged particles away from the earth. Figure 4-15 illustrates how the solar wind is steered away. Notice that the magnetic field on the side of the earth away from the sun is pulled away from the earth. Some particles can pass through the magnetic field and enter the atmosphere. Particles that

Figure 4-16

Auroras are most common near the poles.

enter the atmosphere are trapped by the earth's magnetic field and directed to the North Pole and the South Pole. As the particles collide with gases in the atmosphere in those regions, light is released, creating auroras. An **aurora** is light that is released when charged particles from the solar wind collide with gases within the earth's atmosphere. Particles in the solar wind can disrupt radio communication, disrupt telephone service, confuse compasses used in navigation, and cause power failures.

aurora (dawn)

REVIEW

1. Compare visible light with microwave radiation.
2. What is the solar wind?
3. How does the earth's magnetic field protect living things from the solar wind?

CHALLENGE There is evidence that the magnetic field of the earth changes. There may have been times when the earth had no magnetic field. What effect might this have had on the living things of the earth?

CHAPTER SUMMARY

The main ideas in this chapter are listed below. Read these statements before you answer the Chapter Review questions.

- The sun is the center of the solar system. The planets revolve around the sun in elliptical orbits. (4-1)

- The theory that is most accepted today for the origin of the solar system is the modern nebular hypothesis. The hypothesis states that the solar system formed from a spinning cloud of gas and dust. The sun formed from matter in the center and the planets formed from whirlpools of matter surrounding the sun. (4-2)

- The sun is the largest body in the solar system, containing more than 99.8 percent of the solar system's matter. The sun is made up of layers and produces energy in a process called fusion. (4-3)

- Some features that can be observed on the sun are sunspots, prominences, and solar flares. (4-4)

- The sun gives off many different forms of solar radiation. (4-5)

The key terms in this chapter are listed below. Use each term in a sentence that shows the meaning of the term.

aurora	electromagnetic spectrum	protoplanet
chromosphere	ellipse	radiation zone
collision hypothesis	epicycle	solar flare
convection zone	nebular hypothesis	solar wind
core	photosphere	sun-centered model
corona	prominence	sunspots
earth-centered model		

Chapter Review

Use the key terms from this chapter to complete the following sentences correctly.

1. A slightly flattened circle is called a/an _____.
2. The _____ can be seen as a halo around the sun during a solar eclipse.
3. The _____ suggests that the solar system formed from a cloud of dust and gas.
4. A whirlpool of matter that was the beginning of a body in the solar system is called a/an _____.
5. Energy is produced in the sun's _____.
6. The visible surface of the sun is called the _____.
7. ____ are large dark areas of the sun's surface caused by strong magnetic fields.
8. A looping cloud of plasma held in the corona by a magnetic field is called a/an _____.
9. The different kinds of radiation that the sun produces make up the _____.
10. Light released when charged particles strike gases within the earth's atmosphere is called a/an _____.

CONCEPTS

1. What evidence led Aristotle to believe that the earth was round? (4-1)
2. Why did Aristarchus believe the sun was the center of the universe? (4-1)
3. How does Ptolemy's model of epicycles explain the motion of planets in the sky? (4-1)
4. Describe Copernicus's model of the universe. (4-1)
5. Why was the original nebular hypothesis not complete? (4-2)
6. What are two main arguments against the collision hypothesis? (4-2)
7. Compare the modern nebular hypothesis with the original nebular hypothesis. (4-2)
8. How does the modern nebular hypothesis explain why the planets closer to the sun are different from the planets farther from the sun? (4-2)
9. What is plasma? (4-3)
10. What was wrong with the idea that the sun's energy came from burning gas? (4-3)

11. Describe the interior of the sun. (4-3)

12. What are granules? (4-3)

13. What are spicules? (4-3)

14. Describe how energy is transferred from the sun's core to its surface. (4-3)

15. What did Galileo determine about the sun by observing sunspots? (4-4)

16. Describe the cycle of sunspots. (4-4)

17. Why do sunspots move more slowly at the poles of the sun than near the equator? (4-4)

18. What evidence is there that sunspots affect climate on the earth? (4-4)

19. In what way do the kinds of solar radiation differ? (4-5)

20. Why don't large amounts of harmful solar radiation reach the earth's surface? (4-5)

21. What effects does the solar wind have on the earth? (4-5)

APPLICATION/ CRITICAL THINKING

1. From observations of the sky, how could you tell the members of the solar system from the rest of the universe?

2. The diameter of the sun is 1,392,000 km. The speed at which solar radiation travels through space is 300,000 km/s. Traveling at this speed, about how long would it take energy from the center of the sun to reach the sun's surface? How does this time compare with the actual time?

3. What changes would you observe if
   a. the earth rotated in the opposite direction from what it does now?
   b. the earth rotated faster than it does now?
   c. the earth rotated slower than it does now?

EXTENSION

1. Make a scale model of the earth and sun, showing their relative sizes and distance apart.

2. Ask your teacher for some iron filings and a bar magnet. Place a sheet of paper on top of the magnet, with the magnet at the center of the paper. Sprinkle some iron filings on the paper. Where are the iron filings most concentrated? Where are they least concentrated? Compare the magnetic field of your magnet with the magnetic field of the sun.

READINGS

Frazier, Kendrick. *Our Turbulent Sun*. Englewood Cliffs, N.J.: Prentice-Hall, Inc., 1982.

Solar System. Alexandria, Va.: Time-Life Books, Inc., 1985.

"Graffiti with a Heavenly Message." Time, January 31, 1983, p. 63.

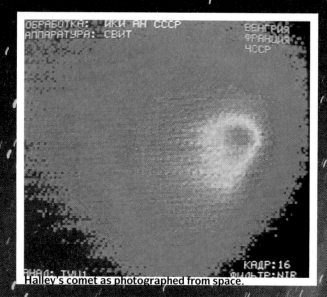

Halley's comet as photographed from space.

THE SOLAR SYSTEM

Have you ever seen a comet? Some comets, like Halley's comet, appear in our skies periodically. Other comets appear unexpectedly, blaze in the sky for several months, and disappear, never to return. Although comets are visitors to the region of space near the earth, they are, like the earth, members of the solar system.

- *What is a comet made of?*
- *Why do comets grow tails as they approach the sun?*
- *Where do comets come from?*

5-1 MEMBERS OF THE SOLAR SYSTEM

On clear nights, away from bright city lights, you may have noticed the positions of the stars. The stars form patterns in the sky. These patterns do not change, although different star groups are visible at different times. A small number of objects, however, seem to wander across the sky. Some grow a tail as they move across the heavens. Others race across the sky and disappear within seconds. These objects that move against the background of the stars are members of the solar system. The **solar system** is the sun and the objects that move around it. The solar system includes the planets and their satellites, comets, asteroids (AS tuh roids), and meteoroids (MEE tee uh roids).

The members of the solar system are much closer to the sun than are the stars. There are nine known planets. Table 5-1 lists the planets in order from the sun. It also gives some data about each planet.

Between Mars and Jupiter, thousands—perhaps millions—of pieces of rock and metal move around the sun. Some of these objects are several kilometers wide, but most are small. The larger of these objects are called asteroids. The region where most of them are found is known as the asteroid belt.

After completing this section, you will be able to

- **describe** the makeup of the solar system.
- **distinguish** between the characteristics of the inner planets and those of the outer planets.

The key terms in this section are
inner planets   solar system
outer planets

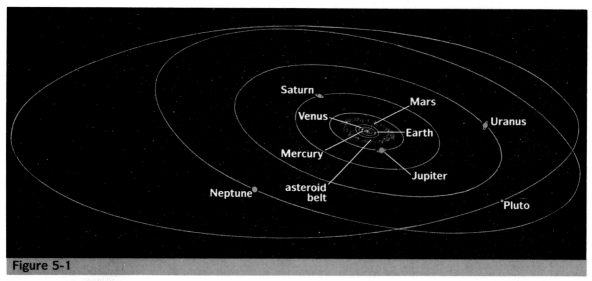

Figure 5-1

The solar system.

The planets between the sun and the asteroid belt are different from the planets beyond the asteroid belt. As a result, scientists divide the planets into two groups, the inner planets and the outer planets.

The **inner planets** are Mercury, Venus, Earth, and Mars, the four planets closest to the sun. It is thought that all these planets have a metal core and a rocky mantle. The earth, Venus, and Mars all have an atmosphere.

The **outer planets**, which are the planets beyond the asteroid belt, are Jupiter, Saturn, Uranus (yu RAY nuhs), Neptune, and Pluto. All of these planets are thought to

Table 5-1 *The Planets*

Planet	Diameter (in km)	Mass (Earth = 1)	Density (H_2O = 1 g/cm³)	Distance from Sun (millions km)	Revolution	Rotation	Tilt of Axis	Gravity (Earth = 1)	Temperature	Satellites (Known)
Mercury	4,878	.055	5.4	57.9	88 d	59 d	0°	.38	430°C daylight −180°C dark	0
Venus	12,100	.8	5.2	108.2	225 d	243 d	3°	.90	475°C	0
Earth	12,756	1	5.5	149.6	365.25 d	23.93 h	23.5°	1	Average 15°C	1
Mars	6,787	.1	3.9	227.9	687 d	24.6 h	25.2°	.38	Average −50°C	2
Jupiter	142,800	318	1.3	778.3	11.86 y	9.9 h	3.1°	2.54	−130°C cloud tops	16
Saturn	120,000	95	.7	1,427	29.46 y	10.7 h	26.7°	1.07	−185°C cloud tops	17
Uranus	50,800	15	1.3	2,870	84 y	16 h	97.9°	.9 (?)	−215°C cloud tops	14
Neptune	48,600	17	1.8	4,497	165 y	18 h	29.6°	1.15(?)	−200°C cloud tops	2
Pluto	3,000(?)	.002	1	5,900	248 y	6.4 d	60° (?)	.03(?)	−230°C	1

ACTIVITY   The Solar System to Scale

OBJECTIVE
Make a scale model of the solar system.

MATERIALS
large piece of white cardboard or paper, metric ruler, drawing compass, local map

PROCEDURE
A. Scale models are useful because they help you understand the relationships among the parts of a system. The scale for this model will be 1 mm = 1000 km. Set up two planet tables. One should list the diameter of each planet in kilometers, and the scale diameter. The other should list the distance of each planet from the sun, and the scale distance. (See Table 5-1 for diameters and distances from sun.)

B. On a piece of cardboard, draw a circle to represent each planet according to your scale measurements. Label each circle with the name of the planet that it represents.

C. Find the location of your school on a local map. The school will represent the sun. Draw a line on the map in any direction from your school through the town. Using your scale and the map scale, mark and label where on the line the planets you have drawn would be placed. For example, if Jupiter was 1 km from the school according to your scale, you would find on your line the point that is 1 km from the school according to the map's scale and then mark it.

RESULTS AND CONCLUSIONS
1. Which planets are clearly larger than the others?
2. The diameter of the sun is 1,400,000 km. How large is it according to your scale?
3. Are the distances greater between the inner planets or the outer planets?
4. According to your scale, how far away would Proxima Centauri be if it is 38,700,000,000 km from the sun? Where would you place it on the map?
5. What are the advantages of making a scale model such as this? What are the disadvantages of this model?

have a rocky core. Jupiter and Saturn have a layer of hydrogen around their cores. This layer acts like a metal because of its high pressure. The hydrogen may be the cause of the strong magnetic fields of Jupiter and Saturn. The metallic hydrogen is covered with a layer of liquid hydrogen and a thick atmosphere.

Uranus and Neptune are very similar to each other. Their rocky cores are surrounded by a layer of ice and then a layer of liquid hydrogen. Both planets have a thick atmosphere.

Pluto differs from all the other planets. Unlike the other outer planets, it is not very big. It is smaller than the earth, and it may even be smaller than Mercury. Unlike the inner planets, Pluto is not very dense. It is thought to consist of rock and frozen gases.

REVIEW

1. What objects make up the solar system?
2. How are the inner planets different from the outer planets?

CHALLENGE Sunlight reaches the earth in $8\frac{1}{3}$ minutes. How long does it take sunlight to reach Pluto? The speed of light in a vacuum is 299,792 km/s.

5-2 THE INNER PLANETS

After completing this section, you will be able to

- **explain** how the characteristics of the inner planets are related to the way that these planets formed.
- **describe** the features of the planets Mercury, Venus, and Mars.
- **compare** Mercury, Venus, and Mars with Earth.

The key terms in this section are

Mars   Venus
Mercury

Mercury, Venus, and Mars, shown in Figure 5-2, are called the *earthlike* planets. Together with the earth, they are the inner planets. These planets seem to have a metal core surrounded by a rocky mantle. They are very different from the giant outer planets. For example, the inner planets contain small amounts of hydrogen and helium. The outer planets are mostly hydrogen and helium.

Why should the inner planets differ from the outer planets? Recall that according to the nebular hypothesis, the solar system formed from a cloud of gas and dust. As matter collected to form the planets, each planet was large and made of the same materials. When the sun began to produce energy, the solar wind removed lighter materials from the bodies closest to the sun. These lighter elements were carried to the outer part of the nebula. In time, only the dense materials that the solar wind could not remove remained close to the sun. In this way the inner planets became smaller and more dense than the outer planets.

Mercury	Venus	Earth	Mars

Diameter (km)   4,878   12,100   12,756   6,787

Figure 5-2

The inner planets.

MERCURY

Mercury is the planet closest to the sun. Its average distance from the sun is only 58 million km. Mercury is difficult to see from the earth. At times, Mercury rises just before the sun. At other times it sets just after the sun. When Mercury is visible it is close to the horizon.

In the spring of 1974, a United States spacecraft, Mariner 10, gave astronomers their first good look at Mercury. Figure 5-3 shows Mercury's surface as photographed by that spacecraft. Notice that Mercury is covered with craters, as is the earth's moon. How might these craters have been formed? Mercury also has long steep cliffs that stretch across the surface.

Figure 5-3

This mosaic of the planet Mercury was taken by Mariner 10.

Mercury is different from the earth in many ways. There is no water on the planet. Mercury is much smaller than the earth, having a diameter of only about 4900 km. The force of gravity on Mercury is about one-third that of the earth's. How much would you weigh on Mercury?

There is a large change in temperature from the sunlit to the dark side of Mercury. Temperature on the sunlit side can be more than 400°C. On the dark side it can drop to less than −180°C.

Mercury moves 1½ times faster than the earth, circling the sun once every 88 days. Its period of rotation is 59 earth days. This combination of a short year and a long day causes a point on Mercury's surface to move slowly through daylight and darkness.

VENUS

Venus is the second planet from the sun. It is the brightest object in the sky except for the sun and the moon. On a clear moonless night, Venus casts shadows on the earth. Venus appears in the sky shortly before sunrise or shortly after sunset because it is close to the sun. It comes closer to the earth than does any other planet.

Venus is about 108 million km from the sun. It takes about 225 earth days to complete one revolution. Its rotation period is about 243 earth days. So Venus's year is shorter than its day.

As shown in Figure 5-4, Venus is wrapped in thick layers of clouds. No sign of the planet's surface can be seen from the earth. How do the thick clouds that cover Venus help account for its brightness?

Several spacecraft have studied Venus. The studies have shown that the clouds in the upper atmosphere of Venus contain sulfuric acid. These clouds are swept along by winds of around 360 km/h. Beneath the acid clouds the wind speed is slower and the atmosphere is mostly carbon dioxide. Near the surface the temperature is around 470°C. The pressure is about 91 times greater than that of the earth's atmosphere.

Figure 5-4

Venus has a thick pattern of cloud cover (*left*). This is an artist's conception, based on measurements by a Pioneer Venus orbiter spacecraft, of the large mountain ranges that occur on Venus (*right*).

MARS

Mars, the fourth planet from the sun, is often called the red planet. Reddish-brown sand and rocks on its surface and dust in its atmosphere give Mars a reddish look.

Mars is like the earth in some ways. Mars rotates on its axis in just over 24 hours. Mars, like the earth, is tilted on its axis. The tilt is almost the same for both planets. As a result, Mars has seasons, as does the earth. The north pole and the south pole of Mars are covered by icecaps, probably made of frozen carbon dioxide and water.

Mars takes about 687 days to travel around the sun. Therefore its seasons are nearly twice as long as those on the earth. The diameter of Mars is 6790 km. That's just a little more than half the earth's diameter. Mars's mass is only one-tenth that of the earth's, and Mars's atmosphere is one-fiftieth that of the earth's. Atmospheric pressure at the surface of Mars is less than one percent of the pressure at the surface of the earth.

The atmosphere of Mars is so thin that it does not trap heat as does the atmosphere of Venus and of the earth. As a result, the surface of Mars is always cold. A summertime high temperature at Mars's equator is 0°C.

Spacecraft that have visited Mars have found huge volcanoes, large craters, areas of lava flow, and deep canyons. The biggest volcano on Mars is 25 km high. Its base would cover the entire state of Ohio. The largest canyon on Mars is 240 km wide and 6.5 km deep in places.

When the two Viking spacecraft landed on Mars in 1976, they probed the surface for signs of life. They studied soil samples and conducted other tests. But they found no evidence of life on Mars.

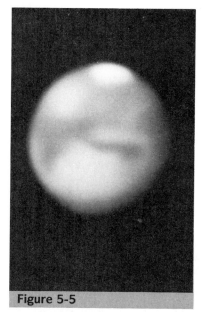

Figure 5-5

Mars as seen through a telescope from the earth.

Figure 5-6

This photograph of the surface of Mars was taken by Viking 2. It shows a thin coating of ice on the rocks and soil.

Mars has two small moons, Phobos (FOH buhs) and Deimos (DĪ mahs). Both moons are irregularly shaped. Phobos, the larger of the two, is only 25 km wide. Deimos is only 15 km across. They look more like asteroids than moons. Some scientists think that these moons may have been asteroids that were captured and held by the pull of Mars's gravity. It was once suggested that these moons were artificial satellites placed in orbit by intelligent beings.

ACTIVITY Measuring Astronomical Distances

OBJECTIVE
Determine the distances to Mercury and Venus.

MATERIALS
metric ruler, drawing compass, protractor

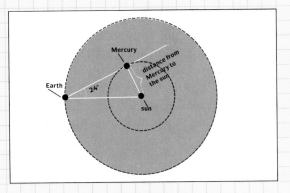

PROCEDURE

A. Early astronomers did not know how far it was from the sun to the planets. Instead, they used the distance from the earth to the sun as a standard with which to compare the other distances. The distance from the earth to the sun is called the *astronomical unit*. Draw a dot in the center of a piece of paper, and label it as the sun. Draw a second dot 10 cm from the first, and label it as the earth. Connect the two dots with a straight line. This distance represents one astronomical unit. Use a compass to draw a circle that is centered at the sun and that passes through the earth. This circle represents the orbit of the earth.

B. As early astronomers measured the position of Mercury in the sky, they noticed that it was never more than 24° from the sun. With a protractor, measure 24° above the line from the earth to the sun, as shown in the figure. Mark this position with a spot. Draw a line from the earth through the spot and past your labeled sun.

C. Use the compass to draw a circle that is centered at the sun and that just touches this new line, as shown in the figure. This circle represents the orbit that brings Mercury no more than 24° from the sun.

D. Measure the distance in cm between Mercury's orbit and the sun. This distance represents the distance from Mercury to the sun.
1. What is this distance?
2. If 10 cm is equal to one astronomical unit, then what is the distance in astronomical units from Mercury to the sun?

E. The farthest Venus is ever seen from the sun is 48°. Repeat steps **B** through **D** to determine the distance from Venus to the sun.
3. How many cm is the orbit of Venus from the sun on your diagram?
4. How many astronomical units is that distance?

RESULTS AND CONCLUSIONS
1. How far is Mercury from the sun?
2. How far is Venus from the sun?
3. Would this system of measuring work for the other planets? Why or why not?

REVIEW

1. The inner planets share the same general characteristics. They are very different from the characteristics of the outer planets. How do scientists explain this?
2. Describe the features of Mercury. How does Mercury differ from Venus?
3. Compare Mars with the earth, pointing out how they are alike and how they are different.

CHALLENGE Suppose that you are viewing Venus through a telescope. You notice that it is almost full—that is, circular. Sketch the relative positions of the sun, the earth, and Venus for Venus to appear almost full.

5-3 THE OUTER PLANETS

With the exception of Pluto, the outer planets are much larger and less dense than the inner planets. Jupiter, Saturn, Uranus, and Neptune, shown in Figure 5-7, are known as the gas giants. Each is mostly made up of the light elements hydrogen and helium. They also contain some heavier elements.

Astronomers think that the outer planets were able to collect and hold the light elements because these planets formed far enough from the sun. Recall that some scientists think that the solar wind drove the light elements from around the inner planets to the outer regions of the nebula. The outer planets collected the light elements and grew to great size.

After completing this section, you will be able to

- **explain** how the characteristics of the outer planets relate to the way they formed.
- **describe** the features of Jupiter, Saturn, Uranus, and Neptune.
- **compare** Pluto with the inner and the outer planets.

The key terms in this section are
Jupiter   Saturn   Pluto
Neptune   Uranus

	Jupiter	Saturn	Uranus	Neptune	Pluto
Diameter (km)	142,800	120,000	50,800	48,600	3,000 (?)

Figure 5-7

The outer planets.

JUPITER

Jupiter, the fifth planet from the sun, is by far the largest planet in the solar system. Jupiter's total mass is more than twice that of all other objects in the solar system except the sun. Jupiter is about 778 million km from the sun. It takes about 12 earth years for Jupiter to complete one orbit.

Jupiter's diameter of 142,800 km is 11.2 times greater than the earth's diameter. A thousand Earths would be needed to match Jupiter's volume. Since Jupiter is relatively low in density, however, it would require only 318 Earths to equal its mass.

Jupiter turns on its axis about every 9 hours and 50 minutes. This is a very rapid rate of rotation. A point on Jupiter's equator moves at 45,200 km/h. Jupiter's rapid rotation causes the giant planet to bulge at the equator and flatten at the poles.

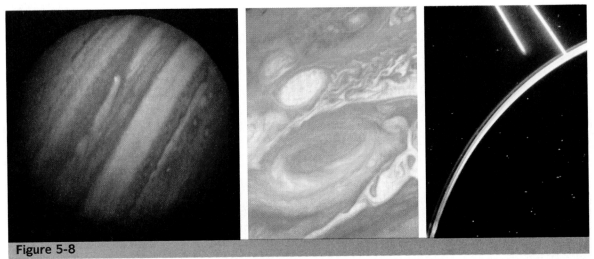

Figure 5-8

A photograph of the planet Jupiter taken by Pioneer 10 (*left*). The red spot photographed by Voyager 1 (*middle*). A color composite of Jupiter's rings, photographed by Voyager 2 (*right*).

Jupiter gives off more energy than it receives from the distant sun. The tremendous pressure caused by Jupiter's great mass produces temperatures of around 30,000°C at the planet's core. This heat energy radiates through Jupiter and into the planet's atmosphere. The temperature at the top of Jupiter's clouds is about − 130°C.

As heat radiates through Jupiter's atmosphere, it causes some parts of the atmosphere to be warmer and less dense than other parts. As a result, Jupiter's atmosphere is in constant motion. Swirling storms appear as colored spots in the atmosphere. The most striking of these is the great red spot, shown in Figure 5-8.

Jupiter's atmosphere is 88 percent hydrogen and 11 percent helium. It also contains small amounts of water, methane, and ammonia. Pressure within Jupiter's atmosphere increases with depth. The gases in the atmosphere become thicker and denser until, finally, they become liquid. An ocean of liquid hydrogen surrounds the core. Deep within the planet, increased pressure produces metallic hydrogen. This metallic hydrogen, along with the planet's rapid rotation, creates a strong magnetic field.

Jupiter has 16 known moons. The four largest were first seen by Galileo. Ganymede is shown in Figure 5-9. Each Galilean moon is larger than Pluto.

Figure 5-9

Ganymede is one of Jupiter's moons that was discovered by Galileo.

SATURN

Saturn, the sixth planet from the sun, is the second biggest planet. It has a diameter of about 120,000 km. Saturn is over 1400 million km from the sun. It takes over 29 years for Saturn to orbit the sun. The temperature in the upper atmosphere is about $-185°C$.

Saturn's system of rings can be seen in Figure 5-11. Unlike the rings around other planets, the rings of Saturn can be seen from the earth with the help of a small telescope. Thousands of small bands form seven main regions in Saturn's ring system. The ring system is about 67,000 km wide but might be no more than 10 m thick.

Saturn's rings are probably made of flecks of frozen gases and tiny chunks of matter covered with ice. Sunlight bouncing off these materials makes the rings appear more solid than they actually are. The Pioneer 11 spacecraft passed through the rings without serious damage.

Figure 5-10

Saturn as viewed through a telescope from the earth.

Figure 5-11

A Voyager 2 photograph of Saturn shows that there are several rings.

Like Jupiter, Saturn is made up mostly of hydrogen. Also like Jupiter, it gives off more energy than it takes in. Saturn is thought to have a very dense, very hot core surrounded by metallic hydrogen. This, and the planet's rapid rotation, creates a strong magnetic field.

Saturn turns on its axis in 10 hours and 40 minutes. This rapid rotation causes bands of clouds to form in Saturn's atmosphere. How would the rapid rotation rate affect the shape of Saturn? Saturn has a stormy atmosphere.

URANUS AND NEPTUNE

Uranus and **Neptune**, shown in Figure 5-12, are often called twin planets. Uranus is about 2900 million km from the sun. Neptune is about 4500 million km from the sun. These planets are much alike. Each has a diameter about four times that of the earth. Each is composed mostly of hydrogen and helium. These planets appear bluish-green with shaded bands. Atmospheric temperatures on both planets are about −200°C.

It is difficult to measure the rotation periods of these remote, cloudy planets. Uranus appears to rotate once in about 16 hours. Neptune appears to rotate once in about 18 hours.

Uranus is tilted more on its axis than is any other planet. As you can see in Figure 5-12, Uranus could be described as lying on its side. As a result of this tilt, at certain places in its orbit Uranus's north pole points almost directly at the sun. On the other side of its orbit, the north pole points away from the sun.

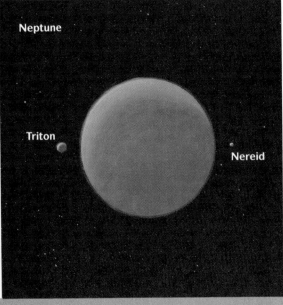

Figure 5-12

Uranus (*left*) and Neptune (*right*). A photograph of Uranus's moon Ariel is also shown.

A system of dark rings encircles Uranus. Some scientists think that the dark rings contain pieces of rock. In fact, the rings may be moons in the making. In addition to the dark rings, Uranus has a number of moons. No rings have been found around far-off Neptune. But scientists think there may also be dark rings there. Neptune is known to have two moons, and there may be a third.

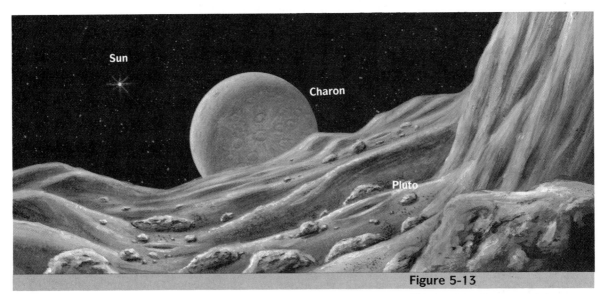

Figure 5-13

This is what Charon and the sun would look like if you were on Pluto.

PLUTO

Pluto was the ninth planet to be discovered in the solar system. Most of the time it is the ninth planet from the sun. Look at Figure 5-1. Pluto's orbit crosses that of Neptune. So at times, Pluto is closer to the sun than is Neptune. This is the case now. Pluto's average distance from the sun, 5900 million km, is greater than that of Neptune. Pluto takes about 248 earth years to move around the sun once.

Pluto is very different from all other planets. It does not have large mass like the other outer planets. Nor does it have high density like the inner planets. It may be the smallest planet in the solar system. Its diameter is estimated to be about 3000 km. It is so small and far away that little is known about it. Some scientists think Pluto is composed of frozen methane, argon, and neon. That would also make it very different from other planets. Pluto has one moon. It is named Charon (KAIR uhn).

REVIEW

1. How might the outer planets have formed with characteristics different from those of the inner planets?
2. Compare the features of Jupiter and Saturn.
3. Why are Uranus and Neptune sometimes called twin planets?
4. How is Pluto different from the other outer planets?

CHALLENGE If a point on Jupiter's equator rotates at 45,200 km/h to complete a rotation, how fast is it going in kilometers per second?

SCIENCE PUZZLER

The existence of Pluto was suspected before it was actually discovered. The suspicion was due to disturbances in the orbit of Neptune. Sometimes, Neptune moved faster than expected. At other times it moved more slowly than expected. Why would such disturbances lead scientists to think that there might be a planet beyond Neptune?

5-4 ASTEROIDS, METEOROIDS, AND COMETS

asteroeides (starlike)

Table 5-2 *Bode's Formula*

Planet	Distance from Sun (AU)	Bode's Distance
Mercury	0.4	0.4
Venus	0.7	0.7
Earth	1.0	1.0
Mars	1.5	1.6
?	2.8	2.8
Jupiter	5.2	5.2
Saturn	9.5	10.0

ASTEROIDS

In 1772 an astronomer, Johann Bode, published a formula that predicted the distances of the planets from the sun. Table 5-2 compares Bode's distances with the actual distances in astronomical units. How well do the distances compare?

As you can see, according to Bode there should be a planet between Mars and Jupiter. Many astronomers looked for such a planet, but they could not find it. Finally, on January 1, 1801, an astronomer named Giuseppi Piazzi found an object there. Later that object was named Ceres (SIHR eez).

Ceres turned out to be very small—just 1000 km across. It seemed far too small and oddly shaped to be a planet. Then in 1802 another small object was found in the region between Mars and Jupiter. A third was found in 1804. By 1890, about 300 rocky objects had been discovered traveling around the sun, between the paths of Mars and Jupiter. These rocky objects of various sizes moving around the sun are called **asteroids**. The region between between Mars and Jupiter, where most of them are located, is called the asteroid belt.

How did the asteroids come to occupy this region of space? Some scientists think that the asteroids may be pieces of a planet that once existed there but was torn apart millions of years ago. Other scientists have suggested that the asteroids are material that never came together to form a planet.

Figure 5-14

Artist's conception of a space probe approaching an asteroid.

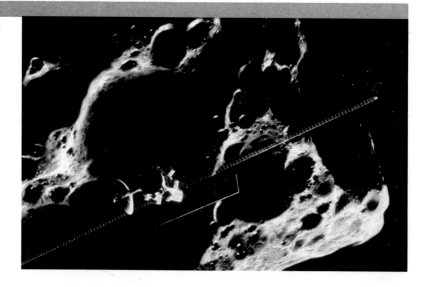

Astronomers track and name the larger asteroids. To date, about 2500 asteroids have been listed. In addition there are hundreds of thousands of small rocky objects in the asteroid belt and elsewhere in the solar system.

METEOROIDS

If you sit outside on a clear night to watch the stars, you may see bright flashes streak across the sky. These flashes of light are called *meteors* (MEE tee uhrs), or shooting stars. Meteors are produced by small bodies that enter the earth's atmosphere. Small bodies of rock or metal that move through the solar system are called **meteoroids**.

Meteoroids passing close to the earth may be pulled in by the earth's gravity. They enter the atmosphere at speeds ranging from 15 km/s to 70 km/s. At such speeds, friction—the rubbing against air particles—will cause a meteoroid to glow white-hot. The result is a meteor.

Most meteoroids entering the atmosphere burn up. Sometimes a larger meteoroid enters the atmosphere. If it is going very fast and at a steep angle, it may glow very brightly. This type of meteor is called a fireball.

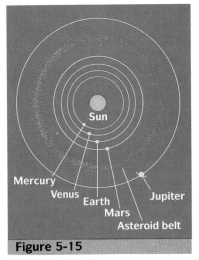

Figure 5-15

The asteroid belt.

Figure 5-16

Barringer Crater, in Arizona.

Rarely, a piece of a large meteoroid does not burn up completely, and it reaches the earth's surface. A meteoroid that strikes the surface is called a *meteorite* (MEE tee uh-rīt). Large meteorites produce craters in the earth's surface. Arizona's Barringer crater, shown in Figure 5-16, is 1.2 km wide. It was probably created by a meteorite 20,000 years ago.

COMETS

Comets are large chunks of ice, frozen gases, dust, and rock. They are often described as dirty snowballs. Comets are perhaps the most unusual objects in the solar system. They appear to move slowly across the sky. They usually grow a bright tail as they approach the sun.

Comets come from the outer region of the solar system, far beyond Pluto. Some scientists say there may be millions of comets out there—great balls of dust and frozen gases traveling around the sun.

cometa (long hair)

As a comet approaches the sun, the sun's energy causes some of the frozen gases to evaporate. As a result, a thick cloud of gases and dust forms around the comet. This cloud is called the coma.

The solar wind causes some of the gases and dust to stream out from the coma and form the tail. Blown by the solar wind, a comet's tail always points away from the sun. Notice in Figure 5-17 that when a comet is approaching the sun, the tail lags behind the comet head. When a comet is moving away from the sun, the tail leads the way.

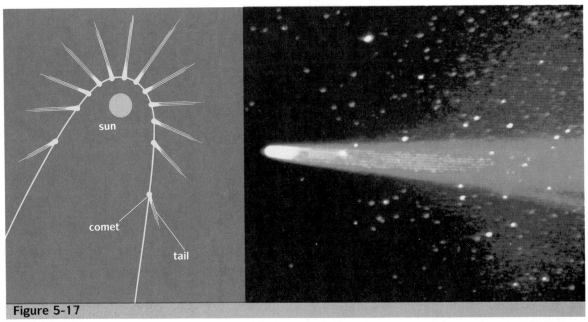

Figure 5-17

Why does the tail of a comet always point away from the sun (*left*)? Computer-enhanced photograph of a comet (*right*).

A comet gives off no light of its own. Sunlight bouncing off the coma and tail causes a comet to glow brightly. On every trip close to the sun, a comet loses part of its mass. In time a comet may break apart. Recently, several spacecraft have flown by Halley's comet. The data obtained by these spacecraft has increased our knowledge about comets.

ACTIVITY   How Do Meteorites Form Craters?

OBJECTIVE
Demonstrate how meteorite impacts could form craters on the surface of a planet.

MATERIALS
20 cm × 20 cm baking pan, sifted flour, paprika, different size pebbles, forceps, metric ruler

PROCEDURE
A. Copy the table.

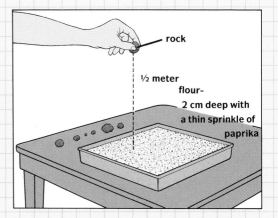

rock

½ meter

flour-

2 cm deep with a thin sprinkle of paprika

Pebble Number	Height	Diameter of Crater
1		
1		
1		
2		
2		
3		
3		

B. Cover the bottom of a baking pan with a layer of flour that is about 2 cm deep. Gently shake the pan to smooth the layer of flour. Lightly sprinkle a thin layer of paprika over the flour. These layers represent the solid surface of a planet or the moon.

C. The pebbles represent meteorites that strike the surface. Hold one of the pebbles 0.5 m above the pan, and drop it into the pan.
   1. What does the crater look like?
   2. What is the distance across the top of the crater? Record the data.
   3. What do you see outside the rim of the crater?

D. Carefully remove the pebble with forceps.
E. Repeat steps **C** and **D** several times with the same pebble but from different heights and over different parts of the pan. Record the results.
   4. How does changing the height from which the pebble falls change the crater?
F. Repeat steps **C** through **E** several times with different pebbles. Record the results.
   5. How does the size of a pebble affect the size of the crater?
   6. How does the shape of a pebble affect the crater?

RESULTS AND CONCLUSIONS
1. How does the material in the pan now resemble the surface of Mercury or Mars?
2. How do you think the craters of the moons and planets might have formed?
3. Why are relatively few craters found on the earth's surface?

REVIEW

1. How do asteroids and meteoroids differ?
2. Describe one hypothesis for the origin of asteroids.
3. Distinguish between a meteoroid, a meteor, and a meteorite.
4. What happens to a comet as it passes close to the sun?

CHALLENGE   Bode's distances are calculated by adding 4 to a series of numbers, called Bode's numbers, and dividing each result by 10. Bode's numbers for planets seven through nine are: seven – 192, eight – 384, nine – 768. Determine the Bode's distances for these planets. How do they compare with the actual distances in astronomical units.

5-5 EXPLORING SPACE

After completing this section, you will be able to

- **list** some of the uses of satellites.
- **explain** how space probes have increased our knowledge of the solar system and the universe.
- **describe** some of the programs that have allowed people to explore space.
- **describe** future space missions and the frontiers of knowledge they might probe.

The key terms in this section are
satellite   **space probes**

A **satellite** is any object that revolves around another object. Moons are natural satellites of planets. When we use the term *satellite* in space exploration, however, we usually mean an artificial satellite.

More than a thousand satellites have been placed in orbit around the earth. There are many different kinds of satellites. Weather satellites have greatly improved the accuracy and speed of weather forecasting. Other satellites allow messages, including TV broadcasts, to be sent around the world almost at once. Landsat satellites study the earth's surface. They keep track of resources, such as croplands, forests, and freshwater supplies.

Exploration of other parts of the solar system has been going on since the 1960s. Spacecraft sent to study the moon and other planets are called **space probes**. Much of the information on the planets that you read about earlier in the chapter was gathered by space probes. For example, the United States has sent Mariner missions to Mercury and Venus. Soviet Venera probes have also studied Venus. American Viking spacecraft have landed on Mars.

Figure 5-18

A photograph of the earth taken by the Seasat satellite.

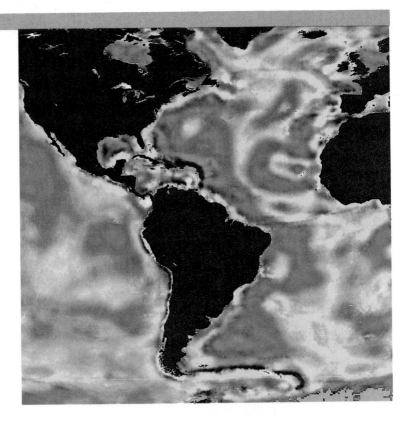

Figure 5-19

Apollo mission liftoff (*left*). Edwin E. Aldrin, Jr., setting up solar wind composition experiment on the moon (*right*). Recovery of an Apollo spacecraft (*middle*).

Exploration of the outer planets of the solar system was started in the 1970s. A great deal of knowledge has been provided by the Voyager missions to the outer planets. Voyager 2 was launched on August 20, 1977, and Voyager 1 followed on September 5. These two spacecraft took thousands of photographs of Jupiter and Saturn. Voyager 2 has also visited Uranus.

Of course, the exploration of space has not been left to machines alone. Since 1961, people have also been going into space. The high point of the United States effort was the Apollo program to put a person on the moon. Before the Apollo program ended, 24 Americans viewed the moon's surface from close-up and 12 walked on it. Apollo astronauts completed 60 experiments on the moon's surface and 30 in orbit around the moon. More than 30,000 photographs and many samples of moon rocks were brought back to Earth.

The space shuttle program began in the 1980s. The space shuttle is a reusable craft. It is launched like a rocket, it orbits like a satellite, and it returns to the earth, like a glider.

The shuttle is used to launch, retrieve, and repair satellites. It is also used for various experiments in orbit. A space shuttle could be used to build a space station in orbit. The crews of the space shuttles are no longer all skilled astronauts. Scientists, engineers, technicians, and doctors have gone into space aboard the shuttle.

Figure 5-20

Using a space shuttle, astronauts may be able to build a space station.

Several future space programs are being planned or considered. They include the Galileo program to put an artificial satellite in orbit around Jupiter. The satellite would then send probes to Jupiter's surface and to some of Jupiter's moons.

Construction of a permanent space station in orbit around the earth is being considered. The station would serve as an observatory, communications center, and launch point for deep-space probes. It would be supplied and serviced by space shuttles.

Some scientists believe that an outpost could be established on the moon. They say there are enough valuable materials on the moon to make such a project pay off.

SCIENCE & TECHNOLOGY

Getting into space is very expensive. But once in orbit, a spaceship could be propelled by ways other than chemical fuel. Sunlight converted to electricity in solar cells could supply the energy to propel a spaceship.

Another approach to propulsion in space is to use solar sails. A solar sail is a large, very thin mirror that would reflect sunlight. The momentum of the sunlight striking the sail would be changed into energy to push the spacecraft. The sail could be folded up during the launch and unfurled in space. A ship powered by such a sail could go to Mars and back in six years. Although this is twice as long as it would take using a chemical rocket, a sail ship might be useful for transporting cargo that did not need to reach a place in a hurry. It would also be cheaper.

REVIEW

1. Identify some uses to which satellites are put.
2. How have space probes increased knowledge about the solar system?
3. What was the Apollo program?
4. What future missions in space are being considered?

CHALLENGE Look back at the section describing conditions on Mars. What needs would have to be supplied to have a team of astronauts spend time on Mars?

CHAPTER SUMMARY

The main ideas in this chapter are listed below. Read these statements before you answer the Chapter Review questions.

- The solar system includes the sun, the planets and their moons, comets, asteroids, and meteoroids. (5-1)

- It is thought that as the inner planets formed, the light elements were pushed away from them by the solar wind. These planets contain a large percentage of rock and metal materials. (5-2)

- Mercury and Venus are closer to the sun than is the earth. Mercury resembles the earth's moon in appearance. Venus has a very thick atmosphere with extremely high temperatures. (5-2)

- Mars, the fourth planet from the sun, is smaller than the earth and has a very thin atmosphere. (5-2)

- It is thought that as the outer planets formed, they were less affected by the forces of the sun than were the inner planets. They contain a high percentage of hydrogen and helium. (5-3)

- Jupiter, the largest planet, gives off more energy than it receives from the sun. (5-3)

- Saturn is the sixth planet from the sun. It is the only planet with rings visible with small telescopes. (5-3)

- Uranus and Neptune are the seventh and eighth planets from the sun. They are similar in both size and composition. (5-3)

- Pluto was the last planet discovered and is the smallest planet. (5-3)

- Other members of the solar system include asteroids, meteoroids, and comets. Asteroids are pieces of rock and metal that revolve around the sun between the orbits of Mars and Jupiter. Meteoroids are pieces of rock or metal that travel through the solar system. Comets are balls of ice and frozen gases that orbit the sun. (5-4)

- Spacecraft have been used to answer many questions about the universe. Spacecraft have tested the ability of technology and people to withstand the conditions of space. (5-5)

The key terms in this chapter are listed below. Use each term in a sentence that shows the meaning of the term.

asteroids	Mars	outer planet	solar system
comets	Mercury	Pluto	space probes
inner planet	meteoroids	satellite	Uranus
Jupiter	Neptune	Saturn	Venus

Chapter Review

Identify each statement as True or False. If a statement is false, replace the underlined term with a term that makes the statement true.

1. <u>Mercury</u> is the planet closest to the sun.
2. The sun and the objects that move around it make up the <u>solar system</u>.
3. <u>Meteoroids</u> are large chunks of ice, frozen gases, dust, and rock.
4. Chunks of rock or metal that move through the solar system and appear as flashes of light as they burn up in the atmosphere are called <u>comets</u>.
5. <u>Venus</u> has a dense atmosphere of carbon dioxide.
6. <u>Mars</u> is the largest planet in the solar system.
7. <u>Neptune</u> has rings that are visible with a small telescope.
8. Small rocky bodies that revolve around the sun between the orbits of Mars and Jupiter are called <u>satellites</u>.
9. <u>Uranus</u> is the next planet beyond Saturn.
10. The planet with the greatest average distance from the sun is <u>Pluto</u>.

CONCEPTS

1. Pluto is usually the farthest planet from the sun. Why is it now closer to the sun than is Neptune? (5-1)
2. In what ways are the inner planets similar? (5-1)
3. In what ways are the outer planets similar? (5-1)
4. How does Pluto differ from the outer planets? (5-1)
5. Where is the asteroid belt located? (5-1)
6. Why do the inner planets contain small amounts of the light elements? (5-2)
7. In what ways are the inner and outer planets different from each other? (5-2)
8. Why has Mercury been difficult for astronomers to study? (5-2)
9. What would account for the similarity of the surfaces of Mercury and our moon? (5-2)
10. Why would Venus not be a pleasant place to live? (5-2)
11. How are Mars and the earth similar? How are they different? (5-2)
12. Why do scientists believe that the outer planets have a large percentage of light elements? (5-3)

13. What causes the colored bands and the great red spot on Jupiter's surface? (5-3)
14. What are the Galilean moons of Jupiter? (5-3)
15. Describe the ring system of Saturn. (5-3)
16. Compare and contrast Uranus and Neptune. (5-3)
17. How is Pluto different from the other outer planets? (5-3)
18. What are asteroids? Where are they located? (5-4)
19. Compare and contrast a meteor and a comet. (5-4)
20. What are the benefits of satellites to scientists and other people? (5-5)
21. What are the advantages of the space shuttle program? (5-5)

APPLICATION/ CRITICAL THINKING

1. If there is life on Mars, to what conditions must it adapt? Where do you think this life would be found? Why?
2. Some astronomers have suggested that if Jupiter were larger, it would begin to give off light, like a star. How might a star in Jupiter's orbit affect life on the earth?
3. What do you think are the advantages of occupied spacecraft over unoccupied spacecraft?
4. If an astronaut landed on the surface of Jupiter what problems would he or she encounter concerning movement? Why?
5. There will be a time in the future when Pluto and Neptune come very close to each other because of Pluto's intersecting orbit. What could possibly happen when this occurs?

EXTENSION

1. What object in the solar system would you most like to visit? Why?
2. If you were going to place on a spacecraft a plaque describing the earth and its people to anything that finds it, what would you include?
3. What provisions must be made for the people aboard an occupied mission to Mars?

READINGS

Allen, Joseph P. *Entering Space: An Astronaut's Odyssey.* New York: Stewart, Tabori, and Chang, 1984.

Fichter, George. *Comets and Meteors.* New York: Franklin Watts, 1982.

Gore, Rick. "The Planets: Between Fire and Ice." *National Geographic,* January 1985, p. 4

Vogt, Gregory. *Mars and the Inner Planets.* New York: Franklin Watts, 1982.

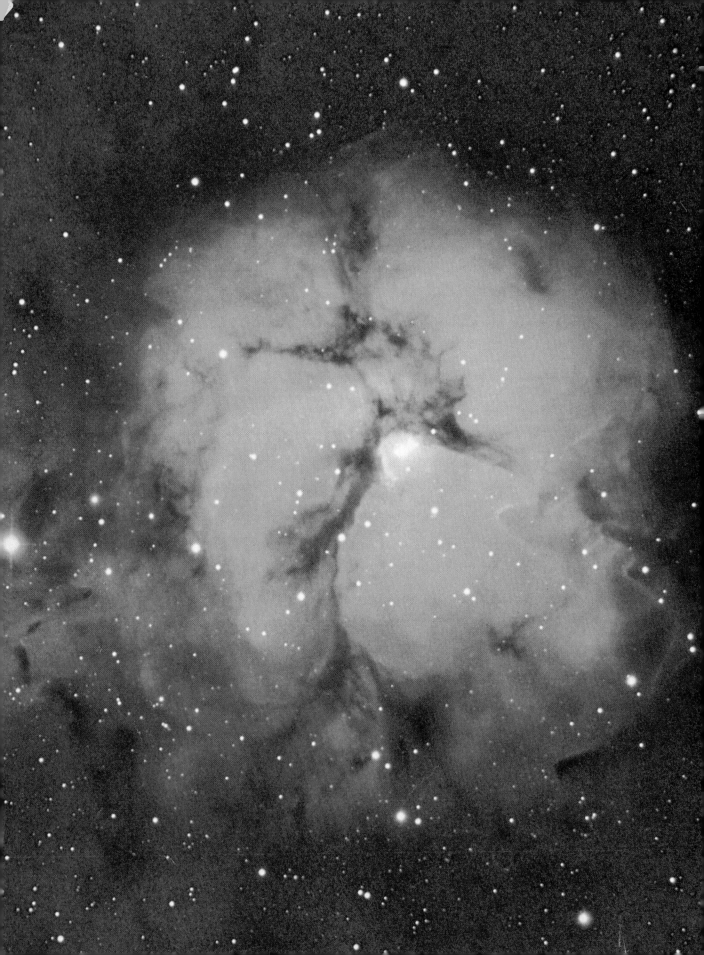

THE UNIVERSE

This photograph shows the Trifid nebula in the constellation Sagittarius. Through a telescope, nebulas appear as cloudy or misty objects among the stars. Most nebulas are clouds of gas and are made up of hydrogen and other substances. Some objects called nebulas are the remains of stars that have exploded. And a few objects thought at first to be nebulas are really systems of stars far beyond are own system.

- *What role do nebulas have in the life of stars?*
- *Why do stars occur in different colors?*
- *What happens to stars as they run out of fuel?*

6-1 OBSERVING STARS

People have always been attracted to and fascinated by the stars and planets. Ancient tablets show that the movements of the planets among the stars were well known before 3000 B.C. Early people were familiar with the positions of the stars in the night sky.

Have you ever seen the Great Bear in the sky? Perhaps you have seen the Twins, or the Big Dog, or the Whale. All of these are constellations. A **constellation** is a group of stars that forms a pattern, or picture, in the sky.

Many constellations were named and described thousands of years ago. Early people imagined that groups of stars formed pictures in the sky. The star groups seldom look like the creatures, people, and objects that their names describe. You must use your imagination to see the pictures in the sky.

A good place to begin a study of the heavens is with the Big Dipper. The Big Dipper is part of the constellation the Great Bear. Locate the Big Dipper in Figure 6-1. The shape of the Big Dipper is easy to recognize. Notice that you have to use your imagination to see the Great Bear. The Big Dipper can be used to find the North Star. As

After completing this section, you will be able to

- **define** the term *constellation*.
- **explain** why different constellations appear during different seasons.
- **describe** several of the instruments used to study the stars.

The key terms in this section are
constellation
radio telescope
reflecting telescope
refracting telescope
spectroscope

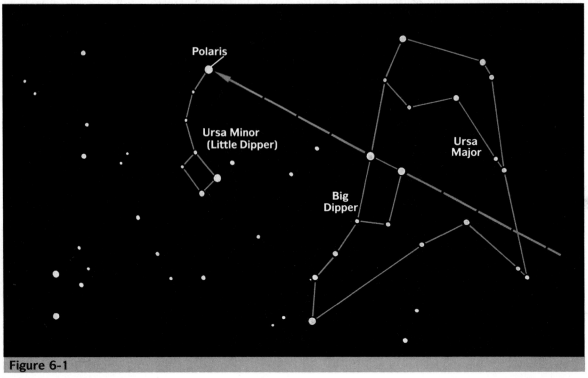

Figure 6-1

The two stars at the outer edge of the bowl of the Big Dipper point to Polaris, the North Star.

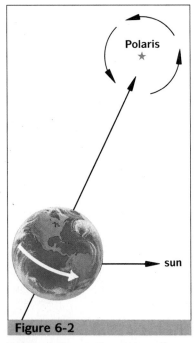

Figure 6-2

Because the earth rotates, the stars appear to circle counter-clockwise around Polaris.

shown in Figure 6-1, a line extended from the two stars at the front of the bucket reaches the North Star, Polaris (poh LAIR ihs). Notice in Figure 6-1 that Polaris is part of the constellation Ursa (ER suh) Minor, the Little Bear. Ursa Minor is also called the Little Dipper.

Why is Polaris called the North Star? Notice in Figure 6-2 the position of Polaris with respect to the earth. Polaris is almost directly over the North Pole. As the earth rotates, stars appear to move from east to west across the sky, just as the sun does. But because it is above the earth's North Pole, Polaris does not move. In fact, all other stars seem to circle Polaris. Stars close to Polaris in the sky remain above the horizon all the time. Other stars rise and set as the earth turns.

Different constellations are visible in the night sky during different times of the year. Why does the night sky change from season to season? As you know, the earth orbits the sun. As you can see in Figure 6-3, the night side of the earth faces in different directions in different parts of its orbit. Notice that in winter, Orion would be visible in the night sky. Which of the constellations shown would be visible on a summer evening?

Stars produce radiant energy, such as gamma rays, X rays, ultraviolet rays, and visible light. As you have learned,

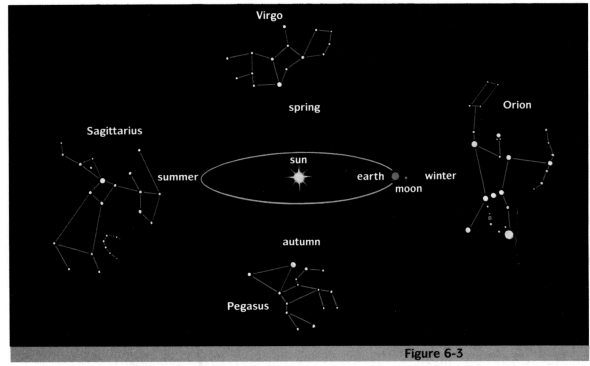

Figure 6-3

Different constellations are visible during different seasons of the year.

these forms of energy make up the electromagnetic spectrum. By studying the energy that a star produces, astronomers learn about the star's makeup, age, and direction and speed of motion.

A **refracting telescope** is an optical telescope that uses a lens to gather light and produce an image. A lens changes the direction of the light rays that pass through it. Figure 6-4 shows how a refracting telescope works. Light rays pass through the lens. The lens causes the light rays that pass through it to change direction. The light rays pass through a second lens, called the ocular. The ocular causes the image formed to be magnified.

A **reflecting telescope** is an optical telescope that uses a curved mirror to gather light rays and produce an image. The curve of the mirror causes light rays that reflect from it to become focused. As shown in Figure 6-4, a flat mirror may be placed in the path of the light. This mirror reflects the light toward the side. An ocular, placed on the side of the telescope, magnifies the image.

Light can be separated into its various colors by a prism. A **spectroscope** is an instrument that separates light into very fine bands of color. Spectroscopes are attached to telescopes so that astronomers can analyze starlight. The bands of color give information about the makeup of stars and their temperatures.

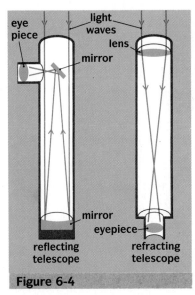

Figure 6-4

A reflecting telescope and a refracting telescope.

OBJECTIVE
Locate Polaris by using the Big Dipper.

MATERIALS
constellation guidebook, flashlight, paper, pencil

PROCEDURE
A. Find a location where you can view the stars. Take the materials listed with you.
B. In the guidebook, find the drawing of the sky as it appears at the time and on the date that you are observing the sky.
C. Locate Ursa Major in the guidebook.
D. Find the Big Dipper in the sky.
E. Starting with the two stars that form the outer part of the bowl, extend a line from the Big Dipper. The first bright star you reach is Polaris.
F. Sketch the positions of the Big Dipper and the Little Dipper (Ursa Minor) as they appear in the sky. Record the time.

RESULTS AND CONCLUSIONS
1. Label Polaris on your sketch.
2. Label the Big Dipper and the Little Dipper on your sketch.
3. Make a sketch showing your prediction for the locations of Polaris, the Big Dipper, and the Little Dipper 6 hours after making your original sketch.
4. Where would you look for Polaris if you were at the North Pole?

A **radio telescope** gathers and focuses radio waves. The radio telescope in Arecibo, Puerto Rico, shown in Figure 6-5, has a diameter of 305 m. A radio telescope gives astronomers different information about astronomical objects than does a light telescope.

Figure 6-5

This radio telescope is built into a natural bowl in the landscape.

REVIEW
1. What are constellations?
2. Use a diagram to explain why constellations visible in the fall sky would not be visible in the spring sky.
3. How do optical telescopes differ from radio telescopes?

CHALLENGE Suppose an eclipse of the sun occurred on a winter day around noon. What season's constellations would be visible in the darkened sky? Explain your answer.

6-2 DISTANCES TO STARS

About 2000 stars are visible on a dark, clear night. It is easy to imagine that these stars are all the same distance from the earth. Astronomers, however, have shown that all stars are not at the same distance.

Figure 6-6 shows the stars of the constellation Cassiopeia and how far three of the stars are from the earth. The screen to the left indicates how these stars appear in the night sky. Notice that the stars are not equally distant from the earth. Some are much farther than others. These stars form a pattern because they are all in the same direction when seen from the earth. But the stars in a constellation are not necessarily all together in one region of space.

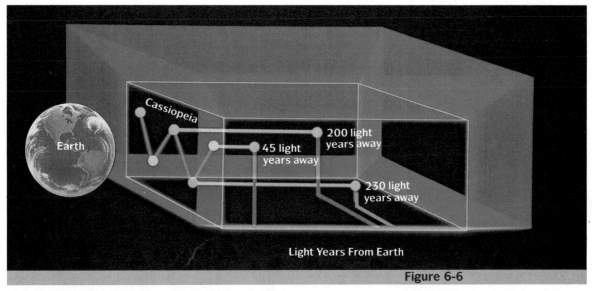

Figure 6-6

The stars in the constellation Cassiopeia appear together in the sky but in reality the stars are not near to each other.

The distances to the stars in Figure 6-6 are measured in light-years (ly). The light-year is based on the speed of light, 300,000 km/s. A **light-year** is the distance light travels in one year, 9,460,000,000,000 km. Distances to the stars are most often measured in light-years because the distances are so large. For example, the distance to Proxima Centauri, the nearest star to the solar system, is about 40,605,000,000,000 km. This distance, however, is also 4.3 ly.

How do astronomers know that the stars are not all the same distance from the earth? One piece of evidence is based on a property called parallax (PAR uh laks). **Parallax** is an apparent shift in the position of an object when it is viewed from different places.

parallaxis (change)

123

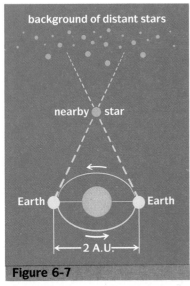

Figure 6-7

Parallax can be used to measure the distance to stars less than 100 light years away.

Parallax can be used to determine distance to nearby stars. The method is shown in Figure 6-7. First, the position of the star compared to other, more distant stars is measured. Then, six months later, the position of the star is measured again. At this time, the earth is on the other side of its orbit, 300,000,000 km from the first view. An astronomer measures the change in position of the star compared to the distant stars. He or she can then determine the distance to the nearby star.

This method of measuring the distances to stars works for stars within 100 ly of the earth. Most stars, however, are so far away that their positions from both sides of the earth's orbit seem to be the same. In such cases, other methods must be used to measure the distances.

You have noticed that some stars are brighter than others. Early astronomers used a system to indicate the brightness, or apparent magnitude, of stars. The system is based on a scale from one to six. The brightest stars were called 1st magnitude stars. The dimmest stars were called 6th magnitude stars. Other stars were rated from 2nd through 5th magnitude.

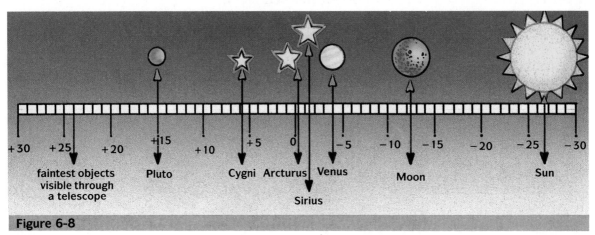

Figure 6-8

The apparent magnitudes of some stars and the sun.

The modern system for measuring apparent magnitude is similar to the original system. Today, astronomers have instruments to measure a star's apparent magnitude. Each step on the magnitude scale marks a change in brightness of 2.5 times. For example, a 1st magnitude star is 2.5 times brighter than a 2nd magnitude star. According to Figure 6-8, how bright is Arcturus? With telescopes, astronomers can see objects that are too dim to be seen with the eye alone. So the scale has been extended so that dim stars can be rated. The dimmest stars that can be seen

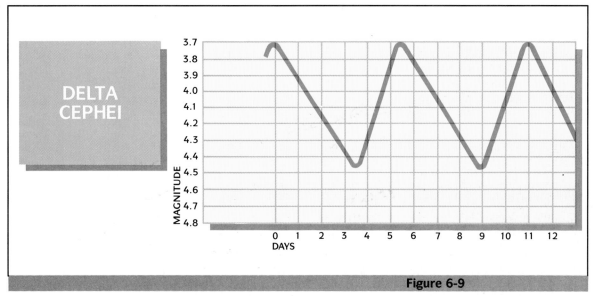

Figure 6-9

The varying magnitude of the star Delta Cephei in the constellation Cepheus.

through a 500-cm telescope are of the 24th magnitude. The sun's magnitude is −26.5 because it is so bright.

Astronomers are interested in knowing how bright a star really is, as well as how bright it looks. The **absolute magnitude** of a star describes how bright that star would be if it were placed a certain distance from the earth. Scientists have agreed to call the apparent magnitude a star would have at 32.6 ly from the earth its absolute magnitude. For example, the absolute magnitude of the sun is +5. Absolute magnitude is a way of comparing the actual brightness of stars. If a star's distance from the earth is known, its absolute magnitude can be figured out from its apparent magnitude.

One way of finding the distances to stars is by using the absolute magnitude of a special kind of variable star. These stars are called Cepheid (SEHF ee ihd) variables. As shown in Figure 6-9, a Cepheid changes in brightness in a regular period of time. How does the magnitude of the star in Figure 6-9 change? What is the period of time for a complete cycle?

It has been shown that the absolute magnitude of a Cepheid is related to its period of variation. The longer the period, the brighter is the star. Cepheid variables are not common stars. But when one is found, astronomers can find its absolute magnitude from its period. Using the absolute magnitude and apparent magnitude, the distance to the Cepheid can be determined. If Cepheids are found with other stars in clusters, the distances to these other stars can be determined.

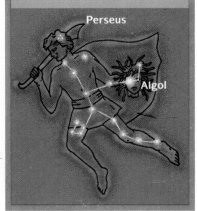

SCIENCE PUZZLER

Algol, a star in the constellation Perseus, undergoes a periodic change in magnitude. However, Algol is not a Cepheid variable. Algol is one member of a double star system. How can the fact that Algol is part of a double star system be used to explain its periodic change in magnitude?

ACTIVITY   Measuring Parallax

OBJECTIVE
Observe the effect of parallax.
Predict the effect of distance on parallax.

MATERIALS
unlined paper, metric ruler, pencil, clay, toothpick

PROCEDURE
A. Place the paper on the table in front of you. Draw a line across the paper 2 cm from the top, as shown in the drawing. Using the metric scale, mark a centimeter scale along the line and number it from 0 to 20.

B. Draw a second line across the paper 5 cm from the top, as shown. Draw a third line down the center of the paper and mark off 5 cm, 10 cm, 15 cm, and 20 cm as shown.

C. Fold the paper along the second line so that the scale stands up on your table.

D. Place the paper in front of you along the edge of your desk. Stand the toothpick in a piece of clay and place it on the 5-cm mark as shown.

E. Crouch down so that when you look at the tip of the toothpick, you see the scale behind it. Close your left eye. While looking with the right eye, line the toothpick up with a mark on the scale. Have your partner record the number of that mark in a data table.

F. Without moving your head, open your left eye and close your right eye. Read the number from the scale that the toothpick now lines up with. Have your partner record that number.

G. Subtract the first number from the second to measure how much the apparent position has shifted. Record the difference in a table.
  1. Predict how the parallax shift will change as the distance increases.

H. Repeat steps E through G with the toothpick placed at 10 cm, 15 cm, and 20 cm. Record your data.
  2. Predict how the parallax shift will change as you move back.

I. Leave the toothpick 20 cm from the scale and move 2 m back from the table. Repeat steps E through G. Record your data.

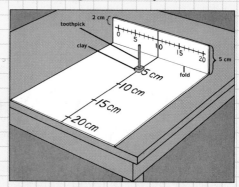

RESULTS AND CONCLUSIONS
1. In which position, 5 cm, 10 cm, 15 cm, or 20 cm, did the toothpick appear to change position the most? The least?
2. When you moved away from the table, did the toothpick appear to move more or less than it did when you were close?
3. Why is it difficult to use this method for measuring the distances to stars when the stars are very far away?

REVIEW
1. Define the term *light-year*.
2. Describe two methods used to determine the distances to stars.
3. Why does a star's apparent magnitude alone tell us nothing about its absolute magnitude?

CHALLENGE Each unit on the magnitude scale indicates a value 2.5 greater than the next unit. Thus a star of magnitude 1 looks 2.5 times brighter than a star of magnitude 2. Suppose star A has an apparent magnitude of 2. Star B has an apparent magnitude of 6. How much brighter does star A appear to be?

6-3 TYPES OF STARS

A close look at stars shows that they vary in many ways. For example, stars are not all the same color. Figure 6-10 shows the constellation Orion, the Hunter. The bright star at Orion's shoulder is a red star called Betelgeuse (BEE-tuhl jooz). The bright star in Orion's leg is a blue-white star called Rigel (RĪ juhl). Stars can appear blue-white, white, yellow, orange, or red in color.

A star's color is determined by the wavelengths of light that it produces. A red star like Betelgeuse produces light of all wavelengths. But it produces more red light than light of other colors. Some stars produce much of their energy in wavelengths that the human eye cannot see, such as ultraviolet waves.

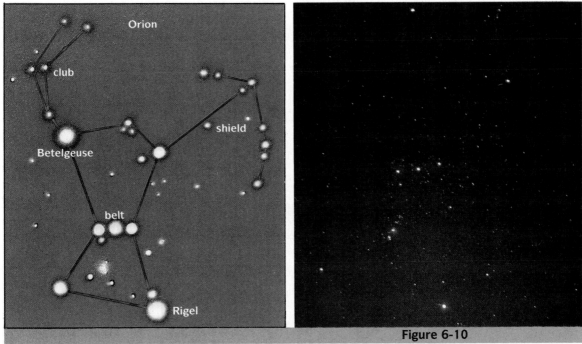

Figure 6-10

A diagram of the constellation Orion (left). A photo of the constellation Orion (right). Can you see the hunter?

The wavelengths of light that a star produces are related to its surface temperature. Perhaps you have watched a toaster as it warms up. As it warms, you first feel heat, but you see no color. As the temperature increases, the heating elements turn red. Increasing the temperature causes them to become brighter. The color may change to orange. If you could continue to increase the temperature, the color would change to yellow and then to white. A star's color is related to its temperature, much as the toaster's heating element is.

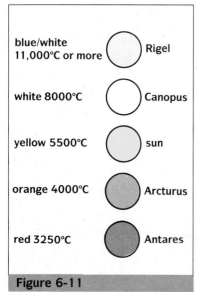

blue/white 11,000°C or more	Rigel
white 8000°C	Canopus
yellow 5500°C	sun
orange 4000°C	Arcturus
red 3250°C	Antares

Figure 6-11

There is a relationship between the colors of the stars and their temperatures.

Figure 6-11 shows the relationship between star color and surface temperature. Stars with a surface temperature of less than 3250°C appear red. If a star has a surface temperature of 5500°C, what color would it appear? In general, stars with high surface temperatures are brighter than stars with low surface temperatures. However, size also is a factor in brightness. A large red star would be brighter than a small white star.

In the early 1900s two astronomers made a graph showing the relationship between the absolute magnitude of stars and their temperature. This graph, shown in Figure 6-12, is often called the Hertzsprung-Russell diagram, or the H-R diagram. It is named for the astronomers who made it. As you read from right to left the surface temperature increases. From the bottom to the top, the absolute magnitude increases. According to the H-R diagram, what are the absolute magnitude and surface temperature of the sun?

DO YOU KNOW?

New information about the brightest star in the night sky, Sirius, has been uncovered. Sirius is a brilliant white star in the constellation Canis Major. But ancient people probably saw Sirius in another color. Astronomers have found that early astronomers saw Sirius as a red star. It was recorded as being red as late as A.D. 585. Around the year 1000, an Arab astronomer first listed it as a white star.

Scientists now know that Sirius is really two stars. And one of them is near the end of its life. In the past, one member of the pair was a red star. This red star is the one that ancient astronomers saw and listed. At some point, the red star collapsed into a white dwarf. It became a small, dim star, no longer blocking out the light of its white companion. It is this white star that we see in the night sky.

But for a star to go from a red giant to a white dwarf so quickly does not fit in with current models of the life of stars. It is thought that a star takes at least 100,000 years to change from a red giant into a white dwarf. If such a change were to occur quickly, it is thought that a violent explosion would occur. But scientists have found no evidence of an explosion in the Sirius system. The short time between the red giant stage and the white dwarf stage has convinced many scientists that current theories about the life of stars will have to be changed.

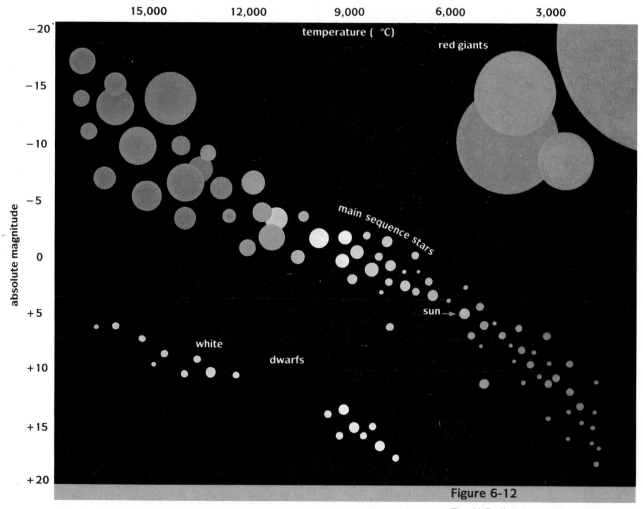

temperature (°C)

Figure 6-12

The H-R diagram.

The H-R diagram has been useful to astronomers in many ways. For example, notice how most of the stars fall in a band that starts in the upper left corner and continues to the lower right of the diagram. This portion of the graph is called the main sequence. **Main sequence stars** are stars that appear on the main sequence of the H-R diagram. About 90 percent of the stars that have been classified are main sequence stars.

When astronomers study the stars of the main sequence, two patterns are seen. First, there is a decrease in surface temperature from stars at the top of the main sequence to stars at the bottom of the main sequence. Second, there is also a decrease in mass from stars at the top of the main sequence to stars at the bottom. These patterns suggest that the mass of a star is important in determining what its surface temperature will be.

There are stars that do not fit into the main sequence. In the upper right are stars that are very bright. To produce

ACTIVITY   Observing Spectra

OBJECTIVE
Observe the types of spectra produced by different materials.
Deduce the way in which spectra can be used to analyze stars.

MATERIALS
safety goggles, spectroscope, lamp, long spoon, small quantities of the salts of sodium, copper, calcium, potassium, Bunsen burner, matches

PROCEDURE
A. A glowing solid produces a continuous spectrum. Put on the safety goggles. Use the spectroscope to observe the glowing filament of a light bulb.
   1. Describe what you see.
B. A glowing gas produces a bright-line spectrum. Light the Bunsen burner. Have your partner place a small amount of the sodium salt on the tip of the spoon.
Caution: Do not taste any salt.

C. Have your partner hold the tip of the spoon in the flame. **Caution:** Hold the spoon in the flame for a short time only, as it will get hot. Observe the glowing color with the spectroscope.
   2. Describe what you see.
D. Repeat steps **B** and **C** using samples of the other salts.
   3. Describe what you see in each case.

RESULTS AND CONCLUSIONS
1. Based on your results, explain what a continuous spectrum is.
2. Based on your results, explain what a bright-line spectrum is.
3. Each element has a unique bright-line spectrum. The sun, and other stars, produce dark-line spectra. The dark lines indicate that wavelengths of light are being absorbed by elements. An element's bright-line and absorption pattern are the same. How can scientists determine a star's composition from its spectrum?

that much light, these stars must be large. For example, a **red giant** is a cool red star that appears very bright because it is so large. There are also blue giants. How would the surface temperature of a blue giant compare with that of a red giant?

In the lower left is another group of stars that is off the main sequence. These stars are called white dwarfs. **White dwarfs** are hot stars that do not appear bright because they are very small. However, they are very dense.

REVIEW

1. What is the relationship between a star's color and its surface temperature?
2. Classify each of the following stars on the H-R diagram.
    a. Star A has an absolute magnitude of +8 and a surface temperature of 8000°C.
    b. Star B has an absolute magnitude of +15 and a surface temperature of 30,000°C.
    c. Star C has an absolute magnitude of −2 and a surface temperature of 4000°C.

CHALLENGE Rigel is a blue giant. Antares is a red giant. Both stars have roughly the same absolute magnitudes. Predict the relative sizes of these two stars.

6-4 THE LIFE OF STARS

As they study stars, astronomers try to learn about the life history of stars. Astronomers have been studying pictures of stars for over 100 years. But stars may exist for billions of years. Very little change occurs in 100 years of a star's life. The stars, however, do change. The nuclear reactions that power them use fuel. In time the fuel runs out. To study stars, astronomers predict how a star might change, and then they search for stars in the predicted stages.

Astronomers think that stars begin as a large, spinning cloud of gas and dust called a nebula. As the nebula spins, it condenses. Astronomers estimate that a nebula that is large enough to condense must have a mass greater than the mass of 1000 stars. Many pockets of matter within the nebula are the beginnings of stars and are called **protostars**. Stars are often seen grouped in clusters because many stars can form within a nebula.

proto- (first)

Figure 6-13

Nebulas are star-forming areas. These are in the constellation Monoceros.

In the beginning, a protostar's diameter may be billions of kilometers. As it condenses, its temperature rises. When the temperature in the center reaches 10,000°C, the atoms are colliding with so much force that their electrons and nuclei separate. A protostar is now about 100,000,000 km across. Imagine that in the beginning the star was the size of the Houston Astrodome. It would now have condensed to the size of a baseball.

A protostar continues to condense, and the temperature inside reaches 150,000°C. The surface temperature now is about 3500°C, and the protostar produces red light. This beginning star is bright enough to be placed on the H-R diagram. It is now 50,000,000 km across. On the H-R diagram this star would appear to the right of the main sequence, just below the red giants. Very few of these young stars have been found. But it is likely that they are hidden by the nebula in which they are forming.

A protostar continues to condense until the temperature inside reaches 10,000,000°C. At this temperature, nuclear fusion begins. A large amount of energy starts to radiate outward. This energy slows the condensing of the protostar's matter and begins the life of a new star. Stars in this stage are main sequence stars.

Figure 6-14

The Pleiades is an open cluster of relatively young stars.

The length of a star's life depends on its mass. The most massive stars may live only 3 million years. A star the size of the sun may live 10 billion years. The smallest, least massive stars may live many billions of years.

When a star begins to run out of hydrogen, it goes through many changes. The nuclear reactions in the core slow down. Around the hot core, a shell of hydrogen continues to react and to release energy. The heat from the core causes the outer layers of gases from the hydrogen shell to be pushed outward. With these changes, a red giant forms and the star moves off the main sequence. The red giant will grow to tremendous size as helium replaces hydrogen as the fuel.

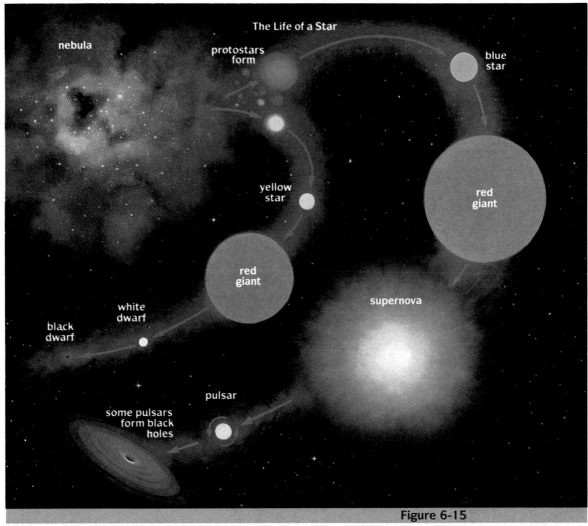

Figure 6-15

The way a star evolves depends on its mass and its composition.

Although most stars go through these changes, the remaining life of a star depends on its mass. Follow these changes in Figure 6-15. Small stars begin a series of changes that lead them to the white dwarf stage. An expanding shell of gases spreads into space and does not return. The remaining matter condenses and heats up. The star becomes a white dwarf. This star produces little light but has a high surface temperature. Its gravity may be 500 thousand times the gravity of the earth. A white dwarf slowly cools until all of its heat is gone. It then becomes a cold piece of matter called a black dwarf.

Stars larger than eight times the sun's mass go through different changes. These stars may expand and contract several times and then explode. The violent explosion of such a star near the end of its life is called a **supernova**.

novus (new)

A supernova may produce as much light as an entire galaxy. Much of the matter from the supernova is shot through space at tremendous speeds, forming a spreading cloud. The remains of a supernova are shown in Figure 6-16.

Figure 6-16

The Crab Nebula is the remains of a supernova that occurred in 1054 A.D.

Two strange kinds of stars may result from supernovas. One of these is called a pulsar, a spinning neutron star. A **pulsar** (PUHL sahr) produces rapid bursts of radio waves that repeat many times per second. Astronomers are unsure about the cause of these waves. Astronomers have estimated that neutron stars contain as much mass as the sun but are only about 15 km in diameter.

If the mass remaining after a supernova is more than four times the sun's mass, it may condense to form a black hole. A **black hole** is an object whose gravity is so strong that even light does not escape it. The matter that creates the black hole may condense to a very small area. Astronomers estimate that there may be 100,000 black holes in the Milky Way galaxy and they are studying the areas around several suspected black holes.

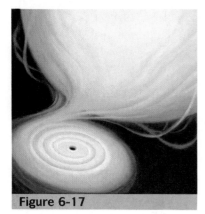

Figure 6-17

An artist's conception of a black hole.

REVIEW

1. Describe the stages in the formation of a star.
2. What is the relationship between the mass of a star and its life cycle?

CHALLENGE Certain stars seem to be streaming matter into space. Scientists think that such stars might be near black holes. Why might scientists suspect black holes to be near such stars?

6-5 GALAXIES

ISLANDS OF STARS

Figure 6-18(*left*) is a photograph of the Andromeda (an-DRAHM uh duh) galaxy. Until the 1920s this object and others like it were thought to be nebulas. They looked like small, fuzzy patches of light. Astronomers believed they were clouds of gas and dust between the stars. In 1924, Edwin Hubble, an American astronomer, used a 250-cm telescope at the Mt. Wilson Observatory, in California, to study these objects. He showed that they were large systems of stars. A large system of stars is called a **galaxy**.

Hubble spent many years studying galaxies. He found that they can be organized into three basic types. One type of galaxy is the elliptical galaxy, shown in Figure 6-18. These galaxies may be nearly round, but most often resemble flattened spheres. The largest galaxies that have been found are elliptical, but many elliptical galaxies are small.

galaxias (milk)

A. elliptical galaxy

B. spiral galaxy

C. irregular galaxy

Figure 6-18

The Andromeda galaxy is very much like the Milky Way (*left*). Three types of galaxies (*right*).

The second most common type of galaxy is the spiral galaxy, shown in Figure 6-18. Notice that this galaxy looks like a pinwheel. It appears to be a spinning disk that is swollen at its center. Most spiral galaxies are brighter than elliptical galaxies. Finally, a small number of galaxies have no regular shape. These are called irregular galaxies. Figure 6-18 shows an irregular galaxy.

It is thought that galaxies start as large clouds of gas and dust called protogalaxies. In time, the cloud will condense and begin to form stars. When the stars begin to shine, the galaxy is born.

One of Hubble's most important discoveries was about the motion of the galaxies. He observed a red shift in their light. A red shift is a change in the spectrum of an object that is moving away. Figure 6-19 shows how spectral lines shift according to the motion of an object. Part *B* shows the position of two dark lines from a stationary object's spectrum. Part *A* shows where these lines might appear when the object moves away from you. Part *C* shows where they might appear if the object is moving toward you. Toward what color do the lines shift if objects are moving away? The faster the object travels the farther the lines shift. Light from nearly all galaxies shows a red shift. This means these galaxies are moving away. The farthest galaxies also move at the fastest speeds.

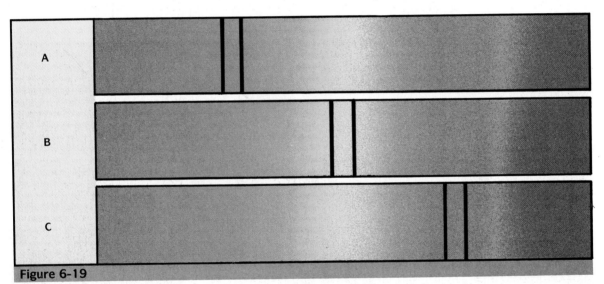

Figure 6-19

As a star moves away, the spectral lines move toward the red end of the spectrum.

The farthest and fastest objects that astronomers have found are called quasars. **Quasars** (KWAY sahrs) are thought to be galaxies that are powerful sources of radio waves. Most quasars are billions of light-years from the earth. Some quasars are moving at 90 percent of the speed of light. One model for a quasar's source of energy says that at the center of a quasar is a black hole. The black hole is gathering matter at a fantastic rate. Energy is released as this matter is pulled into the black hole. Some astronomers believe that quasars are a stage that young galaxies may go through.

THE MILKY WAY

The **Milky Way galaxy**, which contains billions of stars, is the home of the solar system. It is very difficult to study this galaxy because the solar system is located within it. It seems to be a spiral galaxy. The galaxy's disk, which is about 100,000 ly across and 5000 ly thick, is surrounded by many small clusters of stars. The Milky Way galaxy spins around an axis that passes through its center. The solar system completes one revolution in about 250 million years.

Notice in Figure 6-20 that the Milky Way galaxy resembles a pinwheel. Where in the galaxy is the solar system located?

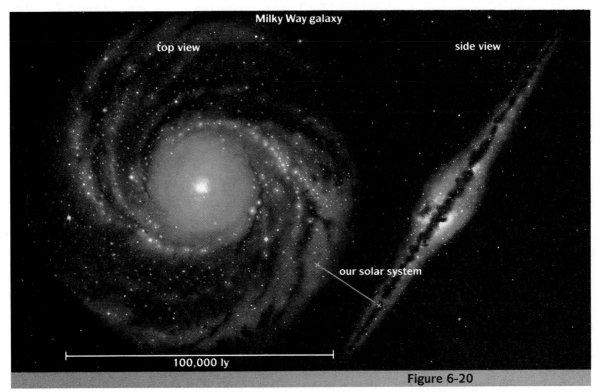

Milky Way galaxy

top view

side view

our solar system

100,000 ly

Figure 6-20

The solar system is part of the Milky Way galaxy.

THE ORIGIN OF THE UNIVERSE

Scientists think that the universe is between 15 billion and 20 billion years old. But how did the universe begin? Three theories have been proposed for the origin of the universe. Each of these theories is based on the idea that the galaxies are moving away from one another.

Based on the evidence that the galaxies are spreading, one can conclude that in the past they were gathered together. But why would matter begin to spread at such fantastic speeds? The answer seems to be a tremendous explosion. The idea that the universe began as a tremendous explosion is called the **big bang theory**. According to this theory, all of the energy and matter in the universe was once concentrated together. Mass, energy, and the forces of nature were all one. The universe, with its matter, energy, and forces, was formed when the big bang occurred. The universe began to expand with the explosion. The big bang theory is the most widely accepted theory on the origin of the universe.

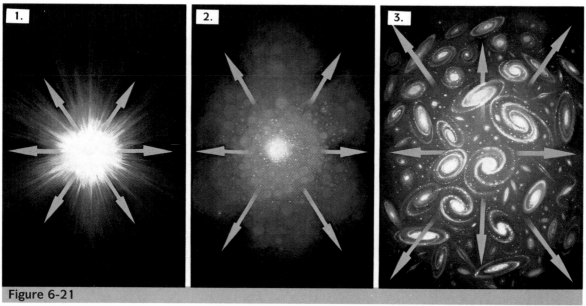

Figure 6-21

The big bang theory.

The **steady state theory** says that the universe is infinite in time. While the galaxies are spreading, new galaxies form in the space between them. There is no change in the density of the universe. As galaxies move away, new ones take their place. There is no evidence that new galaxies are forming in the space between others.

The **oscillating** (AHS uh layt ihng) **universe theory** says that the universe starts with a big bang, but then collapses back together. This change in direction is caused by the total gravity of the matter in the universe pulling everything back together. After the material collapses together, another big bang would start the process again. Many astronomers feel that there is not enough matter, and therefore not enough gravity, to cause this. Other astronomers believe that estimates for the amount of matter in the universe are too small. More data is needed to decide if the universe expands and collapses.

REVIEW

1. How are galaxies classified by shape?
2. Sketch the Milky Way galaxy and indicate the position of the solar system.
3. Why is the oscillating universe theory a variation of the big bang theory?

CHALLENGE Suppose most galaxies showed a blue shift. What conclusions could be drawn from such data?

CHAPTER SUMMARY

The main ideas in this chapter are listed below. Read these statements before you answer the Chapter Review questions.

- A constellation is a group of stars that forms a pattern. Constellations are useful in locating other objects in the sky. (6-1)

- Astronomers use different instruments to study electromagnetic energy from stars. Optical telescopes, radio telescopes, and spectroscopes are examples of instruments used by astronomers. (6-1)

- The light-year, the distance light travels in one year, is used as a standard for measuring distances in space. (6-2)

- Several methods are used to determine the distances to stars. These methods include parallax, and measuring the periods of special stars called Cepheid variables. (6-2)

- Stars are classified according to their temperature and brightness. The H-R diagram is a graph of these two properties. (6-3)

- A star begins as a nebula of gas and dust. The nebula condenses into a sphere of matter. Nuclear fusion produces energy within the star. (6-4)

- Small stars become white dwarfs and eventually, black dwarfs. Large stars may become supernovas, and, possibly, pulsars, or black holes. (6-4)

- A galaxy is a large system of stars. The galaxies all seem to have formed at about the same time and are all moving away from one another. (6-5)

- The big bang theory states that the universe began as a tremendous explosion. The oscillating universe theory states that the universe expands and contracts periodically. (6-5)

The key terms in this chapter are listed below. Use each term in a sentence that shows the meaning of the term.

absolute magnitude	Milky Way galaxy	red giant
big bang theory	oscillating universe theory	reflecting telescope
black hole	parallax	refracting telescope
constellation	protostar	spectroscope
galaxy	pulsar	steady state theory
light-year	quasar	supernova
main sequence stars	radio telescope	white dwarfs

Chapter Review

VOCABULARY

Use the key terms from this chapter to complete the following sentences correctly.

1. The apparent movement of an object caused by a change in the position from which the object is viewed is _____ .

2. The violent explosion of a large star that is near the end of its life is a/an _____ .

3. A huge, cool star that can shine brightly in the sky is a/an _____ .

4. A group of stars that forms a pattern in the sky is called a/an _____ .

5. A theory that says the universe began with a tremendous explosion and that it will probably continue to expand is the _____ .

6. An instrument used to separate light into its various colors is a/an _____ .

7. A hot, very dense star that does not shine brightly in the sky is a/an _____ .

8. A large system of stars is called a/an _____ .

9. The measure of a star's brightness, if it were placed a certain distance from the earth, is its _____ .

10. A telescope that uses a curved mirror to focus light is called a/an _____ .

CONCEPTS

1. The word for ''constellation'' in many foreign languages literally means ''star picture.'' Why are such words appropriate? (6-1)

2. The constellation Sagittarius is only visible during the summer. Why wouldn't Sagittarius be visible in the winter sky? (6-1)

3. Compare how a refracting telescope and a reflecting telescope gather light. (6-1)

4. What information about stars can be obtained by using a spectroscope? (6-1)

5. What is a light-year? (6-2)

6. How can astronomers use parallax to demonstrate that the stars are not all the same distance from the solar system? (6-2)

7. Why does the sun have an apparent magnitude of -26.5 but an absolute magnitude of $+5$? (6-2)

8. How are Cepheid variable stars used by astronomers to measure distance in space? (6-2)

9. In what ways does a star's appearance change as its temperature increases? (6-3)

10. Classify each of the following stars on the H-R diagram. (6-3)
    a. Star A has an absolute magnitude of −4 and a surface temperature of 4500° C.
    b. Star B has an absolute magnitude of +4 and a surface temperature of 10,000° C.
    c. Star C has an absolute magnitude of +16 and a surface temperature of 35,000° C.

11. How do astronomers think a star forms? (6-4)

12. Describe the life cycle of a star having a mass equal to or smaller than that of the sun. (6-4)

13. Describe the life cycle of a star having a mass that is considerably larger than that of the sun. (6-4)

14. Compare the three main types of galaxies. (6-5)

15. Describe the shape of the Milky Way galaxy. (6-5)

16. Compare the big bang theory for the origin of the universe with the steady state theory.

17. Why would an accurate determination of the mass of the universe lead to support for either the big bang theory or the oscillating universe theory?

APPLICATION/ CRITICAL THINKING

1. The relative positions of stars in the sky does not change from night to night. Will the constellations change over thousands of years? Explain your answer.

2. The height of Polaris above the horizon, in degrees, is equal to the latitude from which it is viewed. Where would Polaris appear if one were at the equator?

3. If the current model for the evolution of a star is correct, what is likely to happen to the earth in the next 5–10 billion years?

4. Why is life unlikely to develop on planets that circle very large, very hot stars?

EXTENSION

1. Use a guidebook to the constellations to make your own investigation of the night sky. Identify the first magnitude stars that are visible. Identify several constellations.

2. Using a telescope and sky charts, locate prominent nebulas and galaxies. For example, in winter and spring the nebula in Orion's sword is visible.

READINGS

Dickinson, Terrence. *Nightwatch: An Equinox Guide to Viewing the Universe*. Ontario: Camden House, 1984.

Gore, Rick. "The Once and Future Universe." *National Geographic Society*, June 1983, p. 704.

Science in Careers

You know that geologists study rocks on the earth. How would you learn about the geology of Mars or the Moon? You could study moon rocks collected by the Apollo astronauts, but no rocks have been brought back from Mars.

Astrogeologists study other planets by examining meteorites and data collected by spacecraft. For example, the two Voyager spacecraft took pictures of Mars. They showed geological features, such as ancient river beds, mountains, and volcanoes. These pictures told astrogeologists a lot about the geology of Mars.

Astrogeologists must receive a four-year college degree and should take courses in geology, astronomy, physics, and math. Many continue their education to receive advanced degrees.

If you are interested in astrogeology, you should study earth science, physical science, and math in school. ■

AEROSPACE ASSEMBLER

You don't have to be an astronaut or astronomer to be involved in a space program. As an aerospace assembler, you can put together the machinery and parts that go into spacecraft, telescopes, and equipment used in the aerospace industry.

Aerospace assemblers work for private industry and for the government. They must be able to work with their hands and recognize details. A high school diploma and on-the-job training are usually required. Courses in shop and physical science are also helpful. ■

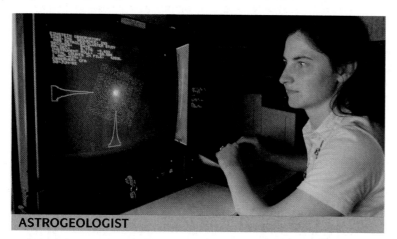

ASTROGEOLOGIST

People in Science

During the 1960s, Dr. George Robert Carruthers, a research physicist, was developing instruments that would improve our ability to detect radiation from space. He knew that stars give off radiation that is invisible to our eyes.

Some of this invisible radiation is located in the ultraviolet region of the spectrum — between X rays and near ultraviolet. Dr. Carruthers also knew that the earth's atmosphere blocks out most of this radiation.

He developed a device that would be used outside the atmosphere, in space. It is called the Far Ultraviolet Camera Spectrograph. It was taken to the moon on Apollo 12 in 1972.

The Carruthers instrument takes pictures of objects radiating ultraviolet radiation. It also separates this radiation into a spectrum. It has allowed astronomers to investigate the chemical and physical properties of stars and interstellar gas in great detail. ■

DR. GEORGE ROBERT CARRUTHERS, PHYSICIST

Until 1961, travel in outer space was just a fantasy. But in that year a Soviet astronaut named Yuri Gagarin became the first person to orbit the earth. Since then the United States and the Soviet Union have landed space probes on the moon, Venus, and Mars. The United States sent the Pioneer and Voyager space probes to photograph Mercury, Jupiter, Saturn, and Uranus. United States astronauts have walked on the moon and re-paired satellites in space. Both the United States and the Soviet Union are now working toward building permanent orbiting space stations.

Space travel continues to be amazing. Television has brought pictures into our homes of astro-nauts walking in space and walk-ing on the surface of the moon. But to some people, space travel in mainly an enormous expense.

NASA's budget for 1985 was over $7 billion. Most of this money was spent on the Space Transportation System, or Space Shuttle. The Space Shuttle, shown in Figure 1, is a reusable vehicle. It can carry people and satellites into orbit. Experiments can also be carried out in space aboard the Space Shuttle.

Critics feel that the money spent on the space program could be put to better use here on earth. Defenders of the space program point to the many bene-fits it brings. Life for us would be very different without the hun-dreds of satellites that orbit the earth. Those satellites would not be there without the space pro-gram. Television satellites help us to see live pictures from all over the world. There are satellites that make long distance phone calls possible. Weather satellites send photographs of weather

patterns to forecasters. These help warn us when severe storms like hurricanes may be on the way.

Earth resources satellites can help us find geological forma-tions on earth that may contain oil. They can spot forest fires and can show pollution in lakes and rivers. They can even pinpoint the locations of large schools of fish in the ocean.

Many products that were orginally developed for the space program are now used in homes. These include freeze-dried foods, latex paint, and improved non-stick coatings for pots and pans.

Special lightweight insulating materials developed for space are now used in blankets, sleep-ing bags, and outerwear. Com-puter programs that were originally used to test rocket sys-tems have been modified to test new cars. And new kinds of bat-

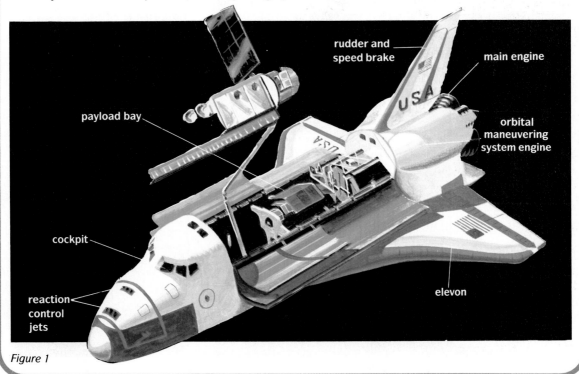

Figure 1

teries and electronic equipment developed for space have improved pacemakers for some heart patients.

Critics don't deny that wonderful things have come from the space program in the past. But they are not sure about the direction the program is taking now.

As mentioned, NASA's budget for 1985 was over $7 billion. That is a small part of the total United States budget. But it is still a lot of money. Most of that money goes for the Space Shuttle. Before the explosion of *Challenger* in January 1986, the United States had four shuttles. Each of them had a value of about $2 billion. Replacing the Challenger will probably cost more than $2 billion. Some people think that is a lot of money at a time when the United States has many people who are either homeless, unemployed, or hungry.

Of course, the shuttle is a reusable vehicle. So it is less expensive in the long run than building a new rocket for each mission. However, each shuttle launch still costs over $200 million. For the nine shuttles sent up in 1985 that adds up to $1.8 billion.

Figure 2 compares the cost of several things, including costs involved in the space program. Use the scale to find the amount of money each item costs.

APPLYING CRITICAL THINKING SKILLS

1. What is the cost for a new Space Shuttle?
2. What would cost less, buying a new Space Shuttle or 20,000 new $100,000 houses?
3. What is the item on this list that costs the least? How much is the cost?
4. The comparisons give you some idea of what the money spent on space flight would buy. Do you think it is worthwhile to spend money on space, or should the money be put somewhere else? If it should be spent on something else, what would you suggest?

5. The total budget of the United States is hundreds of billions of dollars. NASA uses just under $8 billion. Compared with the total U.S. budget, is this too much money? Think of some other things the United States spends money on. If something must be cut, can you think of something other than space travel? What?

What is the United States getting for all of the money spent on the shuttle program? A successful shuttle program brings prestige to the United States and furthers international cooperation by including astronauts from other countries on shuttle crews. And, of course, the shuttle performs many useful services.

The shuttle can put satellites into orbit. It can also bring people into orbit to repair satellites that are broken. Repairing a broken satellite is less expensive than replacing it with a new one.

Many experiments are being performed in the shuttle's zero-

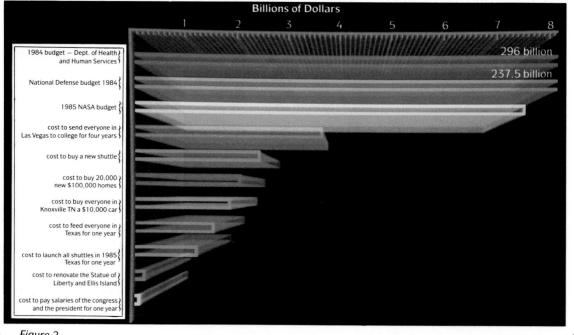

Figure 2

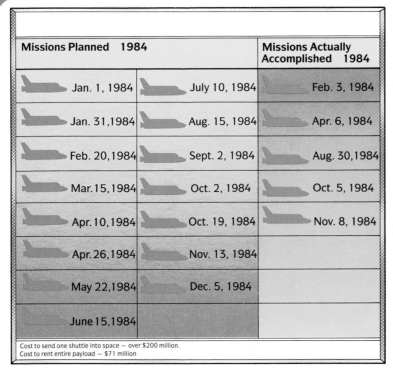

Missions Planned 1984		Missions Actually Accomplished 1984
Jan. 1, 1984	July 10, 1984	Feb. 3, 1984
Jan. 31,1984	Aug. 15, 1984	Apr. 6, 1984
Feb. 20,1984	Sept. 2, 1984	Aug. 30,1984
Mar.15,1984	Oct. 2, 1984	Oct. 5, 1984
Apr.10,1984	Oct. 19, 1984	Nov. 8, 1984
Apr.26,1984	Nov. 13, 1984	
May 22,1984	Dec. 5, 1984	
June 15,1984		

Cost to send one shuttle into space — over $200 million.
Cost to rent entire payload — $71 million

Figure 3

gravity environment. Very pure medicines can be produced. Nearly perfect glass lenses and electronic crystals can also be manufactured. Perhaps someday there may be factories in space because of the experiments done on the shuttle. But some people feel it's wrong to spend taxpayers' money to help businesses manufacture products.

The shuttle is also important to the military. It can be used to test defense systems and weapons. This bothers some people. They don't want to spend billions of dollars to help the military put weapons in space.

The original idea for the shuttle program was to have the shuttle eventually pay for itself. That would be done by having NASA charge anyone who sent something into space. At the end of 1985 the charge to rent all of the payload space on a shuttle was $71 million. Customers pay a percentage of that price depending on the amount of space they use. After 1988 the price is expected to be more than $87 million. But that still will not pay the over $200 million it costs every time we launch a shuttle. The rest of the money will have to come from the American taxpayer.

Notice in Figure 3 that NASA planned to send the shuttle into space many more times than it actually did. This means it will take longer for the shuttle to start paying for itself than originally thought.

The shuttle is now getting some competition for customers as well. In 1975 a group of European countries formed the European Space Agency (ESA). ESA's Ariane rocket can perform many of the jobs the shuttle can. If the price of using the shuttle goes too high, private companies will use the Ariane instead. And NASA will lose more money.

At this time the Space Shuttle *is* the American space program. But some scientists think that projects other than the Space Shuttle should get more of a share of NASA's budget. Should the space program continue with just the shuttle? Or should shuttle flights be cut back to allow money for other projects in space? What about the use of space probes without astronauts, which are less expensive? Americans need to think carefully about whether they are getting what they want for their money.

APPLYING CRITICAL THINKING SKILLS

1. When was the first shuttle flight in 1984 planned to take place? Did it go off on time? When did it take place?
2. How many shuttle flights were originally planned between January 1, 1984 and December 5, 1984? How many actually took place in that time?
3. What can you conclude about the original scheduling of the shuttle?
4. NASA charges money for use of the shuttle. What was the cost of launching shuttles in 1984? How much did NASA receive if each flight was fully rented? How much did it cost taxpayers to launch the shuttle in 1984?
5. A proposed program to send a space probe to Halley's comet was cancelled by NASA. Suppose the probe cost $600 million. How many scheduled flights of the shuttle would have to have been cancelled to pay for the probe?
6. Space exploration using space probes without astronauts is less expensive than shuttle flights. What are the advantages and disadvantages of each type of exploration? Which do you prefer? Why?

GEOLOGY

*E*lements and compounds that are solid and that have a crystal structure are called minerals. Over two thousand minerals occur in the earth. Rocks are mixtures of minerals. Rocks and minerals help form the earth's crust. The crust of the earth has many features, such as mountains and plateaus. Earth scientists depict the earth's surface with topographic maps. In this unit you will study the structure of the earth. ■

▲ A thin slice of shist, a type of metamorphic rock, was photographed under a microscope using polarized light.

◀ Major J.W. Powell, the second director of the U.S. Geological Survey, with Tau-guan, an Indian chief. Together they helped map the terrain of the West in the 1900s.

▼ Petroleum and its products are vital factors in the everyday life of all people. A Texas crude oil derrick (below) pumps out this valuable material.

◀ *Gold mining in California is shown in this lithograph made in 1871 by Currier & Ives. Gold, one of the first minerals used by people, is valued because of its beauty and scarcity.*

▲ *View toward the La Sal mountains, Arches National Park, Utah.*

STATE OF CALIFORNIA

Made from 42 multispectral images received from

the NASA/G.E. Earth Resources Technology Satellite

EARTH'S STRUCTURE

Do you recognize the photograph at left? It is a mosaic of the state of California made up of 42 images taken by a Landsat satellite. Different colors indicate different types of terrain. Lakes and bays can be seen in the photograph. The Pacific Ocean appears to the left of the land area.

- *What kinds of information about the earth can be obtained by using satellites?*
- *What is the earth like below the thin crust on which we live?*
- *How can maps represent the features of the earth's surface?*

7-1 THE ORIGIN OF THE EARTH

The earth is a planet that revolves in orbit around the sun. The earth and other planets move around the sun in the same direction. Why do the planets move around the sun in the same direction? How were the planets formed?

Some time ago some scientists developed the nebular (NEHB yuh luhr) hypothesis to explain how the solar system began. The **nebular hypothesis** states that the sun and the planets formed from a spinning dust cloud, or nebula. According to the hypothesis, the particles of dust and gas in the cloud were evenly spread out at first. As the cloud spun, the particles of dust and gas condensed, or came closer together. This spinning motion could be compared to the spinning of an ice skater. Ice skaters spin faster and faster as they pull in their outstretched arms.

The spinning motion of the cloud caused a dense bulge to form in the center. Around the center was an area of less dense dust and gas. The central bulge of the cloud continued to condense, and it became much hotter than the surrounding materials. The bulge, called a protostar, later became the sun. The material around the protostar condensed at various places and formed protoplanets. A **protoplanet** is a collection of condensed gas and dust particles that is thought to form a planet. It is

After completing this section, you will be able to

- **describe** the nebular hypothesis for the origin of the earth.
- **define** *protoplanet.*
- **explain** how the earth's oceans and atmosphere may have formed.

The key terms in this section are
nebular hypothesis
protoplanet

nebula (mist, cloud)

proto (first)

thought that 10 million to 100 million years were required to form protoplanets from the cold, dark dust cloud.

The protoplanets were probably much larger than the planets are today. Each was probably surrounded by a thick atmosphere. Inside the protoplanets, solid particles combined to form large chunks. The heavier particles probably settled toward the centers of the protoplanets. In time, true planets formed.

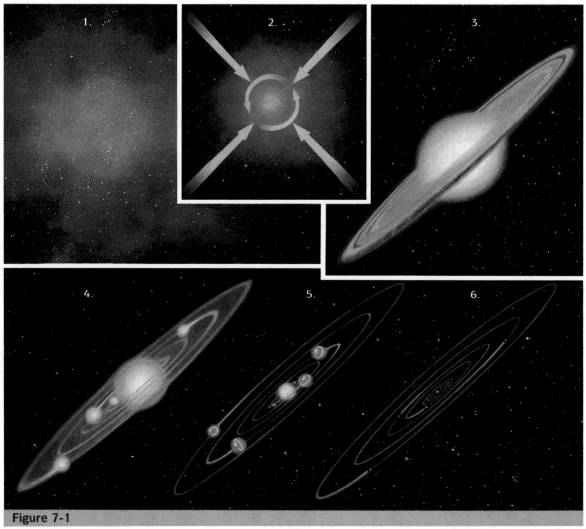

Figure 7-1

The nebular hypothesis.

Figure 7-1 shows the stages in the formation of the solar system according to the nebula hypothesis. The dust cloud, or nebula, is shown in step 1. Notice how the spinning cloud has condensed in step 2. Identify the protosun in step 3. Identify the protoplanets in step 4. Steps 5 and 6 show the final stages in the formation of the solar system.

Figure 7-2

Volcanoes helped form the earth's primitive atmosphere.

Water makes up a large part of the earth's surface. How can the origin of the oceans be explained? Water is made up of hydrogen and oxygen. Hydrogen is abundant in dust clouds in space. Oxygen is also found in such clouds. The earth probably formed from a dust cloud. So water may have formed on the early earth.

The earth's water probably collected inside the earth. Much water was probably trapped inside minerals made mostly of silicon and oxygen. Such minerals would have been found within the earth shortly after it formed. The water may have escaped from the earth's interior through volcanoes. The water may then have collected in the atmosphere as steam and vapor. As the earth cooled, rain fell and water collected on the surface. Figure 7-2 shows rain falling on the early earth.

The earth's primitive atmosphere was probably quite different from the atmosphere today. Much of the gas surrounding the protoplanet would have escaped into space. However, volcanic activity on the early earth would have produced a primitive atmosphere. Figure 7-2 shows what conditions may have been like on the early earth. What gases may have made up the primitive atmosphere, according to the figure? Oxygen was probably added to the atmosphere by early living things. Like today's plants, such organisms may have produced oxygen during food-making activities.

ACTIVITY

What Model Can Illustrate the Nebular Hypothesis?

OBJECTIVE

Construct and **analyze** a model of the nebular hypothesis.

MATERIALS

safety goggles, round pot or pan, hot plate, water, beaker, 2 eggs, 2 culture dishes, slotted spoon, spoon

PROCEDURE

A. Obtain a pair of safety goggles and put them on.

B. Place a round pot or pan on a hot plate. Pour water from the beaker into the pan. Make sure the water is at least 8 cm deep. Plug in the hot plate.

C. Carefully crack an egg on the edge of a culture dish and empty the egg into the dish.

D. When the water is almost boiling, unplug the hot plate. Slowly slide the egg into the hot water. Place it in the center of the pan. Allow the egg to cook; observe its shape.

E. Remove the cooked egg with the slotted spoon and place it back in its dish.

F. Repeat steps **B** and **C**.

G. Using a spoon, slowly begin to stir the water after it almost comes to a boil.
   Caution: Be very careful that you do not spill or spash the hot water.
   1. If you were to place an egg into this moving water, what do you predict would happen?

H. While you continue to stir the water, have your partner carefully slide the egg into the center of the pan.

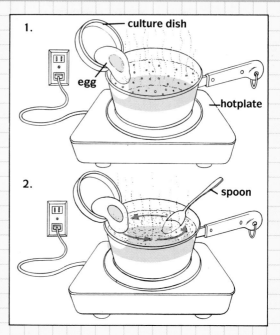

2. What do you observe?
3. What shape does this egg have?

I. After the egg has stopped cooking, stop stirring and remove the egg with the slotted spoon. Return the egg to its dish.

RESULTS AND CONCLUSIONS

1. Compare the cooked eggs. How are their shapes different?
2. Was your prediction about what would happen to the second egg correct?
3. In what way does this model represent the nebular hypothesis?
4. In what way does this model differ from the nebular hypothesis?

REVIEW

1. How does the nebular hypothesis explain the origin of the earth?
2. Distinguish between a protoplanet and a planet.
3. How might volcanic activity have been involved in the formation of the earth's oceans and in the formation of the earth's atmosphere?

CHALLENGE Unlike the earth, the moon has almost no atmosphere. How can you account for the lack of an atmosphere on the moon?

7-2 THE STRUCTURE OF THE EARTH

The earth is composed of three layers: the core, the mantle, and the crust. Identify these layers in Figure 7-3. The crust and upper mantle of the earth are called the **lithosphere** (LIHTH uh sfihr). The heaviest layers are within the earth, and the lightest layer is at the surface.

Most geologists think the earth was once molten. If the earth was once molten, where did the heat come from? Scientists think the heat in the earth was produced by radioactive elements. **Radioactive elements** are elements that change into other elements, giving off energy in the process. Large amounts of radioactive elements, such as uranium and thorium, were probably found among the matter that formed the earth. The heat produced by the breakdown of these buried elements could not escape. As the heat built up, it melted much of the rock that formed the earth. Since the earth is no longer completely molten, radioactive heating must have decreased. It is believed that convection currents in the upper mantle brought some of the heat to the surface, where it escaped.

The *core,* located in the center of the earth, is divided into the inner core and the outer core. As you might guess, it is very hot in these areas. The inner core is solid, and the outer core is molten. Both regions vary in density and temperature.

> *After completing this section, you will be able to*
>
> - **identify** the layers of the earth and describe their locations.
> - **explain** how the earth's structure relates to the way the earth formed.
> - **list** evidence that supports the existence of a metallic core in the earth.
>
> *The key terms in this section are*
> lithosphere
> radioactive elements

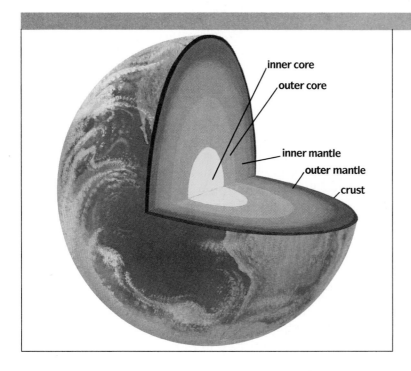

Figure 7-3

The layers of the earth.

inner core
outer core
inner mantle
outer mantle
crust

The core of the earth may have been formed by the sinking of heavy melted materials, such as iron, toward the center. The melting probably took place more than 4 billion years ago.

Notice in Figure 7-4 that the temperature of the inner core is believed to be 4300°C. The temperature of the upper mantle is 1480°C. That is quite a temperature difference. Even today, much heat is generated within the earth. The heat probably results from the breakdown of radioactive elements in the earth's interior.

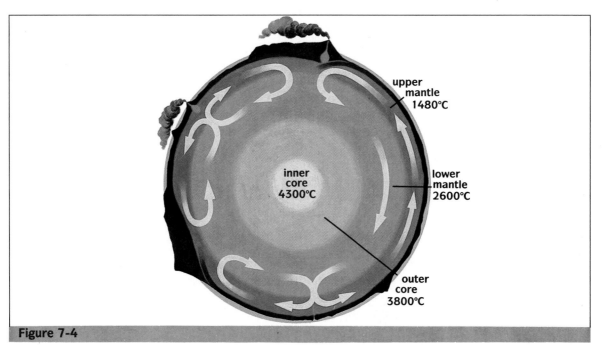

Figure 7-4

The layers of the earth vary in temperature.

But how does the idea of an iron core relate to hypotheses about the origin of the earth? According to the nebular hypothesis, the elements in a dust cloud formed a protoplanet. The layering of the earth developed because the matter became molten and gravity pulled the heavier elements—nickel and iron—inward. Some iron, other metals, and rock formed the less dense mantle. Materials that were even lighter separated out of the mantle and formed the outermost layer, the crust.

Scientists think that complete melting was not needed for this separation of materials into layers. The high temperature and high pressure may have caused the elements to move to the different layers. If the earth had melted completely, some elements would have escaped as gases. These would no longer be found on the earth.

Figure 7-5

Many meteorites contain iron.

The study of meteorites lends support to the idea that the core contains iron. Figure 7-5 shows a meteorite made of iron. These may have once been pieces of the core of a planet that broke up. Iron meteorites are evidence that the earth's core is made of iron.

Another piece of evidence for the existence of an iron core is the earth's magnetic field. The earth behaves as if it contains a magnet. If iron had sunk to the center of the earth, it would account for the magnetic field of the earth.

Evidence that the outer core is liquid comes from the study of earthquakes. When an earthquake occurs, the energy that is released moves through the earth in the form of waves. Some of these waves, which do not pass through liquid, do not pass through the outer core. Therefore, it is believed that the outer core is like a liquid.

What evidence is there for a solid inner core? Pressure affects the melting point of matter. High pressure raises the melting point. It is thought that the pressure in the inner core is so great that the inner core remains solid. The melting point of the matter in the inner core is higher than the temperature of the outer core.

Why must scientists collect all this information about the earth's mantle and core in an indirect way? Remember, the mantle is about 3000 km thick, and the core is located below the mantle. To date, the deepest holes drilled for oil are only 8 km deep. New information about rocks beneath the ocean floor was gathered when the equipment on the ship *Glomar Challenger* drilled closer to the mantle. However, at this time it is not possible directly to sample materials from deep in the mantle or from the core. Therefore, we must use indirect ways to find out about a region we cannot study firsthand.

Scientists also study the moon and other planets in the solar system in the hope of learning more about the earth and its origin. Like the earth, the moon has different internal regions. Identify these regions in Figure 7-6. Many scientists think the moon was formed from a dust cloud about 4.6 billion years ago, along with the earth. As on the earth, heat from radioactive elements may have caused melting. The outer part of the moon melted to a depth of several hundred kilometers. Some minerals formed a crust and the moon's surface was hit by meteorites.

As has been said, many scientists think the earth and the moon formed together. If the earth and moon did form together, from the same nebula, they should have a similar composition. However, the moon may lack an iron core. Therefore, in some ways its formation differed from that of the earth.

Figure 7-6

The layers of the moon.

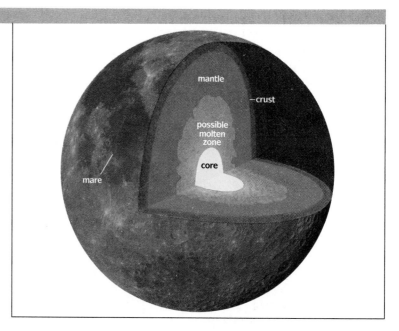

REVIEW

1. Draw a diagram that shows the main layers of the earth. Label the layers.
2. Describe how a molten earth could have led to the layered structure that exists today.
3. What evidence supports the existence of an iron core in the earth?

CHALLENGE Radioactive elements eventually change to nonradioactive forms. How can this information be used to explain the change from a molten earth to a more solid earth?

7-3 THE LAYERS OF THE EARTH

No matter where you are right now, you are more than 6000 km from the center of the earth. The innermost layer of the earth is called the **core**. The core, which has a radius of 3500 km, is thought to be 85 percent iron with a smaller amount of nickel. The average density of the core is about 10.7 g/cm³. The average density of the earth itself is about 5.5 g/cm³.

Notice in Figure 7-7 that the core has two layers: the inner core and the outer core. The **inner core**, with a radius of about 1500 km, is solid and is probably a mixture of iron, nickel, and cobalt. The **outer core** is about 2000 km thick and is probably composed mostly of iron. The temperature of the molten outer core is 3800°C.

The layer within the earth that surrounds the core and that is located below the crust is called the **mantle**. Unlike the core, the mantle is composed mainly of rock rather than metal. The density is about 4.5 g/cm³, or less than half the density of the core. Hot temperatures within the earth's mantle can cause rock to melt. The melted rock, or *magma* (MAG muh), may be as hot as 1110°C.

The mantle is approximately 3000 km thick. Scientists believe the mantle is solid because earthquake waves

> After completing this section, you will be able to
>
> - **describe** the composition of the core, the mantle, and the crust.
> - **compare** the characteristics of the layers of the earth.
>
> *The key terms in this section are*
> asthenosphere   mantle
> core   Moho
> crust   outer core
> inner core

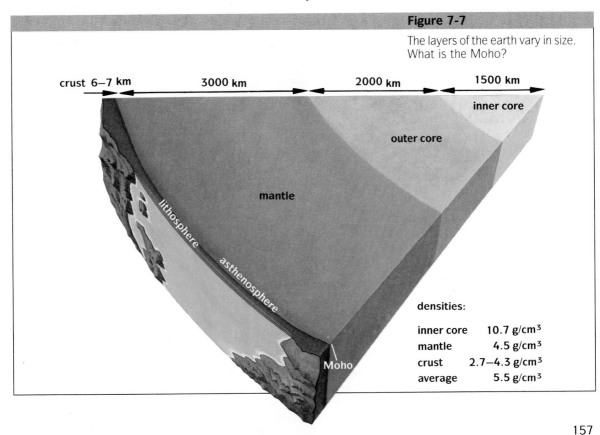

Figure 7-7

The layers of the earth vary in size. What is the Moho?

crust 6–7 km   3000 km   2000 km   1500 km

inner core

outer core

mantle

lithosphere

asthenosphere

Moho

densities:

inner core	10.7 g/cm³
mantle	4.5 g/cm³
crust	2.7–4.3 g/cm³
average	5.5 g/cm³

asthenes (weak)
sphere (sphere)

crusta (rind)

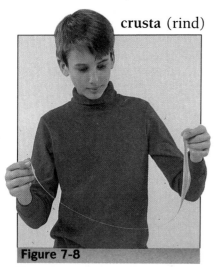

Figure 7-8

The upper region of the mantle is called the asthenosphere. It has properties similar to those of plastic putty.

that do not travel through liquid travel through the mantle. However, under certain conditions the rock in the mantle seems to flow. If you have handled plastic putty, you know that even though it is a solid, the putty flows. The ability of a solid material to flow is called *plasticity* (plas TIHS uh-tee). The **asthenosphere** (as THEHN uh sfihr) is a zone within the upper mantle that has the property of plasticity. The rock at the top of the mantle may be more rigid than the rock near the outer core. Why, do you think, may this upper rock be more rigid?

The outermost layer of the earth—the surface on which we live—is called the **crust**. The thickness of the crust compared with that of the earth is like the thickness of the skin of an apple compared with the apple. Like the skin of an apple, the earth's outer layer is very thin. The crust is about 6 km thick beneath the oceans. There it has a density of about 3 g/cm^3 and is composed mostly of the rock basalt. The crust under the continents is thicker, 20–70 km. The crust in this area is less dense than the ocean crust, about 2.7 g/cm^3. The continents are made up mostly of the rock granite.

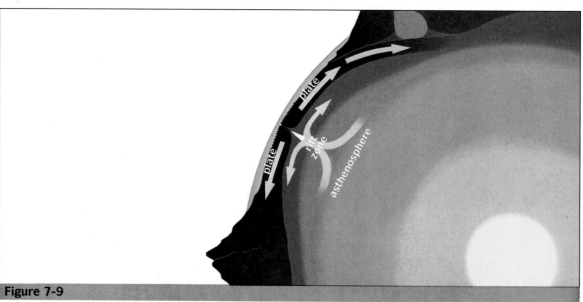

Figure 7-9

The plates of the earth float on the asthenosphere.

The crust of the earth is broken into *plates,* or large pieces. The plates are 5 km to 100 km thick and less dense than the mantle material. As shown in Figure 7-9, the plates float in the asthenosphere. Currents in the asthenosphere cause these plates to move. Their motion is so slight that we are unaware of it. The boundary between the mantle and the crust is called the **Moho**.

ACTIVITY — How Would You Determine the Average Density of the Earth?

OBJECTIVES
Determine the densities of rocks and iron.
Propose an average density of the earth.

MATERIALS
balance, plastic graduated cylinder, water, rock samples (basalt, granite, and slate), sample of iron

PROCEDURE
A. Make a chart like the one below. DO NOT WRITE IN THIS BOOK.

	Mass	Volume	Density
basalt			
granite			
slate			
average	—	—	
iron			

B. Determine the mass of each of your rock samples. Record the data on your chart.

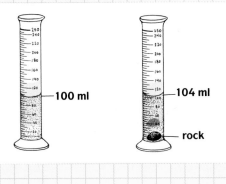

100 ml

104 ml

rock

C. Determine the volume of each of your rock samples by the water displacement method. Follow the steps in the drawing. Record the data on the chart.

D. Using the same procedures you used for the rocks, determine the mass and volume of the iron sample. Record the mass and volume on your chart.

E. Density is the mass of an object divided by its volume.

$$\text{Density} = \frac{\text{mass}}{\text{volume}}$$

Determine the density of basalt, granite, and slate. Add the three densities and divide by 3 to get the average rock density. Record your results on your chart.

F. Determine the density of the iron. Record the density of iron on your chart.
  1. Would the density be different if you had a larger sample?

RESULTS AND CONCLUSIONS
1. What is the average density of your rock samples?
2. What is the density of iron?
3. How does the density of the rocks compare with the density of iron.
4. What layer of the earth do the rocks represent?
5. What layer of the earth does the iron represent?
6. Suppose that the earth is made up of equal volume of mantle and core. What would you propose the average density of the earth to be?
7. The known density of the earth is 5.5 g/cm^3. How does your proposal of the average density of the earth compare with this?

REVIEW

1. How do the inner core and outer core differ? How does the core differ from the mantle in composition?
2. Compare the characteristics of the mantle and the crust.

CHALLENGE How would the earth's characteristics differ if the earth were composed totally of rock, without any layers?

7-4 FEATURES OF THE SURFACE

After completing this section,
you will be able to

• **identify** several surface
features of the earth.

You have probably noticed different landscapes in pictures and when you have traveled. The features that make up landscapes include mountains, plains, and rivers.

Mountains are a main feature of the continents. *Mountains* are elevated sections of the earth's surface. They can occur in chains on the land or on the ocean floor. To be considered mountains, land must be at least 600 m higher than the surrounding surface. Hills are elevated sections under 600 m.

Mountains and other high land separate the surrounding sections of lowland. An area of high land between sections of lowland is called a *divide*. The rivers and streams on either side of a divide are usually kept separated by the divide.

Figure 7-10

Mountains, plains, and plateaus are some of the earth's surface features.

When horizontal rock layers are elevated, *plateaus* are formed. Plateaus may be many kilometers in length. An example of a plateau is the Colorado Plateau, west of the southern part of the Rocky Mountains. Much of the land in the United States is covered by mountains and plateaus.

Rivers often cut through plateaus, forming *valleys*. Such is the case in the Colorado Plateau. *Rivers* have cut into the rock layers, forming deep valleys. The Grand Canyon was formed by a river cutting into the rock layers.

Plains are also horizontal rock layers that are somewhat elevated. Both plains and plateaus are large, flat areas, but plateaus are at higher elevations than plains. Hills and valleys occur where a plain has been raised. The region between the Rocky Mountains and the Appalachian Mountains is called the Great Plains. The Great Plains is an area of intense agricultural activity.

Look at the map or globe of the world. What parts of the world contain mountain ranges? Identify some plains throughout the world. What is the major landform in the area where you live?

REVIEW

1. How do plateaus and mountains differ?
2. What are plains?

CHALLENGE The Rocky Mountains are often referred to as the Continental Divide. Study a map of North America and then explain why the Rocky Mountains form the Continental Divide.

161

7-5 MAPPING THE EARTH'S SURFACE

After completing this section, you will be able to

- **distinguish** between relief maps and topographic maps.
- **distinguish** between contour lines and index contours.
- **interpret** a topographic map.

The key terms in this section are
  bench marks
  contour interval
  contour line
  index contours
  relief map
  topographic
    map

contour (encircle)

It is evident that the earth's surface is not flat and smooth. The variation in elevations of areas on the earth's surface is called *relief*. A map that shows mountains, valleys, plains, and their elevations is called a **relief map**. Such a map may use color as a symbol to indicate the altitude, or height, of the land above sea level. *Sea level* is the average level of the sea where it meets the land. Figure 7-11 shows a relief-map key. Notice that the shading changes as the land becomes more mountainous. How is color used to show the depth of water?

Although relief maps show that the earth's surface has different heights, there are other maps that show the shapes of the land at various heights. These maps are called topographic (tahp uh GRAF ihk) maps. A **topographic map** is a map that shows the shapes and heights of the land by using lines that connect points that have the same elevations. A line that connects points of the same elevation on a topographic map is called a **contour line**.

A contour line is not drawn for every elevation. Contour lines are drawn at regular intervals. An interval may be 5 m, 20 m, or even 100 m. The **contour interval** is the

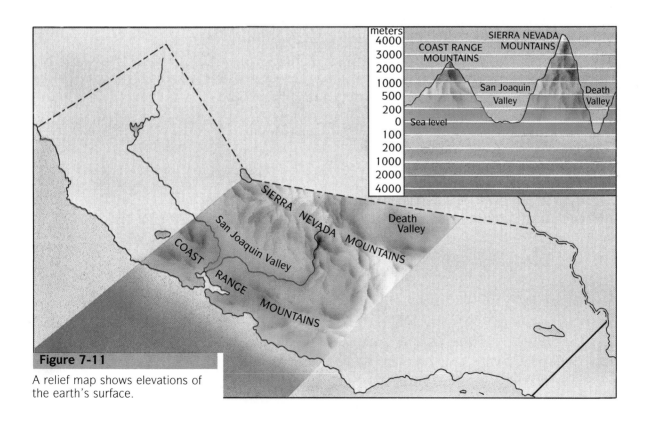

Figure 7-11

A relief map shows elevations of the earth's surface.

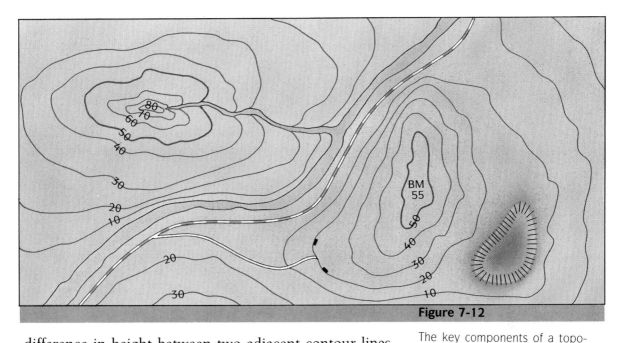

Figure 7-12

The key components of a topographic map.

difference in height between two adjacent contour lines. What is the contour interval in Figure 7-12? What is the highest elevation in meters?

It will require practice for you to interpret topographic maps correctly. Here are some important things to remember when working with topographic maps.

1. A contour line connects points of equal height. A contour interval is the difference in height between two adjacent contour lines. If the contour interval on a map is 5 m, contour lines will be shown for elevations of 5 m, 10 m, 15 m, 20 m, and so on.

2. Every fifth contour line is usually darkened. A dark contour line is called an **index contour**. Index contours make the map easier to read.

3. Contour lines that are close together mean a steep slope. Contour lines that are far apart mean a gradual slope or nearly flat land.

4. Contour lines can never cross or split. Contour lines always close. However, the map may not be large enough to show them closing.

5. Contour lines form a $\bigvee$ shape when a stream is crossed. The $\bigvee$ in the contour lines points upstream, or in the direction from which the stream flows.

6. The exact elevation of a point on a map can be determined if the point is located on a contour line. The elevations of specific points that are not located on contour lines are shown by marks called **bench marks**.

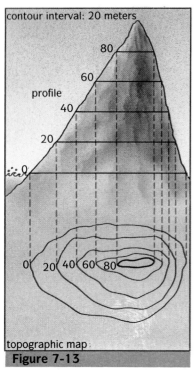

contour interval: 20 meters

80

60

profile

40

20

0

topographic map

Figure 7-13

A profile of a hill.

Bench marks are shown by **X** or **BM**, and the exact elevation is printed in brown or black ink near the mark on the map. What is the elevation of the bench mark in Figure 7-12? The United States Geological Survey (USGS) measures exact elevations at many locations across the United States and marks these areas with metal plates called bench marks.

Notice the short lines drawn in the small area between the 10- and 20-m contour lines in Figure 7-12. These lines are called hachures (ha SHOORZ), and they indicate the direction the land slopes. In Figure 7-12, the hachures indicate a depression.

Topographic maps are very useful, because they give a detailed view of the land from above, as if seen from an airplane. Sometimes it is helpful to have a side view of the elevations. A profile is a side view of the elevation along a particular line, or baseline. A profile shows how the land would appear if a slice were made along the baseline. Figure 7-13 shows an example of a profile.

Topographic maps are sometimes called *quadrangles*. A quadrangle is the area of land shown on an atlas sheet of the USGS. The maps published by the USGS are marked by parallels of latitude and meridians of longitude. The *parallels* are marked on the sides of the map. The *meridians* are marked at the top and bottom in degrees and minutes.

Many of the quadrangles published by the USGS are for an area that covers 7.5 minutes of longitude and 7.5

SCIENCE & TECHNOLOGY

Clay is the basis for ceramics. Ceramics include pottery, bricks, tiles, and china. Ceramic products are strong and do not corrode. These features are expanding the uses for ceramics.

Optical fibers are an example of a new kind of product made from ceramics. These threads of glass are only about 0.1 mm thick. They allow light signals to travel through them. A single glass fiber can replace 10,000 telephone wires.

A special kind of ceramic is used in tools for cutting rocks, steel, diamonds, and other hard substances. New ceramic coatings can triple the life of the tools.

Other types of ceramics are being developed for use in engines. Ceramics wear down very slowly. So they can be used for bearings, which help engine parts move smoothly. And ceramic bearings would not need lubrication. Since ceramic materials can be as strong as metal but much lighter, ceramic parts save weight. New uses for ceramics, particularly in electronics and as structural components, are being studied.

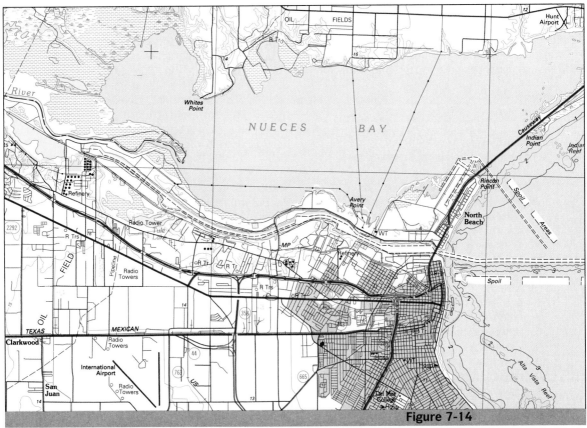

Figure 7-14

A topographic map of the area near Corpus Christi, Texas.

minutes of latitude. Maps with other dimensions of longitude and latitude are also available.

It is important to know the relationship between the distance measured on a map and the actual distance on earth. A ratio is used to compare the distance on a map with the actual distance on the earth's surface. This ratio is called the *map scale*. The USGS produces maps drawn to a scale of 1:62,500. There are 63,360 inches to a mile, so this scale is approximately one inch to one mile. The USGS is converting to a metric scale.

Elevation of the land is only one of the features shown on a topographic map. Lakes, rivers, cities, bridges, and railroads are also shown. Symbols for these and other features are listed in the map's legend, or key. Colors are significant on topographic maps also. In Figure 7-14 what color represents an urban area? What colors represent buildings and roads? What bay is shown on the map?

Topographic maps are used by geologists and by people who plan highways and dams. People who enjoy hiking and exploring also use topographic maps to find trails, steep slopes, and places to fish.

OBJECTIVES

Interpret symbols on a topographic map.
Measure distances on a topographic map.

MATERIAL

metric ruler

PROCEDURE

A. Study the map below and answer the following questions.
1. What is the map scale?
2. What is the contour interval?
3. How many feet are between the index contours?
4. What is the highest elevation?
5. Where is the highest elevation?
6. What kind of road passes over the Big River?
7. Is the coastline along Mendocino Bay steep?
8. Where on the map is the steepest elevation?
9. How many schools are shown?
10. How many churches are shown?
11. How many cemeteries are shown?
12. Where is a swamp? How do you know?
13. Where do most of the people live? How do you know?
14. Describe the contour of the land in areas where the contour lines are far apart.
15. Describe the terrain that the city of Mendocino was built on.

16. Notice that there is a light-duty road running along the north shore of the Big River. Why does this road curve and twist the way it does?
17. Using your ruler, measure how large the town of Mendocino is. Is this a large or a small town?
18. How far is Jackson State Forest from Union High School?

RESULTS AND CONCLUSIONS

1. Do you find it difficult to read a topographic map? Why or why not?
2. What is the most difficult part about interpreting topographic maps? Explain.

EXTENSION

1. Make a topographic map of the area around your home and school.
2. Obtain topographic maps for your area.

East of the Mississippi River
(including Minnesota):
Branch of Distribution
U.S. Geological Survey
1200 South Eads Street
Arlington, VA 22202

West of the Mississippi River
(including Alaska, Hawaii, and Louisiana):
Branch of Distribution
U.S. Geological Survey
Federal Center, Denver, CO 80225

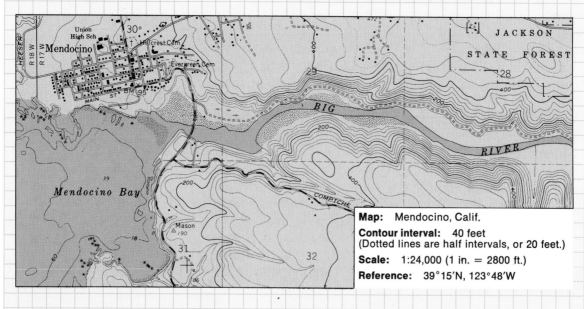

Map: Mendocino, Calif.
Contour interval: 40 feet
(Dotted lines are half intervals, or 20 feet.)
Scale: 1:24,000 (1 in. = 2800 ft.)
Reference: 39°15′N, 123°48′W

REVIEW

1. What is the difference between a relief map and a topographic map?
2. How does a contour line differ from an index contour on a topographic map?

CHALLENGE What features would you look for on a topographic map to indicate a stream that is surrounded by steep slopes?

CHAPTER SUMMARY

The main ideas in this chapter are listed below. Read these statements before you answer the Chapter Review questions.

- The nebular hypothesis states that the earth and the rest of the bodies in the solar system formed from a spinning dust cloud. (7-1)

- Volcanic activity may have been involved in the production of the earth's atmosphere and in the production of the earth's oceans. (7-1)

- The earth is composed of core, mantle, and crust. (7-2)

- Evidence such as the earth's magnetic field indicates that the core of the earth is metallic. (7-2)

- The inner core is solid, consisting of iron and nickel. The outer core is molten, consisting mostly of iron. (7-3)

- The mantle and the crust are made mostly of rock. The plates of the crust float on the mantle. (7-3)

- Mountains, plateaus, plains, and rivers are the main surface features of the earth. (7-4)

- A map that shows elevations of surface features of the earth is called a relief map. (7-5)

- A topographic map uses contour lines to show elevations and the features of the land. (7-5)

The key terms in this chapter are listed below. Use each term in a sentence that shows the meaning of the term.

asthenosphere	index contour	outer core
bench marks	inner core	protoplanet
contour interval	lithosphere	radioactive elements
contour line	mantle	relief map
core	Moho	topographic map
crust	nebular hypothesis	

Chapter Review

VOCABULARY

Write the letter of the term that best matches the definition. Not all the terms will be used.

1. The innermost layer of the earth
2. A map that shows mountains, plains, and valleys and that often uses color to indicate elevation
3. The upper mantle and the crust
4. The source of the heat that may have caused the earth to become molten
5. The earth's outer layer
6. A map that shows elevation and shape by using lines to connect points having the same elevations
7. Solid and composed of iron and nickel
8. The earth's middle layer
9. The condensed gas and dust particles from which the earth formed
10. The plates of the crust float in this zone

a. radioactive elements
b. mantle
c. asthenosphere
d. Moho
e. topographic map
f. core
g. protoplanet
h. outer core
i. lithosphere
j. relief map
k. inner core
l. crust

CONCEPTS

1. What is the relationship between protoplanets and the nebular hypothesis? (7-1)
2. Describe how the earth's oceans may have formed. (7-1)
3. What gases might have been part of the earth's primitive atmosphere? How was this atmosphere formed? (7-1)
4. Describe the structure of the earth, including the names of the layers. (7-2)
5. How does the way the earth formed explain the fact that it is made up of layers? (7-2)
6. What makes scientists think the earth's core is metallic? (7-2)
7. Why is the inner core of the earth thought to be solid and the outer core liquid? (7-2)
8. Compare the core, the mantle, and the crust with regard to composition. (7-3)
9. List the layers of the earth's interior in order of increasing density. (7-3)

10. What is the relationship between the plates of the crust and the asthenosphere? (7-3)

11. What are mountains? (7-4)

12. How might rivers cause an old plateau to appear to be mountains? (7-4)

13. Distinguish between relief maps and topographic maps. (7-5)

14. What is the relationship between index contours and contour lines? (7-5)

15. How are the contour lines on steep slopes different from contour lines on gentle slopes? (7-5)

16. If point *A* is at sea level, what is the elevation of point *A*? (7-5)

17. Why don't contour lines cross? (7-5)

18. A topographic map has a contour interval of 15 m. List, in order, the elevations of all contour lines on this map from 50 m to 110 m. (7-5)

19. What are several landforms that can be shown by contour lines on a topographic map? (7-5)

20. How do contour lines provide information about the direction of water flow? (7-5)

APPLICATION/ CRITICAL THINKING

1. Assuming that the earth and the moon formed from the same cloud of gas, propose a hypothesis to account for the lack of a metallic core in the moon.

2. Predict the shape and direction of contour lines between streams.

3. Discuss the usefulness of a contour interval of 300 m on a map of an extensive area of flat land.

EXTENSION

1. Find out at least one reason that contour lines of different elevations might cross.

2. Do some research to find out what areas outside the United States have been mapped by the USGS.

READINGS

Gore, Rick. "Our Restless Planet Earth." *National Geographic,* August 1985, p. 142.

Weisburd, Stefi. "The Earth's Magnetic Hiccup." *Science News,* October 5, 1985, p. 218.

EARTH'S MINERALS

Although mineral deposits are widespread, the places where they are found concentrated are not. Most of the minerals essential to modern industry are found in a few places around the earth. What causes mineral deposits to become concentrated in only a few places? One place where a mineral deposit forms is the Danakil Depression, Ethiopia, shown in the photograph. A hot sulphur spring bubbles out of the ground, leaving deposits of sulphur.

- *What is the color of sulphur?*
- *Where does the sulphur come from?*
- *What does the hot spring shown tell about the inside of the earth?*
- *What causes the sulphur to be deposited by the spring?*

8-1 MATTER

What do a bicycle, orange juice, and bromine gas have in common with each other? How are they different? These materials are all made of matter. **Matter** is anything that has mass and takes up space. Mass is a measure of the amount of matter in a material. Everything you can see, touch, or taste has mass and takes up space, so everything is made of matter.

How can you tell one type of matter from another? Properties are useful in distinguishing between different kinds of matter. A **property** is a characteristic that describes a material. There are two general types of properties—physical properties and chemical properties. A **physical property** is a characteristic of matter that can be observed without changing the material. Color, odor, taste, and density are examples of physical properties. A **chemical property** is a property that describes how the particles of matter will react and change with other kinds of matter. Paper will burn in the presence of oxygen. Paper has the chemical property of reacting with oxygen and burning.

Matter exists in different states, or phases. These states are solid, liquid, and gas. A *solid* is matter that has a

After completing this section you will be able to

- **describe** matter.
- **distinguish** between the states of matter.
- **distinguish** between a chemical property and a physical property.

The key terms in this section are
chemical property
matter
physical property
property

Figure 8-1

In nature, water is found in all states of matter. Water vapor is invisible. Fog forms when water vapor condenses.

Figure 8-2

The amount of orange juice is the same in each of these glasses. Yet the orange juice takes the shape of the container it is in.

definite shape and has a definite volume, or occupies a definite amount of space. A *liquid* is matter that has a definite volume but does not have a definite shape. Notice in Figure 8-2 that the orange juice takes the shape of the container it is in. The volume, or amount of space it occupies, does not change if you pour it into a larger container. A *gas* is matter that has no definite volume and no definite shape. One way to show that a gas takes up space is to stuff a piece of paper towel in the bottom of a glass. Place the glass upside down in a container of water and observe what happens. Even though the glass is completely covered by the water, the paper towel remains dry. Why, do you think, does the water not enter the glass?

As shown in Figure 8-3, matter can change from one state to another. You know that ice is formed when liquid water becomes very cold and freezes. In changing to ice, the water does not become another material, it just changes from one phase to another. Liquid water can also be changed to a gas—water vapor—if it is heated until it boils.

The temperatures at which matter changes from one state to another are physical properties. These temperatures are called freezing point, boiling point, and melting point. *Freezing point* is the temperature at which a liquid changes to a solid. Each kind of matter has its own freezing point. The freezing point of water is 0°C.

The temperature at which a solid changes to a liquid is called the *melting point.* Each kind of matter has its own melting point. The melting point and freezing point for a particular type of matter are the same. For example, copper melts at 1083°C, which is also its freezing point. What is the melting point of ice is?

The temperature at which a liquid changes to a gas is the *boiling point.* Each kind of liquid has its own boiling point. You probably have noticed what happens to water that is heated until it boils. Bubbles form, rise to the surface, and burst. When water boils, it changes to the gas called water vapor. Some materials have a low boiling point. In fact, the liquid called Freon will boil from the heat of your hand. Freon is used as a coolant in refrigerators and air conditioners.

Figure 8-3

The melting point of gallium is so low that it melts in the hand (*left*). Liquid nitrogen boils at room temperature. Does it have a high boiling point or a low boiling point?

REVIEW

1. What is matter?
2. Compare the various states of matter.
3. Why isn't freezing point a chemical property?
4. How is melting point different from freezing point?

CHALLENGE Water boils at 100°C at sea level. In Denver, which is about 1.6 km above sea level, water boils at 95°C. What factor or factors might cause it to boil at the lowered temperature?

8-2 THE ATOM

While many materials can change from one state to another state, some materials can be changed into different materials. Early scientists did not know how or why certain materials could be changed this way. In the Middle Ages, in fact, people called alchemists tried to change metals—lead, for example—into gold.

As scientists would learn later, the reason why lead cannot be changed into gold is that lead and gold are elements. An **element** is a material that cannot be changed by chemical means into a simpler material. Copper and iron are other examples of elements. There are about 90 elements that occur naturally on the earth and about 16 elements that have been made by scientists in laboratories.

Figure 8-4

An atom of carbon.

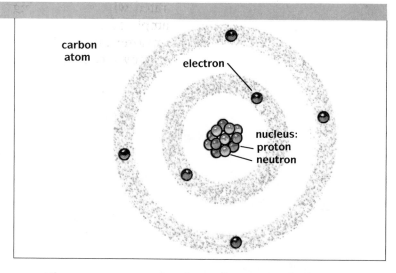

a (without) **tomas** (cutting)

nucleus (kernel)

Elements are made of small units called atoms. An **atom** is the basic unit of an element. Every iron atom has the same chemical properties as every other iron atom. All copper atoms are also alike. However, every copper atom is different from every iron atom.

Figure 8-4 shows the structure of a typical atom. Atoms can contain three types of smaller particles—protons, neutrons, and electrons. Protons and neutrons make up the **nucleus**, or center, of the atom. A **proton** is a particle with a positive electrical charge. A **neutron** has no charge. An **electron** is a particle with a negative charge that moves around outside the nucleus. An atom usually has an equal number of protons and electrons. Atoms of different elements have different numbers of neutrons in their nuclei.

While atoms cannot be changed by chemical means into other atoms, they can combine with atoms of the same element. They can also combine with atoms of different elements to form a chemical compound. A **compound** is the chemical combination of atoms of two or more elements. An example of a compound is salt, sodium chloride (NaCl). Elements that make up a compound usually cannot be recognized in the compound.

componere (come together)

Atoms combine with other atoms in chemical reactions to form new substances. The number of electrons in an atom helps to determine whether the atom will combine with another atom in a chemical reaction. So the number of electrons in an atom helps to determine the chemical properties of the atom.

Sometimes atoms do not combine chemically but are only mixed together. A **mixture** is a combination of different materials that can be separated without involving a chemical reaction. Soil is an example of a mixture. The pieces of rock, leaves, and twigs making up the soil can be removed by hand. Figure 8-5 shows two materials. Which is a mixture?

mixtura (to mix)

Figure 8-5

Aluminum pots are elements (*left*). A salad is a mixture (*right*).

REVIEW

1. What particles make up an atom? Describe each particle.
2. How does a compound differ from a mixture?

CHALLENGE If you were given a jar of salt water, describe how you might find out whether this material was a compound or a mixture.

8-3 WHAT IS A MINERAL?

minera (a mine)
krystallos (clear ice)

As you have learned, early in the earth's history, the planet was very hot. As it cooled, atoms began to combine with each other to form minerals. A **mineral** is a solid element or compound that has a specific composition and crystal structure. Some minerals, such as gold and diamonds, are made up of single elements. Other minerals—salt, for example—are made up of compounds.

Every mineral has its own set of properties that distinguishes it from every other mineral. One of these properties is the shape of its crystals. A **crystal** is a solid with a regular shape and flat sides. The shape of a crystal is determined by the arrangement of its atoms. One way scientists can see this orderly arrangement is by using X-ray photography. Several mineral crystals can be seen in Figure 8-6.

Crystals can form when a material changes from a liquid into a solid if the atoms of the material arrange themselves into a fixed, orderly pattern. Crystals may also form when liquids evaporate. For example, salt crystals are formed when seawater evaporates.

Figure 8-6

Crystals of copper sulfate (*top left*), pyrite (*top right*), azurite (*bottom left*), and sulfur (*bottom right*).

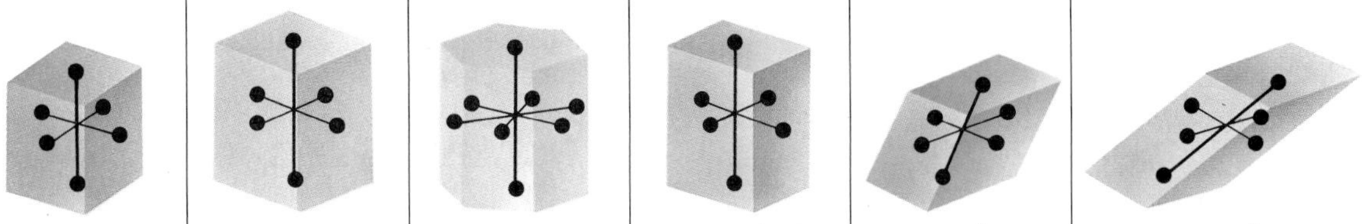

cubic	tetragonal	hexagonal	orthorhombic	monoclinic	triclinic
examples: halite galena	examples: zircon chalcopyrite	examples: quartz calcite	examples: sulfur staurolite	examples: mica gypsum	examples: feldspar rhodonite

Figure 8-7

The six basic crystal shapes.

Crystal shape is an important physical property used in identifying minerals. Every mineral has a specific crystal structure. There are six basic crystal shapes, as shown in Figure 8-7. The six basic crystal shapes have imaginary lines called axes. The atoms that make up a mineral are arranged along the axes, giving the mineral its specific crystal shape.

Halite, or salt, is an example of a mineral with a cubic crystal. The crystal is made up of sodium and chlorine atoms. When the atoms are grouped together, they make an orderly pattern that repeats over and over. If you could see the individual atoms of sodium and chlorine, they would look like those shown in Figure 8-8. What pattern have these atoms formed?

Figure 8-8

The cubic structure of table salt is formed by sodium ions and chloride ions.

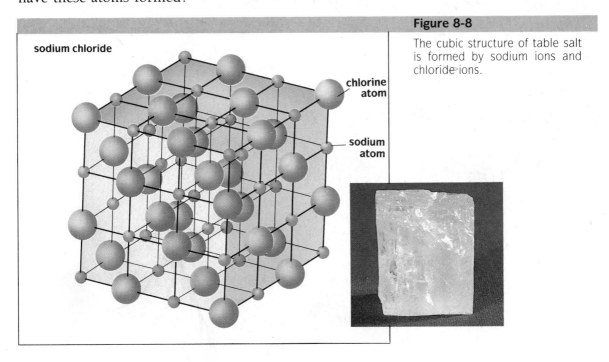

sodium chloride

chlorine atom

sodium atom

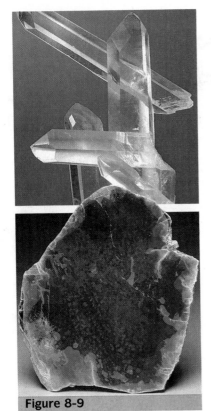

Figure 8-9

Quartz crystals (*top*) are formed from silicon and oxygen. Mica also contains silicon and oxygen, but it appears quite different from quartz.

As has been said, some minerals are themselves, elements. Other minerals are compounds, being made up of two or more elements chemically combined. Quartz is an example of a mineral crystal that is formed from two of the most abundant elements in the earth's crust: silicon and oxygen. Minerals containing these elements are very abundant in the earth's crust. A quartz crystal is shown in Figure 8-9. What is the crystal shape of quartz? Check your answer by referring to Figure 8-7. Other minerals, such as mica and feldspar, also contain silicon and oxygen. Crystals of mica are also shown in Figure 8-9. How are mica crystals different from quartz crystals? Mica splits into thin sheets because its crystals are in sheets. How do mica crystals compare with salt crystals? Use Figure 8-7 to help you make these comparisons.

REVIEW

1. What is a mineral?
2. How are minerals formed in nature?
3. What is a crystal?
4. What is the relationship between the arrangement of atoms and the crystal shape of minerals?

CHALLENGE Some diamonds are much larger than other diamonds. What factors might determine the size of a crystal?

8-4 IDENTIFYING MINERALS

Figure 8-10 shows objects that are minerals. One is a diamond. The other objects are called zircons. As you can see, the zircons looks identical to the diamond. However, these minerals differ greatly in value. A zircon is worth only a fraction of what a diamond is worth. How, then, can you identify which of these minerals is the diamond and which are the zircons?

In order to identify a specific mineral, you must examine its properties. Crystal type, hardness, and color are examples of some of the physical properties that can be used to identify and distinguish between minerals. It is important to remember that more than one property must be used to correctly identify a mineral.

Hardness is a physical property that is useful in identifying minerals. **Hardness** is the resistance a mineral shows to being scratched. Ten common minerals are used as references in a hardness test. They are arranged on a number scale in the order of hardness.

Figure 8-10

A natural diamond (*left*) and synthetic diamonds (*right*).

The number scale for determining the hardness of minerals is called the **Mohs scale** of hardness. Each of the reference minerals in the Mohs scale is given a number between 1 and 10. Notice in the Mohs scale that talc is the softest mineral; it is given the number 1. Talc can be scratched by every other mineral. Diamond is the hardest mineral; it is given the number 10. Diamond scratches all other minerals.

Table 8-1 *Moh's Scale*

Mineral	Hardness
Talc	1
Gypsum	2
Calcite	3
Fluorite	4
Apatite	5
Orthoclase	6
Quartz	7
Topaz	8
Corundum	9
Diamond	10

Table 8-2 *Hardness of Objects*

Object	Hardness Number
fingernail	2.5
copper penny	3.5
nail	4.5
knife blade	5.5
glass	5.5
steel file	6.5

The hardness of an unknown mineral is found by learning which minerals on the scale it can scratch and which minerals it cannot scratch. For example, gypsum scratches talc, but it does not scratch calcite. Therefore gypsum is harder than talc but softer than calcite. Since talc has a hardness of 1 and calcite has a hardness of 3, gypsum must have a hardness of 2. Refer to Table 8-1 to describe in words the hardness of fluorite. What minerals on the Mohs scale could a mineral with a hardness of 3 scratch? What minerals could scratch this mineral?

Not all minerals can be given an exact number on the scale. Some minerals test between two numbers. For example, any mineral that scratches feldspar but not quartz has a hardness on the Mohs scale between 6 and 7. A number value of 6.5 could be assigned.

In doing the hardness test, it is a good idea to examine the scratch to determine whether it is a scratch or a mark that can be rubbed off. Soft minerals can leave marks on harder minerals. A true scratch cannot be removed. Test the unknown mineral on the known mineral and then reverse the test.

The Mohs scale is very useful. But if you are away from a laboratory, you probably won't have the set of 10 minerals with you. In this case there are some other objects you can use to perform a hardness test. These objects include your fingernail, a copper penny, a nail, and a steel file. These objects and others, along with their hardness numbers, are shown in Table 8-2.

An easy, but often misleading, clue to the identity of a mineral is **color**. Some minerals are always the same color. For example, the mineral sulfur is always bright yellow. Some minerals occur in various colors, depending

Figure 8-11

Some minerals streak a different color than they appear.

on what elements the minerals contain. The mineral fluorite, for example, may be violet, green, or blue in color, depending on what other materials are present in a particular sample. Thus fluorite cannot be identified by color alone. A streak test gives a better clue to the identity of a mineral than does color. A **streak** is the color of the powder mark made by a mineral as it is rubbed against a piece of porcelain. The mineral hematite produces a red streak. Iron pyrite produces a black streak.

Luster is a physical property that describes the way the surface of a mineral reflects light. A mineral can have either a metallic luster or a nonmetallic luster. A mineral with a metallic luster shines like a metal. Pyrite, shown in Figure 8-12, is a mineral that has a metallic luster. A mineral that does not shine like a metal is said to have a nonmetallic luster. Quartz has a nonmetallic luster. It has a glassy luster. Other types of nonmetallic lusters include pearly, waxy, and dull.

Cleavage and fracture are two other physical properties that are very useful in identifying minerals. **Cleavage** is a property that describes how a mineral splits apart along one or more smooth surfaces. Cleavage can occur in one or more directions for some minerals. Mica cleaves in one direction, forming sheets. Galena cleaves in three directions, forming cubes.

Some minerals break unevenly or along curved surfaces. A **fracture** is a break along an irregular surface. Iron pyrite is a mineral that fractures. The surface of this mineral is rough and uneven. There are also minerals that break along a curved surface like that of a piece of broken glass. A fracture of this type is called a *conchoidal* (kahng-KOI duhl) *fracture.*

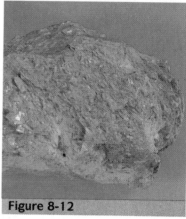

Figure 8-12

Pyrite has a metallic luster (*top*). Talc has a nonmetallic luster (*bottom*).

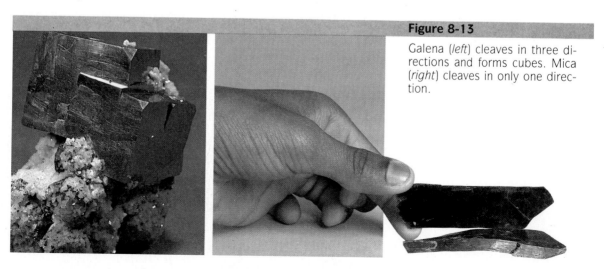

Figure 8-13

Galena (*left*) cleaves in three directions and forms cubes. Mica (*right*) cleaves in only one direction.

OBJECTIVES

Observe a piece of halite.

Identify the cleavage pattern of halite.

MATERIALS

halite, hand lens, safety goggles, hammer, tray

PROCEDURES

A. Copy the table and record your observations in it.
B. Observe a piece of halite with a hand lens. Draw a sketch of the halite. Describe the luster and the appearance of the halite in your table.
C. Put on safety goggles. **Caution:** Safety goggles must be worn when splitting rocks and minerals. Place the piece of halite on a tray. Tap the halite gently with a hammer. The halite should break into smaller pieces. Observe the pieces with the hand lens. Record your observations in your table.
D. Gently tap a piece of the halite with the hammer until the mineral splits again. Notice how the corners of the halite meet.

Cleavage of Halite

	Before Cleavage	After Cleavage
Sketch		
Luster		
Surface appearance		

RESULTS AND CONCLUSIONS

1. Did the halite cleave? How do you know? Explain.
2. Describe how the corners of the cleaved halite meet.
3. How can cleavage be used to identify minerals?

You may have noticed that some minerals are heavier than others. Specific gravity and heft are two tests in which size is used to identify and compare minerals. The **specific gravity** of a mineral is determined by comparing the mass of the mineral with the mass of an equal volume of water. If you determined the mass of 1 cm^3 (1 mL) of water, you would find that it was 1 g. If you determined the mass of 1 cm^3 of gold, you would find that it was 19.3 g. The specific gravity of gold, then, is 19.3 g/1.0 g, or 19.3.

The **heft** of a mineral is the relative weight of a mineral. You can determine the heft of two minerals by holding one mineral in one hand and the second mineral in the other hand and then deciding which mineral feels heavier. How do you think the heft of gold compares with the heft of halite, or salt?

REVIEW

1. The mineral gypsum has a hardness of 2.0. Explain what this means.
2. Describe how to test the hardness of a mineral.
3. Outline a procedure for testing an unknown mineral sample for luster, streak, cleavage or fracture, and heft.

CHALLENGE   Suppose you did a streak test but could not see any colored powder. Propose two reasons for this.

8-5 SPECIAL MINERAL PROPERTIES

You can identify minerals by the physical properties of color, hardness, luster, and streak. All minerals have these properties. Some minerals, however, have other, special properties. The special properties can be used to identify these minerals.

Light can pass through some minerals. These minerals can be identified by this property. Some of these minerals have the property of double refraction. *Double refraction* occurs when a beam of light is split in two by a material. This produces a double image of objects viewed through the material. Calcite is a mineral that has the property of double refraction.

Magnetism is another property that may help identify only a few minerals. Minerals with this property are attracted to a magnet. Magnetite is a magnetic mineral.

The property of fluorescence (flu uh REHS uhns) was named after the mineral fluorite, which has the property. *Fluorescence* is the glowing of a mineral while it is under ultraviolet light. Fluorescent minerals absorb ultraviolet light rays and release visible light rays. Such minerals look dull in ordinary light.

Some minerals will continue to release visible light after the source of ultraviolet light has been turned off. The minerals may continue to glow for several minutes.

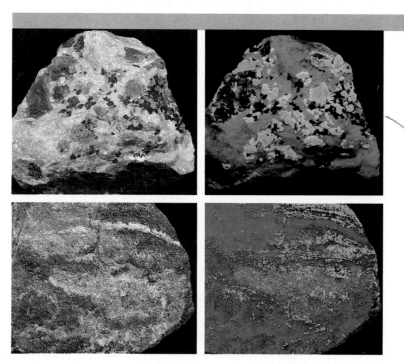

Figure 8-14

Minerals with fluorescence glow under ultraviolet (UV) light. Willemite-calcite under white light and UV light (*top*). Cleiophane-willemite under white light and UV light (*bottom*).

ACTIVITY   Identifying Minerals

OBJECTIVES
Observe the physical properties of unknown minerals. **Classify** minerals based on their physical properties.

MATERIALS
8 unknown mineral samples, copper penny, nail, knife, porcelain tile, hand lens

PROCEDURE
A. Copy the table. Make eight columns in the table. In each column, write the name of a mineral sample.
B. Determine the hardness, streak, luster, cleavage or fracture, color, and heft for each of eight unknown minerals.
C. Record these properties in your table.
D. Use the mineral table in the appendix to identify your samples. Mineral samples vary, so do not be concerned if your results do not exactly match those in the table.

	Mineral Samples		
Physical property			
Hardness	3		
Streak	Yellow		
Luster	Metallic Bright		
Cleavage or fracture	Fracture		
Color	Gold		
Heft	Heavy		
Mineral name	Gold		

RESULTS AND CONCLUSIONS
1. Have your teacher check your answers. Did you correctly identify all the mineral samples?
2. What physical property was most useful in identifying the minerals?

This property is called phosphorescence (fahs fuh REHS-uhns). *Phosphorescence* is the release of visible light, resulting from the absorption of ultraviolet light, after the source of ultraviolet light has been turned off. Sphalerite (SFAL uh rīt) is phosphorescent after being scratched.

Several minerals contain radioactive elements, such as uranium and radium. *Radioactivity* is the decay of the nucleus of an atom into a lighter nucleus. Radioactive minerals are sometimes fluorescent. A device called a Geiger counter, which can detect energy from radioactive elements, is used to identify radioactive minerals.

REVIEW
1. How would you determine whether a mineral was fluorescent? How would you determine whether it was phosphorescent?
2. The mineral calcite is one of four similar-looking minerals in a box. How could you identify calcite?

CHALLENGE Fluorescent lamps produce invisible ultraviolet light. Fluorescent light bulbs are coated with powdered minerals called phosphors. Why are the minerals needed?

8-6 IMPORTANCE OF MINERALS

Minerals are important in our lives. We eat some minerals, use others for jewelry, and use still others for building materials. Some minerals are more valuable than others. A mineral deposit in the earth that contains materials which can be mined for profit is called an **ore**. All mineral deposits are not ores. The value of a mineral deposit may vary from time to time. This value determines whether a material is considered to be an ore at a particular time.

Ores that contain minerals which are metals are *metallic ores*. Metals obtained from metallic ores have a variety of uses. For example, the metals aluminum and copper are used in wires because they are good conductors of electricity. Silver and gold are expensive metals and are used for a variety of purposes. Gold is used in jewelry and medicines. Silver is used in photography.

Figure 8-15

Silver ore (*left*), gold ore (*middle*), and asbestos ore (*right*).

Metals are useful to us because they have properties that other materials do not have. For example, gold is a metal that can be made into very thin sheets. The ability of a material, such as gold, to be hammered into thin sheets without breaking is called *malleability* (mal ee uh-BIHL uh tee). Other metals are useful because they can easily be made into wire. Silver and copper are examples of metals that have the property called ductility. *Ductility* (duk TIHL uh tee) is the ability of a material to be drawn into wire.

185

Figure 8-16

These gems are all varieties of the mineral corundum. The red gems are rubies, and the blue one is a sapphire.

SCIENCE PUZZLER

Gold is one of the most valuable ores on the earth. Like many ores, gold may form in large underground cracks called veins. One method of obtaining gold involves digging a mine into a vein and removing the gold. Another method, called panning, is used by gold prospectors. Panning involves swirling some water and gravel from a stream in a pan until any gold in the gravel is separated and collected.

If gold forms in underground veins, how does it end up in streams? What properties of gold enable it to be separated from gravel by panning? Gold is also found dissolved in seawater. How do you think it gets into seawater? Design a method for removing gold from seawater.

Nonmetallic ores are materials that contain minerals which are nonmetals. Nonmetallic minerals are used in making steel, fertilizers, chemicals, and building materials. Limestone, sand, and gravel are examples of nonmetallic minerals that are used in great amounts in construction materials. Sulfur is a nonmetallic mineral that is used in drugs, rubber, and fertilizers. The agricultural industry uses nonmetallic minerals such as potash, nitrates, and phosphates in fertilizers to help crops grow.

What do you think of when you see the word *gem*? Do rubies and diamonds come to your mind? Like ores, gems are minerals. A **gem** is a mineral that is unusually colorful and reflects much light. There are many factors that determine the value of gems. Some of those factors include the color, hardness, size, availability, and the lack of imperfections.

Gems may be considered to be either precious stones or semiprecious stones. The difference between the two groups is based primarily on the value and availability of the gem. *Precious stones* are minerals that are valuable because of desirable physical characteristics and lack of availability. *Semiprecious stones* are minerals that are less valuable and more abundant than precious stones.

REVIEW

1. Distinguish between the properties of malleability and ductility.
2. How is a gem different from an ore?
3. Explain how a metallic ore is different from a nonmetallic ore. Give an example of each.
4. How is a precious stone different from a semiprecious stone?

CHALLENGE Some special books have names or decorations printed on their covers in gold leaf. What do you think *gold leaf* means? What property of gold makes it possible to form gold leaf?

8-7 GROUPS OF MINERALS

Of all the elements found in the earth's crust, eight elements are found more than any others. These elements are oxygen, silicon, aluminum, iron, calcium, sodium, potassium, and magnesium. Two of these elements—oxygen and silicon—are found in the greatest amounts.

The group of minerals made up of oxygen and silicon are called **silicate minerals** or silicates. More than 92 percent of the earth's crust consists of silicates.

The feldspars make up one family of silicates. About 50 percent of the earth's crust is made up of feldspars. In addition to containing silicon and oxygen, feldspars contain the elements aluminum, sodium, potassium, and calcium. Feldspars have a hardness of 6. Orthoclase is one example of a feldspar.

The second most common silicate is quartz. Quartz is made up of only silicon and oxygen. Quartz may be colorless, white, pink, purple, or brown. It has a nonmetallic luster. Most sand consists of quartz grains.

A third family of silicates is mica. Micas have a hardness of about 2.5. Other examples of silicates are hornblende, augite, olivine, garnet, and talc.

After completing this section, you will be able to

- **distinguish** between silicate minerals and nonsilicate minerals.
- **give examples of** silicate minerals and nonsilicate minerals.

The key terms in this section are
nonsilicate minerals
silicate minerals

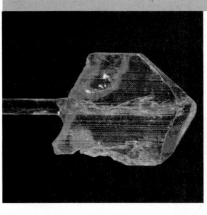 

Figure 8-17

Olivine (*left*) and garnet (*right*) are silicates.

Not all minerals are silicates. Minerals that do not consist of silicon and oxygen are called **nonsilicate minerals**. There are several families of nonsilicate minerals.

In one family of nonsilicates are the sulfide minerals. Sulfides contain sulfur and one or more metals. Galena and pyrite, or fool's gold, are examples of sulfides.

In a second family of nonsilicates are the carbonate minerals. Carbonates consist of carbon and oxygen. Calcite, or calcium carbonate, is the most common carbonate mineral.

The earth has a limited amount of oil. Nearly 50 percent of our oil is used to make gasoline. New kinds of catalysts are being designed to help produce gasoline from natural gas. Catalysts speed up reactions without themselves being used up.

One catalyst now in use in the gasoline industry is zeolite. Zeolite is an excellent catalyst for breaking down petroleum into gasoline. Scientists have made synthetic zeolites that are even more efficient than the natural mineral.

Scientists are getting closer to finding economical ways of converting natural gas to gasoline. Processing natural gas into gasoline first involves changing methane to methanol, an alcohol. Methanol then is converted to gasoline. Researchers are using a zeolite catalyst to complete the second part in this process.

The real challenge lies in finding a catalyst to turn methane, the basic component of natural gas, into methanol. Currently, this process takes many steps and involves much energy and expense. If the process could be done in one step with a catalyst, natural gas could become an economical source of gasoline.

Sulfate minerals make up a third family of nonsilicate minerals. Sulfates contain the elements sulfur and oxygen. Gypsum, or calcium sulfate, is the most common example of a sulfate mineral.

Oxide minerals make up a fourth family of nonsilicate minerals. Oxygen is a key element of all oxides. Two examples of oxide minerals are magnetite and hematite.

Table 8-3 *Groups of Minerals*

Group	Type	Example	Hardness
Silicate minerals	Feldspar	Orthoclase	6
	Quartz	Amethyst	7
	Mica	Biotite mica	2.5
Nonsilicate minerals	Sulfide	Pyrite	6
	Carbonate	Calcite	3
	Sulfate	Gypsum	2
	Oxide	Hematite	5–6
	Halide	Fluorite	4

In a fifth family of nonsilicate minerals are the halide minerals. Halide minerals contain the elements chlorine or fluorine, and sodium, potassium, or calcium. The minerals fluorite and halite are halide minerals.

Minerals make up all the rocks on the earth. The silicates make up the largest group of rock-forming minerals. In the next chapter you will learn how rocks form from minerals.

REVIEW

1. What is the difference between a silicate mineral and a nonsilicate mineral?
2. What causes silicate minerals to be different from each other?
3. Give two examples of silicate minerals and two examples of nonsilicate minerals.

CHALLENGE Olivine makes up 1.5 percent of the earth's crust. Quartz makes up 18 percent. The feldspars make up 50 percent. Mica makes up 4 percent. How many cubic meters of an average 5926 m^3 piece of the earth's crust would be feldspar? How many would be quartz? How many would be mica? How many would be olivine?

CHAPTER SUMMARY

The main ideas in this chapter are listed below. Read these statements before you answer the Chapter Review questions.

- Physical and chemical properties are used to distinguish between different kinds of matter. (8-1)

- The smallest piece of an element is called an atom. An atom consists of protons and neutrons which make up the nucleus, and electrons, which move around the nucleus. (8-2)

- Minerals have specific crystal structures. There are six basic crystal shapes. (8-3)

- A mineral can be identified by studying its properties. Hardness, color, streak, luster, cleavage, fracture, specific gravity, and heft are examples of physical properties of minerals. (8-4)

- Double refraction, fluorescence, phosphorescence, and radioactivity are special mineral properties that can be used to identify some minerals. (8-5)

- Minerals are used to season food, as jewelry, in medicines, and for building materials. (8-6)

- Every mineral can be placed in one of two groups—those that contain oxygen and silicon, called the silicates, and those that do not, called the nonsilicates. (8-7)

The key terms in this chapter are listed below. Use each term in a sentence that shows the meaning of the term.

atom	element	mineral	physical property
chemical property	fracture	mixture	property
cleavage	gem	Mohs scale	proton
color	hardness	neutron	silicate minerals
compound	heft	nonsilicate minerals	specific gravity
crystal	luster	nucleus	streak
electron	matter	ore	

Chapter Review

VOCABULARY

Write the letter of the term that best matches the definition. Not all the terms will be used.

1. Any mineral that can be mined for profit
2. A property that describes how light reflects from the surface of a mineral
3. A solid with a regular shape and flat sides
4. A property that describes how a mineral splits along smooth surfaces
5. A solid element or compound with a specific crystal shape
6. Any characteristic that describes matter
7. The particle with a positive electrical charge in the nucleus of an atom
8. A property that describes the color of a powdered mark left by a mineral on a porcelain tile
9. The smallest piece of an element
10. Any mineral that contains oxygen and silicon

a. property
b. crystal
c. proton
d. ore
e. atom
f. silicate mineral
g. mineral
h. fracture
i. luster
j. cleavage
k. streak

CONCEPTS

1. Distinguish between a physical property and a chemical property. (8-1)
2. Compare freezing point, melting point, and boiling point. (8-1)
3. Explain why boiling point is not a chemical property. (8-1)
4. What is an atom? (8-2)
5. Distinguish between a proton, a neutron, and an electron. (8-2)
6. Make a sketch of an atom that contains 6 protons, 5 neutrons, and 6 electrons. (8-2)
7. How is a compound different from a mixture? Give an example of each. (8-2)
8. Define the terms *mineral* and *crystal*. (8-3)
9. Describe the Mohs scale. (8-4)
10. Evaluate how useful color is in identifying a mineral. (8-4)
11. Distinguish between color and streak. (8-4)
12. What is luster? (8-4)
13. How would you distinguish between a fracture and cleavage? (8-4)

14. Arrange these minerals in increasing order of hardness: diamond, talc, quartz. (8-4)

15. Distinguish between fluorescence and phosphorescence. (8-5)

16. What is radioactivity? How is a mineral tested for radioactivity? (8-5)

17. What is an ore? Give three examples of ores and describe a use for each. (8-6)

18. What is a gem? Give an example of a gem. (8-6)

19. What is a silicate mineral? Give two examples of silicate minerals. (8-7)

20. Describe three families of nonsilicate minerals. (8-7)

APPLICATION/ CRITICAL THINKING

1. Name one possible use for a fluorescent material. Name one possible use for a phosphorescent material.

2. A snowflake has a regular crystal pattern. Is a snowflake a mineral? Explain your answer.

3. In what ways could a mineral that is as hard as a diamond be useful.

4. Suppose you found a mineral that has a hardness of 2 produces a white streak, and cleaves in two directions. Use the table in the appendix to identify the mineral.

EXTENSION

1. Certain minerals have been designated as birthstones for different months. Find out about the birthstone for the month in which you were born. Write a short essay about your birthstone, including the properties and uses for the mineral.

2. Find out about the ores obtained in your state or province. In what ways are each of these ores used?

3. Make paper models of as many crystal shapes as you can. Display your models with pictures of minerals that have each crystal shape.

4. Dissolve two tablespoons of table salt in a half pint of boiling water. Carefully pour the solution into a saucer. Place a string in the solution and over the edge of the saucer. After a couple of days, observe the salt crystals that form on the string.

READINGS

Fenton, C.L., and M.A. Fenton. *The Rock Book*. New York: Doubleday and Co., Inc., 1970.

Shaub, B.M. *Treasures from the Earth — The World of Rocks and Minerals*. New York: Crown Publishers, Inc., 1975.

Shedenhelm, W.R.C. *The Young Rockhound's Handbook*. New York: The Putnam Publishing Group, 1978.

EARTH'S ROCKS

Rocks are the building blocks of the earth's crust. By studying rocks, scientists can learn about the earth's processes that formed them. The photograph shows Stair Hole in Dorset, England. Ocean waves have eroded softer parts of the rock, leaving the harder parts. Thus the rock we see is the result of the balance between the forces that build the land and those that wear it down.

- *What do the folds in the rock layers tell about how the cliffs formed?*
- *Where could the broken pieces of rock have come from?*
- *What could have broken the rock into small pieces?*

9-1 ROCKS

On the evening of November 8, 1982, a rock crashed through the roof of a home in Wethersfield, Connecticut. This rock was not an ordinary rock. It was a meteorite—a rock that fell from space.

The way scientists looked at this "alien" rock is similar to the way they look at earth rocks. By studying its texture, or the size of its mineral crystals, as well as its composition, they learned something about the conditions that existed when the meteorite formed. These same characteristics can be studied in earth rocks.

Scientists have found that rocks have one thing in common: they are made up of minerals. What is the difference between rocks and minerals? Rocks are the solid materials that make up the earth's crust and are each composed of one or more minerals. Minerals are the solid materials that make up rocks and are each composed of a single substance. This difference can be compared to the difference between houses and the materials used to build them. Just as rocks are made of minerals, houses are made of building materials, such as wood, brick, and glass.

After completing this section, you will be able to

- **explain** how rocks and minerals are different.
- **describe** main ways rocks form.

The key terms in this section are
igneous rocks
metamorphic rocks
sedimentary rocks

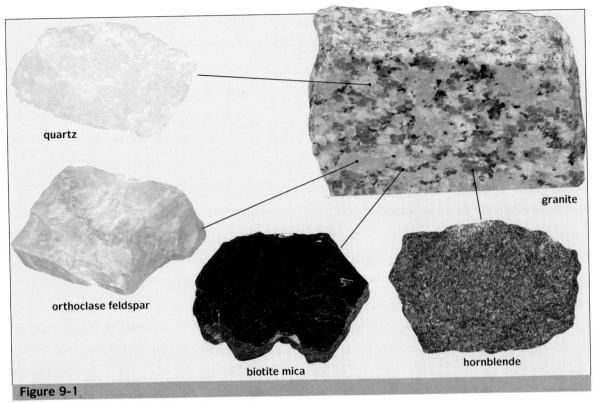

Figure 9-1

Granite and the minerals that form it.

Figure 9-2

The rock limestone (*top*) is made of one type of mineral, calcite (*bottom*).

Most rocks are made up of many minerals. For example, look at the rock shown in Figure 9-1. The rock is called granite (GRAN iht) and is made up of the four minerals shown. What are the names of the minerals?

A few rocks are made up of only one mineral. For example, look at the rock shown in Figure 9-2. The rock, called limestone, is made up of a single type of mineral, calcite. How does the appearance of the limestone differ from the appearance of the granite?

The lines show places where the minerals can be found. Because granite is a mixture, the proportion of each mineral can vary from sample to sample. In addition, the colors of the minerals can vary from one sample to another. Thus the appearance of granite can vary greatly, depending on the proportions and colors of its minerals.

Of the minerals contained in granite, only quartz and feldspar are found in all granites. Quartz and feldspar are called essential minerals in granite. *Essential minerals* are minerals that always occur in a particular rock.

A number of other minerals, such as mica and hornblende, may appear in granite. These minerals are called accessory minerals. *Accessory minerals* are minerals that do not always appear in a particular rock.

Does each kind of rock contain a different group of minerals? Geologists have been able to identify over 2000 minerals in the earth. Of these minerals, only about 12 are commonly found on earth. These minerals are called rock-forming minerals. The most common ones are shown in Table 9-1. The rock-forming minerals make up more than 90 percent of the rock found on the earth. The feldspars, the most abundant minerals, make up more than 50 percent of the earth's rocks. What is the next most abundant mineral?

As you can see, most rocks have a number of minerals in common. The minerals can combine in many different ways to form a wide variety of rocks. But how do rocks form?

Rocks form in three main ways. Based on how rocks form, they can be classified into three groups. **Igneous** (IHG nee uhs) **rocks** are rocks formed from molten rock material as it cools and hardens. The word *igneous* means "from fire." The second group of rocks is called sedimentary (sehd uh MEHNT uh ree) rocks. **Sedimentary rocks** are rocks formed from *sediments* (SEHD uh muhnts) that have been pressed together. Sediment may come from plant or animal remains, from minerals that were once dissolved in water, or from large rocks that have been broken up into smaller pieces by water, wind, or ice. The third group of rocks is called metamorphic (meht uh MOR-fihk) rocks. **Metamorphic rocks** are rocks that have been changed by heat or pressure.

As you have read, the study of rocks can provide information about their past. The mineral composition can often be used to tell where the rocks formed. For example, some minerals usually form in oceans. If such a mineral is found in a rock, the rock likely formed in the ocean. Some rocks also provide clues about the conditions that existed when the earth first formed. In order to see how this is done, we must first learn about the characteristics and properties of each group of rocks.

Table 9-1 *Rock-Forming Minerals*

Mineral	Abundance
Plagioclase feldspar	39%
Orthoclase feldspar	12%
Quartz	12%
Augite	11%
Hornblende	5%
Micas	5%

ignis (fire)

sedimentum (to settle)

meta (change)
morphe (form)

REVIEW

1. What is the difference between minerals and rocks?
2. Explain three main ways rocks form.

CHALLENGE Meteorites are rocks on the earth's surface that have come from outer space. When falling through the earth's atmosphere, they were heated by the friction with the air. How might this distinguish them from rocks formed on the earth?

9-2 IGNEOUS ROCKS

The diver in Figure 9-3 is watching molten, or melted, rock erupt from the ocean floor. When the molten rock hardens, it will become part of the ocean floor. Molten rock indicates to geologists that the inside of the earth must be very hot. By studying molten rock, geologists can find clues about how rocks form inside the earth.

Molten rock is formed when heat inside the earth causes some rock to melt. Molten rock below the surface of the earth is called *magma* (MAG muh). Magma has a temperature usually between 550°C and 1200°C. It is lighter than the solid rock around it and therefore tends to rise toward the earth's surface. Often the magma reaches the earth's surface. The molten rock that comes out onto the earth's surface is called *lava* (LAH vuh).

Figure 9-3

Molten rock on land (*left*) and under the ocean. Is this magma or lava?

ex (out)
trudere (thrust)
in (in)
trudere (thrust)

All igneous rocks are formed either from lava or from magma. Igneous rocks that form from lava are called **extrusive** (ek STROO sihv), or *volcanic,* **rocks**. Igneous rocks that form from magma are called **intrusive** (ihn TROO-sihv), or *plutonic,* **rocks**.

One way of distinguishing between extrusive and intrusive rocks is by texture. *Texture* refers to the size or arrangement of the mineral crystals, or grains, in an igneous rock. The texture can be determined by how fast or slow the molten rock cools and hardens. The longer it takes molten rock to cool and harden, the larger the crystals will be. This is because mineral crystals require time to grow.

Figure 9-4

Basalt often forms in columns.

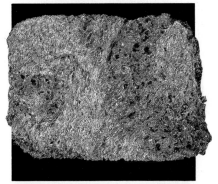

Extrusive rocks usually have small mineral crystals and are called fine-grained rocks. A microscope is usually needed to see the mineral crystals. A fine-grained igneous rock called *basalt* is shown in Figure 9-4.

Some types of extrusive rock do not have mineral crystals. These rocks are formed when molten rock cools so quickly that the crystals do not have time to form. An example of such a rock is called *obsidian,* shown in Figure 9-5 (*top*). Why is obsidian also called volcanic glass?

Another kind of extrusive rock that does not have crystals comes from the top part of lava. Sometimes the lava at the surface cools so quickly that the hot gases mixed with the lava do not have time to escape. The gases become trapped inside the hardened lava, resulting in a rock called *scoria,* shown in Figure 9-5 (*middle*). Another extrusive rock that cools quickly is *pumice.* Pumice, shown in Figure 9-5 (*bottom*), forms from lava thrown out of volcanoes during explosions. Pumice contains so many holes that it can float when placed in water.

Intrusive rocks usually have large mineral crystals and are called coarse-grained. The mineral crystals in a coarse-grained rock are usually large enough to be seen without magnification. Granite is an example of a coarse-grained intrusive rock.

An igneous rock with both large and small mineral crystals is called a **porphyry** (POR fuh ree). A porphyry forms when some mineral crystals in magma grow before others begin to form. Mineral crystals can become large

Figure 9-5

Obsidian (*top*), scoria (*middle*), and pumice (*bottom*).

OBJECTIVE

Identify the effect of the rate of cooling on crystal size.

MATERIALS

safety goggles, graduate, 60 mL water, 100-mL glass beaker, 8 g alum, hot plate, spoon, 2 petri dishes, bowl of ice cubes, paper towel, pencil or pen, paper

PROCEDURE

A. Put on safety goggles. Place 8 g of alum into a beaker containing 60 mL water.

B. Heat the beaker on a hot plate and stir until the alum dissolves.

C. Pour the liquid into each petri dish until it covers the bottom.

D. Set one dish on a table and set the other in a bowl of ice cubes. Observe the liquid in each dish for 5 to 7 minutes.

E. Make a sketch of a crystal from each dish. Try to show the actual sizes of the crystals. One way to make a sketch is by tracing around the alum crystals. To do this, remove a crystal from the liquid, pat it with a paper towel, and then lay it on your paper and trace around it.

RESULTS AND CONCLUSIONS

1. What effect did the rate of cooling have on the size of the alum crystals? Why?
2. Why are there differences in the sizes of mineral crystals in igneous rocks?

Figure 9-6

Granite porphyry (*top*), porphyry (*bottom*) have both large and small mineral crystals.

as magma cools slowly deep in the earth. If the magma were brought to the surface suddenly, as from an erupting volcano, the magma would cool quickly and form small mineral crystals.

What does the texture of an igneous rock tell us about the rock? The texture, or crystal size of the minerals, is determined by how quickly magma cools. An igneous rock with large crystals probably formed from magma that cooled and hardened slowly, below the earth's surface. An igneous rock with small crystals probably formed from lava that cooled quickly, at the earth's surface. Numerous holes tell us that the rock was once part of the surface of lava or was thrown out of a volcano during an explosion. An igneous rock with both large and small crystals indicates that it began as magma cooling below the earth's surface and was pushed up to the surface before cooling and hardening completely.

REVIEW

1. How can you distinguish between extrusive rock and intrusive rock?
2. How is texture of an igneous rock affected by the rate of cooling?
3. Give four kinds of information that can be read from the texture of an igneous rock.

CHALLENGE Under what conditions could an extrusive rock have larger mineral crystals than an intrusive rock?

9-3 CLASSIFYING IGNEOUS ROCKS

The structure in Figure 9-7 was formed from molten rock. This structure is Devils Tower National Monument in Wyoming. Not all igneous rocks look like the rock in Devils Tower. In fact, no two igneous rocks are exactly the same. Igneous rocks can differ in their mineral composition and in texture. What are some kinds of igneous rocks you can find, and how could you identify them?

Does every different kind of igneous rock form from a different kind of magma? Geologists have found that as magma cools, some minerals crystallize before others. As minerals crystallize in different parts of magma, different igneous rocks form. Thus many kinds of igneous rocks can form from one kind of magma.

Table 9-2 organizes some common igneous rocks according to their textures, colors, and the minerals they contain. Notice that the rocks vary in color from dark to light. Dark-colored igneous rocks usually contain dark-colored minerals, such as *olivine* and *augite*. Light-colored igneous rocks usually contain light-colored minerals, such as quartz and the feldspars. Why is *peridotite* (pehr uh-DOH tīt) dark in color?

Table 9-2 *Common Igneous Rocks*

	Dark ←	← Color →		Light
Coarse-grained	Periodotite	Gabbro	Diorite	Granite
Fine-grained	None	Basalt	Andesite	Rhyolite
Main minerals	Olivine, augite	Plagioclase feldspar, augite, olivine	Plagioclase feldspar, hornblende, biotite	Orthoclase feldspar, quartz, biotite, muscovite

The igneous rocks *basalt* and *gabbro* are dark-colored rocks but are lighter in color than peridotite. This is because they contain plagioclase (PLAY jee uh klays) feldspar, a light-colored mineral. Notice in Table 9-2 that basalt and gabbro have the same minerals but different textures. What are these minerals? Compare the size of the mineral grains in basalt and gabbro.

Andesite (AN duh zīt) and *diorite* (DĪ uh rīt) are igneous rocks that are lighter in color than basalt and gabbro because they contain more light-colored minerals. In addition to containing plagioclase feldspar, which is light in

Figure 9-7

Devils Tower in Wyoming (*top*). Peridotite (*bottom*).

199

color, andesite and diorite contain hornblende, another light-colored mineral. Andesite and diorite have the same minerals, but differ in texture.

Rhyolite and *granite* are igneous rocks that contain mostly light-colored minerals. They are lighter in color than andesite or diorite. Rhyolite and granite have the same minerals. Look at Figure 9-8. How could rhyolite and granite be distinguished?

Rhyolite is called a felsite when it contains mineral crystals too small to be seen. A **felsite** is a light-colored igneous rock with crystals that cannot be seen with the naked eye. Felsites form from lava that contains light-colored minerals.

Figure 9-8

Common igneous rocks.

REVIEW

1. How are igneous rocks classified?
2. Why are granite and rhyolite lighter in color than gabbro and basalt?
3. Compare granite and basalt.

CHALLENGE Devils Tower in Wyoming was once inside a volcano. Explain what may have happened to the volcano.

9-4 SEDIMENTARY ROCKS

WHERE SEDIMENTARY ROCKS COME FROM

Most of the rocks you find on the earth's surface are sedimentary rocks. In fact, sedimentary rocks make up 75 percent of the rocks at the earth's surface. From this you might conclude that most rocks below the surface are also sedimentary rocks. However, just below the earth's surface, sedimentary rocks make up less than 10 percent of the rocks.

Sedimentary rocks have not always existed on the earth. About four billion years ago, the earth's surface was covered with igneous rocks. The igneous rocks were formed when molten rock cooled and hardened. The earth's surface at that time probably resembled the way the moon's surface looks today.

Since the time igneous rocks first formed on the earth's surface, they have been exposed to water, wind, and ice. Rocks that come into contact with water, wind, or ice are broken down into smaller pieces over time. This process is called *weathering*. You probably have seen the effects of weathering on old sidewalks. Old sidewalks are rough and cracked, whereas new sidewalks are smooth and free of cracks. The processes that cause sidewalks to become rough and cracked are the same processes that break apart rocks on the earth.

Most rocks on the earth's surface come into contact with water. Water can enter small cracks in rocks. The water freezes when the temperature drops below 0°C. When water freezes, it expands, making the cracks larger. If this process happens enough times, the rock will break into smaller pieces. Water from rain can also dissolve certain minerals in rocks. Rain water becomes a weak acid when it dissolves some of the carbon dioxide in the air as it falls. Certain minerals, such as calcite, are broken down into sediments by rain water.

After large rocks are broken down into sediments, running water may pick them up. The sediments are carried by the running water until the running water slows down or stops. The water may slow down as it nears a lake or an ocean. When running water slows down, it can carry fewer sediments than when it was moving faster. As a result, some of the sediments fall to the bottom. Over time, the sediments collect on the bottom. The materials that have been deposited in water form most sedimentary rock. However, materials deposited by wind and ice can also form sedimentary rock.

Figure 9-9

Water seeps into cracks in a rock. When the water freezes, it expands and breaks the rock apart.

FORMING SEDIMENTARY ROCKS

Usually, sediments build up very slowly. It may take a thousand years for sediments to build up a layer one centimeter thick. A layer will grow in thickness until the environment changes. For example, a layer of sand might be formed where a river enters an ocean. If the river dries up, the layer of sand stops growing. When the river starts flowing again, a new layer of sand is started.

Over many thousands of years, layers of sediment become covered by other layers of sediment. The sediments are squeezed together by the weight of the layers above. Sometimes the spaces between the sediments are filled by minerals dissolved in water, which act like cement. When a layer of sediments hardens, sedimentary rock is formed.

As you have learned, all sedimentary rocks form from sediments. The sediments can be loose pieces of rock. In order for sediments to form rocks, the sediments must undergo a process that holds them together. One way in

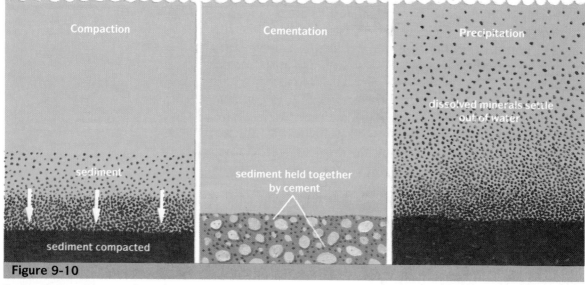

Figure 9-10

Sedimentary rocks can form in three ways; compaction, cementation, and precipitation.

which pieces of rock are held together is through a squeezing process called **compaction** (kuhm PAK shuhn). Pieces of rock become compacted as the weight of the sediments deposited above squeezes out air and water from between the pieces of rock. This action is similar to squeezing a handful of wet soil. As water is squeezed out, the soil holds together. Look at Figure 9-10. What happens to the thickness of the rock layers as they are compacted?

Another way in which sediments are held together is through minerals acting like cement in the process called **cementation** (see muhn TAY shuhn). Sediments can be cemented together when the spaces between the pieces are filled with minerals, usually left by ground water. Quartz and calcite are common cementing materials.

Sediments can be made up of either chemical sediments or the remains of living things. Sedimentary rocks made up of chemical sediments are called **chemical rocks**. Sedimentary rocks made up of the remains of living things are called **organic rocks**.

Chemical sediments form when dissolved minerals in water precipitate or are left by evaporating water. **Precipitation** (prih sihp uh TAY shuhn) is a process by which dissolved materials in water settle out of solution. For example, dissolved minerals in water precipitate by forming solids that sink to the bottom.

Over time, an entire body of water may evaporate, leaving a deposit of minerals. A chemical rock that has formed from these mineral deposits is called an **evaporite**. Rock gypsum, shown in Figure 9-11, is an evaporite. It was formed from the mineral gypsum that was left as a body of salt water evaporated.

Organic sedimentary rocks are a second type of nonclastic rock. Organic sedimentary rocks are formed from organic sediments. **Organic sediments** are sediments made up of the remains of living things. These sediments include skeletons, shells, and plants. For example, chalk, a type of limestone, is an organic sedimentary rock formed from tiny pieces of seashells. The cliffs shown in Figure 9-12 are made of chalk.

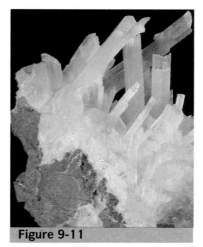

Figure 9-11

Rock gypsum is left when an entire body of water evaporates.

Figure 9-12

These white cliffs, at Dover, England, are made of chalk.

203

FEATURES OF SEDIMENTARY ROCKS

The presence of layers is the most common feature in sedimentary rocks. Look at the layers in the sedimentary rock shown in Figure 9-13 (*left*). What causes the layers in the rock to show up?

Sediments can be deposited by water, wind, or ice. The conditions under which sediments are deposited usually change. For example, mud might be settling to the bottom of a lake. Over time, the lake may evaporate, and the layer of mud stops forming. However, if another lake forms over the same area, a new layer of mud begins to form on top of the old layer. The new layer may contain sediments different in color or size or minerals from those in the older layer. If these layers harden, rock layers containing different sediments or minerals are formed and they can easily be distinguished.

Figure 9-13

The different colors of these layers of rock are due to the different environments that existed when the layers formed (*left*). Sedimentary rocks can have ripple marks formed by wind or moving water (*right*).

In addition to layers, another common feature found in sedimentary rocks is fossils. A *fossil* is a record of past life, such as a footprint made by a dinosaur, or the actual remains, such as a dinosaur bone.

Ripple marks are a feature found in some sedimentary rocks. *Ripple marks* are formed by air or water moving over a layer of fine sediments, such as sand, silt, or clay. This is similar to the way water waves are formed when air blows over a body of water.

Figure 9-14

Concretions.

Concretions (kahn KREE shuhnz) and geodes (JEE-ohdz) are features found in some sedimentary rock layers. A **concretion** is a ball-shaped rock. Concretions range in diameter from several centimeters to a few meters. They are made up of cementing minerals, usually silica, that precipitate from ground water.

The concretions shown in Figure 9-14 were formed from minerals once dissolved in ground water. Concretions can form when ground water comes into contact with a fossil, such as a bone. The minerals precipitate and are deposited around the fossil. Over time the fossil decays, leaving a ball-shaped deposit.

The Grand Canyon is, in some places, 1.6 km deep and more than 16 km wide. The Colorado River, seen at the bottom, carved out the canyon. Why is the canyon wider than the river?

205

ACTIVITY   Chemical Sediments

OBJECTIVE
Investigate one way in which sediments may form.

MATERIALS
safety goggles, graduate, two 50-mL beakers, balance, calcium chloride, filter paper, sodium carbonate, stirring rod

PROCEDURE

A. Put on safety goggles. Using a graduate, measure 20 mL of water. Pour the water into a 50-mL beaker.

B. Again measure 20 mL of water and pour into another 50-mL beaker.

C. Using a balance, measure 1 g of calcium chloride on a piece of filter paper. Place the calcium chloride into one of the beakers of water. Using the stirring rod, gently stir the solution until the calcium chloride dissolves.

D. Using the balance, measure 1 g of sodium carbonate. Place the sodium carbonate into the other beaker. Using the stirring rod, gently stir the water until the sodium carbonate dissolves.

E. Carefully pour the contents of one beaker into the other. Observe what happens.
  1. What did you observe when you mixed the contents of the beakers?

F. Gently stir the contents of the beaker. Observe what happens.
  2. What did you observe when you stirred the contents of the beakers after they were mixed?

RESULTS AND CONCLUSIONS
1. Identify the chemical process you observed in this investigation.

2. Compare stirring the contents of the beakers after they were mixed with stirring the contents when they were in separate beakers.

3. How might rocks be formed by this process?

---

geodes (earthy)

A ball-shaped rock that resembles a concretion is a geode. A **geode** is a hollow rock with mineral crystals lining the inside surface. Geodes can range in diameter from several centimeters to about 30 centimeters.

Figure 9-15

Geode.

REVIEW

1. How do sediments form?
2. Describe two ways in which sedimentary rocks form.
3. Give three examples of sediments.
4. What is the difference between a concretion and a geode?

CHALLENGE Suppose the earth had no atmosphere. How would this affect the amount and kind of rock that makes up the earth's surface?

9-5 CLASSIFYING SEDIMENTARY ROCKS

CLASTIC ROCKS

Sedimentary rocks that form from pieces of other rock are called **clastic rocks**. Pieces of rock, or sediments, can vary in size. Depending on the size of the sediments they contain, clastic rocks are classified as conglomerates (kuhn-GLAHM uhr ihts), breccias (BREHCH ee uhz), sandstones, siltstones, or shale.

Conglomerates and *breccias* are clastic rocks that contain the largest sediments. They contain pebbles of many different sizes. Conglomerates contain pebbles that are rounded, whereas breccias contain pebbles that are angular, or sharp-cornered.

Sandstones are clastic rocks that contain sand-size sediments that are cemented together. The sediments are usually small grains of quartz, basalt, or calcite.

klastos (broken)

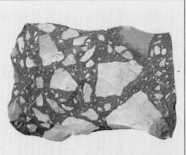

Figure 9-16

Conglomerate (*top left*), breccia (*middle*), sandstone (*top right*), siltstone (*bottom left*), and shale (*bottom right*) are all clastic rocks.

Siltstone is a clastic rock that is similar to sandstone. However, siltstone contains smaller sediments than sandstone. The sediments in siltstone cannot be seen without a magnifying glass.

Shale is a clastic rock with the smallest sediments. It contains clay particles pressed together so tightly that water will not pass through. Shale, which looks like hardened mud, is the most common type of sedimentary rock.

Figure 9-17

Coquina is a sedimentary rock formed from shells.

NONCLASTIC ROCKS

Sedimentary rocks that are formed from dissolved minerals in water or from the remains of past life are called **nonclastic rocks**. Nonclastic rocks are classified by their composition. Nonclastic rocks may contain calcite, halite, gypsum, or quartz.

Limestone is a nonclastic rock formed from dissolved calcite in seawater or from pieces of seashells. Calcite in seawater comes from calcite on land that is dissolved by rain water and washed into the sea. Dissolved calcite may precipitate and settle to the bottom of the sea.

Most limestone forms from tiny seashells or pieces of seashells that collect in large amounts on the floor of the sea. For example, chalk is a kind of limestone that contains tiny seashells pressed together. Coquina (koh-KEE nuh) is a kind of limestone that contains seashells. In Figure 9-17 you can see the seashells in coquina.

Figure 9-18

White Sands National Monument in New Mexico (*left*). Chert (*right*).

Rock salt, rock gypsum, and *chert* are nonclastic rocks formed by the precipitation of dissolved minerals in seawater or by minerals that are left when seawater evaporates. Rock salt is mainly composed of the mineral halite. The salt used in seasoning food comes from rock salt. Rock gypsum is mainly composed of the mineral gypsum. The white sand at White Sands National Monument, New Mexico, shown in Figure 9-18 (*left*), is almost pure gypsum. The gypsum was precipitated from seawater before the water evaporated. Chert, shown in Figure 9-18 (*right*), is mainly composed of quartz. Chert is also known as flint. Why do you think chert was once used to make arrowheads?

One of the most important nonclastic rocks is *coal*. It is used as an energy source. Coal, shown in Figure 9-19, contains hydrocarbons, materials that formed from plant material buried in swamps millions of years ago. It is usually found underground in layers, between layers of shale, limestone, or sandstone.

Table 9-3 *Common Sedimentary Rocks*

Rock	Texture	Composition	Comments
Conglomerate	Coarse, 2 mm	Rounded pebbles	Rounded pebbles, sand, and clay can easily be seen.
Breccia	Coarse, 2 mm	Angular pebbles	Angular pebbles, sand, and clay can easily be seen.
Sandstone	Medium, .0625–2 mm	Quartz, other minerals and rock fragments	Sand grains can be seen; rough surfaces.
Siltstone	Fine, .004–.06 mm	Quartz, clay	Has gritty feel.
Shale	Microscopic, .004 mm	Clay, micas	Has muddy appearance.
Limestone	Coarse to fine	Calcite, shells	May contain fossils, seashells; fizzles when in hydrochloric acid.
Chert	Fine	Quartz	Is light-colored; also called flint; once used for arrowheads.
Rock gypsum	Coarse to fine	Gypsum	Is commonly used as plasterboard.
Rock salt	Coarse to fine	Halite	Has salty taste; table salt.
Coal	Fine	Hydrocarbons	Is dark-colored; is used as a fuel.

Figure 9-19

Coal is a nonclastic rock that is a fuel source.

REVIEW

1. Name five clastic rocks and explain why they are classified as clastic rocks.
2. Name five nonclastic rocks and explain why they are classified as nonclastic rocks.
3. Compare how clastic rocks are classified with how nonclastic rocks are classified.

CHALLENGE Explain why conglomerates may be found farther downstream than breccias.

9-6 METAMORPHIC ROCKS

It may seem that solid rocks never change. Over long periods of time, however, all rocks change. A rock can change if it is put under great pressure and heat. A rock changed by great pressure or heat is called a metamorphic rock. Metamorphic means "changed in form."

Metamorphic rock probably forms at great depths within the earth's crust. Great pressure is put on rocks when they are buried by many layers of sediment. The weight of the layers compresses the rocks, causing the minerals in the rocks to change shape. Great pressure on rocks also occurs during mountain building. Rocks such as the one shown in Figure 9-20 are found in mountains. How can you tell this rock was once under great pressure?

Figure 9-20

Great pressure causes sedimentary rock layers to bend.

Under great heat and pressure, igneous or sedimentary rock can be changed into metamorphic rock. This is shown in Figure 9-20 (*left*). Rocks are changed by heat when they come into contact with or are near magma. Although the heat is not great enough to melt the rocks, it can change their structure. The heat can cause the minerals in rocks to recrystallize into larger or different minerals. Heat can also cause the minerals to line up in layers.

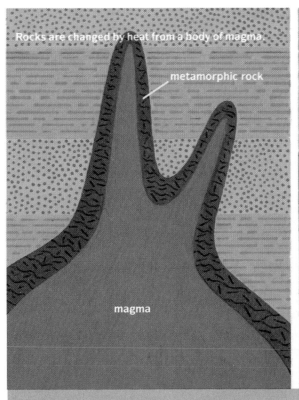
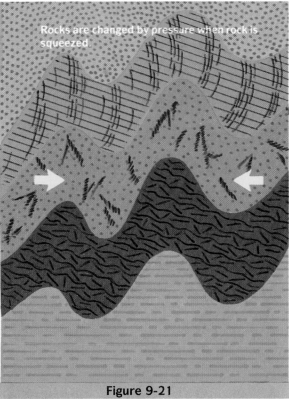

Figure 9-21

Metamorphic rocks are formed by heat and pressure.

Metamorphic rocks can be formed where large areas of rocks are lifted up to form mountains. The pressure on the rocks also causes the temperature to rise. The pressure and heat change the rocks into metamorphic rock. The process by which wide areas of rocks are changed by great heat and pressure is called **regional metamorphism**.

A second process that forms metamorphic rocks takes place by contact. This can happen when molten rock or magma pushes its way into solid rock layers. The surrounding rocks are changed by great heat from the magma. The high temperature of the magma "bakes" the rocks. The metamorphism that occurs when solid rocks come into contact with molten rock is called **contact metamorphism**.

REVIEW

1. Describe how heat and pressure can change a rock.
2. Compare the way metamorphic rocks form in mountains with the way they form near magma.

CHALLENGE A layer of basalt is found between two sedimentary rock layers. How can knowledge of metamorphism be used to tell whether the basalt formed from a lava flow or pushed its way in between the two layers?

9-7 CLASSIFYING METAMORPHIC ROCKS

After completing this section, you will be able to

- **explain** how metamorphic rocks are classified.
- **give** the names of seven metamorphic rocks and the sedimentary rocks from which they are formed.

The key terms in this section are

foliated rocks	nonfoliated rocks

As you learned in the preceding lesson, *metamorphic* means "changed in form." One feature that can be seen in some metamorphic rocks is the arrangement of minerals into bands, or lines. Another feature that can be seen in some metamorphic rocks is layers. Metamorphic rocks that have minerals arranged in bands or that are made up of layers are classified as **foliated** (FOH lee ayt uhd) **rocks.** Metamorphic rocks that do not have minerals arranged in bands or are not made up of layers are classified as **nonfoliated rocks.**

FOLIATED ROCKS

Some foliated rocks contain bands of minerals that appear as bands of different colors. For example, alternating bands of dark-colored and light-colored minerals can be seen in the rock shown in Figure 9-22 (*left*). This rock is called *gneiss* (nīs). Gneiss is formed from granite, an igneous rock, under great heat and pressure.

Figure 9-22

Gneiss (*left*), schist (*right*).

Another foliated rock that shows banding of minerals is *schist* (shihst). Schist is one of the most common of the metamorphic rocks and usually is formed from shale, a sedimentary rock. As you can see in Figure 9-22 (*right*), schist does not have the well-defined bands that are seen in gneiss. Some of the minerals, such as mica, appear as flakes of minerals instead of as bands. The shiny specks seen in schist are mica flakes. They are formed when the clay particles in shale recrystallize into different and larger minerals.

The amount of change a rock undergoes depends on the amount of heat and pressure applied to it. Two foliated rocks that are formed from shale, but which undergo less heat and pressure than does schist, are *phyllite* (FIHL īt) and *slate*. Because phyllite and slate are formed by less heat and pressure than is schist, their mineral crystals are smaller than the mineral crystals in schist. Phyllite has tiny mica flakes, whick give it a shiny appearance. Look at Figure 9-23 (*top*). Compare the appearance of phyllite with the appearance of schist.

Slate is similar to phyllite in that it also has layers. However, slate is formed under less heat and pressure than is phyllite. For this reason, slate has smaller crystals than phyllite. The crystals in slate are too small to be seen without a microscope. Often, slate resembles shale.

Figure 9-23

Phyllite (*top*), slate (*bottom*).

NONFOLIATED ROCKS

Nonfoliated rocks are metamorphic rocks that do not have bands of minerals or layers. Rocks in this group are usually composed of one mineral whose crystals are recrystallized. Nonfoliated rocks do not show banding of minerals, because all the mineral crystals look the same.

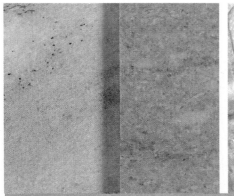

Figure 9-24

Marble (*left*), quartzite (*middle*), and hornfels (*right*) are all unfoliated metamorphic rocks.

An example of nonfoliated rock is *marble*. Marble is formed by the recrystallization of the mineral calcite in limestone. Sometimes, colorful veins can be seen in marble. Look at Figure 9-24 (*left*). Why, do you think, is marble used to make table tops?

Quartzite and *hornfels*, shown in Figure 9-24 (*middle*

OBJECTIVE
Classify rocks based on their characteristics.

MATERIALS
hand lens, numbered samples of rock:
conglomerate, coquina, gneiss, granite, pumice,
sandstone, schist, slate

PROCEDURE
A. Using a hand lens, examine each numbered rock sample for characteristics that would show it formed from molten material.

B. Using the hand lens, examine each rock sample for characteristics that would show it formed from pieces of other rocks.

C. Using the hand lens, examine each rock sample for characteristics that would show it formed under heat and pressure.

RESULTS AND CONCLUSIONS
1. Which rock samples are igneous rocks?
2. Which rock samples can be classified as sedimentary rocks?
3. Which rock samples can be classified as metamorphic rocks?

EXTENSION
Collect rock samples. Identify them and prepare a display of the collection.

and *right*), are also nonfoliated rocks. Quartzite is formed from sandstone, a sedimentary rock. Hornfels can be formed from basalt, an igneous rock, or from limestone or shale, which are sedimentary rocks. Using Table 9-4, determine the mineral compositions of quartzite and hornfels.

Table 9-4 *Common Metamorphic Rocks*

	Rock	Major Minerals	Texture
Foliated	slate	micas, quartz	fine
	phyllite	quartz, muscovite	fine
	schist	biotite, muscovite, hornblende, quartz, feldspars	medium
	gneiss	feldspars, quartz, micas, hornblende	medium to coarse
Nonfoliated	marble	calcite, dolomite	medium to coarse
	quartzite	quartz	medium
	hornfels	quartz, micas, feldspars	fine

REVIEW

1. How are metamorphic rocks classified?
2. Name four metamorphic rocks and give the name of the rock from which each formed.

CHALLENGE How can the layers in foliated rocks be distinguished from the layers often found in sedimentary rocks?

9-8 THE ROCK CYCLE

The changes that form metamorphic rocks are only one step in a never-ending process. This process is called the rock cycle. The **rock cycle** shows how the different types of rocks are related and how rock material is used and reused.

The rock cycle diagram, Figure 9-25 (*left*), shows that igneous rock forms from molten rock. When igneous rock is exposed to water, wind, or ice, it can break down into sediments. The sediments can be carried away and deposited in layers. The layers may be pressed together by the weight of material above them, or the sediments may become cemented together by minerals in water. The sediments can harden into sedimentary rock. This rock may become buried by other layers. Below the surface of the earth, heat and pressure can change the sedimentary rock into metamorphic rock.

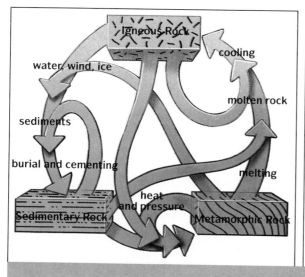
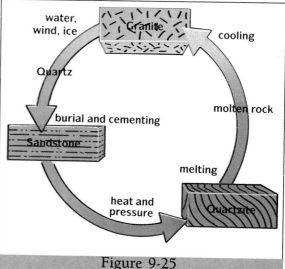

Figure 9-25

The rock cycle.

If the metamorphic rock melts, it may be used again to form new igneous rock, and the rock cycle may continue. However, the metamorphic rock may follow other paths. For example, the metamorphic rock may be brought to the surface of the earth during mountain building. There, it can be exposed to the process of weathering and form sedimentary rock. What other pathways can you see in the rock cycle?

Figure 9-25 (*right*) shows how some rocks can develop in the rock cycle. Magma in the earth hardens to form granite, an igneous rock. Mountain building occurs and granite is pushed up toward the earth's surface. Over

A Florida company called Microgravity Research Associates wants to grow crystals in outer space for use in electronics. Research has shown that crystals grow better under conditions with little gravity and other earthly disturbances. This is because gravity prevents crystals from growing past a certain size. Also, since crystals grow by adding layer upon layer of only atom-thick material, any disturbance, such as moving air, causes a flaw in the finished product. When flawed crystals are used in circuits, not as much electricity will flow through them. Thus the entire electrical system's performance and reliability are affected. However, in space, without gravity or air currents, crystals grow quickly and freely in all directions. They also have fewer flaws.

Microgravity Research Associates wants to use the mineral gallium arsenide for the crystals. Gallium arsenide crystals would be used in sophisticated devices that demand utmost performance and durability. These might include supercomputers that perform billions of computations every second. The crystals would also be suitable for strategic defense systems and satellite communications.

Other companies are taking advantage of the ease with which crystals can be grown in space. Microgravity Technologies, Inc., in California, wants to grow gallium arsenide and other compounds in space to use in producing lasers and optical fibers.

a long period of time, rain, ice, and wind wear away the rock material above the granite, exposing it. The rain, ice, and wind now slowly weather the granite, breaking it into smaller pieces. Eventually, the granite is broken down into smaller pieces and into its minerals. One of the minerals, quartz, is small enough to be carried away by running water or wind. As the running water or wind slows down, the quartz is deposited as a layer of sediment. It becomes covered by more layers of sediment over time and becomes pressed together. The quartz grains are also cemented together by minerals left by water to form sandstone, a sedimentary rock. As the sandstone becomes buried by more layers of sediment, the pressure and heat increase. With enough pressure and heat, sandstone becomes the metamorphic rock quartzite. As the quartzite is buried deeper, the increasing pressure and heat cause it to melt. When the magma hardens, igneous rock forms, and the rock cycle continues. As you can see, the earth's rocks are constantly changing form.

REVIEW

1. How are igneous, sedimentary, and metamorphic rocks related, according to the rock cycle?
2. Briefly describe the changes that granite may go through, according to the rock cycle.

CHALLENGE   Is it possible to tell what paths a certan rock will take in the rock cycle? Explain your answer.

CHAPTER SUMMARY

The main ideas in this chapter are listed below. Read these statements before you answer any Chapter Review questions.

- Rocks are classified according to how they formed. The three main groups of rocks are igneous rocks, sedimentary rocks, and metamorphic rocks. (9-1)

- All rocks show characteristics that are the results of the conditions under which they formed. (9-1)

- Igneous rocks form from molten rock material as it cools and hardens. (9-1)

- Igneous rocks can be put into two groups: extrusive rocks, which form from molten rock at the earth's surface, and intrusive rocks, which form from molten rock deep in the earth. (9-2)

- Igneous rocks can differ in their mineral composition and texture. (9-3)

- Sedimentary rocks form from pieces of other rocks, from minerals, or from the remains of things once alive. (9-4)

- Sedimentary rocks can be put into two groups: clastic rocks and nonclastic rocks. Clastic rocks form from pieces of rock, and nonclastic rocks form either from minerals dissolved in water or from the remains of past life. (9-4, 9-5)

- Metamorphic rocks are rocks changed by great pressure or heat. (9-6)

- Metamorphic rocks can be put into two groups: foliated rocks, which have bands or layers of minerals, and nonfoliated rocks, which are mainly composed of one mineral. (9-7)

- The rock cycle shows how the different types of rocks are related and the pathways rocks may follow when changing from one type of rock to another. (9-8)

The key terms in this chapter are listed below. Use each term in a sentence that shows the meaning of the term.

cementation	felsite	organic rocks
chemical rocks	foliated rocks	organic sediments
clastic rocks	geode	porphyry
compaction	igneous rocks	precipitation
concretions	intrusive rocks	regional metamorphism
contact metamorphism	metamorphic rocks	rock cycle
evaporite	nonclastic rocks	sedimentary rocks
extrusive rocks	nonfoliated rocks	

Chapter Review

VOCABULARY

Write the letter of the term that best matches the definition. Not all the terms will be used.

1. The processes by which rock material is used and reused
2. Rocks formed under great pressure and heat
3. An igneous rock with both large and small crystals
4. Igneous rocks formed below the earth's surface
5. Rocks made of sediments
6. Rocks made by chemical sediments
7. A hollow rock lined with mineral crystals
8. A squeezing together of rock
9. Formed from the hardening of molten rock
10. Rock formed from sediments pressed or cemented together
11. Igneous rocks formed at the earth's surface
12. Rocks formed from the remains of living things.

a. metamorphic rocks
b. compaction
c. nonclastic rocks
d. geode
e. rock cycle
f. porphyry
g. sedimentary rocks
h. igneous rocks
i. clastic rocks
j. extrusive rocks
k. intrusive rocks
l. organic rocks

CONCEPTS

1. What do all rocks have in common? (9-1)
2. What are the characteristics of each of the three main groups of rocks? (9-1)
3. Distinguish between rocks and minerals. (9-4)
4. Explain how the rate of cooling affects crystal size in igneous rocks. (9-2)
5. How can extrusive rocks and intrusive rocks be distinguished? (9-2)
6. Why is basalt called a fine-grained version of gabbro? (9-3)
7. How are felsites formed? (9-3)
8. What are some ways in which sediments can form? (9-4)
9. Describe two ways that clastic rocks can form. (9-4)
10. Explain how chemical rocks and organic rocks form. (9-4)
11. Describe how layers of sedimentary rock might form. (9-4)

12. Compare and contrast chalk and coquina. (9-5)

13. Distinguish among the main groups of clastic rocks. (9-5)

14. How are metamorphic rocks formed? (9-6)

15. What is the difference between the process that forms metamorphic rocks and the process that forms igneous rocks? (9-2, 9-6)

16. Describe the process of regional metamorphism. (9-6)

17. Why do some metamorphic rocks have bands or layers? (9-7)

18. Why aren't bands of minerals found in nonfoliated rocks? (9-7)

19. Identify two metamorphic rocks and the sedimentary rocks from which they form. (9-7)

20. Why is the rock cycle called a never-ending process? (9-8)

APPLICATION/ CRITICAL THINKING

1. Identify the rocks used to construct your school building. Why, do you think, were these particular types of rock used?

2. Explain each of the following observations.
   a. In a cemetery, the writing on some gravestones is more worn than on other gravestones.
   b. Most rocks found at the earth's surface are sedimentary rocks.
   c. Shale is the most common type of sedimentary rock found on the earth's surface.
   d. The most common feature seen in sedimentary rock is layers.
   e. Granite is used as a building material in many buildings.

3. Why are fossils rarely found in metamorphic rocks?

4. Some rocks that have formed from lava have a red color. The red color is caused by iron that rusted in the lava when exposed to the air. In which part of the lava—top, middle, or bottom—do you think the red rock formed?

EXTENSION

1. Add gravel, sand, and soil to a jar of water and mix with a spoon. Pour this mixture into another jar. When all the particles have settled, use a small hose to siphon off the water. How does this explain how sediments settle in water to form layers? What must happen to the layers in order for them to become rock?

2. Hold a piece of obsidian up to a light. Try to look at the light through a thin edge of the obsidian. The edge should appear to be a lighter color than the rest of the obsidian. Find out what gives obsidian its dark color.

READINGS

MacFall, Russell P. *Rock Hunter's Guide: How to Find and Identify Collectible Rocks.* New York: Thomas Y. Crowell, Co., 1980.

Pough, Frederick H. *A Field Guide to Rocks and Minerals,* 4th ed. Boston: Houghton Mifflin Co., 1976.

EARTH'S RESOURCES

Natural resources are materials we use from the earth. The photograph shows a granite quarry, a place where blocks of granite are mined. The granite will most likely be used in constructing buildings.

- *Why is granite considered a resource?*
- *Why are water and air also considered natural resources?*
- *What problems can be caused by using too much of a resource?*

10-1 THE ENVIRONMENT

An *environment* (ehn vī ruhn mehnt) is all the living and nonliving things that surround an organism. In an environment, living things are supplied with conditions that are necessary for their survival.

The earth is our environment. It supplies us with air, water, and food, which are necessary for our survival. It also supplies us with metals such as iron, copper, and gold and with energy sources such as petroleum, natural gas, and coal. Air, water, food, minerals, and energy sources are examples of natural resources.

A **natural resource** is any material that can be used from the earth. There are two kinds of natural resources. They are renewable resources and nonrenewable resources. A *renewable resource* is a resource that can be renewed or replaced. For example, trees are a renewable resource. Trees can be harvested, and new trees can be planted in the same area. A *nonrenewable resource* is a resource that cannot be replaced. Minerals are an example of a nonrenewable resource. Once used, they cannot be replaced. Nonrenewable resources must be used very carefully.

> *After completing this section, you will be able to*
>
> - **describe** the effects of overpopulation.
> - **list** five examples of natural resources.
> - **distinguish** between renewable resources and nonrenewable resources.
>
> *The key term in this section is*
> **natural resource**

Figure 10-1

The increasing world population.

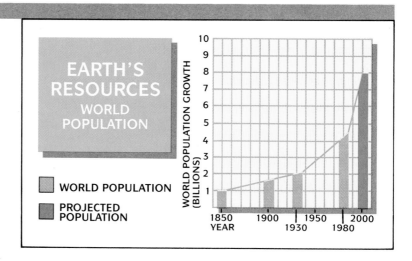

EARTH'S RESOURCES
WORLD POPULATION

☐ WORLD POPULATION
■ PROJECTED POPULATION

The demand for natural resources in the world has increased rapidly. One factor for the increased demand for natural resources is the rapidly increasing world population. In 1650, there were about 500 million people on the earth. In 1850, the number of people on the earth had doubled, reaching 1 billion. By 1930, the earth's population had doubled again, reaching 2 billion. The time needed for the earth's population to double had decreased from 200 years to 80 years. The earth's population now is over 4.5 billion people, and it is doubling at the rate of every 33 years. Using the graph in Figure 10-1, predict what the earth's population will be in the year 2000.

One of the most serious problems caused by overpopulation is the inability to grow enough food to feed the earth's people. One reason for this is that many areas of land do not have the right type of soil or climate. Another reason is poor farming methods in many areas of the world. Farmers in underdeveloped areas cannot afford to buy fertilizers and machinery, which would greatly increase the amount of food that could be grown.

REVIEW

1. What effect does overpopulation have on food resources?
2. Name five natural resources.
3. What is the difference between a renewable resource and a nonrenewable resource?

CHALLENGE One prediction is that if the earth's human population continues to increase at the present rate, there will be one person for every 30 cm² of the earth's surface in 700 years. Can this happen? Explain your answer.

10-2 RENEWABLE RESOURCES

The area shown in Figure 10-2 was once a forest. The forest was destroyed by fire. Over many years, a new forest will eventually grow here. This is an example of how one natural resource can be renewed. The human population needs and uses natural resources. Humans depend on water for drinking, on fuel to run machines, and on wood to build houses.

A forest is not the only natural resource that can be renewed. Water, soil, and air are also natural resources that can be renewed. A natural resource that can be renewed or replaced is called a **renewable resource.**

Figure 10-2

A burned forest takes many years to be replaced.

WATER

The earth's water supply is represented in Figure 10-3. According to the figure about how much of the water is in the oceans? About 2 percent is locked up as ice. The remaining 1 percent is the earth's water supply for the needs of humans.

Water use in the United States can be divided into three types: household, industry, and farming. The average person uses about 266 L of water a day. Almost all the water used in households and industry can be returned to the earth's water supply, or can be reused. However, water used for watering crops is not as easily returned to the earth's water supply for reuse as water in households and industry. This is because much of the water is taken up and held by plants, or it seeps into the ground. However, even this water is eventually returned to the water supply. Water is a resource that is never used up. It is called a renewable resource.

EARTH'S RESOURCES
WATER SUPPLY

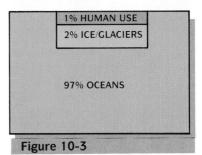

1% HUMAN USE

2% ICE/GLACIERS

97% OCEANS

Figure 10-3

The earth's water supply.

223

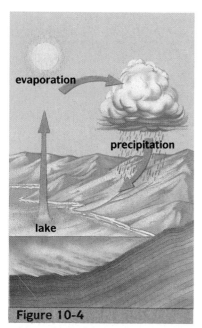

Figure 10-4

Water becomes purified naturally through the water cycle.

Water that is returned to the earth's water supply after being used can be made pure again by a natural process called the *water cycle*. Look at Figure 10-4. What causes liquid water on the earth to evaporate? When water evaporates, it leaves behind any impurities it may have contained. Therefore, when the water returns to the earth as precipitation, it is free of those impurities. The water cycle is a natural process that purifies water.

SOIL

Soil is an important resource. One of the most important uses of soil is for the growing of food to feed the world's people. As you have learned, the world's population is increasing rapidly, and how to grow enough food to feed everyone is a serious problem.

Soil contains nutrients that are used by all plants, including food crops and grasses. Nutrients can be returned to the soil by natural processes, such as decay of plant and animal remains. Thus soil can be reused. However, if some crops are planted in the soil too often, the soil nutrients may be used faster than they can be replaced.

Another problem caused by planting crops too often is soil erosion, or the carrying away of soil by wind or water. Before crops are planted, soil must be tilled, or turned over. This exposes bare soil, or soil with no plant cover. Without a protective covering, the soil can be blown away by wind or washed away by water. Notice the condition of the land in Figure 10-5. In 1934, a layer of soil

Figure 10-5

Old and harmful agricultural practices could cause another dust bowl, like the one in the Midwest during the 1930s.

more than a meter deep was blown off the "dust bowl" region of the American Midwest. In one day, over 300 million metric tons of topsoil would be removed. The plant cover had been destroyed by plows and by livestock.

Soil can be kept from blowing away or washing away. In the method called *strip cropping*, shown in Figure 10-6, grass crops are grown in rows. Between the rows of grass crops, other food crops are grown. When the food crops have been harvested, the grass crops remain, protecting the soil by stopping the flow of running water and by shielding the bare soil from wind.

Another method that protects the soil is *contour plowing*, shown in Figure 10-6. In this method, soil is plowed across the slope, or slant, of the land. This method slows down the movement of running water.

Figure 10-6

By strip cropping (*left*), and contour plowing (*right*), farmers can reduce erosion.

AIR

Air is a mixture of gases and solid particles. Some of the gases and particles in air come from natural processes. For example, solid particles such as dust can come from volcanoes.

Many gases and solid particles in air come from human activities. For example, burning fuels produce a gas called sulfur dioxide. Burning fuels also produce solid particles, such as smoke, that are released into the air. Sulfur dioxide and smoke particles can be harmful to human health.

Figure 10-7

An area can have clean air one day (*left*) and unhealthful air the next day (*right*).

Substances such as sulfur dioxide and smoke are constantly being added to the air. However, air can be purified by rain and wind. Rain can wash certain gases—for example, sulfur dioxide—out of the air by dissolving them and carrying them to the ground. Rain can also wash solid particles out of the air by collecting them as it falls. Wind can cleanse the air by carrying away gases and particles from human activities and bringing in fresh air. Without wind to carry away air and bring in fresh air, people would not be able to live in many major cities. Figure 10-7 (right) shows what happens when harmful gases and particles build up in the air faster than they can be removed.

REVIEW

1. How can water, soil, and air be renewed?
2. Make a diagram of the water cycle, labeling its parts.
3. What are two methods that can prevent soil from being blown away or washed away.

CHALLENGE An average of 10 metric tons of soil per acre of farmland in the United States is lost each year due to soil erosion. New soil forms at the rate of about 1.5 metric tons per acre each year. How many years would it take for new soil to replace the soil lost on one acre in one year because of soil erosion?

10-3 NONRENEWABLE RESOURCES

Imagine saving your money for a lifetime and then spending it in a few seconds. Could you replace that money? Just as money can be spent faster than it can be replaced, so, too, some of our valuable resources can be—and are being—used up faster than they can be replaced.

A **nonrenewable resource** is a natural resource that cannot be replaced. One type of nonrenewable resource that must be used carefully is our mineral resources. Mineral resources take millions of years to form. In addition, many mineral resources, including metals, are found in the earth's crust in very small amounts. Once they have been used up, new sources will not likely be found.

Some mineral resources contain materials that are useful to humans. For example, minerals that contain such metals as copper, aluminum, and iron are useful. Copper is used in wire, aluminum is used in building materials, and iron is used in steel. Some minerals contain useful nonmetals, such as phosphates and sulfur. Phosphates are used in fertilizers and sulfur is used in medicines.

Some rocks contain larger amounts of a mineral than are ordinarily found. Rocks that contain an unusually large amount of a mineral are called **mineral deposits**. A mineral deposit that contains enough of a mineral so that the mineral can be mined at a profit is called an **ore**. The value of the mineral largely determines whether or not a mineral deposit is an ore. For example, a mineral deposit would have to contain about 5 kg of copper per metric ton of rock to be an ore. However, a metric ton of rock would only have to contain about .0021 kg of gold to be an ore.

Metals make up only a very small part of the earth's crust. For example, copper makes up only 0.0058 percent, silver makes up only 0.000008 percent, and gold makes up only 0.0000002 percent of the crust. If metals were evenly spread throughout the crust, they could not be recovered economically. However, certain processes occur that cause metals to become concentrated enough in the crust to become ores.

In one process, ores form from minerals dissolved in hot water. The hot water may come from ground water heated by magma, or it may come from the magma itself. As the hot water moves upward toward the earth's surface, the hot water dissolves and carries along minerals in surrounding rock. If the hot water enters openings or cracks in cooler rocks, the minerals settle out of the water, filling in the openings or cracks, and forming mineral deposits.

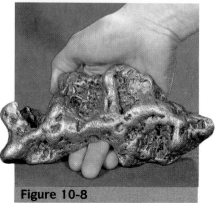

Figure 10-8

A gold vein (*top*). A gold nugget is practically pure gold (*bottom*).

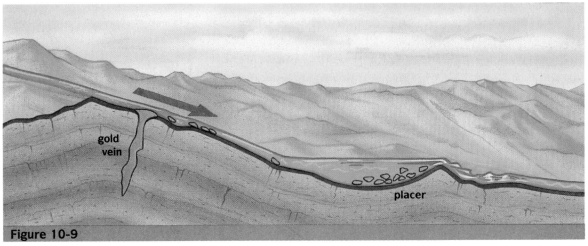

Figure 10-9

When a vein of gold is exposed to weather conditions, some of the gold will wash downstream. A deposit of such gold is called a placer.

A deposit of minerals that has formed in openings or cracks in rocks is called a *vein*. Copper, silver, and gold minerals can be found in veins.

Another process that forms ores occurs as magma cools. Within the cooling magma, some minerals may separate and settle to the bottom. The minerals form an ore that is part of a large body of igneous rock. The ores of chromium and nickel are usually formed in this way.

The metals in metallic ores can be separated from the rock material by the action of wind and water and by changes in temperature. Under these conditions, the ores are broken down into smaller pieces. The pieces may be picked up by moving water or wind. In places where the water or wind slow down, the heavier pieces, which usually include the metals, are deposited. Water or wind deposits that contain valuable metals are called *placers* (PLAYS-uhrz). Most placers are formed in water. They are usually mixtures of gravel and pebbles, with tiny pieces of metal. Gold is often found in a placer. Look at Figure 10-9. Why is the placer found downstream of the vein?

REVIEW

1. What is an ore?
2. Describe two ways in which ores can be formed.
3. How do metals become naturally separated from ores?

CHALLENGE Gold nuggets found in placers in streams near veins are sometimes angular in shape and have rough surfaces. Gold nuggets found in placers farther downstream are rounded in shape and have smooth surfaces. How do you explain this?

10-4 ENERGY RESOURCES

After completing this section, you will be able to

- **define** the term *fossil fuel.*
- **name** three fossil fuels and tell from what materials each forms.
- **describe** the four stages of coal formation.
- **list** four possible alternative sources to petroleum and natural gas.

The key terms in this section are

biomass	fossil fuels
energy	natural gas
coal	petroleum

About 94 percent of the energy used in the world today comes from fossil fuels. **Fossil fuels** are fuels that form from the remains of plants and animals. The fossil fuels are petroleum, natural gas, and coal. They form over millions of years, but once they are used, they cannot be replaced.

PETROLEUM

Petroleum is a mixture of many liquid hydrocarbons. Hydrocarbons are compounds made up of the elements hydrogen and carbon. Petroleum is also called crude oil. About 45 percent of the energy used in the world comes from petroleum. The main use of petroleum is for fuel, such as gasoline and heating oil.

Petroleum forms from the remains of sea life buried by sediments of mud on the ocean bottom. The remains decay over millions of years into the liquid hydrocarbons that form petroleum. As other sediments are deposited on top of the mud, petroleum and water are squeezed out of the mud by the weight of the sediments. The petroleum may enter porous rocks, or rocks that have many tiny open spaces. Sandstone and limestone usually have openings that the petroleum and water can pass through. Eventually, the petroleum and water are stopped by layers of impermeable rock, or rock that does not allow liquids to pass through.

Petroleum must be separated into different substances before it can be used. As shown in Figure 10-11, what are the substances petroleum is separated into?

oil rig
impermeable rock
natural gas
water
oil
permeable rock

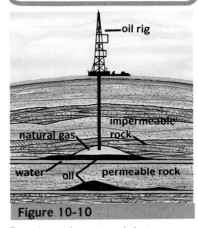

Figure 10-10

Petroleum is trapped between layers of impermeable rock.

propane, butane, ethane
gasoline
kerosene, light gas oil
lubricating oil, fuel oil, grease, waxes
coke, asphalt
crude oil
petroleum refinery

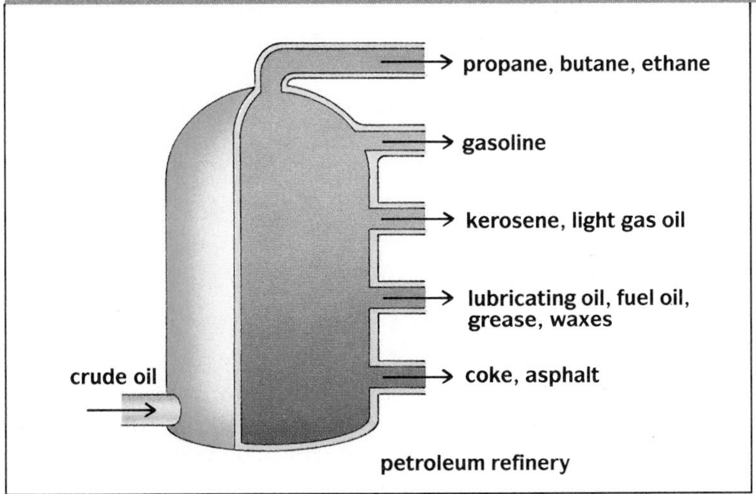

Figure 10-11

Some of the products of petroleum refining.

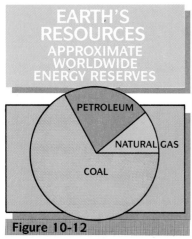

EARTH'S RESOURCES
APPROXIMATE WORLDWIDE ENERGY RESERVES

Figure 10-12

Approximate worldwide energy reserves.

NATURAL GAS

A fossil fuel that is commonly found with petroleum is natural gas. **Natural gas** is made up mostly of methane, a gaseous hydrocarbon. When found with petroleum, natural gas is trapped between the petroleum and a layer of impermeable rock. Natural gas can also be found in porous rock by itself. The processes that form petroleum are the same as the processes that form natural gas. Natural gas forms over millions of years from the remains of sea life. Natural gas is a nonrenewable energy source.

COAL

According to Figure 10-12, about how much of the world's reserves of fossil fuels is coal? **Coal** forms from the remains of plants. The plants lived in forests and swamps millions of years ago. When the plants died, their remains may have become buried by water and mud. The remains decayed under the water and mud for millions of years, forming coal.

As shown in Figure 10-13, there are four stages in the formation of coal. The first stage is the formation of peat. *Peat* is plant material that is buried and changed slightly. It is brownish in color and looks like rotted wood.

Peat buried under the weight of mud and water changes to lignite (LIHG nīt) during the second stage. *Lignite* is a form of coal that is brownish-black, soft, and gives off a lot of smoke when it burns.

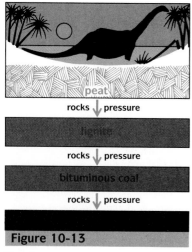

Figure 10-13

The formation of coal (*above*), peat (*top left*), lignite (*top right*), bituminous coal (*bottom left*), and anthracite coal (*bottom right*).

Under pressure, lignite changes into *bituminous* (bī-TOO mih nuhs) *coal* in the third stage. Bituminous coal burns with a smoky flame and is harder and darker in color than lignite. It is also the most abundant form of coal.

If there is more pressure on bituminous coal, a type of coal called *anthracite* (AN thruh sīt) will form. Anthracite is harder than lignite and black in color. It burns without much smoke.

Coal is found in layers called *seams*. It can be removed from the land by two methods: strip mining and underground mining. In *strip mining,* shown in Figure 10-14, the land surface above a coal seam is removed. In underground mining, a tunnel is dug to reach the coal seam. One factor in deciding which method to use is the depth of the coal seam. If the coal seam is deep, too much rock may have to be removed to use strip mining.

Figure 10-14

Underground mining is dangerous and unhealthful to the miners. Strip mining, shown here, is a safer, less expensive way to mine coal, but restoring the damaged surface is costly.

Mining coal can cause damage to the land and harmful effects to health. Removing the land surface during strip mining removes vegetation. Without vegetation, surface water quickly erodes the land. Strip mining also removes the topsoil, which plants need to grow in. Laws have been passed that require companies to restore the land surface after this mining operation.

Underground mining of coal does not damage the land surface. However, it can be dangerous to the health of the miners. Two dangers are mine explosions and mine collapses. In addition, the air in underground coal mines may be filled with coal particles. Health problems can be caused by breathing this air.

Figure 10-15

Tar sand (*top*) and oil shale (*bottom*).

FUTURE SOURCES OF OIL AND GAS

At the present rate of use, the supplies of petroleum and natural gas will be used up in the twenty-first century. The supply of coal should last longer, into the twenty-second century. But using coal has some serious health and environmental problems. New ways of producing more petroleum and natural gas will be needed to meet the world's energy needs.

One potential main source of petroleum is oil shale. *Oil shale* is rock that contains dark organic matter. Oil shale can be heated to remove a liquid similar to petroleum. However, producing oil from rock is expensive. In addition, mining oil shale would damage the land, because large amounts of rock must be removed.

Another potential main source of petroleum is *tar sands*. Tar sands are deposits of sand coated with tar. Tar is a thick liquid that comes from petroleum that passed upward from porous rock underground. One reason tar sands have not been used as a source of petroleum is cost. Also, tar is very thick and difficult to remove from sand.

Since 1900, fuel has been produced from plants. Energy from plant material is called **biomass energy**. For example, corn is one kind of plant material that can be used to produce alcohol. In some areas today, alcohol is being added to gasoline to produce *gasohol*. One problem with making alcohol from plant material is that this process uses more energy than can be produced from alcohol. In addition, growing crops to produce alcohol uses up land that could be used for growing food.

The large supply of coal can be used to produce fuel in a process called coal gasification. In *coal gasification,* coal is heated to produce cleaner burning oil and gas. The oil can be converted to gasoline, heating oil, or diesel fuel. The gas can be converted into methane, which can be burned.

REVIEW

1. What is fossil fuel?
2. What are three fossil fuels? From what materials did each form?
3. Describe the four stages of coal formation.
4. What are the problems with mining coal?
5. Give four potential sources of petroleum and natural gas.

CHALLENGE The United States contains about 6 percent of the world's population but uses about 33 percent of the world's energy. How do you explain this?

10-5 OTHER ENERGY RESOURCES

Less than 200 years ago, most people in the United States lived on farms. People used wood to heat homes and cook food. Most people traveled only as far as they could walk. How is life different today?

One way the United States has changed in the last 200 years is in the amount of energy it consumes. In addition to heating homes and cooking food, energy is now needed to run cars, lights, and electrical appliances. Almost all this energy comes from fossil fuels, which cannot be replaced. However, there are energy sources that are abundant and will never run out.

Energy from the sun is called **solar energy**. Solar energy can be used to heat homes and to make electricity. One way of heating a home with solar energy is to build a house with windows facing the sun to let sunlight into the house. Heating a house with solar energy without the use of pumps, fans, or any other mechanical devices is called *passive solar heating*.

Another way solar energy can be used in a home is to use a solar collector to absorb the sun's energy. A solar collector is usually a glass-covered box that contains metal pipes. Look at Figure 10-16. Where is the solar collector placed on the house? A pump can be used to circulate water or air throughout the house. Using solar energy with the help of pumps, fans, or any mechanical devices to circulate the heat is called *active solar heating*.

sol (the sun)

passive solar heating

Figure 10-16

Passive solar heating using the sun's energy to heat a house *(left)*. A house with an active solar heating system *(right)*.

A third way solar energy can be used is by turning sunlight into electricity. Sunlight can be changed into electricity with the use of solar cells. *Solar cells,* shown in Figure 10-17, are made mostly of silicon. Solar cells are very expensive and are used on spacecraft.

Solar energy is a renewable energy source. Solar energy can never be used up. In addition, it does not add harmful substances to the environment. The amount of solar energy that reaches the earth's surface, however, is not constant. It can vary from day to day, depending on the weather.

Another renewable energy source is geothermal energy. **Geothermal energy** is energy that comes from heat produced within the earth's interior. The heat may come from magma, or molten rock in the crust, which can heat ground water. The hot water and steam produced when ground water is heated can be used to heat houses and other buildings. The steam can also be used to run generators to produce electricity.

Moving water on the earth's surface can be used as a renewable source of energy. Electrical energy that is produced from water flowing downward is called **hydroelectric energy**. For example, water flowing downward at a dam can be used to run generators to produce electricity. After the water runs the generator, it eventually flows to the sea. There it is evaporated by the sun and may return to the flowing water as rain. What renewable energy source is the ultimate source of hydroelectric energy?

Figure 10-17

Photovoltaic cells turn solar energy into electricity.

geo- (earth)
therme (heat)
hydro- (water)

Figure 10-18

A hydroelectric power plant utilizes a fast-moving river to turn turbines to generate electricity.

234

Figure 10-19

Windmills need a constant flow of strong wind to generate power.

Tidal energy is energy produced by the rise and fall of water due to the tides. A dam is used to trap water at high tide. Water is released at low tide. The running water is used to run generators to produce electricity.

Energy produced by the wind is called **wind energy**. Wind can be used to move the blades of a windmill. Some windmills run generators to produce electricity. Windmills work best on the tops of mountains, along seacoasts, and on open plains.

ACTIVITY   Making a Solar Collector

OBJECTIVE
Determine how color affects the efficiency of a solar collector.

MATERIALS
sheet of aluminum foil, 3 small plastic trash bags of equal size and thickness (1 each of black, white, green), water, tape, 3 thermometers, 3 twist ties

PROCEDURE
A. Place a sheet of foil, shiny side up, on the ground outside in the sun.
B. Make a tiny hole in each of three plastic bags and insert a thermometer in each hole. Tape around the holes so that the bags will not leak. Do not tape the thermometer to the bag.
C. Fill each bag with 2 L of water. Squeeze the air out. Using a twist tie, tie each bag closed.
D. Record the temperature of each bag. Then place the bags on the aluminum foil.
E. After about 15 minutes, record the temperature of each bag again.

RESULTS AND CONCLUSIONS
1. What was the temperature of each bag before and after heating?
2. Were there differences in the temperatures of the three bags? Explain your answer.
3. Which color trash bag was the best solar collector? Explain.
4. Which color bag was the poorest solar collector? Explain.
5. Predict what might have happened to the temperatures if the bags were placed directly on the ground, not on aluminum foil.

Figure 10-20

Nuclear power plants supply some of the world's energy.

Nuclear energy is energy produced from changes in the nucleus, or center of the atom. Energy from the nucleus of the atom is produced when the nucleus splits into two or more smaller nuclei in the process called *fission*. The atoms used in the fission process come from the element uranium. A piece of uranium the size of the end of your thumb can produce as much heat as 1 metric ton of coal.

Scientists can control fission reactions in a nuclear power plant. The tall structures, shown in Figure 10-20, are the cooling towers of a nuclear plant.

The waste produced by nuclear power plants is radioactive and dangerous. The waste will release radiation for hundreds or thousands of years. Some of this waste has been dumped into the oceans or stored in underground salt mines. People are questioning whether these places are good disposal sites.

Nuclear energy may also be generated by fusion. *Fusion* is the combining of the nuclei of atoms to form other nuclei. A large amount of heat energy is released when nuclei join. The heat energy can be used to run generators. However, temperatures in the millions of degrees are required for fusion reactions to take place. It is difficult to control reactions that produce such heat.

Conservation can be thought of as a type of energy resource, because it can make our present energy resources last longer. **Conservation** is a method of saving resources

OBJECTIVE

Demonstrate fission, using a model.

MATERIALS

small glass container, 100 mL rubbing alcohol, water, metal teaspoon, paper towels, 10 mL cooking oil, metal butter knife

PROCEDURE

A. Fill a small glass container about half full with rubbing alcohol. Add enough water to fill the glass two thirds full. Stir the liquid mixture with a metal teaspoon.

B. Wipe the spoon dry and fill it with 10 mL of cooking oil. Carefully lower the spoon to the surface of the liquid in the glass. Gently tip the spoon. A single blob of oil should be floating in the middle of the liquid. (If the oil is on the surface, add a spoonful of alcohol. If the oil sank, add a spoonful of water.)

  1. Sketch the shape of the oil drop.

C. Use a knife to break the drop in half.

  2. Sketch the shapes of the oil drops after splitting.

  3. Compare the shapes of the oil drops before and after splitting.

RESULTS AND CONCLUSION

1. Is energy needed to split an oil drop?

2. This demonstration took place in a glass container. Where does a controlled nuclear reaction occur?

3. Compare splitting a uranium nucleus with splitting an oil drop.

---

by controlling how they are used. One way of conserving is by using less. By using less energy, the short supply of oil and coal would be extended. This would also provide the much needed time to develop other energy sources, such as fusion.

Another way of conserving energy is by recycling many of the materials we use. **Recycling** is a process in which wastes are reused or changed into reusable products. For example, it takes much less energy to recycle paper than to make new paper. Making new paper requires energy to cut down trees, energy to transport them to a factory, and energy to run the machines in the factory.

Recycling also saves natural resources. For example, recycling a metric ton of waste paper would save about 17 trees. The recycling of natural resources that are in short supply, such as some mineral resources, may be the only way to extend the supply.

REVIEW

1. What are two ways solar energy can be used in homes?
2. What is the difference between fission and fusion?
3. How can energy from heat in the earth's crust be used?
4. How is electricity produced from water and wind?
5. What are two ways of conserving energy?

CHALLENGE Solar collectors on roofs are positioned to face the sun. However, the sun moves during the day, and its path across the sky is higher in the summer than in the winter. What would be the best direction for the solar collector to face?

Figure 10-21

Recycling metal has become a profitable business.

10-6 POLLUTION

On a damp morning in southern California, a fog moved in from the Pacific Ocean. When the fog mixed with the air, a special type of fog formed. Some people in the area covered by the fog complained that they had trouble breathing. When the fog had disappeared, drops of almost pure acid were left behind.

The type of fog that formed in southern California is called an *acid fog.* It forms when harmful substances given off by the burning of coal, gasoline, and oil mix with the water droplets in a fog. The adding of harmful substances to the environment is called **pollution.** Today, harmful substances are affecting our most valuable resources—land, water, and air.

LAND POLLUTION

The adding of harmful substances to the land is called *land pollution.* One way in which land can be polluted is by the use of chemicals in agriculture, such as pesticides

SCIENCE & TECHNOLOGY

Japan is reusing garbage in a new way—by building on it. Tokyo, Japan's capital city, stretches across Tokyo Bay on 18 artificial islands. These islands reach about 3 km out from the shoreline into the open bay, adding several thousand hectares to the city. The islands are being built to help solve Japan's population problem. Though slightly smaller than California, Japan has half the population of the whole United States. The country is very hilly, with few flat areas on which to build.

City planners in Tokyo say that some of the garbage islands could be filled in with sand and rubble to make them more solid. Power plants and other industrial facilities, which now take up valuable flat space inland, could be built on these islands. Some of the islands will be used for parks.

The Japanese do have problems to overcome before the idea works. Garbage, for example, is not very firm. Even if packed with sand, it will not stand up to intensive city development. The islands are also increasing water pollution. Building them has blocked the natural flow of tides, which helps cleanse the water in Tokyo Bay.

With careful planning, though, these problems are being solved. Japan is making progress in creating land for its growing population.

(PEHS tuh sīdz). Pesticides are used to kill insects and small animals that are harmful to crops. Chemicals that are used on or pollute the land can seep into the ground with rain and contaminate ground water. More than half of the population of the United States uses ground water from wells for drinking water. A pesticide called *ethylene dibromide,* or *EDB,* has been found in well water in Florida. EDB may cause cancer in humans.

Another way in which land can be polluted is by the disposal of chemical wastes on land. Chemical wastes are mostly produced by the chemical, petroleum, and metals industries. The most harmful chemical wastes are toxic wastes. *Toxic wastes* are wastes that are very poisonous. Some toxic wastes, such as *dioxin* (dī AHK suhn), are also believed to cause cancer and birth defects in humans.

Chemical wastes placed in open ponds or buried in containers can leak out and contaminate soil. As you can see in Figure 10-22, the chemicals can be carried into ground water from the soil by rain. How does this affect drinking water from wells?

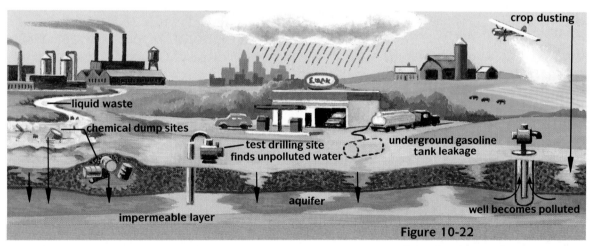

Figure 10-22

Ground water can become contaminated in various ways.

WATER POLLUTION

Chemicals in the soil can also be washed into rivers by surface runoff from rain. The adding of harmful substances to water is called *water pollution.* Some factories have dumped chemicals directly into bodies of water. For example, one factory had dumped chemicals called *polychlorinated biphenyls,* or *PCBs,* into the Hudson River in New York for 20 years. When PCBs were found in fish caught in the river and in people who ate fish from the river, the dumping of PCBs into water was banned. PCBs have been found to cause cancer in laboratory animals.

Figure 10-23

Oil spills pollute water and kill wildlife.

Water can be polluted when untreated sewage is dumped into water. Untreated, or raw, sewage contains germs that can cause disease. Oxygen in the water can break down many of these wastes into harmless substances. However, if too much sewage is added, there will not be enough oxygen for the water to purify itself.

Some chemicals added to water are nutrients. Nutrients are chemicals that help plant life grow. When nutrients are added to water containing plant life, the plant life grows rapidly. The plant life uses up the oxygen in the water, causing fish to die. In addition, without oxygen, wastes cannot be broken down.

Sewage can be treated before being put into water. In a process called *water treatment*, solid wastes are first removed from raw sewage. Then germs are killed and oxygen is added to the sewage before being released into water.

Some power plants use water from lakes or rivers for cooling. For example, nuclear power plants produce great amounts of waste heat. They take water from lakes or rivers to remove the heat. When the water is returned, it is warmer than when it was removed. The addition of heat to the environment is called *thermal pollution*. Adding heat to lakes or rivers can kill fish, because the warmer water that results holds less oxygen than cooler water.

SCIENCE PUZZLER

The concentration of pollutants is often greater in the organisms of ponds than in the water itself. Furthermore, the concentration in small, plant-eating fish is less than that found in large, carnivorous fish. Birds, such as egrets, that feed on fish in the ponds also have high concentrations of the pollutants in their bodies. Explain what is happening in such situations.

AIR POLLUTION

Air pollution is the adding of harmful substances to the air. One harmful substance that is added to air is sulfur dioxide. Sulfur dioxide is a gas that is produced when oil or coal is burned. The sulfur dioxide can be dissolved by rain, forming **acid rain**. Acid rain destroys the leaves on trees and plants. It can also destroy fish and plants in lakes by making the water too acidic for life.

Gases given off by automobiles can form a type of air pollution called smog. **Smog** forms when certain gases given off by automobiles react in the presence of sunlight. As you can see in Figure 10-24, smog looks like a heavy fog. It is made up of solid particles and gases. Smog can cause throat irritation, coughing, and breathing problems.

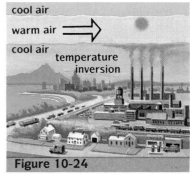

cool air

warm air

cool air   temperature inversion

Figure 10-24

A blanket of smog prevents air pollutants from leaving the air (*left*). A temperature inversion (*right*).

ACTIVITY   Air Pollution Detectors

OBJECTIVES
Build air pollution detectors.
Collect data on air pollution in your area.

MATERIALS
three 10 cm × 10 cm cardboard pieces, 12 thumbtacks, three 9 cm × 9 cm wax paper sheets, paper towels, jar of petroleum jelly, hand lens or microscope

PROCEDURE

A. To make each air pollution detector, use four thumbtacks to attach a piece of wax paper to each cardboard square. Then spread a thin, even layer of petroleum jelly on the wax paper of each of the three squares. The squares will be your pollution detectors.

B. Place the pollution detectors in three different places in your community.
C. Collect them in 7 days. Examine each detector with a hand lens.

RESULTS AND CONCLUSIONS
1. Make a data table like the one shown that summarizes your results. It should include the locations of the detectors, the dates they were in place, the types of particles found, a sketch of each pollutant, and a possible source of each pollutant.
2. Which of the pollutants might be from the activities of people?
3. Compare your results with your classmates' results. Which particles were similar? Which particles were different?

Location of Detector	Date	Description of Particles	Sketch	Possible Source

Harmful substances that are added to air are normally blown away by wind. However, if the air is not moved out and replaced by fresh air, the air will become more and more polluted. This can happen when a layer of cool air becomes trapped below a layer of warm air. This may occur in areas near the oceans. Cool air over the ocean may blow toward land and push under warm air above the land. Since cool air is heavier than warm air, the cool air remains near the ground. The warm air acts like a lid, preventing any cool air from escaping. When a layer of cool air becomes trapped below a layer of warm air, it is called a *temperature inversion*. Any smoke or other gases that are produced also remain trapped below the layer of warm air. Smog can become trapped for many days during a temperature inversion.

REVIEW

1. What is pollution?
2. Give at least two ways in which each resource can be polluted: land, water, and air.
3. Explain the effect of adding nutrients to water.
4. How can a temperature inversion be harmful?

CHALLENGE   Explain the meaning of the saying, "The solution to pollution is dilution." What is your reaction to this solution?

CHAPTER SUMMARY

The main ideas in this chapter are listed below. Read these statements before you answer the Chapter Review questions.

- As the human population increases, greater demands are placed on the earth's natural resources. (10-1)

- Renewable resources are natural resources that can be renewed or replaced. Water, soil, and air are examples of resources that can be renewed. (10-2)

- Nonrenewable resources are natural resources that cannot be replaced once they have been used. (10-3)

- Almost all of the energy used today comes from fossil fuels. Oil, gas, and coal are examples of fossil fuels. (10-4)

- Renewable energy resources will have to be used as the supply of fossil fuels runs out. Solar energy, nuclear energy, wind energy, geothermal energy, and tidal energy could be used in the future. (10-5)

- Conservation can save energy and natural resources. (10-5)

- Some of the most serious problems today involve the pollution of land, air, and water. (10-6)

The key terms in this chapter are listed below. Use each term in a sentence that shows the meaning of the term.

acid rain	mineral deposits	pollution
biomass energy	natural gas	recycling
coal	natural resource	renewable resource
conservation	nonrenewable resource	smog
fossil fuels	nuclear energy	solar energy
geothermal energy	ore	tidal energy
hydroelectric energy	petroleum	wind energy

Chapter Review

VOCABULARY

Write the letter of the term that best matches the definition. Not all terms will be used.

1. Any material that can be used from the earth
2. Any fuels that form from the remains of plants and animals
3. Fuel that forms from the remains of plants buried in swamps
4. Fuel made mostly of methane
5. Energy from the sun
6. Fuel made of liquid hydrocarbons
7. Energy from the heat in the earth
8. Energy from the nucleus of the atom
9. Electrical energy from flowing water
10. Rocks that contain an unusually large amount of a mineral

a. biomass energy
b. coal
c. fossil fuels
d. geothermal energy
e. hydroelectric energy
f. mineral deposits
g. natural gas
h. natural resource
i. nuclear energy
j. petroleum
k. solar energy

CONCEPTS

1. Why is the earth considered to be our environment? (10-1)
2. How does the increase in world population affect the supply of natural resources? (10-1)
3. Describe several ways in which natural resources are used. (10-1)
4. Give an example of a renewable resource and a nonrenewable resource. Explain how they are different. (10-1)
5. Why are water, soil, and air called renewable resources? (10-2)
6. Explain how the water cycle purifies water. (10-2)
7. How could farmers have prevented the soil from being blown off in the "dust bowl" region in 1934? (10-2)
8. Why aren't all mineral deposits considered to be ores? (10-3)
9. What are two ways in which ores are found? (10-3)
10. Compare gold found in placers to gold found in veins. (10-3)
11. Why are petroleum, natural gas, and coal called fossil fuels? (10-4)
12. Compare the way petroleum and natural gas form with the way coal forms. (10-4)
13. Compare and contrast peat, lignite, bituminous coal, and anthracite. (10-4)

14. Describe problems with several potential main sources of petroleum and natural gas. (10-4)

15. Compare and contrast active solar heating with passive solar heating. (10-5)

16. Why can't fusion be used to produce energy in nuclear power plants? (10-5)

17. What are two benefits of conserving energy? (10-5)

18. Give examples of substances that pollute the environment. (10-5)

19. How can land pollution cause water pollution? (10-5)

20. Explain how a temperature inversion forms. How does this explain why some cities have more serious air pollution problems than others? (10-5)

APPLICATION/ CRITICAL THINKING

1. Explain why fossil fuels are an indirect source of solar energy.

2. What are the benefits of recycling aluminum cans?

3. Humans have increased the amount of carbon dioxide in the atmosphere by using fossil fuels. Carbon dioxide traps the sun's heat. What effects does this have on the earth's climate?

4. A drop of water in the water cycle may remain in the ocean for 3000 years and up to 10,000 years in deep ground water. Does this mean the water cycle is not balanced? Explain your answer.

EXTENSION

1. Collect the trash that you would ordinarily throw away in one day. Ask your teacher for permission to bring it into class and weigh it. Record the weight and dispose of the trash properly. Then multiply the weight by 365 to obtain the weight of trash you might throw away in one year.

2. Compare how far you can coast on a bicycle with the tires inflated to the recommended pressure with how far you can coast with the tires at one half the recommended pressure. How would driving a car with underinflated tires affect gas mileage?

3. Design an experiment to show the heat loss in an insulated cup, such as a styrofoam cup, as compared with heat loss in an uninsulated cup. What would be the effect of insulating a house?

READINGS

Boraiko, Allen A. "Hazardous Waste." *National Geographic,* March 1985, p. 318.

St. John, Jeffrey. *Noble Metals.* Alexandria, Va.: Time-Life Books, Inc., 1984.

"Energy." *National Geographic.* February 1981.

Oil, gas, valuable minerals, and other natural resources are always being sought. You have learned that many minerals are found as ores. Suppose an important mineral deposit is found in the ground. A mining company will want to know how much of the deposit is in the ground. They will also want to know what form the mineral is in.

Minerologists can answer such questions. These experts know the different forms of minerals and where they are usually found. Minerologists take samples from mineral deposits. In laboratories, they use chemical and physical tests to analyze the samples.

Minerologists work for private industry and for the government. They must have at least a four-year college degree, and they often go on to receive advanced degrees. If you are interested in minerology, you should take courses in earth science, chemistry, physical science, and math. ■

MINEROLOGIST

SOLAR EQUIPMENT TECHNICIAN

The use of solar energy systems is growing. People who build, repair, and service these systems are called solar energy technicians. They usually travel to places where solar energy systems are being used. Much of their work is outdoors.

A solar energy technician may install piping for a solar collector or solar heater on a roof. He or she usually works for a private company.

The job requires ability to work with your hands, a diploma from a high school, trade school, or two-year college, and on-the-job training. If you are interested in being a solar technician, you will benefit by taking courses in shop, mechanical drawing, and meteorology. ■

People in Science

DR. J. TUZO WILSON, GEOPHYSICIST

Ideas are very important in science. Many scientists make contributions by building on old ideas.

Dr. J. Tuzo Wilson is a Canadian geophysicist who has made important contributions to geology. He did this by adapting Wegener's theory of continental drift to modern geology.

At a time when many scientists did not believe the old theory was useful, Dr. Wilson and others adapted it to form the modern theory of plate tectonics.

Dr. Wilson used the new theory to explain why many active volcanoes are found at the boundaries between plates. He pointed to the Hawaiian island chain as evidence for hot spots. Hot spots are places deep in the earth's mantle where magma rises and melts holes through the earth's plates. He also discovered the transform fault. And thanks to his imagination, we now know that part of Florida was once attached to Africa, and part of New England was attached to Europe. ■

Issues and Technology

The energy needs of the United States are growing. Unfortunately, the resources that now produce most of the nation's energy—oil, natural gas, and coal—are not.

The energy resources that the United States depends on are mostly nonrenewable. That means that only certain amounts of these substances exist in the earth's crust. When these supplies are used up, there will be no more. That is the case with fossil fuels—oil, natural gas, and coal.

The United States has some reserves of crude oil. However, the United States uses much more oil than it produces. Therefore the United States must import much of its oil from other countries. Figure 1 shows world crude oil reserves. Notice that North America does not have nearly as much crude oil reserves as some other countries.

Recognizing that reserves of fossil fuels have been decreasing, government and private industry have been searching for new sources of energy.

Some of the research on developing new energy sources has concentrated on renewable energy sources. Renewable energy sources will not run out. They include the sun, the wind, the earth's heat, and the sea. These sources may not pollute the environment.

Some research has also concentrated on the development of nonrenewable sources. For example, oil shale and tar sands are plentiful and could be used to produce energy. But they have been almost totally overlooked until recently.

Figure 2 shows sources of the world's energy in 1980 and projected figures for the year 2000. The sizes of the wedges indicate the relative amounts of energy obtained from the various sources.

APPLYING CRITICAL THINKING SKILLS

1. Is shale oil represented as an energy source in 1980? Is it represented in estimates for 2000? What conclusions can you draw from this information?
2. Could the estimates for the sources of energy for the year 2000 change? Explain your answer.
3. From which energy sources did most of the world's energy in 1980 come—renewable or nonrenewable? How is this expected to change in the year 2000? What conclusions can you draw from this?
4. Just one energy source will provide less of the world's energy needs in 2000 than it does now. Which energy source is this? Why, do you think, will this be so?

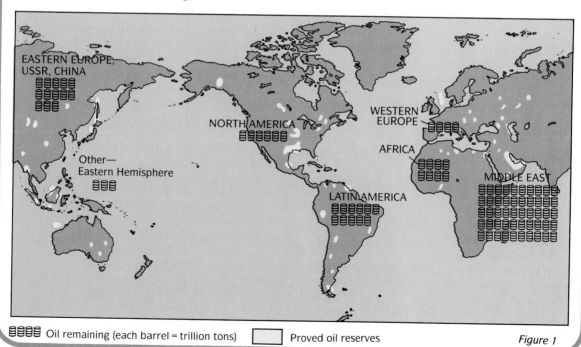

EASTERN EUROPE, USSR, CHINA

Other— Eastern Hemisphere

NORTH AMERICA

LATIN AMERICA

WESTERN EUROPE

AFRICA

MIDDLE EAST

🛢🛢🛢🛢 Oil remaining (each barrel = trillion tons)　　　☐ Proved oil reserves　　　*Figure 1*

247

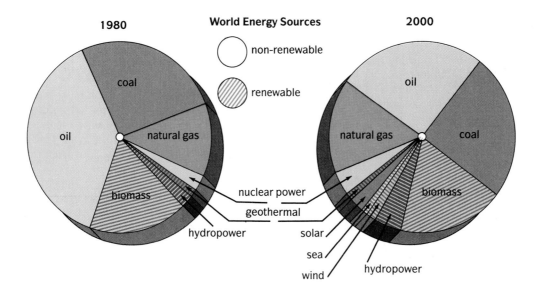

Figure 2

5. Three sources of energy that were not important in 1980 are expected to be important in 2000. Which energy sources are these?

6. Which renewable resource was the most widely used in 1980? Which renewable resource was the second most important?

7. The estimates for 2000 show that renewable energy sources, such as hydro-electric power, solar energy, energy from the sea, thermal energy, and wind energy, will still make up less than 25 percent of the total. Why, do you think, will this be so? Does this seem like a good thing? Why or why not?

Oil shale is the popular name for a layered rock called laminated marlstone. This rock contains a rubbery material called kerogen. Using oil shale as an energy resource depends on removing the kerogen from the rock.

First the oil shale must be removed from the ground and broken into pieces. Then the oil shale is heated to about 500°C. The oil turns into vapor as it separates from the rock. The vapor is drawn off and cooled. It then becomes a thick liquid that can be refined and used like crude oil.

Geologists estimate that there is more oil shale under the hills of the western United States than there is crude oil under all of the deserts of the Middle East.

Oil from shale could keep the United States supplied with an additional energy resource for many years to come. It is also an oil supply that cannot be cut off by a foreign government.

So why isn't oil shale providing a large part of America's energy needs? The answer is that there are drawbacks to using oil shale. It takes three barrels of water to recover one barrel of oil from shale. This could present a problem for the dry areas of our West, where most of the oil shale deposits are found.

There is also the problem of what to do with the rock that is left over after the oil has been removed. Oil shale expands and breaks up when it is heated. That means there is a greater volume of rock after processing than when the shale is removed from the ground. So the rock can't simply be put back into the same hole it was taken out of. Some other place must be found for it.

The volume of rock to be disposed of is not the only problem. Shale oil contains a number of poisonous and carcinogenic, or cancer-causing, substances. These are released during the retorting process. The substances can be removed from the finished oil. But they remain in the water used in processing the shale. They also remain in the rock from which the oil was extracted. Many cases of skin cancer have been reported over the years in people coming into contact with shale oil and its by-products. Piles of waste shale rock that build up could leak these poisons into the soil. The ground water in areas where oil-shale mining and retorting are done could become contaminated.

Aside from causing environmental problems, it is also costly to obtain oil shale. As long as there is cheaper crude oil, why should anyone pay more for oil shale? The price of conventional oil would have to rise enough to make the price of oil from shale competitive.

There is a process for extracting oil from shale that avoids some of the environmental problems. In this process, the shale is not removed from the ground. Controlled burning of the oil shale is done while it is in the ground. Then the oil is pumped out. This process is cheaper than removing the shale and breaking it up. But it doesn't eliminate all environmental concerns.

The question remains, is it wise to produce oil from shale? Should industry be working on ways to extract oil from shale safely now, while there is still time? Will waiting until the next oil crisis be a mistake? And can the United States afford to let such a large energy source remain unused?

If we use shale, what about the environmental problems? Is oil shale too costly and risky to be widely used? Do we have any better energy alternatives?

As the demand for energy rises, these are questions that will need to be answered.

Figure 3 shows the locations of most American oil shale and crude oil reserves. It also shows, in pictograph form, the amount of oil shale and crude oil estimated to be left in these places.

APPLYING CRITICAL THINKING SKILLS

1. Is there more oil shale or more regular crude oil left in the ground?
2. How many barrels of shale oil are in the ground?
3. How many barrels of crude oil are left in the ground?
4. If the United States today uses nearly 6 billion barrels of oil each year, how many years of crude oil are left in the United States reserves?
5. How many extra years of oil could the United States have, at the present rate of consumption, by using oil shale?
6. Right now the United States does not use its oil shale reserves. Why?
7. What could cause the United States to begin developing oil shale as an energy resource?
8. In what part of the United States are most oil-shale deposits located? Is this a problem? Why or why not?
9. Many of America's national parks and wilderness areas are located in areas where oil shale is found. How could this cause a problem?
10. What alternatives can you offer to using oil shale as an energy resource?
11. Should the United States plan to use oil shale as an energy source? Explain your answer.

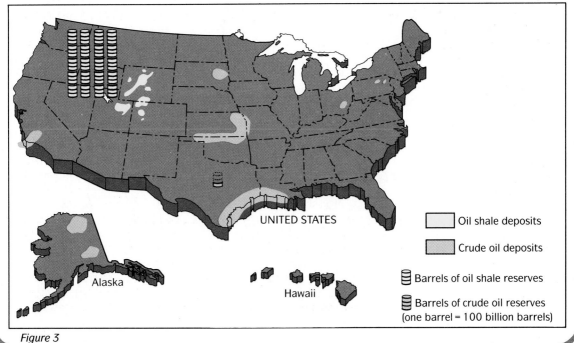

UNITED STATES

☐ Oil shale deposits

☐ Crude oil deposits

🛢 Barrels of oil shale reserves

🛢 Barrels of crude oil reserves
(one barrel = 100 billion barrels)

Alaska

Hawaii

Figure 3

THE CHANGING EARTH

The earth is often thought of as solid and unchanging. Yet, in a matter of minutes, an earthquake, volcano, avalanche, or mudslide can alter the landscape. Wind, rain, ocean waves, and glaciers can also change the surface of the earth. Scientists think that the continents themselves are in motion. In this unit you will study ways in which the earth is constantly changing. ■

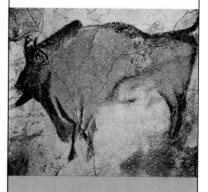

▲ *Early paintings, some over 10,000 years old, enable us to hypothesize about what life may have been like in the past.*

▼ *A volcano is an example of a sudden, violent change occurring on the earth. This is Mt. Etna, in Sicily, in 1983.*

▲ *This recently-discovered flower fossil is over 70 million years old.*

▼ *False-color radar image of an arid, mountainous region of the Sinkiang Province in China, taken from space. The mountain ranges were formed by the uplift of sedimentary rocks. The displacement along the ranges indicates a major fault zone.*

▲ *Stephen Bishop* (top), *the first tourist guide to Mammouth Cave, was very knowledgable in geology and other sciences related to caves. Mammouth Cave, Kentucky* (above) *was formed by water dissolving limestone.*

WEATHERING

A landslide can cause a whole mountainside to tumble into a valley in a matter of minutes. The landslide shown on the facing page was triggered by an earthquake. What seems to be fog is actually dust being stirred up as rocks fall.

- *What force causes the rock material to slide down the mountain?*
- *How might an earthquake cause a landslide on a steep slope?*
- *Explain how a mountain can be changed by landslides.*

11-1 WHAT IS WEATHERING?

You have learned that rocks are not as permanent as they may seem. New rocks are always being formed while others are being broken apart and changed. When rocks are exposed to air, water, and temperature changes, they slowly crumble into smaller pieces. The breakup and change of rocks and minerals, mainly from the action of air, water, and frost, is called **weathering**.

There are two main types of weathering: mechanical weathering and chemical weathering. **Mechanical weathering** is a process that breaks large rocks into smaller rocks. Each smaller rock has the same mineral composition as the original rock. Another name for mechanical weathering is *disintegration*.

Chemical weathering is a process that forms new substances from minerals in a rock. Air, water, and dissolved substances in water break down the minerals in a rock. This type of weathering is also called *decomposition*, because minerals decompose and new substances are formed. Chemical weathering usually works together with mechanical weathering to break up and decompose rocks on or near the earth's surface.

Both types of weathering produce rock fragments of different sizes. These pieces of rock gradually break into even smaller pieces. By breaking down rocks and minerals, weathering eventually produces soil.

> *After completing this section, you will be able to*
> - **define** the term *weathering*.
> - **distinguish** between mechanical weathering and chemical weathering.
> - **list** factors that affect the rate of weathering.
>
> *The key terms in this section are*
> chemical weathering
> mechanical weathering
> weathering

Figure 11-1

Rocks at the base of a mountain fell down the mountainside. What kind of weathering is this?

Weathering is usually a very slow process, and the rate of weathering is not constant. There are a variety of factors that affect the rate of weathering. Two of these factors are the type of rock being weathered and the type of climate. In cities, the amount of air pollution and water pollution present is also an important factor.

The type of rock being weathered will affect the rate of weathering. For instance, rocks that contain the mineral quartz weather slower than rocks that don't contain quartz in them. This is because quartz is very resistant to weathering. Quartz is found in granite. The mineral calcite, on the other hand, weathers rapidly. Calcite is found in limestone and marble. The rates at which limestone and granite weather in a desert have been compared. The Egyptians used limestone to build pyramids; they used granite to construct statues. The limestone weathered much faster than the granite. How would the weathering of marble compare to the weathering of granite?

Climate is another factor that affects the rate of weathering. Generally, all rocks weather faster in warm, humid climates than in dry, desert conditions. This is because water is a primary weathering agent. Cleopatra's Needle demonstrates the effect of climate. The Egyptians built Cleopatra's Needle about 3500 years ago. This giant structure stood in the desert, so weathering was slow. After many centuries, the writing on the stone structure was still clear. In 1880, Cleopatra's Needle was moved to New

Figure 11-2

Little weathering takes place where the air is dry (*left*). Weathering is much greater where the air is moist (*right*).

York City, where the moist air speeded up the weathering process. In less than 100 years, the lettering on the windward side was almost completely removed.

In cities, air pollution and water pollution also influence the rate of weathering. Automobiles and factories burn fossil fuels that release carbon dioxide, sulfur, and nitrogen oxide gases. These gases combine with moisture to produce weak acids. These acids eat away at rock and increase the rate of weathering. Look at the statue in Figure 11-3. This statue is made of marble and has been decomposing rapidly due to the large amounts of air pollutants.

REVIEW

1. What is weathering?
2. What is the difference between mechanical weathering and chemical weathering?
3. What factors affect the rate of weathering?

CHALLENGE Would you expect weathering to occur more rapidly in Boston than in Phoenix? Why?

Figure 11-3

This statue at the Field Museum in Chicago is disintegrating from pollution and acid rain.

11-2 TYPES OF WEATHERING

MECHANICAL WEATHERING

There are several forces in the environment that cause mechanical weathering. Temperature changes account for some mechanical weathering. The temperature change between day and night does not seem to be severe enough to cause rocks to break apart. However, forest fires, volcanic areas, and hot springs may heat rock to higher than usual temperatures. A surface layer on the rock may expand from the left and break off in a sheet. Sometimes the heat from forest fires is so intense that it causes rocks to split apart. This kind of temperature change does cause mechanical weathering.

Rocks under the earth's surface are under a lot of pressure. If a rock that has been buried is finally exposed at the surface, it will be under less pressure. When that happens, the outer layers of the rock will expand and peel off. This peeling off of slablike sheets of rock is called **exfoliation**. Granite is the rock most sensitive to this kind of mechanical weathering. An example is Liberty Cap, in Yosemite National Park, shown in Figure 11-4. Notice that the granite has peeled off, leaving a dome-shaped rock.

A similar event may occur in a mine. As rock is dug out, the pressure is reduced on the underlying layers. These layers may expand quickly and spring out of the walls. Sometimes a mine shaft may be filled with "flying" rocks, which can injure miners and damage equipment.

Figure 11-4

Exfoliation occurs as slabs of rock peel off in sheets (*left*). Exfoliation of the rock making up Liberty Cap in Yosemite National Park (*right*).

ACTIVITY   The Disintegration of Rocks

OBJECTIVES

Compare the effects of mechanical weathering on rocks.

Graph the change in mass as rocks undergo mechanical weathering.

MATERIALS

Graph paper, a few samples of each of three types of rocks (such as granite, shale, or sandstone), balance, container with a tight-fitting lid, water, filter paper, funnel, magnifying glass, paper towels, colored pencils

PROCEDURE

A. Examine the rock samples that you have.
   1. Which one would you predict would weather fastest? Why?
B. Place all the samples of one type of rock on the balance and find their mass. Record the mass in a table similar to the one shown.
C. After you have recorded the mass of the rock samples, place all the rocks of one type in a container. Add water to cover the rocks and put the lid on tightly.
D. Shake the rocks vigorously for 100 shakes.
E. Pour off the water through the filter paper that has been placed in a funnel. Look at the filter paper under a magnifying glass.
   2. What do you see?

F. Remove the wet rock samples, dry them, and determine their mass. Record their mass in your data table.
G. Repeat steps C through F nine times. Record the mass of the rocks in your data table after every 100 shakes.
H. Repeat this procedure with your other rock types. Record your data in your table.
I. Devise a graph, with the "mass of rock samples" on the vertical axis and the "number of shakes" on the horizontal axis. Plot your data, using a different color for each type of rock.

	MASS		
	Granite	Sandstone	Shale
before shaking 100 shakes 200 shakes 1000 shakes			

RESULTS AND CONCLUSIONS

1. Which rock decreased in mass the most?
2. Which rock disintegrated the fastest?
3. What kind of weathering did you imitate?
4. What specific example in nature would cause rocks to weather in this way?

The freezing action of water acts as the most important agent of mechanical weathering. Rain water seeps into cracks and crevices in the rock. When water freezes, it expands by about 10 percent, and this expansion creates pressure on a rock. When water thaws, it contracts, and pressure is reduced. As the water in cracks in rocks expands and contracts, the pressure on the rocks increases and decreases. Eventually, pieces of rock will break apart. This freezing of water in cracks of rocks, causing the rocks to break apart, is a type of mechanical weathering called *frost action*. In mountain regions, frost action is common.

Plants and animals contribute to mechanical weathering. Earthworms and insects burrow in the soil and open up holes to the rock below. Water seeps through these holes, speeding up weathering. Some plants grow in crevices of rocks, and their roots force the rocks apart. How is the tree in Figure 11-5 causing mechanical weathering?

Figure 11-5

Mechanical weathering can be caused by the roots of trees.

CHEMICAL WEATHERING

Chemical weathering occurs when the minerals in a rock are chemically changed. Chemical weathering may occur in a number of ways.

Falling raindrops dissolve tiny amounts of carbon dioxide (CO_2), which is found in the air. When CO_2 combines with water, it forms carbonic acid. This is the same weak acid that is found in soft drinks. The reaction of carbonic acid with other substances is called **carbonation**. Carbonation is harmless to humans. However, rocks can be weathered by it. Carbonic acid can break down many minerals, such as feldspar, hornblende, augite, and mica, leaving only clay behind. Carbonic acid can also dissolve pure calcite, gypsum, and halite.

Limestone, which is made of calcite, dissolves easily in carbonic acid. In some areas, where limestone deposits occur, large caves are formed. These caves frequently contain ground water. If the ground water is removed, the roofs of the caves lose their support. The ground may collapse, forming huge holes in the earth's surface, as shown in Figure 11-6.

Figure 11-6

This limestone cave was formed by water dissolving the limestone (*left*). Ground water dissolved the rock below the surface, causing the ground to collapse in Winter Park, Florida (*right*).

The process of **hydration** occurs when water combines with minerals. Water is a major agent in chemical weathering. Some minerals, such as feldspar, combine with water. The water removes the element potassium from feldspar. As this happens, the feldspar swells up, which causes the outer layers to peel off. Eventually, the feldspar is changed into clay. In this example, chemical weathering and mechanical weathering work together. Chemical weathering changes the feldspar, and mechanical weathering causes it to peel off. Both types of weathering often work together.

Oxygen combining with other substances is a process called **oxidation**. During oxidation a new substance is formed. For example, oxygen combines easily with minerals such as pyrite, and magnetite, which have iron in them. Oxidation of these minerals produces a new substance called iron oxide, or rust. Rust is the reddish substance often found on iron objects exposed to the air. When water is present, oxidation occurs more rapidly.

There are other acids in the environment that contribute to chemical weathering. The decay of plant and animal material produces acids. Some organisms, such as lichens, produce acids. As they grow on rocks, the acids they produce dissolve some of the minerals in the rocks.

Automobiles and factories also affect chemical weathering. Gases, such as sulfuric oxides and nitrogen oxides, are released into the air when fossil fuels are burned. These compounds are combined with water droplets in the air to form weak sulfuric acid and nitric acid. They fall to the ground as *acid rain*. In some areas, acid rain is acidic enough to decompose rock structures.

SCIENCE PUZZLER

The unusual rock formation shown is Natural Bridge in Kentucky. Natural Bridge is believed to have formed from the action of ground water. How could ground water produce such a formation? What is probably the nature of the rock material in the bridge? Give reasons for your answer.

ACTIVITY   Carbonation and Decomposition

OBJECTIVES
Predict the effect of carbonic acid on different kinds of rock.
Compare the effect of carbonic acid on rocks with the effect of water on rocks.

MATERIALS
balance, two small samples each of limestone, sandstone, marble, and granite, eight 30-mL beakers, eight labels, distilled water, dilute carbonic acid

PROCEDURE

A. Prepare a data table like the one shown.

Rock	CARBONIC ACID				
	Initial Mass (g)	Immediate Response	After 15 min	After 24 hr	Mass After 24 hr
Limestone					
Sandstone					
Marble					
Granite					

Rock	WATER				
	Initial mass (g)	Immediate Response	After 15 min	After 24 hr	Mass After 24 hr
Limestone					
Sandstone					
Marble					
Granite					

B. Using what you have learned about carbonation, predict what will happen to your rock samples if they are placed in carbonic acid.

C. Label the beakers as follows: Limestone and Carbonic Acid, Limestone and Water, Sandstone and Carbonic Acid, Sandstone and Water, Marble and Carbonic Acid, Marble and Water, Granite and Carbonic Acid, and Granite and Water.

D. To the four beakers with "Carbonic Acid" on their labels, add carbonic acid until they are three quarters full. To the other four beakers, add water until they are three quarters full.

E. Find the mass of one sample of limestone. Record the mass in the data table. Place that piece of limestone in the beaker labeled "Limestone and Carbonic Acid." Record what happens to the rock. Determine the mass of the other piece of limestone and place it in the beaker labeled "Limestone and Water."

F. Repeat step **E** with the other rock samples. You should have a sample of each rock in carbonic acid and a sample in water.

G. Wait 15 minutes and observe all the rock samples again. Record your observations.

H. After 24 hours, observe your rock samples. Record your observations in the data table. Dry each piece of rock and then determine its mass. Record the mass in the appropriate column in the data table.

RESULTS AND CONCLUSIONS
1. In which beakers did you observe a chemical reaction taking place?
2. Which type of rock reacted the fastest?
3. Which rock sample changed the most in mass?
4. In which beakers did the rocks change the least?
5. Draw conclusions about this type of chemical weathering.
6. Compare the effect of carbonic acid on the rocks with the effect of water on the rocks.

REVIEW
1. How does water cause mechanical weathering?
2. What is exfoliation?
3. Compare the roles of hydration, oxidation, and carbonation in chemical weathering.

CHALLENGE   Suppose a scientific study indicated that the rate of carbonation was higher in industrial areas than in other areas. How could the higher rate be explained?

11-3 MASS MOVEMENTS

Wherever there is a steep slope on the earth's crust, gravity will eventually cause rock material to fall, slide, or move. The movement of large amounts of weathered rock and other earth materials down a slope is called **mass movement**. This movement can be rapid or slow. Look at Figure 11-7 and notice the large pile of rocks at the base of the mountain. A large pile of rocks at the base of a hill or mountain is called a *talus*. A talus is evidence that mass movement has occurred.

Even though gravity is the primary cause of mass movement, there are other contributing factors. Water is one of the major factors. As heavy rains fall on sand, the sand may begin to ooze. Gravity can pull the sand more easily down a slope. Water can also wet the surface between two layers of rock. One layer may begin to slip over another and move down a mountainside.

Mass movement also occurs after wind, rain water, or a river has worn away the base of a mountain. When support for the higher rock formations is removed, eventually those formations will tumble down.

There are different types of mass movements. One type is the landslide. A **landslide** is a rapid movement of rock and other earth materials down a slope. A large amount of rain, a river cutting into the base of a mountain, or an earthquake will cause a landslide.

After completing this section, you will be able to

- **define** the term *mass movement*.
- **identify** the causes of mass movements.
- **describe** the various types of mass movements.

The key terms in this section are
creep
landslide
mass movement
mudflow
slump

Figure 11-7

The large pile of rocks found at the bottom of Capitol Reef National Park, in Utah, is called talus.

Figure 11-8

Slump in Anchorage, Alaska (*left*). A mudflow from Mount St. Helens, Washington (*right*).

When a large block of material suddenly slips along a curved surface, down a slope in a single mass, the movement is called a **slump**. Figure 11-8 (*left*) shows a slump that occurred during the Anchorage, Alaska, earthquake in 1964. A slump leaves the mountainside with a curved surface, as if material was scooped out with a giant spoon.

In dry mountain areas, heavy rains may wash dirt and loose rock material into valleys. As the water and dry material mix, they form mud. This mud may move along the valley floors. A moving mass of mud is called a **mudflow**. Observe Figure 11-8 (*right*), which shows a mudflow caused by Mount Saint Helens. The mudflow occurred in 1980 when Mount Saint Helens erupted in Washington State. Ash and dust poured out of the volcano, and the heat from the eruption melted the ice and snow. The meltwater mixed with the ash and dust and created a huge mudflow that moved at 48 km/h.

Creep is a slow form of mass movement and occurs on gentle slopes. As the land slowly moves downward, it causes fenceposts and telephone poles to lean downhill, as shown in Figure 11-9. Otherwise, creep is hardly noticeable. Scientists believe that creep results from gravity and mechanical weathering. As soil freezes and expands, particles are raised upward. When the soil thaws, the particles settle back to the surface. Because the surface is sloped, the particles settle back slightly downhill. This gradual downhill movement produces creep.

Figure 11-9

Soil creep has caused this tree to move downhill.

ACTIVITY   Investigating Mass Movements

OBJECTIVE
Compare conditions that cause mass movements.

MATERIALS
stream table (with hose attached), two bricks, bucket, watering can, clay, sand, pebbles, water, a metric ruler

PROCEDURE
A. Set up a stream table as shown. Place a brick under one end as shown.
B. Measure the height of the stream table on the brick end as shown.
C. Record the measurement in a table like the one shown. Do not write in this book.

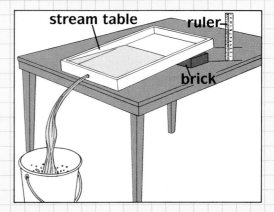
stream table   ruler
brick

Material	Height of Stream Table	Speed of Movement
Sand (top), clay (bottom)		
Sand (top), clay (bottom)		
Pebbles (top), clay (bottom)		

D. Place a thin layer of clay on the bottom of the stream table. Place a layer of sand on top of the clay.
E. Using a watering can, pour water on the sand.
F. Record your observations in the data table.
G. Increase the height of the stream table by adding a brick. Measure the height of the table and record it in the data table.
H. Rearrange the sand as it was for step **D**. Pour water on the sand as you did before.

I. Record your observations in the table.
J. Remove the sand from the stream table and cover it with pebbles.
K. Pour water over the pebbles. Observe what happens and record the results in the data table.

RESULTS AND CONCLUSIONS
1. What was the effect of increasing the slope on the movement of the sand?
2. Which mass movement was the slowest?
3. What kind of mass movement in nature would this slowest kind resemble?
4. What kind of mass movement was demonstrated in step **H**?
5. What kind of mass movement was demonstrated in step **K**?
6. Which of the three types of mass movement that you created would be the most destructive?
7. What are the causes of mass movement?

EXTENSION
Repeat the activity using loam soil. You may even wish to try building terraces to see if they can eliminate destructive mass movements.

REVIEW
1. What is mass movement?
2. What factors can cause mass movements?
3. What are various types of mass movements?

CHALLENGE An avalanche is a mass movement of snow. Which type of mass movement is an avalanche most similar to? Explain your answer.

11-4 WHAT IS SOIL?

Soil is the loose material on the earth's surface in which plants with roots can grow. All life depends on soil. Generally, soil includes four ingredients: weathered minerals, organic materials, water, and air.

Quartz, feldspar, and calcite are common minerals in the soil. Soil also contains organic materials. These materials are formed from the decay of plants and animals. Bacteria and fungi are the two primary agents that cause decay. These organic materials make up the dark-colored part of the soil called *humus*. The presence of humus is essential for the growth of plants.

In addition to organic material and weathered rock, soil contains water and air. Water and air speed up weathering. They are also necessary for the survival of plants, animals, and other organisms in the soil.

Soil forms as rock is weathered and broken into smaller pieces. Eventually, a thin soil layer may cover the underlying rock. This underlying, unweathered rock is called **bedrock**. With the right conditions, a thicker layer of soil may develop over the bedrock. The rock from which soil is formed is known as the soil's **parent rock**.

DO YOU KNOW?

In China, there are 1.1 million km² of desert. But only 61 percent of this amount represents true desert caused by only a tiny bit of rain each year. The rest has been caused by people. The addition of desert land to China is just one example of the encroachment of deserts all over the world.

In their quest for food and fuel, people have cut down forests for pastureland and firewood and have allowed animals to overgraze on grasslands. With no vegetation on the land, winds can remove soil, leaving areas of deserts. In the United States, overgrazing by sheep has stripped the vegetation from lands in Arizona and New Mexico, transforming once-rich grassland to desert.

Some programs to reclaim deserts are underway. In China, people have covered thousands of acres in the Gobi Desert with trees.

But despite attempts with old and new technology, fighting the growth of deserts is an uphill battle.

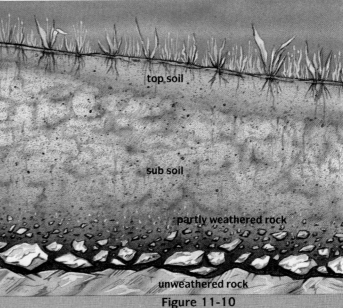

top soil

sub soil

partly weathered rock

unweathered rock

Figure 11-10

A soil horizon showing layering of the soil (*left*). Topsoil, subsoil, partly weathered rock, and unweathered rock are illustrated (*right*).

As soil develops, it forms layers called **horizons**. These horizons make up the *soil profile*. Look at the soil profile in Figure 11-10. Distinct horizons can be seen. The top layer is known as the *A-horizon*, or *A-zone*. This top layer of soil is also referred to as the **topsoil**. Fertile topsoil is soil that contains humus and the weathered minerals that plants need to grow. Corn, wheat, and rye can grow only in topsoil. Animals such as ants, worms, moles, and shrews also live in the layer of topsoil.

Below the layer of topsoil is the *B-horizon*, or *B-zone*. This layer below the topsoil is also called the **subsoil**. Minerals from the topsoil are carried downward by water and deposited in the subsoil. The subsoil may also contain some humus and living organisms.

Beneath the subsoil lies partly weathered rock. This rock is producing new soil. Plant roots may extend even as far as this rock. What layer lies below the layer of partly weathered rock?

Sometimes soil remains on top of its parent rock. Soil that remains on top of its parent rock is called **residual soil**. The soil, however, may be moved to a new location by wind or water. Over time, humus may be added to the soil. If earthworms are present, they will grind up soil and organic materials. This activity increases the soil's fertility. Earthworms also create passages in the soil. These passages allow water and air to enter.

Various types of soil are found over the earth's surface. The differences in soil can be explained by many

Figure 11-11

Weathered limestone around Meteor Crater, in Arizona, produces a soil rich in calcium carbonate.

factors. One factor is the type of rock that formed the soil. If limestone is the parent rock, it will produce a different type of soil than if sandstone were the parent rock. The composition of the parent rock affects the soil's fertility. For example, potassium feldspar contains potassium. During chemical weathering, potassium is removed from the feldspar and deposited in the soil. Plants need potassium to grow. Therefore the soils that form from rocks that have potassium feldspar in them are usually fertile soils.

Soil is also formed by mechanical weathering. Mechanical weathering breaks down the parent rock into smaller pieces of rock. The soil that results is similar in composition to the parent rock. Soil is formed by both the processes of mechanical weathering and chemical weathering.

Time is a factor that affects soil. In general, if weathering has been going on for a short time, the layer of soil will be thin. When weathering has occurred over a longer period, the layer of soil may be thicker.

The type of surface on which weathering occurs also affects soil. The soil often cannot build up on a steep slope because gravity pulls the soil downward. Water also washes it away. Soil may build up on a gentle slope. However, plants must be present to hold the soil in place. Soil can become even thicker on a level surface. Plants growing on the surface help to prevent wind and water from removing the soil.

A very important factor affecting soil is climate. In warm, moist regions, chemical weathering can proceed rapidly. As a result, soils can be created rather quickly. These soils support a great number of plants and animals. When they decay, their organic material is added to the soil. This material further enriches the soil.

By contrast, weathering proceeds more slowly in dry areas. In such areas, rocks are broken down mainly by mechanical weathering. This type of weathering creates poor, rocky soils. The soil builds very slowly and forms only a thin layer on the surface.

REVIEW

1. What are four of the ingredients in soil?
2. How is soil formed?
3. What factors cause different types of soil?

CHALLENGE Is soil that has formed in a dry area likely to differ much or little in composition from the bedrock? Explain your answer.

11-5 TYPES OF SOIL

The diameters of the particles that make up soil determine **soil texture**. There are two types of soil texture: sand and clay. **Sand** is made up of particles that are larger than those in clay or loam. Sand is produced through chemical weathering. It is usually composed of gypsum, calcite, or quartz grains. **Clay** is produced by the chemical weathering of feldspar and other minerals and is made up of very small particles. Some soils, called **loam**, contain a combination of sand, clay, and pieces of sedimentary rock called silt. Compare the particle size of loam, in Figure 11-12, to the particle size of sand and clay.

North America has a variety of types of soil. *Forest soil* exists primarily in the forests in the eastern part of the United States and Canada. In the north, forest soil looks gray-brown. In the south, forest soil appears yellow to red. The topsoil generally contains decayed leaves, animal matter, and particles of sand. The subsoil contains aluminum, iron, and particles of clay.

After completing this section, you will be able to

- **describe** the two types of soil texture.
- **list** different types of soil and **state** where these types of soil are found.

The key terms in this section are

clay	sand
loam	soil texture

Figure 11-12

Sand (*left*), clay (*middle*), and loam (*right*).

In the central part of North America *grassland soil,* or *prairie soil,* is found. Wheat, rye and corn flourish in this soil. The grasslands and prairies form the heart of America's agricultural area. The topsoil in this area is often thicker and more fertile than it is in the forest soil. This fertile soil was deposited by glaciers that covered much of North America thousands of years ago. Grassland and prairie soils have a top layer that is dark brown. Underneath, however, the soil is often whitish, because it contains calcium carbonate.

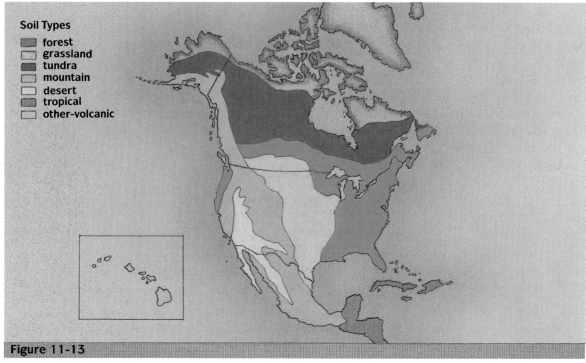

Figure 11-13

Soil types of the United States.

Soil Types
- forest
- grassland
- tundra
- mountain
- desert
- tropical
- other-volcanic

Along the mountain slopes of western North America lies *mountain soil*. This type of soil is produced mainly by mechanical weathering. The layer of topsoil is thin and contains large bits of rock. Only a limited variety of plants can grow in the mountain soil.

America's western deserts contain *desert soil*. Desert soil is made up mostly of sand and minerals. The soil is extremely dry, because deserts receive little rain. When desert soils are irrigated, crops can grow in them too. For example, proper irrigation of desert areas in California, Arizona, and New Mexico have turned desert land into productive farmland. Look at Figure 11-13. What river irrigates the western deserts?

Tundra soil is another type of soil found in North America. *Tundra soil* lies in the polar regions of Alaska and Canada. The weather in these regions remains below freezing much of the time, and the surface of the land is often covered with ice. During warmer weather, the topsoil thaws. However, the soil beneath the surface remains frozen. Tundra soil is formed primarily by mechanical weathering. It is thin and not very fertile. The tundra receives very little moisture, and only hardy plants like mosses and lichens survive there.

Tropical soil is another soil type. It is not found in Canada or the United States. *Tropical soil* forms in warm, tropical regions, located in Africa, Asia, and South America. Tropical soil is red in color because it contains iron oxide. However, this soil has few other minerals and little humus. As a result, tropical soil is poor for growing crops.

REVIEW

1. Distinguish between the two types of soil, based on texture.
2. What are the different types of soil? Describe where each type is found.

CHALLENGE A sample of topsoil is brown. Traces of calcium carbonate are found in the soil. Identify the type of soil and from where in North America it was taken.

CHAPTER SUMMARY

The main ideas in this chapter are listed below. Read these statements before you answer the Chapter Review questions.

- Weathering involves the breakup and change of rocks, mainly from the action of air, water, and frost. The two types of weathering are mechanical weathering and chemical weathering. (11-1)

- The rate of weathering is mainly affected by the type of rock being weathered, the climate, and the amount of air pollution and water pollution present. (11-1)

- Changes in temperature and pressure are factors that cause mechanical weathering. (11-2)

- Hydration, oxidation, and carbonation are some processes involved in chemical weathering. (11-2)

- Mass movement, or the movement of large amounts of earth material down a slope, includes landslide, slump, mudflow, and creep. (11-3)

- Soil forms from weathered rock and also includes organic materials, minerals, air and water. (11-4)

- Factors that affect the type of soil that forms include the nature of the parent rock, the amount of time that the soil has been forming, and the climate. (11-4)

- Soil may be described as sand or clay, based on its texture. (11-5)

- Different types of soil occur in different areas of North America. (11-5)

The key terms in this chapter are listed below. Use each term in a sentence that shows the meaning of the term.

bedrock	horizons	mudflow	soil
carbonation	hydration	oxidation	soil texture
chemical weathering	landslide	parent rock	subsoil
clay	loam	residual soil	topsoil
creep	mass movement	sand	weathering
exfoliation	mechanical weathering	slump	

Chapter Review

Write the letter of the term that best matches the definition. Not all the terms will be used.

1. The peeling off of slablike sheets of rock
2. The breakdown of rock into smaller pieces
3. The slippage of a block of material down a slope as a single mass
4. The combination of water with minerals
5. Layers of soil
6. The process that forms new substances from elements in rock
7. The reaction of carbonic acid with substances in rock
8. The rapid movement of rock and other earth material down a slope
9. Soil containing a combination of clay, sand, and silt
10. The rock from which a particular soil is formed

a. horizons
b. landslide
c. mechanical weathering
d. carbonation
e. parent rock
f. exfoliation
g. oxidation
h. chemical weathering
i. loam
j. hydration
k. slump
l. creep

CONCEPTS

1. What is weathering? (11-1)
2. Describe the processes of mechanical weathering and chemical weathering. (11-1)
3. Identify the factors that affect the rate of weathering and give examples of how each factor affects the rate. (11-1)
4. Explain how high temperatures can cause mechanical weathering. (11-2)
5. What is frost action? (11-2)
6. Give examples of how plants and animals cause mechanical weathering. (11-2)
7. List and explain three processes involved in chemical weathering. (11-2)
8. What factors cause mass movement? (11-3)
9. Distinguish between the four main types of mass movements. (11-3)
10. Describe the composition of soil. (11-4)
11. Explain how soil forms. (11-4)

12. Identify the layers found in soil. (11-4)

13. What factors determine the type of soil that forms in an area? (11-4)

14. How do sand, clay, and loam differ? (11-5)

15. What are the characteristics of forest soil? (11-5)

16. Compare grassland soil with mountain soil. (11-5)

17. Why is tropical soil poor for farming? (11-5)

APPLICATION/ CRITICAL THINKING

1. How would a soil scientist determine whether the soil in a region had been produced primarily by mechanical weathering or by both mechanical weathering and chemical weathering?

2. Some scientific studies indicate that the average temperature and the average annual precipitation will increase in northeastern North America over the next 50 years. Predict the effects that such changes would have on weathering rate.

3. Weathering can be considered part of the process of recycling the earth's materials. Explain what is meant by this statement.

4. Ancient cities that are buried under soil and rock don't age until they are excavated. Explain what is meant by this statement.

EXTENSION

1. Investigate the effects of pollution on an important monument. An example might be the Acropolis in Athens, Greece. What efforts are being made to deal with the effects of pollution?

2. Research a famous landslide. An example might be the landslide in Elm, Switzerland in 1881. What were its causes and effects?

3. In 1981, large holes suddenly appeared in various parts of Florida. Discover the reasons why these holes appeared. What role did weathering play in producing them?

4. Investigate the mudslides that often occur in California. Why do these mudslides happen? How are they similar to landslides? How are they different?

5. Investigate ways geologic features and soil types help to determine land use.

READINGS

Fodor, F.V. *Chiseling the Earth*. Enslow Publishers, 1982.

Gibbons, Boyd. "Do We Treat Our Soil Like Dirt?" *National Geographic,* September, 1984.

EROSION

The slowness of erosion makes the process almost unnoticeable. A rock, for example, may look the same for thousands of years even though it is being worn away. The rock shown in the photograph was carved by the action of windblown sand. By itself, wind has very little effect on rocks. However, when wind picks up sand, the wind can sandblast any rock in its path.

- *Which part of the rock has been weathered the most?*
- *Could the river shown have weathered the rock?*
- *Will the structure remain standing?*

12-1 WEARING AWAY THE LAND

You learned in Chapter 11 that a number of forces cause rocks to break into smaller pieces. For example, large boulders can be split apart by the action of frost. Once they are broken into smaller pieces, the pieces can be carried away in a process called erosion.

Erosion is the wearing away and moving of rock material by natural agents. The main agents of erosion on the land surface of the earth are running water, wind, and glaciers, or moving ice. Along the coasts, ocean waves are the main agent of erosion.

Erosion occurs mainly in two ways. In one way, rock materials are picked up and carried away by an erosional agent. For example, wind can pick up sand and carry it off. Another way erosion occurs is by abrasion. **Abrasion** is a process by which rock is worn away by rock materials carried by an erosional agent. Rock materials can act like tools, grinding down rock. For example, sand that is picked up by wind can abrade, or wear away, rocks in its path. Why do you think sand is used to clean the outside of stone or brick buildings?

> *After completing this section, you will be able to*
>
> - **name** four agents of erosion.
> - **describe** two ways erosion can occur.
> - **explain** how deposition occurs.
>
> *The key terms in this section are*
> abrasion   erosion
> deposition

ab (off)
radere (to scrape)

Figure 12-1

Sand can be used to clean the side of a building (*left*). Wind-blown materials can carve rock structures in a desert (*right*).

Rock material that is carried by erosional agents eventually settles. If the agent is running water or wind, settling occurs when the water or air slows down or stops. With glaciers, rock material settles as the ice melts. The settling of material is called **deposition**.

Each agent of erosion produces different effects on the rock material it moves. For example, running water rounds and smooths the rocks it carries. Wind-blown material is rounded and has pitted surfaces. Rocks moved by ice tend to keep their irregular shapes. The different effects are important to a scientist, because they give clues to the processes that carried the materials to where they are found.

REVIEW

1. What are four agents of erosion?
2. What are two ways erosion can occur?
3. How does rock material on the earth's surface become deposited?

CHALLENGE Explain the existence of many more craters on the moon's surface than on the earth's surface.

12-2 RUNNING WATER

Running water is part of the water cycle. In the cycle, water evaporates from the oceans and enters the atmosphere. The water is carried by wind over land where it falls as rain. Some of the water flows on the land as running water back to the oceans.

Running water usually begins as runoff. **Runoff** is rain water that moves over land. Runoff usually forms as a thin sheet, or layer, of water. The sheet can be broken into narrow streams of water by rocks. The water carves out narrow channels called *rills*. With each new rainfall, more water collects in the rills. Running water deepens and widens the rills to form larger channels called *gullies*.

As gullies are enlarged, more water can collect and flow there. Eventually, running water will be present during a rainfall and also during the times in-between as well.

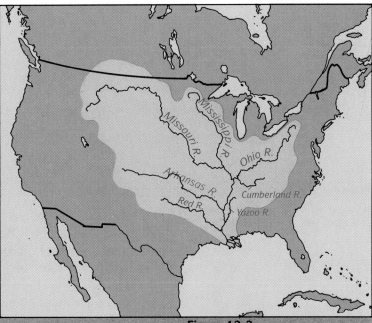

Figure 12-2

The running water becomes a stream. A **stream** is a naturally flowing body of water.

Small streams may come together to form larger ones. All the streams in an area join to form one main flowing body of water called a **river**. Streams that flow into larger streams or a river are called **tributaries** (TRIHB yuh tehr-eez). Identify the tributaries of the Mississippi River, shown in Figure 12-2. The area that supplies water for a river is called a **watershed**.

After a rainfall, water forms gullies along the side of this mountain (*left*). The watershed of the Mississippi River (*right*).

THE DEVELOPMENT OF A RIVER

As a river erodes its channel, it can pass through various stages of development. Depending on the characteristics it develops, a river can be classified as young, mature, or old. A young river flows rapidly along a steep, rugged course. The river's energy is directed mainly at cutting its channel lower, not wider. Thus the river threads its way through steep-sided, narrow valleys. It forms a V-shaped valley, like that shown in Figure 12-3 (*left*). This type of valley is typical for many young rivers.

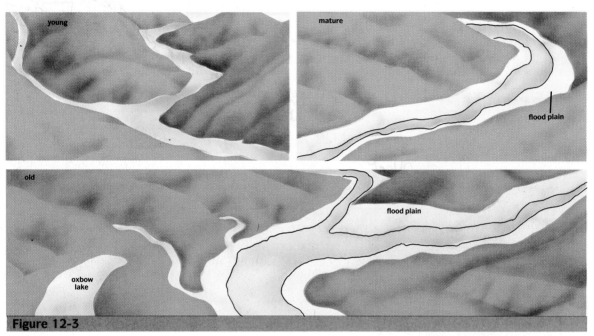

Figure 12-3

A young river (*left*), a mature river (*middle*), and an old river (*right*).

Eventually, the river is unable to cut its channel much lower. It passes into the mature stage. At this stage the river mainly erodes its banks and winds back and forth. Gradually, the river valley begins to expand, producing a broad valley or a flood plain. The flood plain is that area which the river fills when it overflows its banks during a flood. As it flows onto the flood plain, the river loses velocity. It drops its load of sediments, making the plain smooth and flat. The sediments enrich the soil, making it more productive for agriculture.

Mature rivers have curves along their channels. A river flows faster on the outside of a curve, thus more channel erosion occurs there. As the river slows down on the inside of a curve, sediments are deposited. Where are the sediments deposited in the mature river shown in Figure 12-3 (*middle*)? This process produces large, sweeping curves called *meanders*.

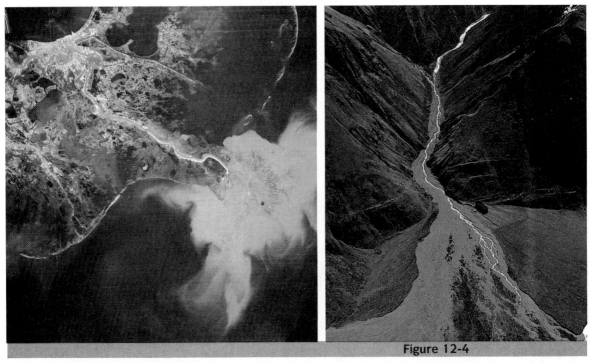

Figure 12-4

The delta of a river (*left*). An alluvial fan (*right*).

In time, a river enters old age. The sweeping curve of a meander may form a narrow neck at one end. Eventually, the river will break through this neck of land and form a straight channel. Then the river deposits material across the meander until it is cut off. Abandoned meanders that are filled with water form oxbow lakes. Old rivers are characterized by numerous meanders and oxbow lakes as well as wide flood plains.

At its end or mouth, a river may enter a larger body of water, such as an ocean, a gulf, or a lake. If it enters quiet waters, the velocity of the river slows suddenly. The river then drops its load of sediments and produces a large triangular formation that is called a *delta*.

When a mountain stream reaches a flat plain, its velocity slows quickly also. The stream deposits its material on the plain in a fan-shaped formation called an *alluvial fan*. How does the formation of an alluvial fan differ from the formation of a delta?

THE WORK OF RUNNING WATER

Erosion by running water begins with raindrops falling on soil. Each drop loosens soil particles. The raindrops from a single rainstorm hitting an area of land the size of a football field can loosen almost 100 t of soil. Rushing water from runoff can carve rills and gullies into the soil.

OBJECTIVE

Predict what will happen to the particles of different size when they are deposited by water.

MATERIALS

large glass jar with tightly fitting lid, sand, gravel, pebbles, water

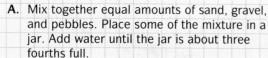

PROCEDURE

A. Mix together equal amounts of sand, gravel, and pebbles. Place some of the mixture in a jar. Add water until the jar is about three fourths full.

B. Put a lid on the jar. Carefully shake the jar until its contents are thoroughly mixed.

C. Allow the contents to settle.

RESULTS AND CONCLUSIONS

1. What happened to the contents of the jar when you set the jar down? Explain your observations.
2. Describe the contents of the jar at the end of the activity.
3. How do you think materials settle in a river or a stream?

Figure 12-5

In the young river (*left*), notice the rapid flow of water. The old river (*right*) has wide flood plains, large meanders, and oxbow lakes.

Running water in streams and rivers causes most of the erosion of the earth's surface. The water can wear away rock in three ways. One way is by dissolving rocks. For example, limestone can be dissolved by acids that are present in running water.

Another way running water can wear away rock in a stream is by using the force of the water. This force can widen cracks and remove pieces of rock from the channel.

The third way running water can wear away rock in a stream or channel is by abrasion. When materials such as sand and gravel are picked up by the water, they scrape against the rock of the channel like sandpaper scrapes against wood. Larger materials, such as pebbles, roll and bounce along the stream bottom and chip away the rock.

SCIENCE & TECHNOLOGY

Making energy from glaciers sounds like a mammoth task, but the Norwegians have already done it. They have produced energy from the Bondhus Glacier, a valley glacier in southwestern Norway. The pressure from the weight of the glacier causes the bottom layers to melt. The meltwater forms streams running under the glacier. To get at the water, Norwegian engineers dug horizontal tunnels into the bedrock under the glacier. Then vertical shafts were drilled upward into the glacier into these streams. The water from the glacier runs into the shafts, through the tunnel, and then into a reservoir. From there, the water flows downhill to generators that produce energy.

The technique used at the Bondhus Glacier has been very successful. In one summer the glacier yielded as much as 15.8 billion gallons of water and produced enough electricity for 6000 Norwegian households for one year. The Norwegians are studying the nature of glaciers from the tunnels already made in the Bondhus Glacier. They hope they can use this knowledge to tap other glaciers for energy.

Several factors affect how fast a river can erode its channel. One factor is how fast the water is flowing. A fast-flowing river can carry more material than a slow-moving river. The more material a river carries, the faster it can erode the channel. Another factor is how much water is flowing. A river with a large volume of water can carry more material and erode the channel faster than a river with a small volume.

A third factor is the type of material a river carries. A river carrying a hard material, such as quartz, will erode the channel quickly. A fourth factor is the type of rock that makes up the channel. A river channel made of soft rock, such as limestome, will erode quickly.

REVIEW

1. How does a river form?
2. Describe the three stages in the life of a river.
3. What are three ways a river can erode the land?
4. What are four factors that affect the rate of erosion by running water?

CHALLENGE Rivers that enter the ocean along the Atlantic coast do not have deltas. Explain why.

12-3 THE WORK OF WIND

After completing this section, you will be able to

- **describe** two ways that wind causes erosion.
- **explain** how a dune forms.
- **compare** the material found in loess with the material found in dunes.

The key terms in this section are

deflation   loess
dune

Travelers through the deserts in the southwestern United States can find their cars stripped of paint and their windshields pitted after a sandstorm. This illustrates one property of wind. When wind picks up sand, it can sandblast objects in its path.

WIND EROSION

Wind can pick up loose rock material and move it in a process called deflation. **Deflation** is the lifting and carrying away of loose material by wind. Deflation occurs mainly in dry areas where there is little plant life to hold soil in place. In these areas, wind can pick up and carry away lightweight particles, such as clay, silt, and sand. Heavier objects, such as pebbles and small rocks, cannot be picked up by wind and so remain on the surface. What eventually remains is a layer of pebbles and small rocks called a *desert pavement*. As you can see in Figure 12-6, a desert pavement forms a cover that can protect the surface from further wind erosion.

Another way wind erodes is by abrasion. In this process, sand blown by the wind breaks down material on a rock's surface. This can occur because particles of sand have sharp edges. This is similar to the way a sandblaster is used to clean the outside of a stone or brick building.

Figure 12-6

Desert pavement forms when wind blows away the lighter particles and leaves the larger, heavier stones (*left*). A desert pavement (*right*).

Figure 12-7

Mushroom Rock, in Death Valley, California, was formed by the wind blowing sand against a block of basalt (*left*). Loess deposits in the midwestern United States (*right*).

Abrasion usually occurs near the surface of the land. This is because sand is not often lifted more than a meter high. Below a meter, windblown sand can leave rocks with polished, pitted surfaces, or sharp edges. How can you tell that the rock shown in Figure 12-7, has been abraded by the wind?

WIND DEPOSITS

Material carried by wind is deposited when the wind slows down or stops. The lightest materials, such as sand, silt, and clay can be carried great distances. When the wind slows down, it deposits them on the surface in a thick layer. In some areas of the world, the surface is covered with deposits of wind-blown silt called **loess** (LOH-ihs). The thickest deposits are found in China, where the loess can be more than 60 m thick. Loess is also found in the midwestern United States, along the Mississippi River.

The speed of the wind can be slowed down by an object like a rock, fence, bush, or even a mound of sand. Objects that slow down the speed of wind are called *wind-breaks*. When the wind in a desert reaches a windbreak, it deposits sand in a mound behind the windbreak. The mound of sand grows as it blocks more wind, causing more sand to accumulate. Eventually, a hill of sand called a **dune** forms. Dunes are the most common feature formed when the wind deposits its cargo of sand.

Figure 12-8

Small sand dunes form behind windbreaks such as grass.

Dunes form in many areas along coasts. Winds blowing in off the ocean push and carry sand inland from the beach. The sand is dropped when the wind encounters windbreaks, such as grass or buildings. Look at Figure 12-8. What causes the sand to pile up on the beach? The side of the dune facing the wind has a gentle slope. The side facing away from the wind has a steeper slope. Look at Figure 12-9. Sand is blown up the gentle slope and over the top of the dune. Notice how the sand then drops down the steep slope. The sand dune moves as sand is carried from the side facing the wind to the side facing away from the wind.

Dunes slowly move in the direction the wind blows. Ordinarily, they move a few meters a year, but where winds are strong and in the same direction, they can move about a third of a meter a day. Dunes can move over farmland, roads, railroad tracks, and houses.

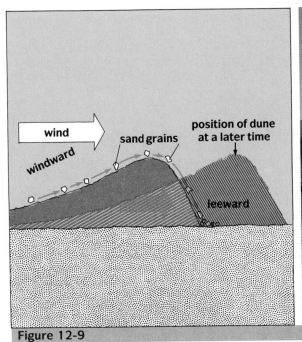

Figure 12-9

Sand dunes move in the same direction that the wind blows (*left*). Some sand dunes can become very large (*right*).

REVIEW

1. What are two ways that wind causes erosion?
2. How does a dune form?
3. How is the material found in loess different from the material found in dunes?

CHALLENGE Explain why piles of rocks are placed around the bases of telephone poles in deserts.

12-4 GLACIERS

During the winter, parts of the United States receive several meters of snow. If you live in one of these areas, you may have noticed a change in the appearance of the snow after a few days. If the snow is trampled by people's feet or flattened by automobile tires, it becomes the hard material ice.

A similar process takes place in nature where temperatures are low enough for snow to collect year after year. This occurs on mountains where there is enough winter snowfall and low enough temperatures in the summer for snow to remain year round.

As more and more snow collects, air is squeezed out of the snow by the weight of the additional snow. As the snow becomes compacted, it changes into ice.

When the ice becomes thick enough, its weight will cause it to move down the mountain slope, under the pull of gravity. A large mass of moving ice is called a **glacier**. When the glacier moves downward, heat caused by the ice scraping against the bedrock below causes some of the ice to melt. A thin layer of water forms under the glacier, allowing the glacier to slide more easily over rock.

glacialis (ice)

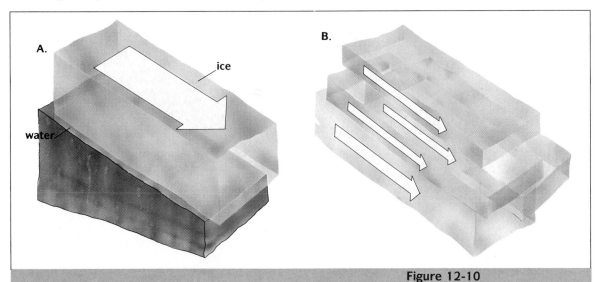

Figure 12-10

A glacier can move down a mountain by sliding on a thin layer of water (*left*). Glaciers can also move when inner layers slip past each other (*right*).

Glaciers can also move because of the pressure inside. Under pressure, the ice forms layers. The force of gravity causes the layers to slide over one another. Look at Figure 12-10. The motion is similar to the movement of cards piled in a stack. The entire stack can be made to move if each card slides forward a small amount.

Figure 12-11

A valley glacier.

There are two types of glaciers: valley glaciers and continental glaciers. Both are masses of moving ice, but they are different because of where they are formed.

Valley glaciers are glaciers that form in mountains. The pull of gravity causes them to flow down the mountains. Look at Figure 12-11. Valley glaciers often look like dirty rivers of ice.

As a glacier moves around curves or over uneven surfaces, the ice near the surface breaks. Large cracks called *crevasses* (kruh VAS ihz) form. Crevasses also form when some parts of a glacier move faster than others.

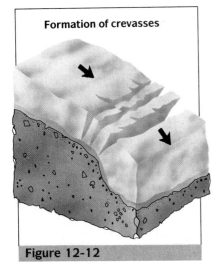

Formation of crevasses

Figure 12-12

As a glacier moves over a hill, the bending of the ice forms crevasses (*left*). Crevasses (*right*).

Figure 12-13
Anarctica is covered by a continental glacier.

The other type of glacier is a continental glacier. A **continental glacier** is an ice sheet that covers a large area of the earth's surface. Today, continental glaciers are found only in Greenland and Antarctica. In Greenland, an ice sheet covers about 1.7 million square km. The ice sheet covering Antarctica is much larger, spreading out over 14 million square km of land.

Even though an ice sheet may rest on ground with little or no slope, it can still move. Look at Figure 12-14. Where is the ice thickest in a continental glacier? The ice forms a dome. The weight of the ice around the center causes the ice sheet to spread outward. The spreading ice can even move over mountains if the dome is higher than the mountains. Eventually, the ice reaches the sea, where huge blocks of ice break off. The blocks of ice that fall into the sea are called *icebergs*.

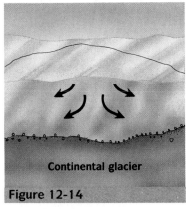

Continental glacier

Figure 12-14

The weight of the ice in a continental glacier causes it to spread outward.

REVIEW

1. How does a glacier form?
2. How does a glacier move?
3. How are valley glaciers and continental glaciers similar? How are they different?

CHALLENGE Snow builds up at the poles near sea level, whereas the snow builds up at the equator above 4500 m. Explain why.

12-5 THE WORK OF GLACIERS

After completing this section, you will be able to

- **describe** two ways that glaciers cause erosion.
- **list** several features left by glaciers.
- **distinguish** between two types of deposits left by glaciers.
- **give** three theories for the cause of the ice ages.

The key terms in this section are

drift   outwash
ice age   till
moraine

EROSIONAL FEATURES

Some of the most spectacular erosional features are found in mountains where valley glaciers form. A valley glacier forms from snow that collects in small hollows on the mountain. Look at Figure 12-15. As the glacier moves down the mountain, it picks up large blocks of rock from the steep slope. The rocks are carried along by moving masses of ice, carving away more rock as well. Rock is scooped away from the hollow, forming a bowl-shaped basin called a *cirque* (serk). A *cirque lake* is formed if water fills the basin after the glacier has left the valley.

Valley glaciers may carve out several cirques close to one another. If the sharp ridges between the cirques join, a peak called a *horn* is formed. The most famous example of this feature is the Matterhorn in Switzerland.

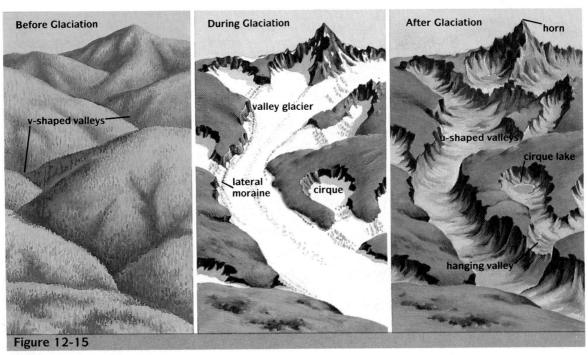

Before Glaciation

v-shaped valleys

During Glaciation

valley glacier

lateral moraine

cirque

After Glaciation

horn

u-shaped valleys

cirque lake

hanging valley

Figure 12-15

Before glacial erosion, a mountain has smooth, rounded surfaces (*left*). Snow and ice collects in hollows on the mountain (*middle*). The mountain is rough and sharp after glacial erosion (*right*).

After flowing down a mountain, a glacier may enter a river valley that is narrower than the glacier. As the glacier squeezes through, it erodes both the floor and the sides of the valley, changing the shape of the valley from a V shape to a broad U shape.

In an area where a large glacier is joined by smaller ones from side valleys, features called hanging valleys are formed. *Hanging valleys* are U-shaped valleys that are above

Figure 12-16
Glaciation caused the parallel grooves or striations in rock.

the level of the floor of the main valley. They are formed when the smaller glaciers erode the side valleys. Streams running in these valleys drop into the main valley in steep waterfalls.

As a glacier moves over land, it leaves many erosional features. For example, large pieces of rock picked up by the glacier can produce long, parallel scratches called *striations* (strī-AY shuhnz) in the bedrock. If the is bedrock is composed of soft rock, the glacier's passage will leave deep *grooves* in the surface of the rock. Small rock materials, such as sand, will polish the surface of the rock bed.

The landscape left by a valley glacier is rugged and filled with sharp peaks. A continental glacier, however, levels the land by eroding everything except the tallest mountains. The landscape it forms is smooth.

DEPOSITIONAL FEATURES

Glacial deposits form when the ice in a glacier melts and rock material is released. The deposits from a glacier are called **drift**. There are two types of drift: till and outwash. **Till** is rock material deposited directly by a glacier when it melts. Till is made up of a mixture of all kinds and sizes of rock particles. **Outwash** is rock material deposited by water produced from the melting of a glacier. Unlike till, the material in outwash has distinct layers, like those produced when sediment settles to the bottom of a lake or stream. When till or outwash pile up, they form various features on the land.

Figure 12-17

Till is a mixture of different sized sediments.

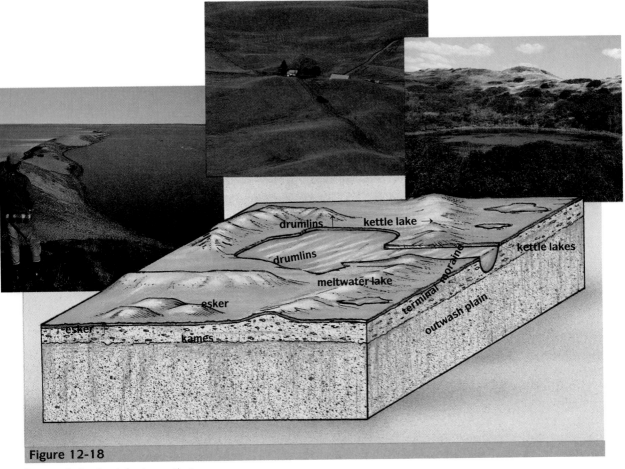

Figure 12-18

Some of the land features that remain after a glacier recedes.

Probably the most common feature made of till is a moraine. A **moraine** is a ridge of till left as a result of the melting of a glacier.

When a ridge of till is deposited at the leading edge of a glacier, it is called a *terminal moraine*. A terminal moraine marks the furthest point of a glacier's movement.

Another feature made of till is a drumlin. A *drumlin* is an oval-shaped hill made of till. A drumlin is usually found as part of a group of drumlins. Groups of drumlins are found near Boston, Massachusetts; Syracuse, New York; and in eastern Wisconsin.

As a glacier melts, meltwater may carry sand, silt, and gravel away from the front of the glacier. When these materials are deposited, they form a feature called an *outwash plain*. Some scientists believe that the loess deposits in the United States were blown from outwash plains.

Features called kettles can be found in an outwash plain. A *kettle* is a depression that forms when a piece of ice breaks off from a glacier and becomes lodged in the

OBJECTIVE

Predict what will happen when a model glacier moves over rock and soil.

MATERIALS

sand, gravel, rocks, metal pie tin, water, flat piece of wood, freezer

PROCEDURE

A. Put sand, gravel, and rocks in a pie tin. Add water, but make sure that some of the rocks extend above the level of the water.

B. Put the tin in a freezer overnight.

C. Remove the tin and invert it on the surface of a flat piece of wood. Push the model glacier along the surface and observe the results.

RESULTS AND CONCLUSIONS

1. What happened to the wood that the "glacier" passed over?
2. What happened to the material carried by the "glacier"?
3. Summarize the effect of erosion by ice on the land.

EXTENSION

Invert the "glacier" so that the side containing sand and gravel is facing up. Place soil on the top of the "glacier." Pour water slowly over the soil.

1. Describe the path of the water as it flows off the "glacier."
2. Where does the soil collect?
3. Does all the soil move? Explain your answer.

plain. When the ice finally melts, a depression is left in the plain. When a kettle fills with water, a *kettle lake* forms.

Long, narrow hills made up of outwash are features called *eskers*. These features are believed to have formed when streams of water beneath a glacier deposited sand and gravel. When the glacier melted, the ridges of drift remained. Another kind of feature formed by an outwash deposit is a kame. A *kame* is a cone-shaped hill of sand and gravel left by glacial meltwater. Kames may have formed from material that collected in openings of the glacier. When the glacier melted, the meltwater deposited the material in steep-sided hills.

ICE AGES

About 20,000 years ago, one third of the land on the earth was covered with ice. Ice covered more than half of North America and northern Europe. In some places in the northern United States, the ice was more than a kilometer thick. During this period, so much water was locked up in ice that the sea level was almost 100 m lower than it is today.

Scientists believe that great amounts of ice formed during periods of time when the earth was much cooler than it is today. These cool periods lasted tens of thousands of years. This allowed ice sheets to grow enormously in size. The ice sheets advanced hundreds of kilometers from the north and south toward the equator. A cool period in which ice sheets advanced is called an **ice age**.

Figure 12-19

Large ice sheets covered much of North America during the last ice age.

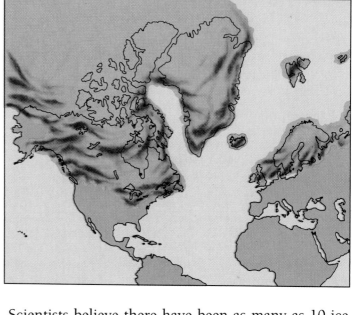

Scientists believe there have been as many as 10 ice ages in the past 2 million years. Each ice age lasted for thousands of years and was followed by a longer, warmer period. During these warmer periods, there were few or no ice sheets on the land. The last ice sheet disappeared from the northern United States about 10,000 years ago.

Many theories have been proposed to explain what caused the ice ages. One theory explains that dust from large numbers of erupting volcanoes could have been put into the atmosphere. How could the dust have caused the earth to cool?

Another theory explains that the ice ages took place during periods of time when the sun gave off less energy. Today it is known that the sun goes through cycles in which it becomes more active and less active. However it is not known if such cycles take place over long periods of time.

A theory that is becoming more accepted by scientists explains that the ice ages were caused by changes in the tilt of the earth's axis and in its orbit around the sun. The tilt of the earth's axis is what causes the earth to have seasons. For example, summer takes place in the Northern Hemisphere when the earth's axis is pointed toward the sun. When the earth's axis is pointed away from the sun, winter takes place. Thus a change in the tilt of the earth's axis can cause a change in the amount of heat the earth receives.

In addition, the earth's temperature could have been affected by changes in the shape of the earth's orbit around the sun. This could have put the earth a little farther from the sun during the summer than it is now. The earth would have had cooler summers, allowing snow to remain in the Northern Hemisphere all year round. The combined changes of the earth's tilt and orbit could have caused the temperature to drop enough for an ice age to occur.

REVIEW

1. What are two ways that glaciers cause erosion?
2. Name and describe several features left by glaciers.
3. What is the difference between till and outwash?
4. Describe three theories for the cause of the ice ages.

CHALLENGE The beaches on the north side of New York's Long Island are made up mainly of a mixture of rocks, gravel, and sand. The beaches on the south side are made up mainly of fine sand. How can this be explained?

CHAPTER SUMMARY

The main ideas in this chapter are listed below. Read these statements before you answer the Chapter Review questions.

- The earth's land surface is worn away in a process called erosion. (12-1)

- The main agents of erosion on the earth's surface are running water, wind, and moving ice. (12-2)

- Over time, a river goes through three stages of development: youth, maturity, and old age. (12-2)

- Wind causes erosion by picking up small particles and carrying them away, and by abrading rocks in its path with the rock particles it carries. (12-3)

- There are two kinds of glaciers: valley glaciers, which form in mountains, and continental glaciers, which form over large areas of land. (12-4)

- Glaciers cause erosion by picking up and carrying away rock material and by abrading bedrock with the rock material they carry.

- A theory that explains the ice ages states that they were caused by changes in the tilt of the earth's axis and in the shape of the earth's orbit. (12-5)

The key terms in this chapter are listed below. Use each term in a sentence that shows the meaning of the term.

abrasion	glacier	runoff
continental glacier	ice age	stream
deflation	loess	till
deposition	moraine	tributaries
drift	outwash	valley glaciers
dune	river	watershed
erosion		

Chapter Review

VOCABULARY

Write the letter of the term that best matches the definition. Not all the terms will be used.

1. An area that provides water for a stream
2. Layered deposit of sand and gravel from a glacier
3. Erosion of rock surfaces by wind-blown sand
4. A period when ice sheets covered large parts of the earth
5. Moving mass of snow and ice
6. Main body of flowing water
7. Removal of weathered rock
8. Carrying away of loose particles by the wind
9. Settling of wind blown material
10. Large mound of sand deposited by the wind

a. erosion
b. abrasion
c. deflation
d. watershed
e. dune
f. loess
g. river
h. glacier
i. ice age
j. outwash
k. tributary

CONCEPTS

1. What are the main agents of erosion on the land surface of the earth? (12-1)
2. Describe two ways that erosion can occur. (12-1)
3. Describe how the deposits of running water, wind, and ice differ. (12-1)
4. Where does the water in rivers come from? (12-2)
5. What is the difference between a stream and a river? (12-2)
6. How is most erosion done by rivers? (12-2)
7. What factors could cause a river to go through its stages of development more quickly? (12-2)
8. What determines the age of a river? (12-2)
9. Name two features caused by wind erosion. (12-3)
10. How does a dune move? (12-3)
11. How does loess form? (12-3)
12. How does a snowfield become a glacier? (12-4)
13. Compare the way a valley glacier moves with the way a continental glacier moves. (12-4)
14. Compare where valley glaciers are found with where continental glaciers are found. (12-4)

15. How is erosion by valley glaciers different from erosion by continental glaciers? (12-5)

16. Explain how each of the following features is formed: cirque, horn, U-shaped valley, hanging valley. (12-5)

17. Compare the material found in a terminal moraine with the material found in an outwash plain. (12-5)

18. How does the material in outwash compare with deposits left by streams? (12-5)

19. Describe the earth's ice sheets during the last ice age, 20,000 years ago. (12-5)

20. Explain how changes in the earth's axis and in the shape of its orbit could have caused an ice age. (12-5)

1. Why must wind have a much greater velocity than water to move the same size particles?

2. The Colorado River has eroded some places in the Grand Canyon to a depth of 1800 m over the past 10 million years. What is the average rate of erosion per year? Will this rate continue forever? Explain your answer.

3. List the observations that would lead you to believe the following agents of erosion had been active in an area: running water, wind, and glaciers.

4. Erosion by running water and wind is more destructive than erosion by glaciers to humankind. Explain why.

1. Set a white pan filled with water outside on a window sill. After a couple of days, observe the water to see if any sediment has collected in the pan. What does this show about air? If possible, try placing several pans at different heights. Observe the pans after a couple of days. Explain any differences in the types and amounts of sediment collected.

2. Rub a fresh ice cube across the surface of wood. Observe any marks made by the ice on the wood. Then put the ice in some sand and rub the ice across the wood again. What do you observe? What type of erosion does this represent?

3. After a heavy rain, look around the school grounds for evidence of erosion. Make a list of your observations.

Bailey, Ronald H. *Glacier*. Alexandria, Va.: Time-Life Books Inc., 1982.

Fodor, R.V. *Chiseling the Earth: How Erosion Shapes the Land*. Hillside, N.J.: Enslow Publishers, 1983.

Page, Jake. *Arid Lands*. Alexandria, Va.: Time-Life Books Inc., 1984.

Pringle, Laurance. *Rivers and Lakes*. Alexandria, Va.: Time-Life Books Inc., 1985.

PLATE TECTONICS

This photograph, showing water bordered on both sides by rock, was taken in Iceland. Notice that the rock material on both sides of the flowing water appears to be the same. Yet scientists do not think that the water is responsible for wearing away the rock. In fact, the rocks on opposite sides of the water seem to be separating.

- *What could cause these rocks to separate, or pull apart?*
- *Why is such a feature found in Iceland?*
- *What other types of movement of the earth's crust occur?*

13-1 DO CONTINENTS MOVE?

Once there were tropical plants in Antarctica and ice sheets in Africa. Much of North America contained tropical forests. What could have caused those climates?

Many years ago scientists did not have much information to explain past climates. It was not until the early 1900s that a theory was introduced that could explain past climates. This theory would answer many other questions about how the earth worked. It is important, however, to take a look at the ideas that came before that important theory.

Look at the coastlines of Africa and South America in Figure 13-1. What observation can you make about the coastlines of these two continents? In the past, many people had observed that the east coast of South America and the west coast of Africa could fit together like the pieces of a puzzle. The first person to try to explain the fit of these continents was Alexander von Humboldt in 1801. Humboldt found that South America and Africa had more similarities than just the fit of their coastlines. He found that several mountain ranges which existed on the east coast of South America seemed to fit with those on the west coast of Africa. He concluded that the continents had become separated by erosion. He believed that the Atlantic Ocean was a valley formed by erosion.

After completing this section, you will be able to

- **list** three reasons why some scientists believed that South America and Africa were once a single land mass.
- **describe** the Mid-Atlantic Ridge.

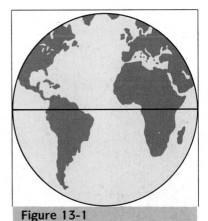

Figure 13-1

Notice the coastlines of Africa and South America.

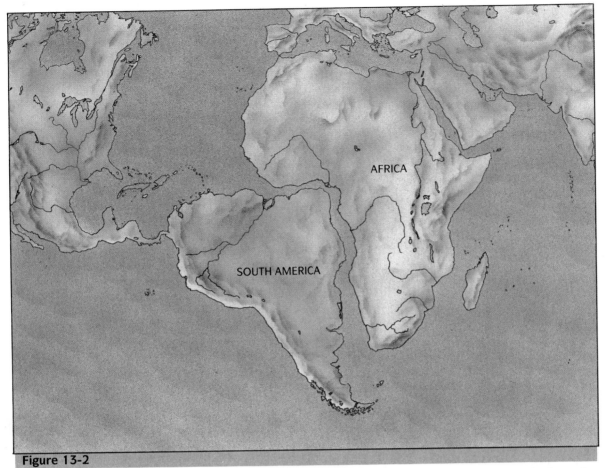

Figure 13-2

The jigsaw-puzzle fit of the coastlines of South America and Africa led some scientists to think that these continents were once joined.

In 1858, Antonio Snider-Pellegrini stated that the similarities of the east coast of South America and the west coast of Africa were evidence that all the continents were once a single land mass that then moved apart.

In 1908, an American geologist named Frank Taylor proposed that a major undersea mountain range between South America and Africa was the place where the two continents began separating. The mountain range was called the Mid-Atlantic Ridge. He said that the mountain range did not move but that South America and Africa moved away from it. Taylor and others were suggesting the startling idea that the earth's continents move.

REVIEW

1. Why did some scientists believe the continents may have been joined together at one time?
2. Describe Taylor's idea about the Mid-Atlantic Ridge.

CHALLENGE Would the discovery of young ocean crust support the idea that the continents are separating? Explain your answer.

13-2 CONTINENTAL DRIFT THEORY

In 1912, a young scientist named Alfred Wegener proposed a theory to explain many of the similarities between the continents. His theory was called the theory of continental drift. The **theory of continental drift** states that the continents were once together and had broken apart and moved to their present positions.

Like many scientists before him, Wegener saw the jigsaw fit between South America and Africa. Wegener compared facing sections of the two continents. He found that the types of rocks on both coasts matched. He also found that a mountain range in South America linked up with a similar mountain range in Africa.

Wegener used his theory to explain climate changes on the earth. For example, Antarctica, which now has a cold climate, once had a warm climate. Scientists know this because remains of tropical plants and animals have been found in Antarctica. Wegener explained that Antarctica was once closer to the equator and had drifted toward the South Pole. As a result, it now has a colder climate. Wegener also used his theory to explain the tropical climate that once existed in North America.

After completing this section, you will be able to

- **describe** the theory of continental drift.
- **list** four pieces of evidence that Wegener used to support the theory of continental drift.
- **explain** why the theory of continental drift was not accepted.

The key terms in this section are
  Gondwanaland
  Laurasia
  Pangaea
  theory of continental drift

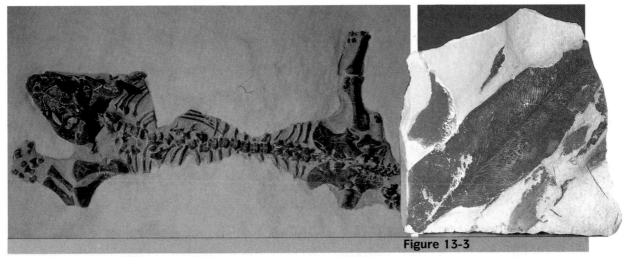

Figure 13-3

Fossils of *Glossopteris* (*right*) have been found in India and Australia. Fossils of *Lystrosaurus* (*left*) have been found in South America and Africa.

As further evidence for his theory, Wegener pointed to similar fossils found on different continents. Fossils are the remains of past life. For example, fossils of the plant *Glossopteris*, shown in Figure 13-3, were found in India and Australia. Fossils of a small reptile called *Lystrosaurus* were found in South America and Africa. Since it was unlikely that plants and animals crossed the oceans, the continents must have been together at one time.

Some scientists proposed a different theory to explain why similar fossils were found on different continents. They said that the continents were once connected by land bridges. Such bridges enabled plant and animal life to move between the continents. They believed that the land bridges eventually sank under the oceans. However, no traces of the bridges were ever found.

Wegener proposed that all the continents were once joined into a single land mass. He called this large land mass **Pangaea** (pan JEE uh). *Pangaea* means "all lands." He said that Pangaea had existed 300 million years ago. He proposed that Pangaea began to separate into a northern continent and a southern continent about 200 million years ago. The northern land mass he called **Laurasia**. It separated into the land masses of North America, Europe, and Asia. The southern land mass he called **Gondwanaland**. It separated into the land masses of India, Australia, Africa, South America, and Antarctica. The land masses then slowly pushed their way along the sea floor to their positions today.

Wegener could not explain how continents could move through the solid crust of the sea floor. Some scientists suggested that even if the continents did move, the coasts of the continents would change. In addition, Wegener could not explain what force could be powerful enough to move continents. Thus the theory of continental drift was not accepted by most scientists at that time.

pan (all)

Figure 13-4

A stamp honoring Wegener's idea of drifting continents.

ACTIVITY   Puzzling Pangaea

OBJECTIVE
Construct a map of how the continents of Pangaea might have been joined.

MATERIALS
scissors, tracing paper, pencil

PROCEDURE
A. Trace and cut out the continents.
B. Try different ways to fit the continents together so that one large continent is formed.
C. Write the name of the continent on each puzzle piece.

RESULTS AND CONCLUSIONS
1. In how many ways do the continents fit together?
2. Fossils on the coastline of continent *E* should match those found on continent _____.
3. Fossils on the coastline of continent *B* should match those found on continent _____.
4. In what direction did continent *C* move to get from Pangaea to its present-day position?

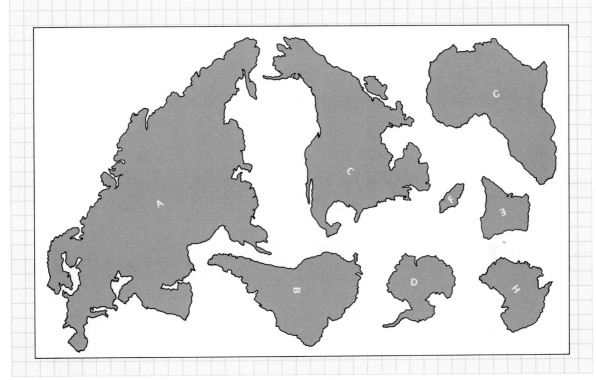

REVIEW

1. Describe the theory of continental drift.
2. On what evidence did Wegener base his theory of continental drift?
3. Why wasn't the theory of continental drift accepted by most scientists?

CHALLENGE Look at Figure 13-2. Why doesn't the east coast of South America perfectly match the west coast of Africa?

13-3 SEA-FLOOR SPREADING

Finding out how continents can move through the solid ocean floor was difficult for scientists. During World War II, however, equipment was developed to locate submarines. Scientists found that they could use this equipment to map and explore the ocean floor.

While mapping the ocean floor, scientists made some surprising and important discoveries. One discovery was that the thick layer of sediment that they supposed had settled on the ocean floor over billions of years was not there. Instead, they found a thin layer of sediment. This layer represented only 100 million to 200 million years of settling. What explanation can you suggest for there being only a thin layer of sediment?

Another discovery was made near the Mid-Atlantic Ridge, a mountain range running through the center of the Atlantic Ocean floor. There, scientists found pillow lava. Pillow lava, shown in Figure 13-5, is a kind of rock that forms when lava cools underwater.

Figure 13-5

Pillow lava forms when lava cools underwater.

Scientists also discovered that the Mid-Atlantic Ridge is connected to other ocean ridges. The ridges form a continuous chain of underwater mountains around the earth. The continuous chain of mountains on the floor of the major oceans is called the **Mid-Ocean Ridge**.

The Mid-Ocean Ridge is the largest surface feature of the earth. The ridge is about 65,000 km long and 500–5000 km wide. The Mid-Ocean Ridge encircles the earth simi-

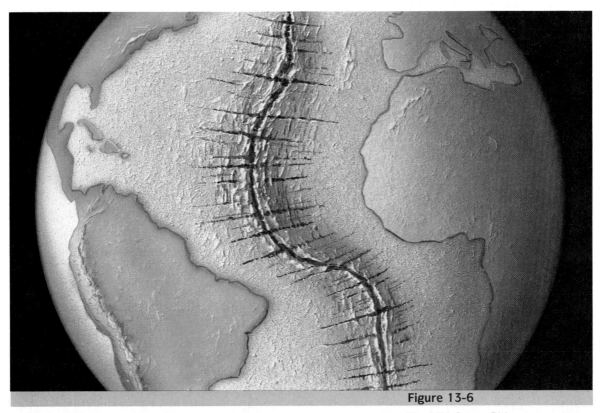

Figure 13-6

The Mid-Ocean Ridge.

lar to the way in which a seam encircles a baseball. Look at Figure 13-6. Notice that the ridge is a continuous chain of mountains between the continents.

Scientists also found a deep, narrow valley called a **rift valley** running through the center of the Mid-Ocean Ridge. They found, too, that the rift valley was warmer than any other part of the ocean floor. Scientists have produced computer-generated maps of the world, based on measurements taken from space. Such maps have led scientists to believe that the Mid-Ocean Ridge was a place where molten rock was rising out of the ocean floor. As the molten rock hardened, it formed new ocean floor.

The idea that new ocean floor formed at the Mid-Ocean Ridge led to a new theory called sea-floor spreading. The **theory of sea-floor spreading** says that the Mid-Ocean Ridge is a crack in the earth's crust through which molten rock rises to the surface. The molten rock spreads out and adds new material to the ocean floor. The new material is carried away from the Mid-Ocean Ridge. Sea-floor spreading explains the existence of pillow lava near the ridge and the absence of thick layers of sediment on the ocean floor. In fact, near the ridge, sediment is not found.

One of the most important contributions of the theory of sea-floor spreading was that it could explain how continents moved. As the ocean floor moved, the continents were carried along like logs in a moving ice floe.

Possibly the most convincing evidence for sea-floor spreading was the information gained from magnetism in rocks. A compass needle lines up with the magnetic poles of the earth. The magnetic poles are near the geographic North Pole and South Pole.

Iron mineral grains in magma also line up in the direction of the earth's magnetic field. When magma hardens into rock, the grains remain lined up in the direction of the earth's magnetic field. Some rocks on the ocean floor were found with iron mineral grains lined up in one direction. Other rocks were found with iron mineral grains lined up in the opposite direction.

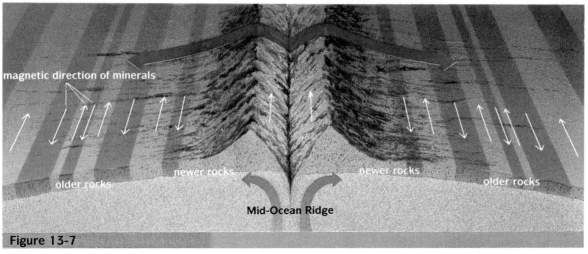

Figure 13-7

The direction in which iron-containing minerals on the sea floor are magnetized varies. This indicates that the sea floor was not all formed at one time.

Some scientists said that reversed positions of the magnetic grains could provide evidence for sea-floor spreading. If molten rock was rising in the Mid-Ocean Ridge, it would be magnetized in the direction of the earth's magnetic field as it cooled. It was thought that the poles had reversed from time to time. If the sea floor was spreading, it would contain bands of rock. These bands would be parallel to the ridge, and would be magnetized in opposite directions. As shown in Figure 13-7, bands of rock were magnetized in opposite directions parallel to the Mid-Ocean Ridge.

In 1968, scientists were able to obtain direct evidence for the theory of sea-floor spreading. Using the research ship *Glomar Challenger,* scientists collected rock samples

ACTIVITY   A Model of Sea-Floor Spreading

OBJECTIVE
Demonstrate the process of sea-floor spreading.

MATERIALS
2 sheets of notebook paper, ruler, scissors

PROCEDURE
A. Using a ruler, measure and draw three 10-cm lines on a sheet of paper, as shown.
B. Draw mountain peaks on the outer side of each end line.
C. Use scissors to make a slit along each of the lines you have drawn.

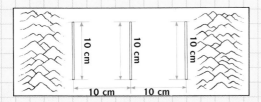

1. If the sheet of paper is the ocean floor, what does the middle slit represent? Label it.

D. Use the second sheet of paper to make two strips, 9.5 cm wide and about 27 cm long. Put the two strips face to face and run them through the middle slit.
2. What do these strips represent? Write this term on each strip.

E. Pull both strips out of the slit about 6 cm. Lay the "ocean floor" on your lap so that the strips underneath are held gently in place by your knees. Insert each strip into the outer slit closest to it. See the diagram. Continue to pull the strips up through the slit and observe.

3. Which part of the strips represent young crust? Old crust? Write the word *old* on the part of each strip you believe represents the old crust.

RESULTS AND CONCLUSIONS
1. How is actual sea-floor spreading similar to your model?
2. Where are the oldest rocks found on the ocean floor? the youngest rocks?

from both sides of the Mid-Ocean Ridge. Studies of these rocks showed that those found nearest to the ridge were the youngest in age. The rocks found farthest from the ridge were the oldest. How are these findings evidence for the formation of new ocean floor and the theory of sea-floor spreading?

REVIEW
1. What is the theory of sea-floor spreading?
2. How is the theory of sea-floor spreading different from the theory of continental drift?
3. Give four pieces of evidence that support the theory of sea-floor spreading.

CHALLENGE If new material is being added to the sea floor and the sea floor is spreading, does this mean that the earth is getting larger? Explain your answer.

13-4 PLATE TECTONICS

The land below you is moving. This movement may be only a few centimeters a year. But over millions of years, a land mass can move across the earth and back. How does a land mass move?

The discovery of sea-floor spreading showed that sections of the earth's crust did move. However, discoveries in science often raise new questions. For example, were other sections of the earth's crust moving? What force could move such huge sections of the earth's crust?

One answer to these questions came from earthquakes. When the locations of earthquakes were plotted on a world map, many were found to occur along the path of the Mid-Ocean Ridge. Also, the locations of earthquakes formed a pattern on a map that appeared to divide the earth's surface into different sections. This pattern led scientists to believe that the earth's crust was broken into

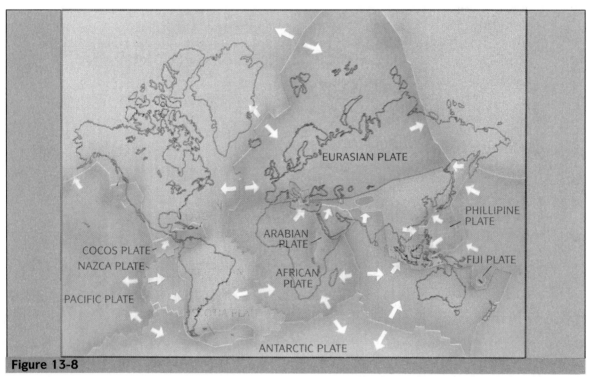

Figure 13-8

The earth's major plates.

sections, or plates. Based on this idea and the ideas of continental drift and sea-floor spreading, scientists proposed the theory of plate tectonics.

The **theory of plate tectonics** states that the earth's lithosphere is broken into moving plates. The **plates** are rigid blocks of the earth's outer crust that are about 50–150 km thick. Scientists have identified about 7 major plates and 18 minor plates. As you can see in Figure 13-8, many of the plates have the same names as the continents they carry. What is the name of the plate you live on? The plates float on a zone in the upper mantle known as the **asthenosphere** (as THEHN uh sfihr). The asthenosphere is about 200 km thick.

asthenia (weak)

Most of the plates have both continental and oceanic crust. Some plates are made up almost wholly of oceanic crust or continental crust. For example, the Pacific Plate is made up almost entirely of oceanic crust.

What force could be moving the plates over the asthenosphere? One answer is the heat inside the earth. It is believed that the heat in the earth causes convection currents in the mantle. A *convection current* is the movement of material caused by differences in temperature. Convection currents can be illustrated by heating water. As water near the heat source is warmed, it rises. As the water cools near the surface, it returns to the bottom. The moving water forms a convection current.

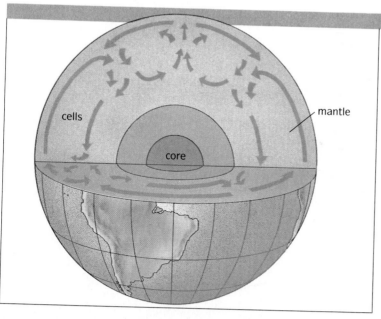

Figure 13-9

Convection currents in the mantle may be involved in the movement of plates.

cells

mantle

core

Scientists believe that heat within the earth causes the material in the mantle to rise in the area of the Mid-Ocean Ridge and spread out. As the material cools, it sinks back down into the mantle.

Scientists do not have much information about how convection currents actually move plates. For example, it is not known how deep in the mantle the convection currents are found. Some scientists believe the currents reach the bottom of the mantle. Others believe they exist only in the upper part, or the first 700 km, of the mantle. Convection currents cannot explain the different sizes of the plates, since different-size convection currents would have to be produced.

Hot plumes of rock might be another possible force that could be moving the plates. Plumes are columns of molten rock that rise from places deep in the mantle called *hot spots*. The plume material then spreads out under the plates, carrying the plates along with it. As with convection currents, the movement of plumes is caused by heat.

Sometimes a plume can melt a hole in a plate. The plume can then rise through the hole and form a volcano. It is believed that the volcanoes that make up Hawaii were formed by plumes as the Pacific Plate moved over a hot spot. The volcano Kilavea is shown in Figure 13-10. As time passes, Kilavea will move away from the hot spot. Why will this occur?

Figure 13-10

The Hawaiian Islands may have formed from volcanic material flowing from a hot spot under the Pacific Plate.

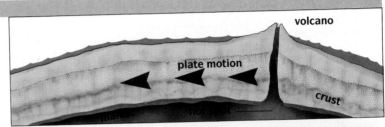

OBJECTIVES

Demonstrate the concept of convection.

Formulate a conclusion about hot spots that supports the plate tectonic theory.

MATERIALS

2-hole rubber stopper to fit vial, 2 pieces of plastic capillary tubing to fit rubber stopper, small vial, 500-mL beaker, red food coloring, hot tap water, cold tap water

PROCEDURE

A. Place 350 mL of cold tap water in a 500-mL beaker.
B. Set up a vial, rubber stopper, and plastic capillary tubing as shown.
C. Add hot tap water to the vial, then add a few drops of red food coloring.
D. Place the vial in the beaker of cold tap water. Make sure the water covers the top of the capillary tubing.
E. Record your observations and explain what is happening.

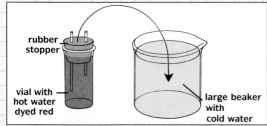

F. Sometimes islands and seamounts are formed over hot spots where plumes of lava rise. The hot spot lies beneath the plate and does not move. Examine the map and answer the following questions.

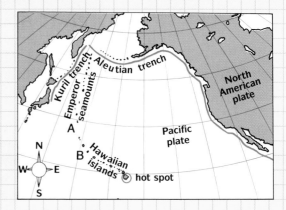

1. If the islands are forming over the hot spot, which one is older, A or B? Why?
2. Which island is younger, A or B? Why?
3. In what direction does the ocean floor seem to be moving at the present time? What evidence supports your answer?
4. What evidence do you have that there has been a change in direction in the movement of the ocean plate?
5. Where do you predict the next island will form?
6. In what direction was the plate moving when the Emperor seamounts were formed?

RESULTS AND CONCLUSIONS

1. What kind of heat transfer did you demonstrate with the hot water and the cold water?
2. How do convection currents support the theory of plate tectonics?
3. How does the occurrence of hot spots support the theory of plate tectonics?

REVIEW

1. What is the theory of plate tectonics?
2. How is the theory of plate tectonics different from the theory of continental drift?
3. What are two explanations for the movement of plates?

CHALLENGE The North American, South American, Eurasian, and African plates move at a rate of about 2 cm a year. The Pacific, Nazca, and Cocos plates move at a rate of about 12 cm a year. Based on Figure 13-8 on page 304, explain what might cause this difference in speed.

13-5 PLATE TECTONIC FEATURES

After completing this section, you will be able to

- **describe** three kinds of plate boundaries.
- **name** two features that can form when plates collide.
- **explain** how the continents formed.

The key terms in this section are

convergent boundary
divergent boundary
plate boundaries
subduction
subduction zone
tranform fault
trench

divergere (to slope in different directions)

PLATE BOUNDARIES

One day southern California will be part of the Alaskan coast. Moving at the rate of about 5 cm a year, it is believed that southern California will collide with Alaska in about 150 million years. This is one example of how the surface of the earth is rearranged.

The plates that make up the earth's crust fit together like pieces of a jigsaw puzzle. No one plate can move without affecting another plate.

The areas where the plates meet are called **plate boundaries**. There are three types of plate boundaries. Each plate boundary describes how the two plates that meet move relative to each other.

One type of plate boundary is called a divergent boundary. A **divergent boundary** is the place where plates move apart, leaving a space between the two plates. Based on Figure 13-11, what is an example of a divergent boundary? The space is filled with molten rock from the asthenosphere as the plates separate. The rock cools to form a new section of the sea floor.

Figure 13-11

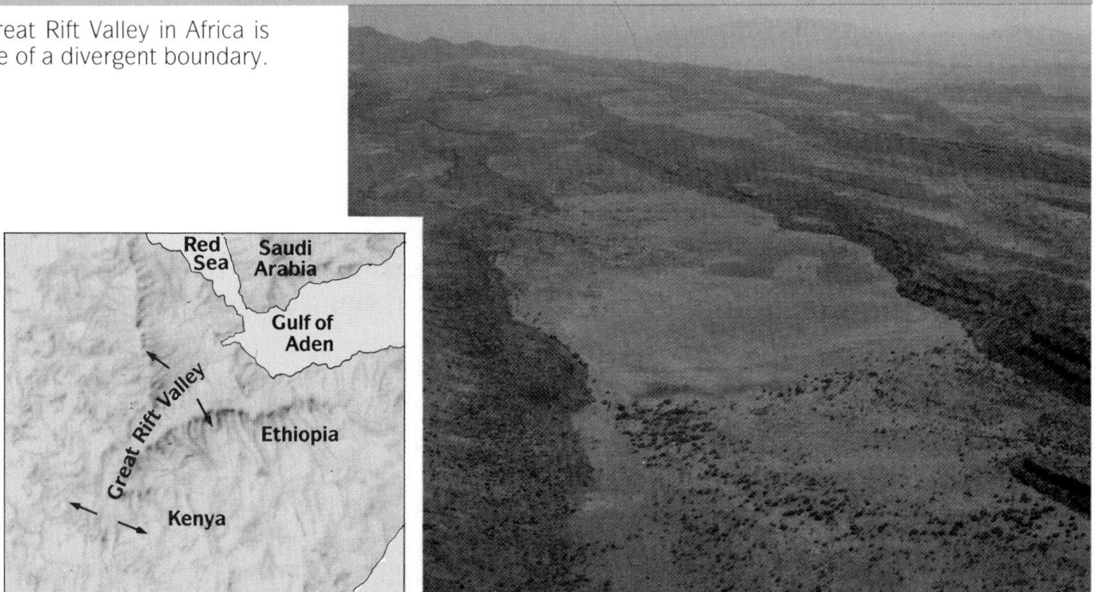

The Great Rift Valley in Africa is the site of a divergent boundary.

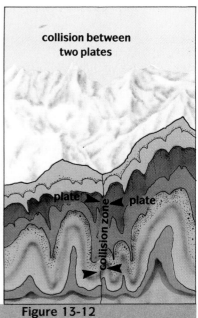

Figure 13-12

When plates carrying continents collide, mountain ranges form.

When two plates separate, there must be a place where other plates come together. A place where two plates come together is called a **convergent boundary**. Collisions can occur between two continental plates, between two ocean plates, and between a continental plate and an ocean plate.

As shown in Figure 13-12, when two continental plates bump into each other, they crumple, forming mountain ranges. The Himalayas were formed when the Indo-Australian Plate collided with the Eurasian Plate.

When two ocean plates collide, the edge of the older plate is bent downward and slides under the edge of the younger plate. This is because the older plate has cooled more than the younger plate and is denser. The process by which one plate is pushed below another because of a plate collision is called **subduction**. The area where a plate is pushed below another plate is called a **subduction zone**. The lower plate bends and sinks into the asthenosphere, where it is destroyed by intense heat and pressure. The lithosphere is destroyed at about the same rate as it is being made.

As the older, denser plate sinks into the earth, it forms a trench. A **trench** is a deep valley feature on the sea floor that is produced next to the subduction zone. A trench can be as much as 11 km deep, 100 km wide, and more than 1500 km long. The Mariana Trench, where the Pacific plate is sinking into the earth, is the deepest part of the sea floor in the world. It is 11 km below the surface of the ocean.

convergere (incline together)

sub (under)

When one ocean plate edge is bent down into a trench, the materials melt, and volcanic activity begins. Volcanoes form on the ocean floor. If the activity goes on, volcanic islands, like the Aleutian Islands, will be formed. A group of volcanic islands formed by subduction is called an *island arc*. Look at Figure 13-13. Notice that a line of volcanic islands has formed. The line of islands is caused by the movement of the plate over the earth's surface.

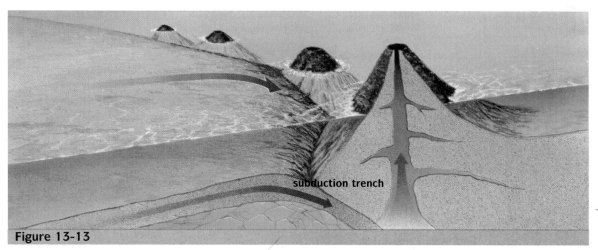

subduction trench

Figure 13-13

Volcanic islands can form along a subduction zone.

Collisions may also occur between plates carrying oceanic crust and continental crust. If the plate carrying continental crust sinks, the lighter continental material does not sink. Instead, its edge folds into mountains, causing some ocean crust to be deposited on top.

If the oceanic plate sinks under the continental plate, the oceanic crust is melted as it plunges into the asthenosphere. The melted materials may rise, forming volcanic mountains, such as the Andes. The Andes were formed when the Nazca Plate sank below the South American Plate.

The third type of boundary is a transform fault. A **transform fault** is a boundary where plates slide past each other. Figure 13-14 illustrates a transform fault. An example of a transform fault is the San Andreas Fault in California. Here the Pacific Plate is moving northwest relative to the North American Plate. Predict what might happen to the peninsula of Baja in California if this movement continues. As the plates move past each other, sections of the plate become locked. Stress builds up until the plates suddenly slip past each other. An earthquake results. Figure 13-14 shows an area along the San Andreas Fault.

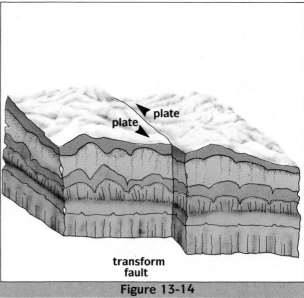

Figure 13-14

Earthquakes are frequent along transform faults.

CONTINENTS

The crust that makes up the continents is very different from the crust that makes up the ocean floor. For example, the continental crust is much older than the oceanic crust. Some parts of the continental crust have been measured to be over 2 billion years old. No part of the ocean floor has been found to be more than 160 million years old. Another difference is in the types of rock that make up each kind of crust. Continental crust is made up mostly of granite, an igneous rock that has low density. Oceanic crust is made up mostly of basalt, an igneous rock that has a high density. How does plate tectonics explain these differences?

As you have learned, the ocean floor is destroyed in subduction zones and created at the Mid-Ocean Ridge. Thus the ocean floor is renewed. However, continents are not renewed. Unlike the ocean floor, continents are permanent features of the earth's crust.

But how did the continents form? One theory explains that the continents formed early in the earth's history, possibly before plate tectonics was active. At that time, the earth was still molten. It is believed that the continents formed when minerals, low in density, floated upward from the mantle to the earth's surface and hardened. This may explain why continents are made up mostly of rocks low in density such as granite. After the continents were formed, they drifted on plates to new parts of the earth through the process of plate tectonics.

SCIENCE PUZZLER

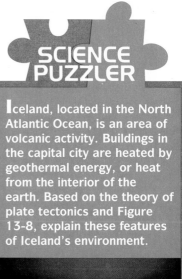

Iceland, located in the North Atlantic Ocean, is an area of volcanic activity. Buildings in the capital city are heated by geothermal energy, or heat from the interior of the earth. Based on the theory of plate tectonics and Figure 13-8, explain these features of Iceland's environment.

311

A technique called seismic profiling is allowing earth scientists to explore deep beneath the earth's crust. Seismic profiling is giving scientists new data on how the continents may have formed.

The basic process of seismic profiling involves sending powerful vibrations, or seismic waves, deep into the earth. Faults and changes in rock composition reflect the waves back to the surface. Special receivers pick up the signals. The data collected is processed by computers. The product is a "snapshot" of the earth's crust from the surface down to the mantle. The snapshot shows the structure of the rock, including faults and other features.

Scientists had long thought that the continents were formed by up-and-down shifting of rocks over time. Data from seismic profiling shows that rocks have shifted sideways as well. This suggests that continents are formed from many chunks of material that are continually being pushed against each other. As a result, large pieces of continents are relatively young.

Using seismic profiling, scientists will unravel some of the earth's mysteries. Perhaps they will be able to predict how the continents will change in the future.

As the continents drifted, they may have collided with smaller land masses. These smaller land masses may have become attached to the edges of the continents, increasing the size of the continents. The process of adding rock material to the edges of continents as a result of plate collisions is called *continental accretion.*

Evidence shows that the continents may have "grown" through continental accretion. For example, the west coast of North America contains pieces of ocean crust and volcanic islands. Many of the rocks found in Alaska show that the area was once a tropical island. In addition, Alaska and the west coast of North America are much younger than the rest of North America. Scientists think these areas were added to North America by continental accretion.

REVIEW

1. Describe three types of plate boundaries.
2. How do trenches and island arcs form?
3. How did the continents form?

CHALLENGE At one time, scientists believed that all living things depended on the sun as a source of energy. However, in 1977, a whole community of living things was found near the Mid-Ocean Ridge, where sunlight does not reach. What source of energy is used here?

13-6 THE CONTINENTS IN TIME

Two hundred million years ago there was just one continent, called Pangaea, surrounded by one huge ocean. Evidence shows, however, that plate tectonic activity had begun before this, about 2 billion years ago. Evidence from magnetism in rocks, fossils, and past climates shows that Pangaea was not the first single continent. Based on this evidence, scientists have reconstructed the earth's surface in the past.

About 500 million years ago, a single "supercontinent" began breaking into four pieces. Two of the northern land masses came together about 110 million years later, forming the land mass called Laurasia. The collision of these two land masses formed part of the Appalachian mountain chain in North America. Laurasia contained the future land masses of North America, Europe, and Asia. The other two land masses south of Laurasia also came together, forming the land mass of Gondwanaland. Gondwanaland contained the future land masses of South America, Africa, India, Australia, and Antarctica.

Then about 250 million years ago, Laurasia collided with Gondwanaland, forming the single continent of Pangaea. Look at Figure 13-15B. What type of land feature probably formed as a result of this collision?

After completing this section, you will be able to

- **list** the kinds of information that scientists have used to plot the past positions of the continents.
- **describe** the possible future positions of the continents.

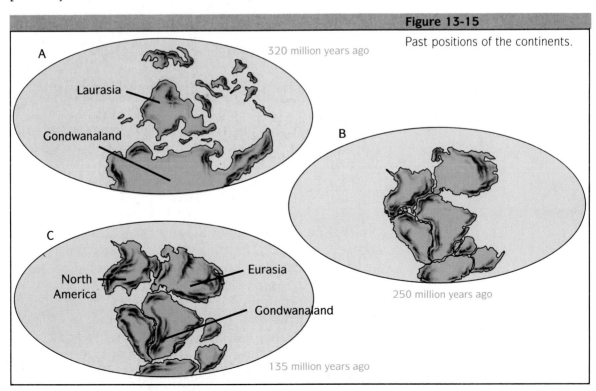

Figure 13-15

Past positions of the continents.

A — Laurasia / Gondwanaland — 320 million years ago

B — 250 million years ago

C — North America / Eurasia / Gondwanaland — 135 million years ago

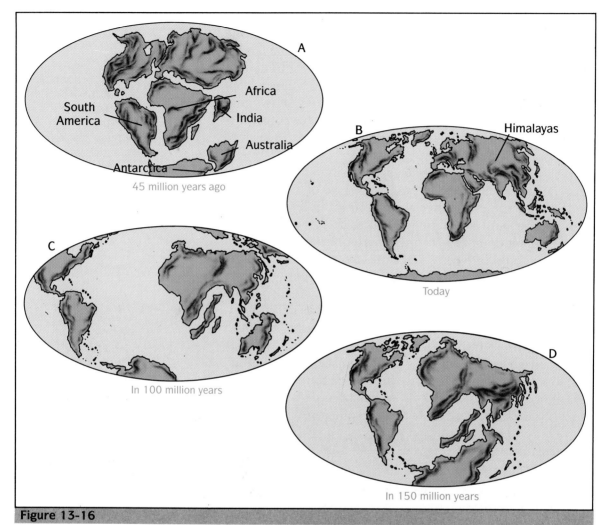

Figure 13-16

The locations of the continents in the future will differ from their locations today.

By about 135 million years ago, Pangaea had split into three land masses. From Figure 13-15C, what were the names of those land masses?

By 45 million years ago, Gondwanaland had separated into five continents. Using Figure 13-16A, what were the names of those continents?

Figure 13-16B shows the positions of the continents today. Notice that The Himalayas are located where India became attached to Asia. What has happened to North America and South America?

If the present plate movements continue, in 100 million years Africa will collide with Europe, the Atlantic Ocean will become the largest ocean, and Africa's Great Rift Valley will become a seaway. Look at Figure 13-16C. What will happen to the Mediterranean Sea?

REVIEW

1. What information have scientists used to plot the past positions of the continents?
2. Describe how the continent of Pangaea formed and what happened to it.
3. If present plate movements continue, how will the positions of the continents change?

CHALLENGE Dinosaurs originated about 200 million years ago on Pangaea. However, they became extinct about 65 million years ago. What changes could plate tectonics have caused that may have led to the extinction of the dinosaurs?

CHAPTER SUMMARY

The main ideas in this chapter are listed below. Read these statements before you answer the Chapter Review questions.

- The apparent fit of South America and Africa led some scientists to believe that the continents were once a single land mass. (13-1)

- The theory of continental drift was used to explain similar rocks, fossils, and mountain ranges and changes in climate on the continents. (13-2)

- The discovery of sea-floor spreading enabled scientists to explain how continents could move. (13-3)

- The theory of plate tectonics states that the earth's crust is broken into moving plates.

- The theory of plate tectonics provides scientists with a way of explaining many features of the earth's crust. (13-4)

- Many of the features of the earth's crust are caused by plates coming into contact with one another. (13-5)

- Using evidence, scientists have been able to plot the past and future positions of the continents. (13-6)

The key terms in this chapter are listed below. Use each term in a sentence that shows the meaning of the term.

asthenosphere	Pangaea	theory of continental drift
convergent boundary	plate boundaries	theory of plate tectonics
divergent boundary	plates	theory of sea-floor spreading
Gondwanaland	rift valley	transform fault
Laurasia	subduction	trench
Mid-Ocean Ridge	subduction zone	

Chapter Review

VOCABULARY

Write the letter of the term that best matches the definition. Not all the terms will be used.

1. The upper layer of the mantle
2. A place where plates come together
3. Southern land mass that separated from Pangaea
4. Means "all lands"
5. Valley between mountain ridges in oceans
6. Process by which one plate is forced beneath another
7. Theory that states that the earth's lithosphere is broken into moving plates
8. Theory that says molten rock rises at the Mid-Ocean Ridge
9. Boundary where two plates slide past each other
10. A valley next to a subduction zone

a. lithosphere
b. theory of plate tectonics
c. Laurasia
d. Pangaea
e. subduction
f. asthenosphere
g. convergent boundary
h. transform fault
i. trench
j. theory of sea-floor spreading
k. rift
l. Gondwanaland
m. divergent boundary
n. plates

CONCEPTS

1. What is the Mid-Atlantic Ridge? (13-1)
2. List supporting evidence that South America and Africa were once a single land mass. (13-1, 13-2)
3. Why was the theory of continental drift not accepted by scientists? (13-2)
4. Compare the theory of sea-floor spreading and the theory of continental drift. (13-2, 13-3)
5. What evidence supports sea-floor spreading? (13-3)
6. Contrast the theory of plate tectonics and the theory of continental drift. (13-2, 13-4)
7. Use the theory of plate tectonics to describe what happens at the Mid-Ocean Ridge. (13-4)
8. How might convection currents cause plates to move? (13-4)
9. Describe the three types of plate boundaries. (13-5)

10. Why are volcanoes associated with plate movement? (13-5)

11. What is the relationship between ocean trenches and island arcs? (13-5)

12. How is the formation of the Andes related to plate movement? (13-5)

13. How does the formation of the Aleutian Islands differ from the formation of the Andes? (13-5)

14. What type of plate boundary is associated with the formation of the Himalayas? (13-5)

15. Where is lithosphere formed, and where is it destroyed? (13-5)

16. Some people predict that parts of California may someday become islands. Use the concept of plate tectonics to explain this. (13-6)

17. What land masses formed Pangaea? (13-6)

18. How did scientists determine the past positions of the continents? (13-6)

19. Describe the possible positions of the continents in 100 million years. (13-6)

20. Describe the possible positions of the continents in 150 million years. (13-6)

APPLICATION/ CRITICAL THINKING

1. There is evidence of large sand dunes in the sandstone formations near London, England. Why would there be sand dunes in England?

2. The Alps are mountains in Europe. Propose the way they may have been formed. Justify your answer.

3. There are submerged volcanoes, or seamounts, on the ocean floor. Some seamounts have flat tops, indicating wave erosion. These seamounts are hundreds of meters below sea level. How could they have flat tops if they are below sea level?

EXTENSION

1. Find out more information about the *Glomar Challenger*. What projects are its scientists working on now? What instruments do they use?

2. Use resource books to learn more about Iceland. What type of plate boundary is associated with its formation? What features on Iceland give clues about its history?

READINGS

Gore, Rick. "Our Restless Planet Earth." *National Geographic,* Aug. 1985, p. 142.

Kiefer, Irene. *A Global Jigsaw Puzzle.* New York: Atheneum Publishers, 1978.

Miller, Russell. *Continents in Collision.* Planet Earth series. Alexandria, Va.: Time-Life Books Inc., 1983.

VOLCANOES AND EARTHQUAKES

The fury of volcanoes and the destructive power of earthquakes are clues to the awesome forces within the earth. Volcanoes and earthquakes are like pieces of a puzzle. When viewed together, these "pieces" tell of the role of plate tectonics in shaping the earth. Volcanoes and earthquakes are only parts of a great cycle of creation and destruction.

- *What type of materials are being given off by the volcano?*
- *What do the materials given off by a volcano indicate about the earth's interior?*
- *How do the materials given off by volcanoes affect the earth?*

14-1 VOLCANOES

Volcanoes can be one of nature's most destructive forces. Their eruptions have been known to wipe out entire civilizations. They have turned landscapes into wastelands, and they may have caused the ice ages. What causes a volcano to suddenly erupt?

A **volcano** is a structure made of materials from within the earth that build up around an opening in the earth's surface. A volcano is formed when *magma*, or molten rock, is forced up to the earth's surface. Magma that reaches the earth's surface is called *lava*.

Some volcanoes, such as Mount Vesuvius in Italy, have been observed for at least 2000 years. Over that time, volcanoes have not been observed to erupt continuously. In fact, some volcanoes have not erupted since they were first observed by humans and are not likely to do so in the future. Such volcanoes are called *extinct* volcanoes. Those called *dormant* or *active* volcanoes have erupted within human history. They could erupt at any time.

The molten rock and gases from volcanic activity can cause great destruction. However, the materials given off by volcanic activity have also been necessary for human life. Molten rock from volcanic activity formed much of

After completing this section, you will be able to

- **define** *volcano*.
- **describe** the locations of volcanoes.
- **explain** three ways in which volcanoes form.

The key term in this secion is
volcano

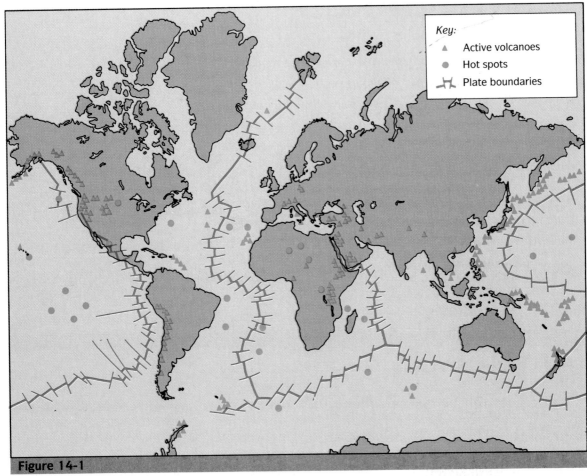

Figure 14-1

Most volcanoes occur in belts on the earth's surface.

the earth's dry land. The air we breathe and the water we drink are believed to have come from the gases given off by volcanoes. Lava and volcanic ash contain nutrients that have enriched some of the earth's best farmland.

There are about 600 known active volcanoes in the world. Most are located in narrow regions called belts. One belt is known as the Ring of Fire. It forms a near circle around the Pacific Ocean. Locate the Ring of Fire in Figure 14-1. What part of the United States lies within this region? Volcanoes are also found in belts near the Mediterranean Sea and in eastern Africa. Iceland and Hawaii have volcanoes as well.

As you learned in the last chapter, the regions in which volcanoes are found are active parts of the earth's crust. Look at Figure 14-1. Where are most of the volcanoes found? Volcanoes can be formed as a result of activity between plates.

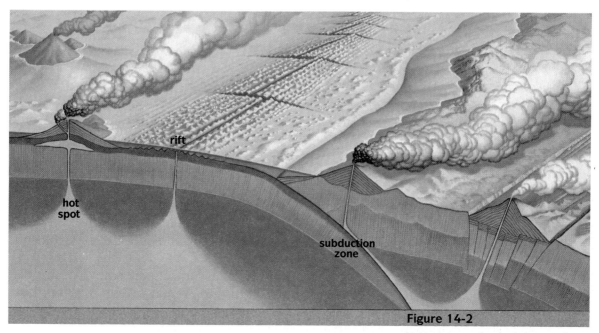

Figure 14-2

Volcanoes are formed above subduction zones, along rifts, and above hot spots.

One kind of plate boundary where volcanoes are formed is a *subduction zone*. In a subduction zone, as two plates collide, one plate sinks under the other. The sinking plate melts as it slowly descends into the mantle. The resulting magma rises through the plate above and forms a chain of volcanoes. The volcanoes in the Ring of Fire were formed in subduction zones.

Another kind of boundary where volcanoes form is a *rift*, which is caused by two plates being pulled apart. Volcanoes along a rift form from magma that rises out of the sea floor as the sea floor spreads. The volcanoes that formed Iceland were formed by magma from a rift in the Mid-Atlantic Ridge.

Some volcanoes, such as those in the Hawaiian Islands, are found in the middle of plates. These volcanoes were formed by rising columns of superhot magma from places in the mantle called *hot spots*. The magma can burn holes in a plate and rise to the surface to form volcanoes. As a plate moves over a hot spot, a chain of volcanoes is formed.

REVIEW

1. What is a volcano?
2. Where do volcanoes occur?
3. Explain three ways in which volcanoes form.

CHALLENGE Metal ores are often found in areas of volcanoes. What does this tell about the interior of the earth?

14-2 VOLCANIC ERUPTIONS

After completing this section, you will be able to

- **compare** two kinds of magma that occur in a volcano.
- **explain** four kinds of volcanic eruptions that occur.
- **describe** three kinds of materials given off by volcanoes.

The key terms in this section are

ash   cinders
bombs   vent

On May 18, 1980, Mount St. Helens, in the state of Washington, exploded with a force of 500 atomic bombs. Ash from the blast blanketed the northwestern United States and southern Canada with a layer of ash as much as 7 cm thick. Heat from the explosion melted snow and ice on the mountain. This formed a huge mudflow that destroyed trees, houses, and bridges.

No two volcanoes behave in exactly the same way. Compared with the violent 1980 eruption of Mount St. Helens, the volcanoes on the Hawaiian Islands have quiet eruptions. Why do volcanoes erupt differently?

Whether a volcanic eruption is quiet or explosive depends on whether the volcano's vent is blocked or open. A **vent** is the channel that connects the source of magma to the opening of a volcano. When a vent is blocked by material such as hardened lava, the buildup of pressure can cause the volcano to explode.

Figure 14-3

Mount St. Helens, in Washington State, erupting violently (*left*). Kilauea has quiet eruptions with slow lava flows (*right*).

The kind of eruption also depends on the kind of magma in a volcano. The magma can be as thick as molasses or as thin as water. It also can contain a large amount of gas, such as water vapor. Quiet eruptions usually happen when the magma is thin and contains little gas. More violent eruptions occur when the magma is thick and contains a large amount of gas.

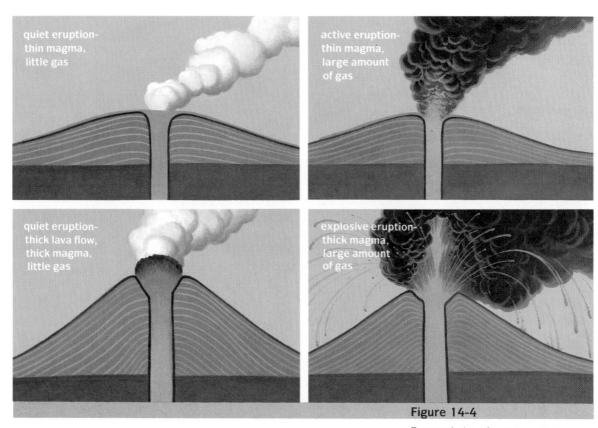

quiet eruption-
thin magma,
little gas

active eruption-
thin magma,
large amount
of gas

quiet eruption-
thick lava flow,
thick magma,
little gas

explosive eruption-
thick magma,
large amount
of gas

Figure 14-4

Four varieties of magma will cause different volcanic eruptions.

There are four basic kinds of volcanic eruptions, based on the kind of magma in a volcano and whether the vent is blocked. A quiet eruption with a watery lava flow occurs when the magma is thin and contains little gas. The thin lava flows out in a steady stream.

A more active eruption can take place when a thin magma contains a larger amount of gas. Such magma occurs in the Hawaiian volcanoes. In a thin magma, gas can bubble up through the magma. As the gas escapes from the surface, the gas causes hot magma to shoot out of the volcano.

A quiet eruption with a thick lava flow occurs when the magma is thick and contains little gas. The thick lava flow usually forms a huge dome.

An eruption can be violent if the magma is thick and contains a large amount of gas. A thick magma can harden before leaving the vent and cause the vent to become blocked. This prevents gas from bubbling to the surface and escaping. The trapped gas builds up pressure under the vent. Any sudden release of this pressure can set off an explosion. For example, the explosion on Mount St. Helens was set off by an earthquake. The earthquake caused a landslide which reduced the pressure near the top.

Figure 14-5

Pahoehoe lava has a ropelike appearance (*left*). Aa lava has a rough appearance (*right*).

When volcanoes erupt, three types of materials are given off: lava, gases, and pieces or rock. There are two main types of lava. One type is called *pahoehoe* (pah HOH-ee hoh ee) lava. This kind of lava is hot, thin, and fast-flowing. When it hardens, it forms a wrinkled surface. The other kind of lava is called *aa* (AH ah) lava. Aa lava is cooler and thicker than pahoehoe lava. When it cools, it forms a rough, block-like surface.

Gases are the second type of material thrown out by volcanoes. One type of gas is water vapor. Water vapor comes from water that is dissolved by magma beneath the surface. In addition to water vapor, other gases such as carbon monoxide, sulfur dioxide, and hydrogen sulfide also escape. It is believed that gases from volcanoes may have been the source for most of the earth's air and water.

The third type of material thrown out by volcanic activity consists of pieces of rock. The smallest pieces of rock thrown out by volcanoes are called *volcanic dust*. Their size is 2 mm or less. Slightly larger rock fragments, about the size of sand particles, are called **ash**. In time, mineral-rich ash becomes fertile soil. Figure 14-6 (*top left*) shows volcanic dust and ash.

Figure 14-6

Rock materials sent out by volcanoes vary in size. Ash (*top left*), cinders (*top right*), bombs (*bottom left*), and blocks (*bottom right*).

Rock particles that are sent out by an eruption and that are several centimeters across are called **cinders**. Larger rocks called **bombs**, measuring up to 1 m across, are also ejected during an eruption. The force of a volcanic explosion is sometimes so great that rocks weighing several tons are thrown out of the volcano. Such rocks are called *blocks*. Compare the sizes of each of the volcanic materials shown in Figure 14-6.

REVIEW

1. What are two ways that magma in a volcano can differ?
2. Describe four kinds of volcanic eruptions that occur.
3. What are three kinds of materials thrown out by volcanoes?

CHALLENGE On November 14, 1985, a volcano erupted in the Andes, in South America. Lava did not flow down the volcano. Instead, a layer of mud flowed down, burying four towns and killing more than 20,000 people. What caused mud instead of lava to flow down a volcano?

14-3 VOLCANIC FEATURES

In a few mintues, a volcanic eruption can throw out millions of kilograms of rock material. Its blanket of ash can destroy life across thousands of kilometers. But material from volcanoes can supply the soil with important nutrients for plant growth.

VOLCANISM

Volcanic activity has formed many of the surface features on the earth. Below the soil, much of the rock was formed from lava. Many mountain ranges were formed by explosive volcanoes. The process by which magma rises into the earth's crust and flows onto the earth's surface is called *volcanism.*

Volcanoes are surface features caused by volcanic activity. They form when lava and rocks from eruptions pile up on the earth's surface and form *cones.* Volcanic cones can be classified by their shapes.

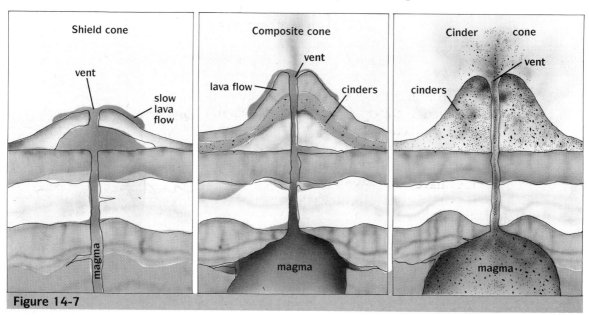

Figure 14-7

Shield cone (*left*), composite cone (*middle*), and cinder cone (*right*).

A **shield cone** has a gentle slope and a broad base. It is formed from layers of thin lava flowing out around the volcano's opening as a result of quiet eruptions.

The second type of cone has steep sides and a narrow base. It is called a cinder cone. A **cinder cone** is a pile of ash and cinders around a volcanic opening.

The composite cone is the third type of cone. A **composite cone** is formed from alternating layers of lava and rocks. The layers are evidence of different types of volcanic

Figure 14-8

Mount Fuji is a composite cone (*left*), and Crater Lake is a caldera (*right*).

activity. For example, there may have been periods of quiet eruptions in which lava was produced. Then at other times there may have been violent eruptions that produced rock fragments. Volcanoes with this layered structure are sometimes called *stratovolcanoes*.

Located at the top of most volcanic cones is a bowl-shaped depression called a **crater**. A crater forms when lava hardens arounds the vent. When magma moves up and out of the vent, it fills the crater before flowing out as lava. If the lava hardens, it forms a plug in the vent.

Some volcanoes have very large craters called **calderas** (kal DIHR uhz). A caldera may form when an explosion that blows off the top of a volcano. It may also form when magma drains out of the crater of a volcano. The magma in a crater helps to hold up the top part of the volcano. When the magma drains out, there is no longer any support from the magma below. The volcano's top collapses and a caldera is formed. Crater Lake, Oregon, shown in Figure 14-8 (*right*), is an example of a caldera. What rock structure can be seen in the middle of Crater Lake?

While volcanoes have added material to the earth's crust, two other kinds of volcanic activity have also shaped parts of every continent. These are flood basalts and ash flows. *Flood basalts* are extremely thin lava flows that come out of cracks in the earth called *fissures*. The lava flows do not build a cone but spread out over a large area. For example, the Columbia River Plateau in the northwestern United States was formed by lava flows millions of years

Figure 14-9

Columbia River flood basalt.

327

Figure 14-10

The Valley of Ten Thousand Smokes, near Mount Katmai, Alaska, has an ash deposit of over 60m deep!

bathos (deep)
lithos (stone)

ago. Flood basalts are believed to come from magma in the upper mantle, or *asthenosphere.*

Ash flows are deposits of volcanic ash that come out of fissures. The fissures form over thick magma that contains large amounts of gases. When the magma rises to the surface, expanding gases cause millions of cubic kilometers of ash to shoot upward out of the fissures. The ash is deposited in a layer that looks like a lava flow.

INTRUSIVE ACTIVITY

Magma does not always reach the earth's surface. It may harden below the surface, forming rock. Volcanic activity below the earth's surface is called *intrusive activity.* Intrusive activity can produce different types of rock structures below the earth's surface. They are seen only when surface rock is worn away by the forces of weathering and erosion.

One type of rock structure formed by intrusive activity is a batholith. A **batholith** is a large mass of igneous rock below the earth's surface. Batholiths often form the inside of mountain ranges. The depth of batholiths is unknown. A small mass of intrusive igneous rock is called a *stock.*

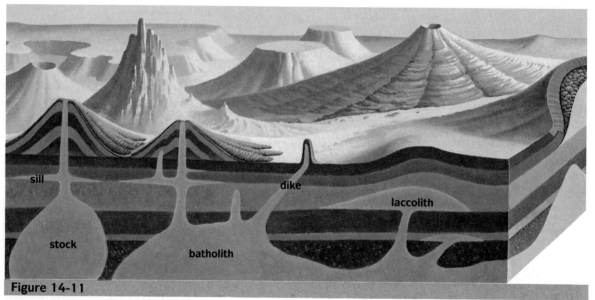

Figure 14-11

Rock structures formed by intrusive activity.

lakkos (storage pit)
lithos (stone)

Another rock structure formed below the earth's surface is a laccolith. A **laccolith** is a mass of intrusive igneous rock that is dome-shaped. This type of structure is formed when magma moves between rock layers and pushes the rock layers above it into a dome shape.

OBJECTIVE

Interpret a topographic map of a volcanic cone and its features.

MATERIALS

topographic map of Crater Lake, pencil, hand lens, ruler, notebook paper

PROCEDURE

Use information from a topographic map of Crater Lake to answer the questions below.

1. What names (two or more) on the map give clues that Crater Lake is found on a volcano?
2. What is the highest elevation on the map?
3. What is the lowest elevation on the map?
4. Notice the peak to the southeast of Crater Lake. How might this peak have been formed?
5. Does the peak have snow on its slopes?
6. What is the contour interval for this map?
7. What is the elevation of the bench mark on Wizard Island?
8. Does Crater Lake have a flat bottom? Support your answer with data.
9. From the map key, what kind of vegetation is found around Crater Lake?
10. Where is the gentlest slope around Crater Lake? The greatest slope?
11. What structure is found in the center of the lake?

RESULTS AND CONCLUSIONS

1. What evidence shows that Crater Lake is located on a volcano?
2. What type of volcanic cone do you think Crater Lake is formed on?
3. What evidence shows that an eruption took place in the crater?

Magma does not always push rock layers upward. Sometimes it fills spaces between the layers. A structure of hardened magma between horizontal rock layers is called a *sill*. A *dike* is formed if magma fills and hardens in vertical cracks in rock. Dikes are longer than they are wide. Look at Figure 14-11. What kind of structure do dikes extend from?

Like all land and structures on the earth, volcanoes are changed by erosion. Some parts of volcanoes are more easily eroded than others. A volcanic neck, or central plug, of an extinct volcano is made of rock that is not easily eroded. The volcanic neck may remain standing long after most of the cone of the volcano has eroded. An example of a volcanic neck is Shiprock, New Mexico, shown in Figure 14-12. What happened to the volcano in which Shiprock formed?

REVIEW

1. How do three types of volcanic cones form?
2. Give two ways in which volcanic material is added to the land besides by volcanic eruptions.
3. What are four features formed by intrusive activity beneath the earth?

CHALLENGE Which is older, a dike or the rock surrounding it?

Figure 14-12

Shiprock, New Mexico.

14-4 EARTHQUAKES

No area in North America is more likely to have a major earthquake than the area around the San Andreas Fault in California. A major earthquake struck near the southern end of the fault in Los Angeles in 1857. In 1906, a major earthquake struck its northern end and destroyed San Francisco. Scientists believe a major earthquake will strike again, somewhere along the fault, by the year 2000.

More than a million earthquakes take place each year. Most are so weak that they barely rattle a teacup. Others, such as the 1906 earthquake in San Francisco, cause great destruction. Whether they are small tremors or large shifts in the earth's surface, almost all earthquakes happen because rock in the crust suddenly moves. The shaking or trembling of the earth caused by the sudden movement of rock is called an **earthquake**.

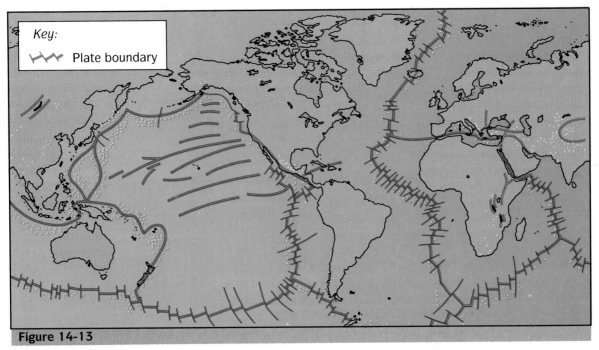

Figure 14-13

Map showing earthquake epicenters. Where do most of the earthquakes take place?

Almost all movements in the earth's crust can be explained by the theory of plate tectonics. As you have learned, the theory explains that the earth's surface is broken into moving plates. As the plates move, they collide, pull apart, or slide past each other along their boundaries. The boundaries are like huge cracks in the crust. A place where rock has moved on one or both sides of a crack in the earth is called a **fault**.

Rocks along plate boundaries are put under great strain. The strain occurs because rocks do not slide past each other easily. The surfaces of the rocks are rough and jagged and cause the rocks along the fault to lock together. As plates move, the rocks are squeezed, pulled, and bent. This causes strain to build up in the rocks. Eventually, the strain becomes too great. Then, like a rubber band that snaps when stretched too far, the rocks slip along the weakest point on the fault. The energy released by this movement is felt as an earthquake.

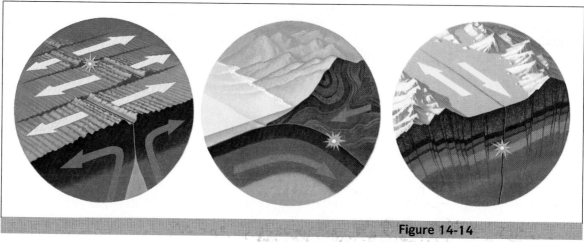

Figure 14-14

Earthquakes can occur along divergent zones, convergent zones, and transform faults.

As you can see in Figure 14-13, most earthquakes occur in belts, or narrow regions. These belts occur along three kinds of plate boundaries: divergent zones, convergent zones, and transform faults.

In a *divergent zone*, where two plates are moving apart, earthquakes occur almost constantly along *rifts*. Along a rift, sections of the rift are pushed out of line. Earthquakes occur where two sections move in opposite directions.

Earthquakes also occur in *convergent zones*, where two plates are colliding, coming together. When two plates collide, one plate may be pushed below the other in a subduction zone. As one plate sinks, it bends and grinds against the other plate, creating great strain. It is believed that the most severe earthquakes occur in subduction zones.

Colliding plates can also cause the earth's crust to buckle upward. As rocks along the fault are squeezed, the great force on the rocks can cause them to fracture, or crack, causing earthquakes.

Along a *transform fault*, two plates slide past each other. As rocks are locked together, strain builds up until it is released by earthquakes. The San Andreas Fault is a transform fault.

Figure 14-15

The San Andreas Fault is a transform fault.

Some earthquakes occur away from plate boundaries. For example, four major earthquakes took place in Missouri in 1811 and 1812. Missouri is near the center of the North American Plate. A large fault has been detected running through Missouri. The fault may be a weak zone of rock in the North American Plate caused by the separating of the continents about 200 million years ago.

Other earthquakes that occur away from the edge of a plate can be caused by volcanic activity. Rising magma can seep into cracks in rock. The heat and pressure of the magma cause the rock to expand. The strain on the rock triggers an earthquake.

Some earthquakes have been brought on by people. For example, more than a thousand earthquakes occurred in Denver between 1962 and 1966. At that time, large amounts of liquid waste were being pumped into wells. Earthquakes resulted when the liquid seeped into faults, making it easier for rocks to slip.

REVIEW

1. What is an earthquake?
2. What is the relationship between earthquakes and plate boundaries?
3. How can earthquakes occur away from plate boundaries.

CHALLENGE Explain how the filling of a large reservoir with water can bring on an earthquake.

14-5 EARTHQUAKE WAVES

The Chinese in A.D. 132 knew that earthquakes could release enough energy to be detected thousands of kilometers away. Today, scientists can locate earthquakes accurately and quickly. This has enabled populated areas struck by major earthquakes to receive help more quickly.

The sudden movement of rock in an earthquake causes vibrations in the form of waves. The waves produced in an earthquake are called **seismic waves**. In the earth, the place along a fault where rock moves is called the **focus**. However, the earthquake is usually felt the strongest on the surface above the focus. The place on the earth's surface directly above the focus is called the **epicenter**.

Just as the snap on one end of a rope causes a ripple to move along the rope, the sudden movement of rock can send seismic waves through the earth. The waves move out from the focus in all directions. When they reach the surface, they cause the ground to vibrate. These vibrations can be recorded by a seismograph. A **seismograph** is an instrument that records vibrations in the earth. Figure 14-16 shows the parts of a seismograph. What are these parts?

seismos (earthquake)

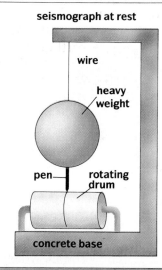
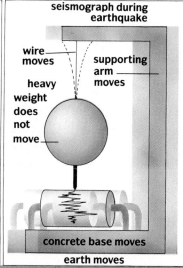

Figure 14-16

The record of seismic waves is called a *seismogram*. Seismic waves are recorded as wavy lines on a seismogram. Seismograms show that there are three types of seismic waves. They are called primary (P) waves, secondary (S) waves, and surface (L) waves.

The National Earthquake Information Service records earthquakes that occur all over the United States (*left*). A seismograph at rest and during an earthquake (*right*).

ACTIVITY   When Will the Earthquake Waves Arrive?

OBJECTIVE
Calculate how long it takes earthquake waves to travel certain distances.

MATERIALS
paper, pencil

| Distance | Time | | Difference |
	S wave	P wave	(S − P)
120 km			
960 km			

PROCEDURE
P waves travel at a speed of 6 km/s and S waves travel at a speed of 4 km/s. Do the following calculations and record your results in a table like the one below.

A. Calculate the time in seconds required for an S wave to travel 120 km.
B. Calculate the time in seconds required for a P wave to travel 120 km.
C. Calculate the time in seconds required for an S wave to travel 960 km.
D. Calculate the time in seconds required for a P wave to travel 960 km.

RESULTS AND CONCLUSIONS
1. What is the difference between the arrival time of the S wave and the P wave (time lag) at 120 km?
2. What is the time lag between the arrival of the P and S waves at 960 km?
3. Which travels through the earth faster, P or S waves?
4. How would knowing the time required for a wave to travel a specific distance be helpful to scientists and to people who live in an affected area?

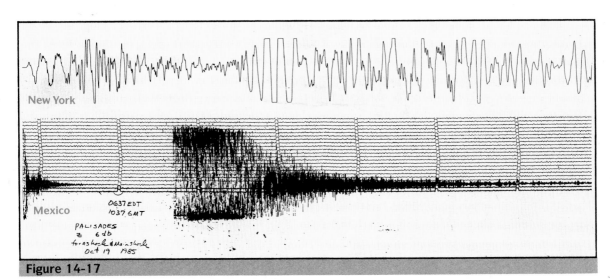

New York

Mexico

0637 EDT
1037 GMT

PALISADES
z 6 db
foreshock & Mainshock
Oct 19 1985

Figure 14-17

Seismograms from earthquakes that occurred in New York and Mexico.

The **primary waves** or **P waves** are the first seismic waves to be recorded by the seismograph. This is because they travel the fastest of the three types of seismic waves. P waves can travel through solid rock and through liquids such as magma and water. As P waves move through rock, they cause the particles in the rock to move back and forth in the same direction the wave is traveling. The motion of the particles is shown in Figure 14-18.

Secondary waves or S waves are seismic waves that arrive after the P waves. They travel slower than the P waves. S waves can travel through solids but not through liquids. S waves cause rock particles to move up and down.

The slowest and last waves to reach the seismograph are the surface waves or L waves. L waves travel along the outer layer of the earth. Why do L waves cause the most damage? They come from P and S waves that reach the earth's surface. L waves cause rock particles to move the same way that waves move on water.

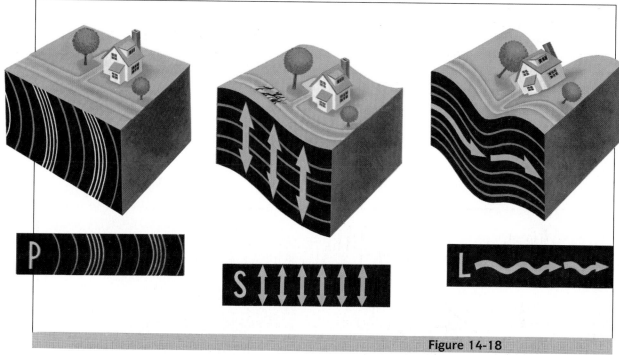

Figure 14-18

The difference in the arrival times of the P and S waves can show how far an earthquake epicenter is from the seismograph. Consider two bicyclists racing, one faster than the other. The longer the race, the greater the difference is in the times the slower and faster bicyclists reach the finish line. The greater the difference in times between the arrival of P and S waves at the seismograph, the farther away the earthquake.

The surface effects of P, S, and L waves.

Seismic waves are used by scientists to study the earth's interior. When seismic waves travel through the earth and return to the surface they contain valuable information about the inside of the earth. For example, S waves cannot pass through the outer core of the earth. Since S waves cannot travel through liquids, the outer core must be liquid.

OBJECTIVE
Locate an epicenter, using three known locations and distances.

MATERIALS
pencil, paper, compass

PROCEDURE

A. By using P and S waves, the distance to an earthquake epicenter can be determined. However, the epicenter cannot be located unless the direction from which the waves came is known. On a sheet of blank paper, trace the map shown below. Mark and label the location of each city.

B. The table below shows the epicenter distances from three cities. Use the map scale to set the radius of a compass to match the epicenter distance from Topeka.

C. Using the compass, draw a circle around Topeka on your map.

City	Epicenter Distance
Topeka	900 km
Denver	400 km
Oklahoma City	750 km

D. Repeat the procedures in **B** and **C** for Denver and Oklahoma City.

RESULTS AND CONCLUSIONS

1. Near what city is the epicenter of the earthquake?
2. How many locations and their epicenter distances were necessary to locate an epicenter?
3. How can the accuracy of locating an epicenter be improved?

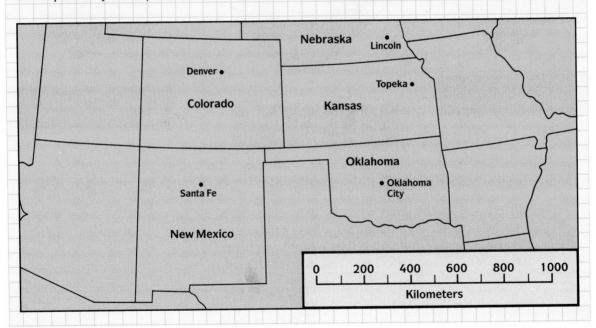

REVIEW

1. Compare the *focus* and *epicenter*.
2. How are seismic waves produced?
3. Name and describe three kinds of seismic waves.

CHALLENGE How can seismographs be used to detect the testing of nuclear weapons in other countries?

14-6 EFFECTS OF EARTHQUAKES

The dangers of an earthquake are important to people. But to scientists who study earthquakes, the energy released by earthquakes is of greater importance. Just as a doctor uses X rays to examine the inside of the body, a scientist can use the energy from earthquakes to examine the earth's deepest interior and the processes going on there. From this information, scientists hope to be able to predict earthquakes.

The total amount of energy released by an earthquake is called **magnitude**. A method of measuring the amount of energy released by an earthquake was developed by Charles Richter (RIHK tuhr). The **Richter scale** is a scale of magnitudes that is used to measure the relative sizes of earthquakes. Earthquakes with magnitudes of less than 2.5 are not felt by humans. The largest earthquakes recorded have had magnitudes near 8.9.

An increase of 1 in magnitude on the scale indicates the release of 10 times the energy of the next lower number. For example, an earthquake with a magnitude of 7 releases 10 times more energy than an earthquake with a magnitude of 6. How many times more energy would an earthquake with a magnitude of 7 release than an earthquake with a magnitude of 5?

The effect of an earthquake depends on its magnitude. Some of the world's most severe earthquakes had magnitudes greater than 8.2. Much destruction happens within minutes. One of the most violent earthquakes to occur in North America took place in Mexico in 1985. That earthquake had a magnitude of about 8.1 on the Richter scale.

After completing this section, you will be able to

- **define** the term *Richter scale*.
- **name** one natural disaster related to an earthquake.
- **list** three ways scientists are using to predict earthquakes.

The key terms in this section are
aftershock   Richter scale
magnitude

magnitudo (large)

SCIENCE PUZZLER

The photograph shows the Transamerica Pyramid, an earthquake-resistant building in San Francisco. In what ways does the structure of the building make it less likely to suffer damage than the buildings surrounding it?

Over 5000 people were killed, and many buildings collapsed. Dozens of aftershocks followed the earthquake. **Aftershocks** are smaller, less intense earthquakes that follow a major earthquake. They are caused by seismic waves given off when the movement of rock along a fault continues. Aftershocks may occur for more than a year after a major earthquake. In Mexico, an aftershock with a magnitude of 7.5 came 18 hours after the earthquake.

Most earthquakes last only a few seconds, but the Mexican earthquake lasted almost a minute. The San Francisco earthquake of 1906 lasted for 40 seconds. Its magnitude was 8.3 on the Richter scale. Over 300 people died, and an equal number of people were reported missing.

Figure 14-19

Surface destruction is vast in a major earthquake.

Earthquakes can cause great destruction. Their tremors can cause buildings to collapse and cause water, gas, and sewer pipes to break. Fires often burn out of control when water pipes are broken. Many lives can be lost.

Oftentimes more people die from an earthquake-related disaster than from the actual earthquake. One example of a disaster associated with earthquakes is the tsunami. A *tsunami* (tsoo NAH mee) is a large ocean wave produced by an earthquake on the ocean floor. The wave may be 30 m high and move at speeds over 500 km/h.

A tsunami was produced by an earthquake in Chile in 1960. It traveled 17,000 km across the Pacific Ocean to Japan in about 22 hours. Many people in Japan were killed as a result of the Chilean earthquake.

Figure 14-20

Tsunamis are caused by earthquakes under the oceans.

Earthquakes have been known to cause volcanoes to erupt. In 1975, Kilauea, Hawaii, erupted less than an hour after an earthquake occurred. The earthquake shook the magma in the volcano, causing the dissolved gases to bubble up rapidly. The cause of the eruption can be compared to the shaking of soda pop in a bottle.

Earthquakes are being used to help predict when volcanic eruptions will occur. Earthquakes are known to occur in large numbers before a volcanic eruption. For example, about 35 earthquakes a month had been taking place for almost a year before the volcano in the Andes erupted. In the few weeks before the Mount St. Helens eruption, up to 41 earthquakes a day occurred.

Earthquakes are not uncommon on the earth. In fact, some places on earth experience as many as 60 earthquakes during a day's time. Earthquake risks do exist. Therefore, people must plan and be prepared in the event an earthquake occurs where they live. Here are some safety ideas.

1. Indoors, stand against a wall or stand in a doorway.
2. Outdoors, stay in the open, away from electrical wires.
3. In a moving car, stop, and stay inside.
4. At school, stay away from windows and get under a desk.

After an earthquake,

5. Stay away from waterfront areas.
6. Expect aftershocks.
7. Do not drink the water or flush toilets until the water and sewer lines have been checked.
8. Stay away from damaged buildings.

It is said that some animals behave strangely before an earthquake. But scientists are looking for more than barking dogs or panicky fish to warn them. They are trying to make accurate predictions about where and when earthquakes will occur.

Earth scientists know that entire crustal plates move a certain amount each year. However, they do not know how much a particular area along the edge of a plate might move, or slip. Some areas haven't slipped for many years. It is believed that pressure is building up in these areas and that these are the places where the greatest earthquakes will occur. Some areas along the San Andreas Fault, in southern California, are such places.

Scientists particularly want to know how the crust behaves just before an earthquake. Instruments such as seismometers and lasers can measure vibration and strain in the crust. Computers can analyze the data gathered by these instruments and give earth scientists a better picture of changes in the earth's crust that lead up to an earthquake.

Planning for safety in an earthquake is also a consideration in the construction business. More engineers are studying the ground they build on and learning how to design buildings that will sway and not crumble when earthquakes occur. For example, engineers have designed shock-absorbing walls for buildings. These walls bend but do not crack when shaken during an earthquake.

In addition to protecting buildings during earthquakes, water pipes, utility lines, and communication lines must be protected. Broken water pipes make fire fighting impossible. When utility lines such as gas pipes are broken, fires can easily be started. Damaged telephone lines prevent rescue efforts.

Some earthquake-prone areas have already taken steps to protect their lifelines. Alaska's main electric generators and gas pipes can be shut off automatically during an earthquake. Japan has a 10-day supply of drinking water in underground caves and earthquake-proof buildings. California has made its water systems more easily reached by repair crews.

Scientists in some countries have made observations that might be useful in predicting earthquakes. The Chinese have found that the depth and temperature of water in wells change before an earthquake. Scientists in the Soviet Union believe the amount of a radioactive gas called radon increases in well water prior to seismic activity.

Earthquakes probably occurred millions of years before us and will continue for millions of years after us. We may never be able to prevent them. Our best chance for safety will probably be in knowing where and when they will occur next.

REVIEW

1. What is the Richter scale?
2. Name one natural disaster related to earthquakes.
3. What are three ways scientists are using to predict earthquakes?

CHALLENGE Another scale used to measure the strength of earthquakes is the Mercalli scale. It is based on the amount of damage done by an earthquake. Why is this scale not always accurate in measuring the strength of an earthquake?

CHAPTER SUMMARY

The main ideas in this chapter are listed below. Read these statements before you answer the Chapter Review questions.

- Volcanoes occur when magma rises from subduction zones, rifts, and hot spots. (14-1)

- The kind of eruption a volcano can have depends on the kind of magma it contains and whether its vent is blocked. (14-2)

- There are three types of volcanic shapes: shield cones, cinder cones, and composite cones. (14-3)

- Flood basalts and ash flows are volcanic activities that have shaped much of the earth. (14-3)

- Earthquakes are caused by sudden movements of rock in the earth. They mainly occur along plate boundaries. (14-4)

- Three types of waves produced during an earthquake are primary (P) waves, secondary (S) waves, and surface (L) waves. (14-5)

- The Richter scale can be used to measure the amount of energy given off by an earthquake. (14-6)

- Earthquakes can cause tsunamis. (14-6)

The key terms in this chapter are listed below. Use each term in a sentence that shows the meaning of the term.

aftershock	crater	Richter scale
ash	earthquake	secondary wave
batholith	epicenter	seismic wave
bombs	fault	seismograph
caldera	focus	shield cone
cinder cone	laccolith	surface wave
cinders	magnitude	vent
composite cone	primary wave	volcano

Chapter Review

Write the letter of the term that best matches the definition. Not all the terms will be used.

1. Crack along which rock moves
2. Large rocks sent out by a volcanic eruption
3. Broad-based volcanic cone
4. Steep-walled pit around the vent
5. Place on earth's surface directly above the focus
6. Instrument that detects seismic waves
7. Wave vibrating up and down
8. Amount of energy released by an earthquake
9. Small earthquake
10. Place along a fault where rock moves in the earth

a. seismograph
b. secondary wave
c. magnitude
d. aftershock
e. focus
f. primary wave
g. epicenter
h. laccolith
i. crater
j. fault
k. bombs
l. shield cone

CONCEPTS

1. How does a volcano form from magma? (14-1)
2. How does the theory of plate tectonics explain the locations of earthquakes? (14-1)
3. Predict where future volcanic eruptions will occur. (14-1)
4. In what ways does the type of magma affect the eruption of a volcano? (14-2)
5. Compare the factors that lead to explosive volcanic eruptions with those that lead to quiet eruptions. (14-2)
6. Make a list of each of the three types of materials given off by volcanoes. (14-2)
7. Explain how each kind of volcanic cone forms. (14-3)
8. Why is volcanic activity important to life on earth? (14-3)
9. Compare the features caused by volcanism with those caused by intrusive activity. (14-3)
10. How does the release of strain in rock cause earthquakes? (14-4)
11. Predict where future earthquakes are most likely to occur. (14-4)
12. Compare the locations of earthquakes with the locations of volcanoes. (14-1, 14-4)

13. Make a list of the different areas where earthquakes can occur and the cause of an earthquake in each place. (14-4)

14. Compare the focus and epicenter of an earthquake. (14-5)

15. What happens to seismic waves after they are produced? (14-5)

16. Compare the seismogram of a distant earthquake with one that is formed by a nearby earthquake. (14-5)

17. How many times stronger is an earthquake with a magnitude of 8 than an earthquake with a magnitude of 5? (14-6)

18. Why is it dangerous to enter buildings after an earthquake has hit the area? (14-6)

19. Make a list of several destructive effects of earthquakes. (14-6)

20. How can earthquakes cause great damage to areas thousands of kilometers away? (14-6)

21. What steps have some countries taken to protect their lifelines during an earthquake? (14-6)

APPLICATION/ CRITICAL THINKING

1. How can volcanoes and earthquakes be used to locate plate boundaries?

2. Why are the focuses of earthquakes much deeper in subduction zones along the edges of continents than in rifts in the Mid-Ocean Ridge?

3. If you look at a map of the Pacific, showing the ocean south-southwest of Iwo Jima, you will find no land. However, if you fly over the area, you will see an island. Explain why.

4. Explain how volcanoes can result from activity that builds plates and also result from activity that destroys plates.

5. How might large reservoirs cause earthquakes?

EXTENSION

1. Create your own volcano and earthquake activity map. Record the location of the volcanoes and earthquakes on a world map as they occur. Using the information in your textbook, draw the plate boundaries on your map.

2. Use library resources to find out about two kinds of seismographs.

3. Does the moon have volcanic and earthquake activity? Conduct some research to find the answer.

4. The volcano Surtsey near Iceland appeared in 1963. Gather as much information about Surtsey as you can.

READINGS

Volcano. Alexandria, Va.: Time-Life Books Inc., 1982.

Walker, Bryce. *Earthquake.* Alexandria, Va.: Time-Life Books Inc., 1982.

THE EARTH AND TIME

Look closely at the photograph on the opposite page. What kind of animal do you think this skull came from? Notice the two, long canine teeth. Do such teeth give you a clue to the kind of animal? The skull is that of a saber-toothed cat. Saber-toothed cats are extinct. Scientists learn about past life by studying fossils, such as the fossil skull shown.

- *What clue do fossils give about living things of the past?*
- *Are all fossils formed in the same way?*
- *How do scientists find the ages of fossils?*

15-1 THE RECORD OF THE ROCKS

What is the story of the earth's past, long before written history? Scientists find many clues in the earth's rocks. Patterns in the rocks provide a record that can be read somewhat like a book. In reading this record, scientists make use of an idea put forth by James Hutton, a Scottish geologist, in 1795. Hutton observed processes such as the *erosion,* or wearing away, of rocks. He had the idea that the same processes must have occurred in time past. This idea is called uniformitarianism (yoo nuh fawr-muh TAIR ee uh nihz uhm). The **principle of uniformitarianism** states that the processes at work today are the same processes that have been at work throughout the earth's history. This idea is stated simply as, "The present is the key to the past."

According to the principle of uniformitarianism, sedimentary rocks formed in the past as they do today. In the process of *deposition,* sediments carried by wind, water, or ice are deposited, or laid down. Slowly, over time, layers of sediment turn into rock. How do the layers in sedimentary rock compare in age? To answer this question, scientists try to determine the order in which the layers were deposited. Suppose you were looking at a cross sec-

After completing this section, you will be able to

- **describe** the principle of uniformitarianism.
- **interpret** the meaning of unconformities in rock layers.
- **explain** the use of the law of superposition and the law of cross-cutting relationships to find relative ages of rocks.

The key terms in this section are
law of cross-cutting
   relationships
law of superposition
principle of uniformitarianism
relative age
unconformity

tion of a sanitary landfill. Which layer of the landfill would have been deposited first? How do you know?

Like the bottom layer in a landfill, the bottom layer in a section of sedimentary rock was deposited first. Rocks near the top were formed from sediments that were deposited more recently. The **law of superposition** states that each layer in an undisturbed section of sedimentary rock is older than those above it and younger than those below it. In Figure 15-1, you can see undisturbed rock layers. Where are the oldest rocks in the formation?

Figure 15-1

Undisturbed rock layers along a highway.

Geologists use the law of superposition to find relative ages of rock layers. **Relative age** is the age of something compared with the age of something else. For example, you might describe your relative age as older than a fifth grader but younger than an eleventh grader. The relative age of a rock can be described in the same way—older or younger than some other rocks.

If rock layers were never disturbed, then reading the rock record would be easy. But disturbances can and do happen. Suppose several rock layers formed and then deposition stopped for a time. As shown in Figure 15-2, erosion might then take away part of the rock record. If new rock layers later formed over the gap, the result would be one type of unconformity (uhn kuhn FAWR muh tee). An **unconformity** is any buried surface that represents a break in the rock record.

Sometimes forces within the earth can cause rock layers to change position. Layers that once lay flat can become slanted or even overturned by faulting and folding.

Figure 15-2

An unconformity in rock layers.

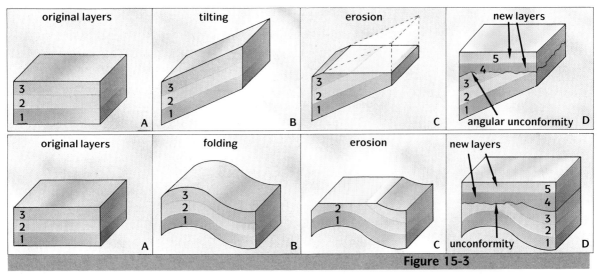

Figure 15-3

Two ways unconformities form.

What force might have changed the rock layers from *A* to *B* in Figure 15-3 (top)? Erosion of the surface of tilted rock layers followed by new rock formation are shown in *C* and *D* of Figure 15-3 (top). The new rock formation is an angular unconformity. Why is it called angular? What is occurring in 15-3 (bottom)?

In finding relative ages, geologists also make use of the **law of cross-cutting relationships**. According to this law, younger features in rock formations cut across older features. Folds and faults are younger than the layers that they cut across. So are intrusions of igneous rock, such as dikes and sills. How does the age of the dike in Figure 15-4 compare with the age of the rocks around it?

REVIEW

1. How is the principle of uniformitarianism a guide to reading the record in the rocks?
2. How is the law of superposition used to find relative ages of rocks?
3. Describe the sequence of events that results in an angular unconformity.
4. Why do unconformities make determining the relative ages of rocks more difficult?

CHALLENGE   Suppose a layer of granite, an igneous rock, is seen below layers of sedimentary rock in a road cut. Using only the law of superposition, can you tell whether the granite is older than the sedimentary rocks or younger? Explain your answer.

Figure 15-4

Dike intrusion at Mount Moran in the Teton Range.

15-2 FORMATION OF FOSSILS

The bone in Figure 15-5 (*left*) is being examined by a paleontologist (pay lee ahn TAHL uh jihst). **Paleontologists** are scientists who study life on the earth in past geologic time. They make inferences about ancient organisms and their environments through the study of fossils. **Fossils** are the preserved remains or traces of plants or animals of the past found in the earth's crust. What might fossil tracks tell about the animal that made them?

PETRIFIED REMAINS

When a plant or animal dies, its remains usually are eaten or they decay completely. But if an organism is quickly buried in mud, sand, or volcanic ash, it may become a fossil. Even then, the soft parts usually decay. But the hard parts—bones, shells, wood—can turn into stone, or be petrified. This process of turning into stone is called *petrifaction* (peht ruh FAK shuhn).

palaio (ancient)
fossilis (to dig)

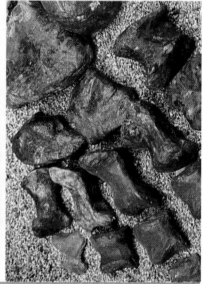

Figure 15-5

A paleontologist is carefully chipping rock away from this dinosaur bone in Colorado (*left*). Petrified wood, Arizona (*middle*). Petrified *Stegosaurus* foot bones, 140 million years old (*right*).

Ground water contains dissolved minerals. During the process of petrifaction, dissolved minerals enter openings in bones and other hard parts of organisms. Little by little, the minerals replace the materials that made up the object. When the minerals harden, the fossil is formed. The mineral pyrite may replace a shell. The mineral silica may replace wood, forming petrified wood. Fine details, even microscopic cells, can be preserved as rock. In Figure 15-5 (*middle*), notice the growth rings.

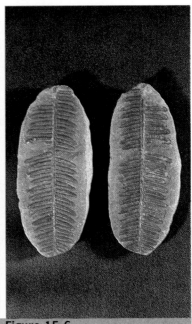

Figure 15-6

Carbon film fossil (*left*), fossil reptile tracks (*middle*), mold and cast of a fern fossil (*right*).

FILMS, IMPRINTS, MOLDS, AND CASTS

Organisms can be preserved as fossils by a process called *carbonization*. Plant and animal remains contain compounds of carbon and other elements. After an organism is buried, pressure within the earth may squeeze out the other elements, leaving a thin film of carbon. The carbon film may show the organism in fine detail, as in Figure 15-6. In some cases, even the carbon is gone, leaving an *imprint*.

Footprints, trails, and burrows leave imprints of another type. These imprints are traces, rather than actual remains, of living things. A *trace fossil* is preserved evidence of an animal's activity. Dinosaur tracks in soft mud that hardens into rock, shown in Figure 15-6, are trace fossils. So are the imprints of burrows of ancient worms.

Sometimes imprints are made by the remains of organisms that then dissolve away. For example, a shell is buried in mud. The mud hardens into rock. Then the shell dissolves, leaving its imprint in the rock. This kind of imprint is called a mold. A **mold** is a hollow space left in a rock by an object that has dissolved. Which object in Figure 15-6 is a mold? If the mold is later filled with minerals or mud, the filling can harden into a cast. A **cast** is a fossil that has the same outer shape as the original object. A cast of a shell looks like the shell itself, not like an imprint.

349

Fossils of an early type of reptile called *Dimetrodon* show that it had long spines arising from its back. In life, the spines may have been connected by a web of skin. Some scientists think that this "sail" helped to regulate body temperature. How would such a structure be useful in maintaining a fairly constant body temperature?

UNCHANGED REMAINS

In some cases, fossils are the unchanged remains of organisms. Examples are the actual teeth and bones of dinosaurs. These have been found in many parts of the United States. The hard parts remained after the soft parts decayed.

Occasionally, a whole animal, including the soft tissues, is found preserved as a fossil. In Poland a woolly rhinoceros was found preserved in asphalt. Woolly mammoths that lived nearly 20,000 years ago have been found in ice and frozen soil in Siberia and Alaska. Hair, skin, and even stomach contents were intact! A mammoth is shown in Figure 15-7 (right). Why, do you think, was its body so well-preserved?

Figure 15-7

A woolly mammoth (*right*) that was discovered frozen in the tundra and a beetle in amber (*above*).

ACTIVITY   A "Fossil" Mold and Cast

OBJECTIVE
Construct models of a fossil mold and a fossil cast.

MATERIALS
small seashell, petroleum jelly, modeling clay, hand lens, 12 g plaster of paris, 5 mL water, plastic dish, plastic spoon

PROCEDURE

A. Coat a small seashell with a thin layer of petroleum jelly.
B. Roll a piece of modeling clay into a ball about twice the size of the shell. Press the outer side of the shell into the clay ball. Remove the shell. Use a hand lens to observe the imprint of the shell in the clay. Record what you observe.
C. Roll another piece of modeling clay into a ball about twice the size of the shell. Press the same shell into the center of the clay ball. Remove the shell.
D. Mix 12 g of plaster of paris with 5 mL of water in a plastic dish. Stir the mixture with a plastic spoon until it is creamy and smooth.
E. Pour the plaster into the imprint made by the shell in the clay. Let dry 30 minutes or overnight.
F. Remove the hardened plaster from the clay. Use the hand lens to observe the plaster. Record what you observe.

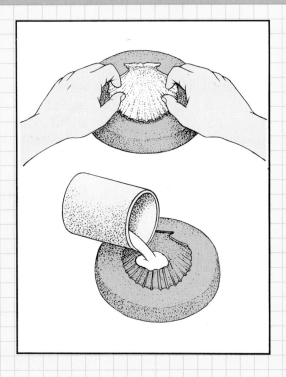

RESULTS AND CONCLUSIONS

1. Compare the imprint of the shell in the clay with the hardened plaster shape. Which is a mold? Which is a cast?
2. How are your models of a fossil mold and fossil cast like real fossils? How are your models different from real fossils?

The fossil insect in Figure 15-7 was preserved inside hardened tree sap called amber. The insect was trapped when the sap was a sticky liquid. Can you suggest a reason why insects are found in amber but not in ice?

REVIEW

1. What is the special field of study of a paleontologist?
2. Describe how a fossil forms by petrifaction.
3. How is a carbon-film fossil formed?
4. How are trace fossils formed?
5. What is the difference between a cast and a mold?

CHALLENGE If you found a fossil bone, tooth, or shell, how could you tell whether it is unchanged, has been petrified, or is a cast?

15-3 FOSSILS AND TIME

Molds and casts of clams are found high on dry land. So are rocks that contain imprints of fish. In fact, most fossils of water animals are dug up or collected on land. How did they get there? Fossils provide us with many clues to past environments. The fossils of clams and fish found on land are evidence that the land was once under water. Further studies may show whether the water was shallow or deep, warm or cold, fresh or salty. Palm trees are tropical plants. Fossils of palm trees are found in the Antarctic. If "the present is the key to the past," what might you say about the past climate of the Antarctic?

The remains of living things that lived only in an unchanging environment are called *facies* (FAY shee eez) *fossils*. Such fossils show that a certain kind of environment existed. For example, corals live only in shallow, warm seas today. When fossil coral reefs are found, we can say that warm, shallow seas existed when the corals that built the reefs were alive.

Scientists use some fossils as index fossils. An **index fossil** is a fossil that can tell the relative age of the rock in which it is found. Organisms that lived for a certain time span in many different places are used as index fossils. Small organisms that lived in great numbers make good index fossils. So do organisms that have distinctive features that make them easy to identify. The trilobite (TRI-luh bīt) is an example of an index fossil. What are some features that help identify the trilobites in Figure 15-8?

Figure 15-8

Trilobites are good index fossils.

Some kinds of dinosaurs serve both as facies fossils and as index fossils. They lived on the land in a warm, moist climate. For reasons that no one knows for sure, the dinosaurs became extinct. Their bones are facies fossils because they indicate the kind of climate in which the dinosaurs lived. The dinosaurs are also index fossils because they were limited to a specific period of geologic time.

Index fossils provide a way of matching rocks of the same age found in different places. The same kinds of trilobites have been found in both the Grand Canyon and in Wales. Since these trilobites lived during a certain geologic time, we can say that the rocks in which they were found formed at about the same time. This process of matching rocks of the same age from different places is called **correlation**. In Figure 15-9, find the fossils in each group of rocks that could be used to correlate the rocks by age.

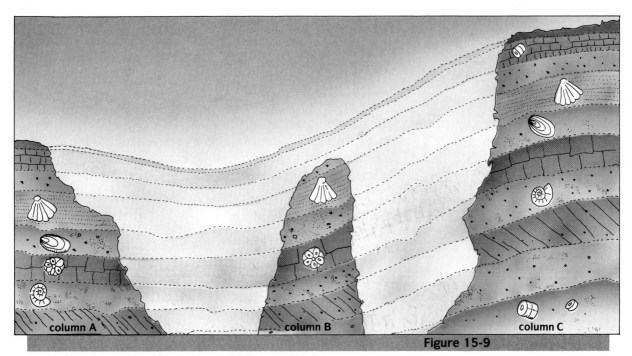

column A   column B   column C

Figure 15-9

Fossils can be used to match up layers of rock from different areas.

The first person to use fossils to match rock layers was William Smith. In the late 1790s, while building a canal in England, Smith studied the rocks and fossils that were dug up. Smith noticed that each rock layer contained fossils found only in that layer. He found that the same kinds of rocks, with certain kinds of fossils, were found in the same sequence in different places. He arranged the

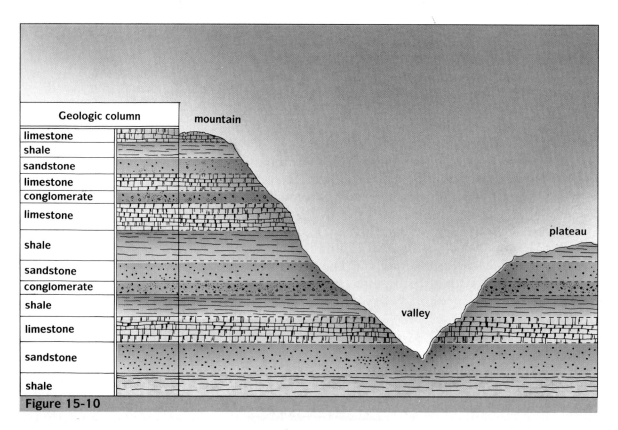

Geologic column
limestone
shale
sandstone
limestone
conglomerate
limestone
shale
sandstone
conglomerate
shale
limestone
sandstone
shale

mountain

plateau

valley

Figure 15-10

The geologic column is a record of rock formations from all over the earth.

rock layers in order of their ages, making a relative time scale. Similar work was done by scientists in other countries. The result was the first geologic column. A **geologic column** is a diagram of the sequence of rock layers in an area in order of age, as shown in Figure 15-10. Such a diagram is made by piecing together layers from separate areas. There is no one place where the entire history of the earth is represented in its rocks. Geologic columns made in the 1800s could show only the relative ages of rock layers. As you will see, scientists have eventually been able to add actual dates to geologic columns.

REVIEW

1. How do fossils provide evidence of changes in environment?
2. Why must a fossil be found in different places to serve as an index fossil?
3. How was the first geologic column constructed?

CHALLENGE Why is there no one place on the earth where all the layers that were ever laid down there are still represented?

15-4 EARLY ESTIMATES OF THE EARTH'S AGE

The study of rocks and fossils tells us much about relative ages of layers in the earth. But what about the earth's actual age in years—that is, its **absolute age?** How many years old are the rock layers? And how long has it been, in years, since the earth began? In the 1800s, several scientists tried various ways to determine the earth's absolute age.

By one method, scientists estimated the total thickness of the earth's sedimentary rock. They compared their estimate with the rate of sedimentation. **Sedimentation** is the process in which materials carried by air, water, or ice are deposited as sediments. You will remember how weathering and erosion remove particles from rocks. These particles become sediments when they fall to the bottom of lakes and seas. There, the sediments eventually turn into sedimentary rock. Several geologists compared the total thickness of sedimentary rocks with the rate of sedimentation. In this way, they thought, they found the age of the earth. But the ages found by different geologists did not agree. They ranged from 3 million to 1.5 billion years.

sedimentum (to settle)

DO YOU KNOW?

Not long ago, water from a creek in eastern Arkansas washed away the last few millimeters of sediment covering part of the creek's bank. The sediment had covered an ancient oyster reef. Using special techniques, paleontologists unearthed fossils from the ancient reef. They found an unusual number of shark teeth as well as bones of fish, reptiles, and mammals.

The fossils were collected and prepared for identification very carefully. The careful collection techniques allowed scientists to identify the fossils. The fossils were those of animals from the Eocene Period and were about 40 million years old. Among the fossils were teeth from four kinds of sharks. These ancient sharks resemble today's tiger shark, lemon shark, sand tiger shark, and cat shark. Bones from fish and reptiles, including those of a 7-m-long snake, were also found. These types of animals indicate that the climate of eastern Arkansas in late Eocene times was warmer than it is today.

Paleontologists around the Gulf states continue to search for evidence of oceans that existed in past geologic times. The use of efficient techniques to study fossils will help scientists uncover more secrets about life and climate in prehistoric America.

Why did the estimates of the earth's age vary so much? Sedimentation can be seen at work today. By the principle of uniformitarianism, we know that sedimentation also occurred in the past. But early geologists did not realize that the rate of the earth's processes can vary at different times and places. Also, they had no accurate way to measure the thickness of the earth's rock layers. For these reasons, those who tried to date the earth had started with different measurements.

Figure 15-11

Rock layering in Big Bend National Park, in Texas.

Another way of dating the earth was by the "salt" method. This method estimated the salt content of the oceans. The estimate was then compared with the rate at which salt is being added to the oceans. Scientists assumed that at first the oceans contained fresh water. The weathering and erosion of rocks carried salt into rivers and then into the oceans. The idea was to calculate how long it took for the oceans to reach their present saltiness. That time was thought to be the earth's age. The results of this method ranged from 9 million to 2.5 billion years. Can you guess why the results did not agree? Each scientist had made different estimates of the amounts of salt. Also, the scientists had not accounted for other ways in which salt is added to or removed from the oceans.

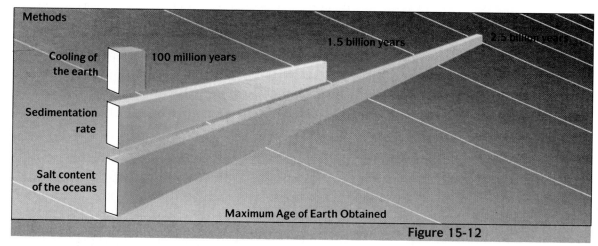

Figure 15-12

The estimated age of the earth varied with the method of dating used.

Lord Kelvin, a British physicist, used another method for dating the earth. Kelvin assumed that at first the earth was so hot that its rocks were molten. Since its beginning, the earth was thought to be losing heat. Kelvin measured the rate of the earth's cooling. He also took into account the heat coming from within the earth and from the sun. Then he calculated how long it had taken the earth to cool to its present temperature. He made several estimates of the earth's age. These ranged from 20 million to 100 million years.

Many scientists thought Kelvin's results were closer to the earth's real age than were the results of the other methods. But it turned out that his results were also inaccurate. At the time, no one knew about radioactivity, which heats the earth from within. This source of internal heat makes Kelvin's estimates far too small.

None of the methods of the 1800s to find the absolute age of the earth worked. However, the results all indicated that the earth was probably very old indeed. Before that time, people generally believed the earth was only a few thousand years old. That belief was beginning to change.

REVIEW

1. State how sedimentation rate, salt content of the ocean, and the earth's heat were each used to estimate the earth's age?
2. Give reasons why each of the three early methods of estimating the earth's age gave inaccurate results.

CHALLENGE How would unconformities make it difficult to measure the total thickness of the earth's sedimentary rocks accurately?

15-5 RADIOMETRIC DATING

In the late 1800s, Henri Becquerel (beh KREHL) discovered that certain elements are radioactive. A **radioactive element** is an element that decays, or breaks down, to form other kinds of elements. **Radioactive decay** is a process in which atomic nuclei break down, giving off particles and energy. The particles and energy are forms of radiation. This release of radiation is radioactivity.

The discovery of radioactivity showed Kelvin's dating of the earth to be wrong. Radioactivity also gave scientists a better way to measure geologic time. This new way of measuring time is called radiometric dating. **Radiometric dating** finds the real ages of rocks and other objects by measuring the rates of decay of radioactive elements in the objects. This method works because the rate of radioactive decay does not change. Changes in pressure and temperature, for example, do not affect the rate of decay. The rate at which a given radioactive element decays is based on the element's half-life. The **half-life** of an element is the length of time it takes for one half of its atoms to decay.

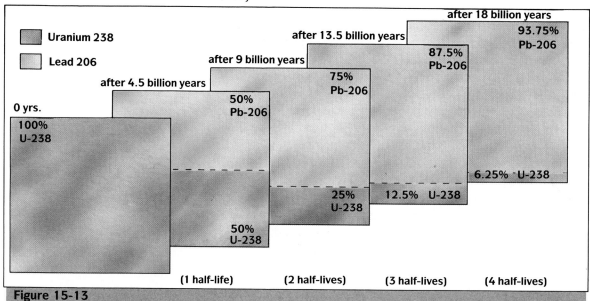

Figure 15-13

Radioactive decay of uranium 238.

Figure 15-13 shows how the amounts of the radioactive element, uranium 238, and its decay element, lead 206, change over time. The decay element, lead 206, is not radioactive. The amounts of uranium 238 and lead 206 after a half-life period are given as percentages. The half-life of uranium is 4.5 billion years. After that time, half of the atoms of a mass of uranium 238 are changed into lead 206. After one half-life the percentage of uranium 238 atoms to lead 206 atoms is 50% : 50%. Use Figure 15-13 to tell the percentage of uranium 238 atoms after 9 billion years. How many half-lives is this? According to Figure 15-13 what percentage of the U-238 remains after four half-lives?

Scientists use uranium 238 as an atomic clock. If uranium 238 is part of a rock when it forms, it becomes locked into the rock. After that, no more uranium-238 can become part of the rock. But as the rock ages, the uranium 238 decays into lead 206. From the half-life of uranium 238 and the ratio of uranium 238 to lead 206, the rock's age can be calculated. The oldest earth rock dated so far by this uranium 238 method was formed 3.9 billion years ago. This means that the earth itself is at least that old. Some meteorites and moon soil dated by radiometric methods are 4.6 billion years old. Most scientists believe the earth's age to be the same—about 4.6 billion years.

Figure 15-14

Scientist using radioactive dating method to find the age of a rock.

Different radioactive elements serve as atomic clocks for things of different ages. Table 15-1 lists some of these elements, their half-lives, and their uses. As Table 15-1 shows, carbon 14 is used to date things that were once part of living things, such as bones, shells, and wood. All living things take in carbon as long as they are alive. Most of the carbon is non-radioactive. This non-radioactive carbon is called carbon 12. A small amount of the carbon is radioactive carbon 14. The percentage of carbon 14 in the living thing stays the same until death occurs. After death the percentage of carbon 14 slowly goes down as it decays. Scientists can compare the amounts of carbon 14 and ordinary carbon in dead organic matter. The older the material, the smaller its percentage of carbon 14. Using the half-life of carbon 14, 5730 years, scientists can figure out the age of the material. However, the method does not work for items older than about 50,000 years.

Table 15-1 *Half-lives of Radioactive Elements*

Element	Half-life	Used for Dating
carbon 14	5730	wood, shells, bone
potassium 40	1.3 billion	rocks
rubidium 87	47 billion	rocks
uranium 235	713 million	rocks
uranium 238	415 billion	rocks

ACTIVITY A Model for Radiometric Dating

OBJECTIVES
Demonstrate a model for radiometric dating.
Interpret data gathered from the model.

MATERIALS
ruler, index cards, scissors, shoebox with lid, graph paper, colored pencil

PROCEDURE
A. Copy the table and record your observations in it.
B. Use a ruler and pencil to mark off 100 squares, 2 cm × 2 cm, on index cards. Make an X inside each square. Then cut the squares apart. In this model, each square represents an atom that undergoes radioactive decay. When the X is facing up, the atom is radioactive. When the square is turned over so that the X faces down, the atom has decayed and is no longer radioactive.
C. Place each of the 100 squares with the X facing up in the *lid* of the shoebox. Place the *bottom* of the box over the lid.
D. Hold the box securely shut and shake it, mixing the squares thoroughly. Put the box down lid-side down and open it. Take out

all the squares that no longer have the X facing up. Count the squares that are left in the lid and record the number in the table.
E. Repeat Steps C and D seven times.

RESULTS AND CONCLUSIONS
1. For each trial, calculate the percentage of squares left in the box from the original 100. Make a graph of the number of trials versus the percentages of squares left in the box.
2. Suppose exactly half the atoms of X decayed during each trial. Calculate the percentage of the original 100 squares that would be left in the box after each half-life period. Use a different colored pencil to add a graph of each of these "perfect" results to your graph.
3. How do you account for the difference between the graph of your results and the graph of the "perfect" results?
4. Suppose the half-life of X is 1000 years. At the end of your trials, how old is the rock represented by the box?

	Trial Number							
	1	2	3	4	5	6	7	8
Number of squares left in box								
Percentage of squares left in box								
Percentage of radioactivity left in "perfect" decay of X	75	50	25	12.5	6.75	3.38	1.69	0.8

REVIEW
1. Explain what it means for an element to have a half-life of 10,000 years.
2. Why is radiometric dating a better method than measuring heat loss for finding the earth's age?
3. How is carbon 14 used to find the age of a bone?

CHALLENGE Suppose scientists knew for sure that there were no earth rocks older than 3.9 billion years. Why would they still believe the earth itself is older than that?

15-6 TIME AND CHANGE IN LIVING THINGS

The oldest known fossils are of simple organisms over 3 billion years old. We know their age from the age of the rocks in which they were found. Fossils of other organisms, from simple to complex, occur in rocks of various ages. Moving from the oldest rocks to the youngest, we find that there is a change in types of fossils from the simplest to the most complex.

Many species, or life forms, that are extinct and found as fossils are similar to, yet different from, species alive today. These extinct and living species seem to be related. Figure 15-15 shows related species of horses, from oldest (small horses) to youngest (larger horses). List some ways in which each horse is similar to, yet different from, one below or above it in time.

After completing this section, you will be able to

- **describe** how fossil evidence supports the theory of evolution.
- **list** the main ideas in the theory of evolution by natural selection.

The key terms in this section are
evolution
natural selection

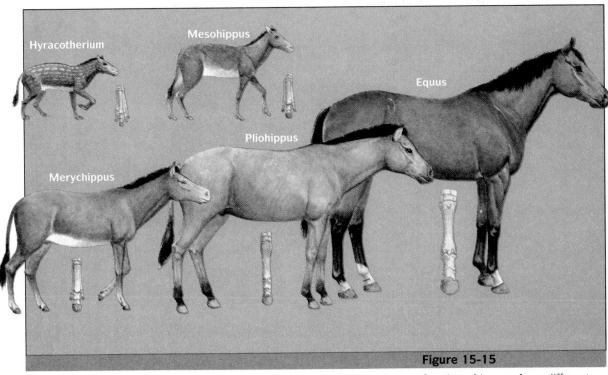

Figure 15-15

Species of horses from different periods seem to be related.

The fossil evidence is that, over time, living things have slowly *evolved*, or changed. Today's species are descended, with changes, from those of the past. The process of change that produces new species from existing species is called **evolution**. How can we explain evolution? Why did animals and plants change as they did throughout geologic time?

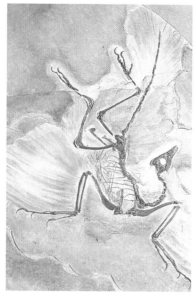

In 1859, Charles Darwin put forth a theory of evolution based on natural selection. **Natural selection** is the idea that those life forms that are best adapted to an environment will survive. Darwin's theory of evolution by natural selection has several parts.

1. There are inborn variations, or differences, among the individuals in a species.
2. Some variations are traits that help the individual to live successfully. Individuals with such helpful traits are well adapted to their environment.
3. The best-adapted individuals are most likely to live long enough to reproduce. In other words, they are selected by nature to pass their traits to their offspring.
4. The selection process is repeated in each generation. In time, new species of organisms are produced.

Figure 15-16

Fossil of *Archaeopteryx* (top). Artist's conception of what *Archaeopteryx* looked like.

Darwin expected that fossils representing links between different species would be found. Many scientists think that *Archaeopteryx* (ahr kee AHP tuhr ihks) is such a link. Look at Figure 15-16. What kind of animal is this? It appears to have some traits of a reptile and some traits of a bird. List those traits that might identify it as a relative of each animal group. In life science and biology courses, you will learn more about the work of Darwin and others in the field of evolution.

REVIEW

1. How do fossils help support the idea that living things evolve?
2. Using an example, explain evolution.
3. How does Darwin's idea of natural selection help explain evolution?

CHALLENGE The duckbill platypus lays eggs, like a reptile. The platypus also has hair and produces milk, like a mammal. Why is the platypus called "living fossil"?

CHAPTER SUMMARY

The main ideas in this chapter are listed below. Read these statements before you answer the Chapter Review questions.

- According to the principle of uniformitarianism, the processes at work on earth today were also at work in the past. (15-1)

- The law of superposition, the study of unconformities, and the law of cross-cutting relationships help geologists to determine relative ages of rocks. (15-1)

- Fossils are the remains or traces of prehistoric life forms preserved in various ways. (15-2)

- Index fossils and facies fossils are used in the correlation of rocks from different areas. (15-3)

- A geologic column shows the sequence, by age, of rocks in an area. (15-3)

- Early methods of estimating the earth's age were based on studies of sedimentation, the saltiness of the ocean, and the earth's cooling. (15-4)

- Radiometric dating uses the half-lives of radioactive elements to determine ages of materials. (15-5)

- The evidence of the fossil record supports Darwin's theory of evolution by natural selection. (15-6)

The key terms in this chapter are listed below. Use each term in a sentence that shows the meaning of the term.

absolute age	law of cross-cutting	radioactive decay
cast	relationships	radioactive element
correlation	law of superposition	radiometric dating
evolution	mold	relative age
fossil	natural selection	sedimentation
geologic column	paleontologist	unconformity
half-life	principle of	
index fossil	uniformitarianism	

Chapter Review

VOCABULARY

Use the key terms from this chapter to complete the following sentences correctly.

1. The process of matching rocks of the same age from different places is _____.
2. The law that describes the relative ages of undisturbed rock layers is the _____.
3. The time required for one half the atoms of a radioactive element to decay is its _____.
4. A fossil that can tell the relative age of the rock in which it is found is a/an _____.
5. A fossil that has the same outer shape as the original is a/an _____.
6. The process in which atomic nuclei give off particles and energy is _____.
7. A buried surface that represents a break in the rock record is a/an _____.
8. A process used in an early method of dating the earth is the rate of _____.
9. The process of change that produces new species of living things over time is _____.
10. A diagram of the sequence of rock layers in an area is a/an _____.

CONCEPTS

1. Give an example of how scientists use the principle of uniformitarianism to study the earth's history. (15-1)
2. Name and state the law that describes the relative ages of rock layers. (15-1)
3. Describe two ways in which unconformities form. (15-1)
4. Give an example of the law of cross-cutting relationships. (15-1)
5. What is a paleontologist's special field of study? (15-2)
6. What is a fossil? How is a trace fossil different from other types of fossils? (15-2)
7. Explain how both a mold and a cast can be formed from the remains of an organism. (15-2)
8. What are two ways in which fossils of whole animals have been formed? (15-2)
9. What are the characteristics of a good index fossil? Give an example. (15-3)

10. How do facies fossils provide information about the past of an area? Give an example. (15-3)

11. Explain how correlation is used to make a geologic column. (15-3)

12. Distinguish between relative age and absolute age. (15-1, 15-4)

13. How was the rate of sedimentation used to date the earth? (15-4)

14. How was the saltiness of the sea used to date the earth? (15-4)

15. What was Lord Kelvin's method of dating the earth? (15-4)

16. Questions 13–15 refer to three early methods used to estimate the earth's age. What were the limitations of each method? (15-4)

17. What happens to the ratio of the amounts of a radioactive element and its decay element as time passes? (15-5)

18. Why might potassium 40 be used instead of carbon 14 to date a certain fossil? (15-6)

19. What does it mean to say that living things evolve? (15-7)

20. How does the fossil record support the idea of evolution? (15-7)

21. What is the main idea of natural selection? (15-8)

APPLICATION/ CRITICAL THINKING

1. Name some animals and plants now living on the earth that would make good facies fossils for future geologists. Explain your choices.

2. Why do geologists use the age of meteorites to help determine the earth's age?

3. Suppose a piece of wood was found to contain one fourth of its original amount of carbon 14. How old is the wood?

4. Why would radiometric dating of rocks be helpful to geologists in locating coal?

EXTENSION

1. Collect fossils in your area. Try to decide which organisms lived in an ocean environment and which did not. Explain your decisions.

2. Use library resources to prepare a paper on the extinction of the dinosaurs. What are some explanations that have been suggested? What is your opinion? Why do you think so?

READINGS

Fenton, Carroll L., and M. A. Fenton. *The Fossil Book: A Record of Prehistoric Life*. Garden City, N.Y.: Doubleday & Co., Inc., 1958.

Gannon, Robert. "How Old Is It?" *Popular Science*, November 1979.

Jeffery, David. "Annals of Life Written in Rock, Fossils." *National Geographic*, August 1985.

EARTH'S HISTORY

Several times during its history, North America was under water. Evidence of this can be found in the Scablands of Washington State, shown in the photograph. At other times, mountains were uplifted, worn away, and uplifted again. Changes in the land surface have been interpreted from the rock record. By reading the rock record, scientists have learned much about the earth's dynamic history.

- *What features in the photograph show that the area in the photograph may have once been under water?*
- *What type of climate does this area have today?*
- *In what ways can a landscape give clues to past environments?*

16-1 GEOLOGIC TIME SCALE

Millions of years ago, giant reptiles called dinosaurs roamed the earth. Some were the largest land animals ever to have lived. Some were fierce hunters with huge jaws and sharp teeth. They reigned over the earth for more than a 100 million years. Then they completely disappeared. What could have caused their disappearance?

The record of life from its earliest forms to the present forms is shown in the rock layers in the geologic column. As you examine the layers in the column many forms of life seen in lower, older layers do not appear in higher, younger layers. Other forms of life suddenly appear in the younger layers. Some forms of life are found throughout the column.

Scientists believe that changes occurred on the earth throughout history that affected living things. For example, a cooling of the climate may have caused the dinosaurs to die out. Changes in sea level can cause the disappearance of one form of life and the appearance of different forms. For example, when the sea level rises, areas of low-land become covered with water. This causes life forms on the land to be replaced with sea life.

> *After completing this section, you will be able to*
>
> - **explain** how the geologic time scale is divided into units.
> - **describe** the types of life forms during the Precambrian era
> - **name** the four eras of the geologic time scale.
>
> *The key terms in this section are*
> epoch
> era
> geologic time scale
> period

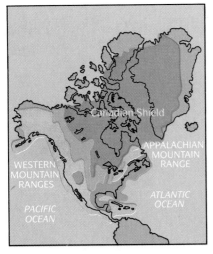

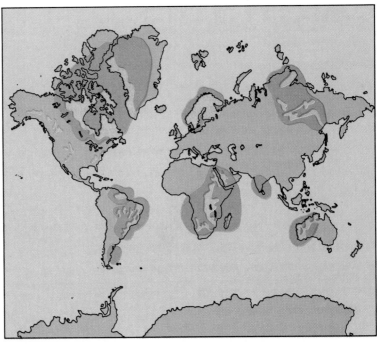

Key:

 Shields

 Precambrian rock outcrops

Figure 16-1

The Canadian Shield contains the largest area of exposed Precambrian rocks.

From the study of the rock record and the fossils it contains, scientists have developed a "story" of the earth's past. With the evidence of changes in the earth's crust and sudden changes in forms of life, scientists have divided the earth's history into units of time. The division of the earth's history into units of time based on the geologic time changes in the earth's crust and sudden changes in forms of life is called the **geologic time scale**.

The geologic time scale, shown in Figure 16-2, is divided into four major parts, called eras. An **era** is a unit of time based on the changes in the earth's crust and on the stages of development of certain life forms.

The oldest and longest era is the Precambrian (pree-KAM bree uhn) Era. It began when the earth came into existence about 4.6 billion years ago. According to Figure 16-2, when did the Precambrian Era end?

Precambrian rocks are usually covered by younger layers of rocks. However, they can be seen at the bottom of the Grand Canyon, where erosion has cut through the younger layers. The largest area of exposed Precambrian rocks is in the Canadian Shield, in the northeastern United States and eastern Canada.

Few fossils are found in Precambrian rocks. Life forms during this era did not have the hard body parts that could form good fossils. Early Precambrian rocks do show some evidence of simple forms of life, such as bacteria and algae.

Figure 16-2
The Geologic Time Scale

ERA	PERIOD	EPOCH	BEGINNING (millions of years ago)	IMPORTANT EVENTS
Cenozoic	Quaternary	Holocene	less than .01	modern humans appear
		Pleistocene	2.5	ice age 
	Tertiary	Pliocene	6	
		Miocene	25	 mammals dominant
		Oligocene	38	
		Eocene	55	 
		Paleocene	65	small mammals
Mesozoic	Cretaceous		140	mass extinction of dinosaurs; flowering plants 
	Jurassic		195	 first birds appear; dinosaurs dominant
	Triassic		230	first dinosaurs and first mammals appear; conifers, reptiles, shellfish, grasshoppers abundant 
Paleozoic	Permian		290	most sea life disappears; mammallike reptiles dominant 
	Carboniferous		345	 first reptiles and first insects appear; club mosses and horsetails abundant; forests and swamps 
	Devonian		400	fish abundant; first amphibians appear 
	Silurian		440	 land plants appear; jawed fish appear 
	Ordovician		500	shelled organisms abundant; jawless fish appear 
	Cambrian		600	trilobites, brachiopods, sponges, snails, jellyfishes, worms abundant 
Precambrian			1500	first jellyfish
			4600	bacteria, algae

ACTIVITY   A Model of Geologic Time

OBJECTIVE
Relate events that occurred in the earth's history to the geologic time scale.

MATERIALS
adding machine tape (5-m length), meter stick

PROCEDURE
A. You will use adding machine tape to make a time line. Then you will plot events from the earth's history on the time line. This can be done by using a scale on which 1 m represents 1 billion (1,000,000,000) years.
   1. How many years would 1 cm represent on this scale? 1 mm?
B. Make a table similar to the one below. Based on the scale of 1 m representing 1 billion years, change each number of years shown to the number of centimeters that will represent it. Record these numbers in your table.

C. Draw a vertical line across the tape near the left end. Label the line "Beginning of Precambrian."
D. Starting at this line, measure the distances on the tape that will represent the events in the table. Draw a line across the tape to mark each event. Label each event.

RESULTS AND CONCLUSIONS
1. Which is the longest geological era?
2. Which is the shortest geological era?
3. Which era do we live in?
4. Compare the time span during which modern humans have been on the earth with the entire span of geologic time.
5. Compare the time span between the appearance of the earliest human and the appearance of modern humans with that between the appearance of modern humans and the first landing on the moon.

Event	Years Before the Present (approx.)	Cm
Humans first land on the moon	10	
Early Egyptian civilization	5,000	
Beginning of last Ice Age	20,000	
First modern human	50,000	
Earliest human	2,000,000	
Beginning of Cenozoic Era	65,000,000	
First birds	150,000,000	
First insects	345,000,000	
Beginning of Mesozoic Era	230,000,000	
First land plants	440,000,000	
Beginning of Paleozoic Era	600,000,000	
Beginning of Precambrian Era	4,500,000,000	

Figure 16-3 shows some of the forms of life that may have lived during the Precambrian era. Rocks of the Canadian Shield show only traces of the algae and bacteria that lived over 3 billion years ago.

Impressions of soft-bodied animals, such as jellyfish, corals, and starfish, have been found in late Precambrian rocks. Some Precambrian rocks are rich in carbon, which may be the remains of once living things.

Figure 16-3

Living things in the Precambrian were relatively simple and did not have hard body parts.

Following the Precambrian Era is the Paleozoic (pay-lee uh ZOH ihk) Era. Many forms of primitive life existed in this era. Paleozoic means "ancient life." According to Figure 16-2 when did the Paleozoic Era end?

After the Paleozoic era comes the Mesozoic (mes uh-ZOH ihk) Era. Mesozoic means "middle life." It was dominated by reptiles, such as the dinosaurs. About 65 million years ago, the Mesozoic Era ended.

The most recent era is the Cenozoic (see nuh ZOH-ihk) Era. Cenozoic means "recent life." It is dominated by warm-blooded animals or mammals.

Eras are divided into smaller time units called periods. A **period** is a time interval into which eras are divided. An era is divided into periods based on certain characteristics of the rocks that formed during that period. For example, the Carboniferous (kahr buh NIF uhr uhs) period was the period of time when coal, or rocks made of carbon, formed.

The periods of the Cenozoic Era are divided into smaller units of time called **epochs** (EP uhk). This is because the Cenozoic Era is the most recent era and contains enough fossil evidence to classify its periods into smaller units of time.

REVIEW

1. On what evidence is the geologic time scale divided?
2. What types of life forms existed during the Precambrian Era?
3. What are the four eras of the geologic time scale.

CHALLENGE   Why isn't the Precambrian divided into periods?

16-2 PALEOZOIC ERA

As you have learned, there is little evidence of life during the Precambrian Era, which lasted about 4 billion years. At the end of this era, an era began in which abundant life forms first appeared. This era is called the **Paleozoic Era**.

The Paleozoic Era was dominated by animals called invertebrates (ihn VER tuh brayts). An **invertebrate** is an animal that does not have a bony skeleton. However, it can contain hard parts, such as a shell. The Paleozoic Era is sometimes called the Age of Invertebrates. The Paleozoic Era is divided into six periods, based on kinds of life forms and changes in the earth's surface that occurred.

The first period in the Paleozoic Era is the *Cambrian* (KAM bree uhn) *Period*. Figure 16-4 (*left*) shows what the earth looked like during the Cambrian Period. As shown, the shapes, sizes, and positions of the continents were

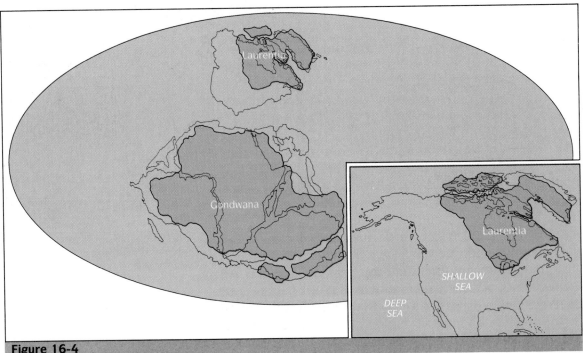

Figure 16-4

The positions and shapes of the continents were different in Cambrian times than they are today (left). Much of the land was covered by shallow seas (right).

very different than they are today. Notice that what is now North America was part of a larger continent. What is the name of this continent?

During the Cambrian Period, much of the continental areas were covered by shallow seas. According to Figure 16-4 (*right*), what part of the United States was once covered by a shallow sea?

Some scientists believe that the warm, shallow seas over the continental areas led to the sudden appearance of sea life. Evidence of land animals or plants during the Cambrian Period has not been found. The most common form of life was the trilobite (TRĪ luh bīt). Figure 16-5 shows a fossil of a trilobite.

Another common animal during the Cambrian Period was the brachiopod (BRAYK ee uh pahd). The *brachiopod* was a hard-shelled animal, somewhat like a clam. Other animals included sponges, snails, jellyfish, and worms. The Cambrian Period lasted for about 100 million years.

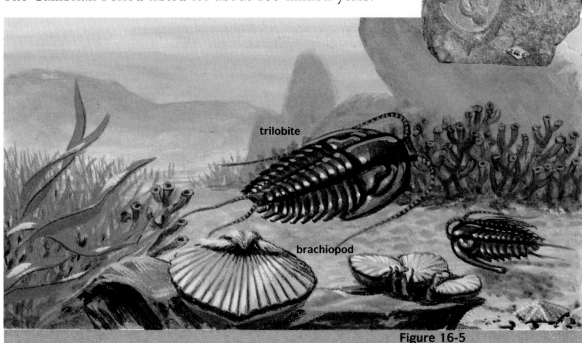

Figure 16-5

Trilobites and brachiopods were common types of animals during the Cambrian period.

The Cambrian period is followed by the *Ordovician* (awr duh VIHSH uhn) *Period*, beginning about 500 million years ago. During this period, life forms similar to clams, squid, and octopuses began to take over as the major life forms. The first vertebrates appeared during this period. A **vertebrate** is an animal with a bony skeleton. The first vertebrates were fish covered with bony plates. The fish also had bones in their fins. The fins may have eventually become the limbs of the first land animals.

The Ordovician Period was marked by many surface changes on the earth. The sea level rose, covering about 70 percent of North America. There was volcanic activity and mountain building along the eastern coast of the future United States. The Ordovician Period ended after about 60 million years.

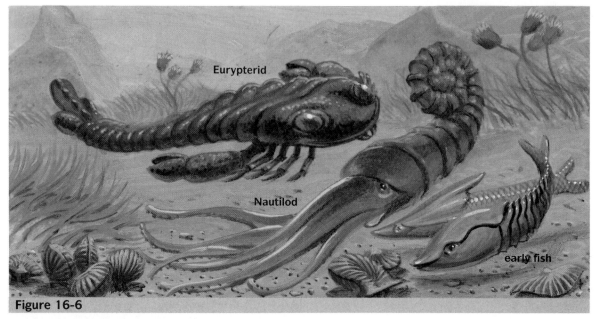

Figure 16-6

Life during the Ordovician period.

Figure 16-7

A frog is a modern amphibian.

The *Silurian* (suh LUR ee uhn) *Period* follows the Ordovician Period. The Silurian Period began about 440 million years ago. During the Silurian Period, the eastern coast of North America was uplifted. A large inland sea formed in the eastern part of the United States. By the end of the period, much of the sea had evaporated. How would such evaporation affect life on the earth? The first land plants, such as lichens and mosses, appeared during this period. Animal life, such as scorpions, lived on the land. The Silurian Period lasted about 40 million years.

The next period is the *Devonian* (duh VOH nee uhn) *Period*, which began about 400 million years ago. By this period, fish had become abundant. Scientists believe that some of these fish developed lungs that could be used to breathe air. These fish are called *lungfish*. The first amphibians (am-FIHB ee uhnz) appeared during this period. *Amphibians* are animals that live in water when they are young but live on land when they are adults. An example of a modern amphibian is a frog. Large land plants appeared, such as giant tree ferns and evergreens.

The Devonian Period is followed by the *Carboniferous Period*. The Carboniferous Period began 345 million years ago and lasted about 55 million years. During this time Pangaea was moving to the north away from the South Pole. How would the climate of Pangaea have been affected? Forests and swamps covered the land. Name some

ferns

conifers

Figure 16-8

During the Carboniferous period forests and swamps covered the land and winged insects were abundant.

of the plants shown in Figure 16-8 that lived during this period. Many insects also developed including a giant dragonfly. It had a wingspan of about 76 cm. With the insects came a new group of vertebrates called reptiles. These animals could live entirely out of the water.

The final period of the Paleozoic Era is the *Permian* (PER mee uhn) *Period*. It began 290 million years ago and lasted 60 million years. The climate became much colder, causing ice ages. This caused parts of present-day Africa, Australia, and South America to be covered with glaciers. Many types of plants and animals could not survive the cold climate. Up to 90 percent of the sea life that was abundant during the Paleozoic Era disappeared. But the reptiles and insects adapted to the changes in climate, and they survived. Conifer (KOH nuh fuhr) trees developed in this period.

REVIEW

1. How do the life forms of the Paleozoic Era differ from the life forms of the Precambrian Era?
2. What were the major life forms and surface changes in each period of the Paleozoic Era?
3. How do invertebrates and vertebrates differ?

CHALLENGE During the ice ages, some land areas became dry. Explain why.

Figure 16-9

A turtle is a modern reptile.

16-3 MESOZOIC ERA

After completing this section, you will be able to

- **describe** the kinds of organisms that lived during the Mesozoic Era.
- **list** the major life forms in each period of the Mesozoic Era.
- **compare** two theories for the mass extinction of the dinosaurs.

The key terms in this section are
Mesozoic Era
meteorite impact hypothesis

The next large division of geologic time to follow the Paleozoic Era is the Mesozoic Era. The Mesozoic Era lasted 165 million years. During this time, Pangaea broke into pieces and formed the continents as we know them today.

Crustal movement created a warm and wet environment. Among the animals, reptiles were better able than other animals to adapt to this environment. The Mesozoic Era is often called the Age of Reptiles.

The land that is now the North American continent took shape. Two mountain chains formed. We know them today as the Sierra Nevada and the Rocky Mountains.

There are three periods during the Mesozoic Era. The first period is the *Triassic* (trī AS ihk) *Period*. During this period, conifers and reptiles were abundant, and mammals appeared. Oysters, lobsters, and clams are some of the marine invertebrates that existed. Grasshoppers, termites, and flies are some of the land invertebrates that existed.

Figure 16-10

During the Mesozoic Era dinosaurs dominated the land.

The next period is the *Jurassic* (ju RAS ihk) *Period*. During this period, reptiles called dinosaurs (DĪ nuh sawrz) dominated. The word *dinosaur* comes from the Greek and means "terrible lizard."

Both large and small dinosaurs existed during the Jurassic Period. The plant-eating dinosaur called the *Brontosaurus* (brahn tuh SAWR uhs) was probably the largest

In 1985 a national park in Arizona yielded the bones of an ancient—but new—dinosaur. This is the oldest dinosaur skeleton in the world. The 225-million-year-old bones of this animal are from the Triassic Period. This is a very early period in the existence of the dinosaurs. Most dinosaurs flourished 35 million years later.

The ancient dinosaur is of a type never before described by any scientist. Researchers who found the dinosaur bones believe that it weighed about 200 pounds. It had large hindquarters and short forearms, much like a very early dinosaur called *Plateosaurus*. As with any newly discovered plant or animal, the dinosaur will be given an official name. It was found near a place called Chinde Point. *Chinde* is a Native American word meaning "ghost." So the new dinosaur may be called *Chindesaurus*—"ghost lizard."

The new find is important because it is a clue to the way life was millions of years ago.

animal that ever lived on land. Fossils indicate this dinosaur was 21 m long and weighed about 70 t. In contrast, some dinosaurs were about the size of a chicken. *Stegosaurus* (stehg uh SAWR uhs) was a dinosaur with plates on the back. A dinosaur that ran on its hind legs and ate meat was *Allosaurus* (AL uh sawr-uhs). Toward the end of the Jurassic period, the first birds appeared.

The final period of the Mesozoic Era is called the *Cretaceous* (krih TAY shuhs) *Period*. Flowering plants appeared at this time. Different types of reptiles appeared. The dinosaur *Tyrannosaurus* (tih ran-uh SAWR uhs) was over 13 m long and weighed about 8 t. It was a large, two-legged meat-eater. Other dinosaurs included *Triceratops* (trī SEHR uh tahps)—a plant-eating, "horned" dinosaur—and the "duck-billed" dinosaur.

By the end of the Cretaceous Period, the dinosaurs and about half of all other life forms had disappeared from existence. When many forms of life die a short period of time, it is called a *mass extinction*. Only small animals survived, such as small reptiles, birds, and mammals.

Many theories have been proposed to explain why the dinosaurs suddenly died. One theory explains that worldwide volcanic activity would have put huge amounts of volcanic dust and smoke into the atmosphere. The dust and smoke could have blocked out sunlight. This may have caused the earth's climate to cool and plant life to die. Dinosaurs that depended on plants for food probably died first. Then the dinosaurs that preyed upon plant-eating dinosaurs died.

Figure 16-11

A duck-billed dinosaur.

ACTIVITY   Name That Mountain

OBJECTIVE
Identify the mountain-building activity that took place in North America during the Mesozoic and Paleozoic eras.

MATERIALS
paper and pencil

PROCEDURE
A. Trace the map of North America.

Period	Activity
Ordovician	Taconic Mountain range forms in northeastern part of United States.
Silurian	Large inland sea forms over the central part of North America.
Devonian	Acadian Mountains form in eastern Canada.
Permian	Appalachian Mountain range forms in eastern United States.
Cretaceous	Rocky Mountain range forms in western North America.

B. Using the information in the table, locate the mountain ranges that formed during the periods of geologic time. Mark their locations on your map by using these symbols: ⋀⋀⋀.

C. Label each mountain range with the name of the period in which it formed.

RESULTS AND CONCLUSIONS
1. What mountain range formed in the United States during the Ordovician Period?
2. Describe the geologic activity that occurred in the Silurian Period.
3. What mountain range formed during the Devonian Period?
4. What mountain range formed during the Permian Period?
5. What mountain ranges formed during the Cretaceous Period?
6. How do the mountains in the eastern United States compare in age with the mountains in the west? Explain your answer.

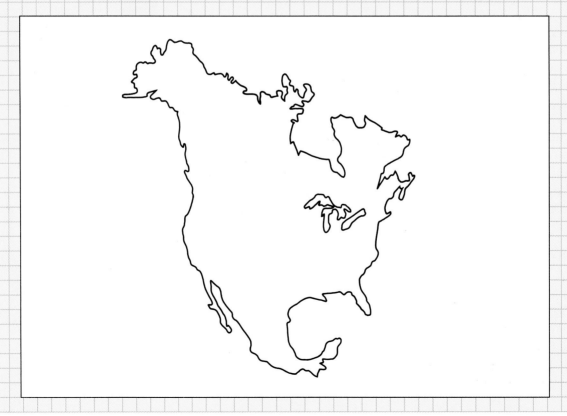

Figure 16-12

A meteorite striking the earth could have led to the extinction of the dinosaurs.

Another theory, called the **meteorite impact hypothesis**, proposes that the dust in the atmosphere came from a meteorite that hit the earth. Upon striking the earth, the meteorite would have exploded, throwing up huge amounts of dust into the air.

Evidence for the meteorite impact hypothesis comes from the study of layers of rock that formed at the end of the Cretaceous Period. In several places on the earth, layers of rock that formed during this period have been found to contain an element called *iridium* (ih RIHD ee uhm). Iridium rarely occurs on the earth, but it is often found in bodies from space, such as meteorites. Some scientists believe the iridium in these layers came from a huge meteorite that struck the earth about 65 million years ago.

REVIEW

1. What kinds of organisms lived during the Mesozoic Era?
2. What life forms existed in each period of the Mesozoic Era?
3. How do the two theories for the extinction of the dinosaurs differ?

CHALLENGE If a large meteorite struck the earth at the end of the Cretaceous period, why is there no evidence of a large crater?

16-4 CENOZOIC ERA

The most recent era is the **Cenozoic Era**. It is the era in which we live and in which mammals became dominant. Figure 16-11 shows some early mammals. What modern mammals do they resemble?

The Cenozoic Era is divided into two periods. The first period is the *Tertiary* (TER shee ehr ee) *Period*. During this period, some of the great mountain ranges formed, including the Alps, Himalayas, Rockies, and Andes.

The other period of the Cenozoic Era is called the *Quaternary* (kwuh TER nuhr ee) *Period*. During this period of time, the climate became much colder and ice sheets advanced.

Figure 16-13

Mammals became the dominant animals during the Cenozoic Era.

Because of the abundance of fossil evidence from the Cenozoic Era, the periods are divided into smaller time units called epochs. The Tertiary Period is divided into five epochs. The first epoch is the *Paleocene* (PAY lee uh-seen) *Epoch*. During this epoch, mammals were small. Plants resembled tropical plants of today.

In the next epoch, the *Eocene* (EE uh seen) *Epoch*, the mammals became larger. Ancestors of modern mammals, such as the whale and horse, appeared.

Figure 16-14

Deer are examples of modern mammels.

Following the Eocene Epoch is the *Oligocene* (OL uh-goh seen) *Epoch*. The climate cooled during the Oligocene epoch. Tropical plants were replaced by grasses and pine trees. Apes, elephants, and members of the cat and dog families are animals that existed.

The next epoch is called the *Miocene* (MĪ uh seen) *Epoch*. Herds of horses eating grasses roamed the plains of North America during this epoch. Mastodons crossed the land bridge between Siberia and Alaska.

After the Miocene epoch is the *Pliocene* (PLI uh seen) *Epoch*. During the Pliocene Epoch, glaciers began to form in the Northern Hemisphere. The sea level fell. Animals crossed land that was no longer covered by water. Land bridges existed between North and South America. There is evidence that in the Pliocene Epoch some animals hunted the herds of horses and deer for food.

The continents looked similar to the way they do today. For example, the shape of North America was almost like it is today. The Sierra Nevada and the Rocky Mountains were lifted to higher elevations. Volcanic activity occurred in what is now the northwestern United States. An ice age began near the end of the Pliocene Epoch. The Grand Canyon was carved out of the rising rock layers. Volcanoes erupted in the northwest, and the lava produced the Columbia Plateau.

The Quaternary Period follows the Pliocene Epoch and has two epochs. The first epoch is called the *Pleistocene* (PLĪS tuh seen). The Pleistocene Epoch, which began about 2.5 million years ago, is often called the Ice Age. It was one of the coldest time periods in the earth's history. Glaciers advanced at least four different times during this

SCIENCE PUZZLER

One of the strangest geologic formations in Missouri is found in Elephant State Park. Giant granite rocks, called elephant rocks, stand end-to-end like a train of circus elephants.

The formation of the rocks began about 1.5 billion years ago, during the Precambrian Era. The granite was then actually magma, or molten rock below the earth's surface.

How did the rocks reach the surface? What could have caused the present shapes of the rocks?

ACTIVITY Correlating Organisms with Geologic Time

OBJECTIVE
Correlate forms of life with the geologic time units to which they belong.

MATERIALS
paper, pencil, ruler

PROCEDURE
A. Make a table similar to the one shown below.

Life Form	Period	Era
A.		
B.		
C.		

K.		
L.		

B. Look at the chart below. Decide when each life form shown in the chart first appeared.

Record in your table the name of each life form. Using the information from the chapter, record the period and era of geologic time in which each one lived.

1. To what period and era do the brachiopods belong?
2. In what period did the first dinosaurs appear?
3. To what period and era do humans belong?
4. Which animals and plants became extinct?

RESULTS AND CONCLUSIONS
1. Describe the changes in life forms over geologic time.
2. Do any of the organisms appear throughout geologic time, from the earliest time to the most recent? Explain why or why not.

A. trilobites B. dinosaurs C. mammals D. brachiopods
E. jellyfish F. amphibians G. squids H. reptiles
I. flowering plants J. birds K. mammoths L. archaeopteryx

epoch. Glaciers began to melt about 10,000 years ago, when the Pleistocene Epoch ended. Because of the cold climate, animals had to either develop protective coverings or move to other regions. Those that could not adapt became extinct. Mammals of the Pleistocene Ice Age included mastodons from Asia, saber-toothed tigers, and mammoths. As this epoch ended, these large mammals became extinct.

The most recent epoch is called the Holocene (HOH-luh seen) Epoch. During this epoch, the earth's climate became warmer, causing almost all of the glaciers formed in the Pleistocene Epoch to disappear. It is in the Holocene Epoch that human civilization arose.

REVIEW

1. How was the climate of the Quaternary Period different from the climate of the Tertiary Period?
2. Compare the life forms of the Cenozoic Era with those of the Mesozoic Era.
3. Describe the events of the Pleistocene Epoch.

CHALLENGE In the future, why may additional periods be added to the Cenozoic Era?

CHAPTER SUMMARY

The main ideas in this chapter are listed below. Read these statements before you answer any Chapter Review questions.

- The earth's history can be divided into units of time based on changes in the earth's surface and sudden changes in life forms. (16-1)

- Little evidence of life forms is found in Precambrian rocks. (16-1)

- An abundance of life forms, mostly invertebrates, appeared during the Paleozoic Era. (16-2)

- Reptiles, including the dinosaurs, dominated the Mesozoic Era. (16-3)

- The era we live in is called the Cenozoic Era. Mammals became dominant during this era. (16-4)

The key terms in this chapter are listed below. Use each term in a sentence that shows the meaning of the term.

Cenozoic Era	invertebrate	Paleozoic Era
epoch	Mesozoic era	period
era	meteorite impact	Precambrian Era
geologic time scale	hypothesis	vertebrate

Chapter Review

VOCABULARY

Write the letter of the term that best matches the definition. Not all the terms will be used.

_____ 1. Subdivision of an era

_____ 2. Era from which oldest rocks are found

_____ 3. Division of the earth's history by time

_____ 4. Subdivision of a period

_____ 5. Present era

_____ 6. A unit of time based on characteristic life forms

_____ 7. Dinosaurs lived mainly in this era

_____ 8. Explains disappearance of dinosaurs

_____ 9. An animal without a backbone

_____ 10. Age of Invertebrates

a. Cenozoic Era
b. epoch
c. era
d. geologic time scale
e. invertebrate
f. Mesozoic Era
g. meteorite impact hypothesis
h. Paleozoic Era
i. period
j. Precambrian Era
k. vertebrate

CONCEPTS

1. Compare the geologic time scale with the geologic column. (16-1)
2. On what evidence is the geologic time scale divided into eras, periods, and epochs? (16-1)
3. Compare the life forms that existed in each of the eras. (16-1)
4. Compare the lengths of the four eras. (16-1)
5. Why is the earth probably older than the oldest Precambrian rocks? (16-1)
6. Why aren't Precambrian rocks commonly found? (16-1)
7. Describe the life forms that existed during the Precambrian Era. (16-1)
8. Describe the fossils found in Precambrian rocks. (16-1)
9. Why is the Grand Canyon an excellent record of the earth's past? (16-1)
10. Why is the Paleozoic Era divided into periods but the Precambrian Era is not? (16-1, 16-2)
11. How did surface changes on the earth affect the life forms that existed in each period? (16-2)
12. Give an example of an invertebrate and a vertebrate that lived during the Paleozoic Era. (16-2)

13. What changes caused much of the life during the Paleozoic to disappear? (16-2)

14. Compare the life forms of the Mesozoic Era with those of the Paleozoic Era. (16-2, 16-3)

15. What surface changes may have led to the appearance and disappearance of the dinosaurs? (16-3)

16. What evidence is there for the meteorite impact hypothesis? (16-3)

17. Compare the climates of the Quaternary and Tertiary periods. (16-4)

18. Compare the life forms of the Tertiary Period and the Quaternary Period. (16-4)

19. Describe the life forms of each of the epochs of the Cenozoic Era. (16-4)

20. What surface change may have caused many animals that lived during the Pleistocene Epoch to become extinct? (16-4)

APPLICATION/ CRITICAL THINKING

1. How could you estimate the size of a dog from the imprints of its feet?

2. If you found an undated newspaper clipping that discussed the events of World War II as happening "today," how could you estimate the date on which the newspaper was printed? How is this similar to finding the age of rocks by using the geologic time scale?

3. Identify a species of animal that is threatened with extinction today and suggest reasons for this. Compare these reasons with those that have been given for the extinction of the dinosaurs.

EXTENSION

1. Work with a partner to build models of the oceans, continents, and prominent features for particular periods of geologic time. The models could be made of salt and flour or joint cement or papier-mâché.

2. A fish called a coelacanth (SEEL uh kanth) was caught alive in the Indian Ocean in 1938. Scientists thought this fish had been extinct for over 70 million years. Find out more about the coelacanth and its special characteristics.

READINGS

Angier, Natalie. "Did Comets Kill the Dinosaurs?" *Time*, May 6, 1985, p. 72.

Cuisin, Michel. *Prehistoric Life*. Morristown, N.J.: Silver Burdett Co., 1980.

Jeffery, David. "Annals of Life Written in Rock: Fossils." *National Geographic*, August 1985, p. 182.

Science in Careers

You have learned about the different kinds of volcanoes. Many active volcanoes are spectacular. Some provide dazzling displays of streaming lava. Still others are life threatening, destroying towns with rivers of boiling mud and clouds of poison gas.

Volcanologists are scientists who study volcanoes. They may take samples of lava from a volcano to learn about the earth's interior. Many volcanologists are trying to discover ways of predicting violent eruptions.

Volcanologists often travel to different parts of the world to visit active volcanoes. They collect samples of volcanic gases, ash, and lava. And they use instruments to record seismic activity and changes in the contours of the land.

Many volcanologists teach at universities. Some work for the government. After receiving a college degree, most go on to receive master's and doctor's degrees. Classes in earth science, physics, chemistry, and math will be helpful for persons who wish to enter this field. ∎

STONEMASON

Have you seen buildings that are decorated with carved stone figures? Perhaps you have noticed buildings in which marble slabs are fitted together to make a pattern. Stonemasons are responsible for these kinds of details in architecture.

A stonemason is both an artist and a builder. He or she often works for a construction company. The work involves measuring, cutting, and carving stones. A stonemason uses hand tools — such as hammers and chisels — and power tools.

Stonemasons learn their craft through apprenticeship, which may take several years. If you are interested in becoming a stonemason, you should take courses in mechanical drawing, fine arts, and geology. ∎

VOLCANOLOGIST

People in Science

Zofia Kielan-Jaworowska is a "time traveler." She explores the earth's ancient past by studying fossils. In other words, she is a paleontologist.

The Polish Academy of Sciences chose her to lead several expeditions to the Gobi desert of Mongolia to hunt for fossils. You may know that the Gobi contains many dinosaur fossils. The aim of the Polish expeditions was to find fossils of Cretaceous dinosaurs and Tertiary mammals.

While in the Gobi, Dr. Keilan-Jaworowska had to endure the harsh desert climate. There were many severe sand storms, and water was scarce.

However, the desert yielded many dinosaur fossils. Before being shipped to Poland, the fossils were embedded in plaster of Paris to keep them from breaking.

By studying the dinosaur bones, Dr. Keilan-Jaworowska and other paleontologists hope to learn the answers to many questions, including why the dinosaurs became extinct while other life forms survived. ∎

DR. ZOFIA KIELAN-JAWOROWSKA, PALEONTOLOGIST

Issues and Technology

It is rotting the bodies of cars and weakening the structures of metal bridges. It is wearing away monuments like the Egyptian temples at Karnak, the Indian cliff dwellings at Mesa Verde, and the Statue of Liberty. It gets into lakes and kills wildlife. It falls on trees and kills them. It is reported to have turned a Swedish woman's blonde hair to a shade of green. What could have such world-wide effects? It is acid rain, one of the most controversial environmental problems today. Everyone knows that acid rain is harmful. But people don't all agree on where it comes from and who should pay for its damage.

Most scientists agree that acid rain forms from gases released by the burning of fossil fuels — oil, coal, and gas. The primary sources of such gases are electric power plants, industrial boilers, and metal smelters. When fossil fuels are burned, sulfur dioxide and nitrogen oxide gases are given off. These invisible gases pour out of smokestacks into the air. Once in the air they react, in the presence of sunlight, with other chemicals. These reactions turn the gases into sulfuric acid and nitric acid. They fall to earth as acid rain or acid snow.

Extremely tall smokestacks — sometimes over 300 m high — have made the problem worse. They were originally built high to remove pollution from areas where factories are located. The idea was that the pollution could be sent soaring high enough into the sky to harmlessly drift away. But the stacks are so tall that they put the pollution into high altitude wind streams. In this way, pollutants are carried hundreds or even thousands of kilometers downwind from the source.

In North America, the industrial areas of the Midwest and Northeast are a main source of sulfur dioxide and nitrogen oxides. Therefore, large amounts of acid rain fall downwind in the northeastern United States and eastern Canada. Tests have shown that sometimes rain in the northeastern United States is 10 to 30 times more acidic than normal rain. A 1978 storm brought rain as acidic as lemon juice to one part of Pennsylvania.

Figure 1 is a pH scale. A pH scale shows how acidic or basic (alkaline) a substance is. This scale shows the pH of several substances, including acid rain. The stronger the acid the lower the pH number. Numbers greater than seven indicate that the material is alkaline. A pH of seven is neutral.

APPLYING CRITICAL THINKING SKILLS

1. What is the acidity of unpolluted rain?
2. What is the range of acidity for acid rain?
3. Is seawater acidic? How do you know?
4. Is unpolluted rain acidic? If so, why is acid rain a problem?

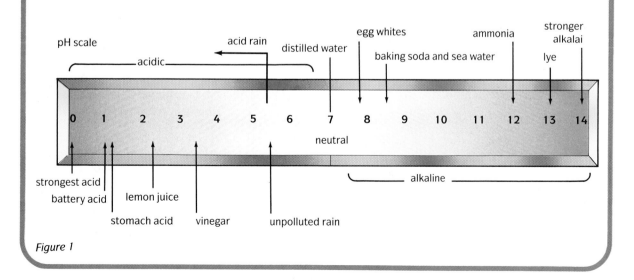

Figure 1

387

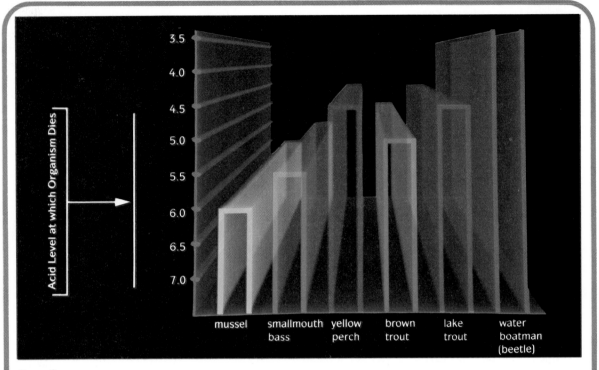

Figure 2

Most of the damage caused by acid rain occurs in spring. Acids are held in snow all winter. Then they are suddenly released as snow melts. The acids enter lakes quickly. The shock of raised acid levels often causes the fish to die. The acidity of the water irritates the gills of fish. So the gills form a protective layer of mucus. But the high levels of acid cause too much mucus to form. It clogs the gills and the fish suffocate.

The acid rain also helps draw metals, like aluminum, lead, and mercury, out of the soil. These metals concentrate in lakes. They kill bacteria, aquatic plants, and animals that are part of the food chain. Lakes attacked by acid rain are often beautifully crystal clear. That is because all life in them has disappeared.

Figure 2 shows the relationship between the acidity of water and its effect on some living things found in lakes. Notice that organisms differ in their ability to tolerate acid rain.

APPLYING CRITICAL THINKING SKILLS

1. Which creature can stand the most acidity?
2. What kinds of creatures can stand the least?
3. Which of these creatures could live in a lake in which the water had the acidity of acid rain?
4. There are also creatures that cannot survive in a strongly alkaline environment. Why would this be a factor in attempting to raise the pH level of lakes to offset acid rain?
5. What activities of humans are likely to be affected by an increase in the acidity of lakes?

In northern Europe the damage caused by acid rain has been similar to that occurring in North America. Foul-tasting, contaminated water supplies, dead lakes, and dying forests are alarming many people. Over 20,000 Swedish lakes are estimated to be without fish. In Germany, one half of the nation's trees have been injured by acid rain.

The problem is also serious in Canada. Since much of Canada's acid rain results from American industrial pollution, this creates a strain between two countries that have been close friends.

There are processes for removing some of the pollution that causes acid rain. Devices called scrubbers work on sulfur dioxide. They shoot jets of wet lime at waste gases before they go up the smokestack. The alkaline lime reduces the strength of the acids that form from sulfur dioxide. In many cases, the scrubbers reduce sulfur dioxide emissions by over 90 percent. That cuts down on acid rain.

Over a dozen European countries and Canada have pledged to encourage the use of scrubbers and other anti-pollution devices.

They want to reduce the amount of sulfur dioxide in the air by 30 percent by the early 1990s. The United States and Great Britain have refused to make such a pledge. However, they are two of the largest producers of these harmful gases.

One reason for holding back is money. It is expensive to install anti-pollution devices. And much of the cost gets passed along to the public. For example, the use of anti-pollution devices in power plants would probably mean a rise in electric bills. The use of such devices in manufacturing plants could mean higher prices for the goods produced in those plants. Many people who would have to pay the increased costs do not live in areas affected by acid rain. Is it fair for them to pay for a problem thousands of kilometers away?

Meanwhile, some people say that the source of acid rain has not yet been proven. They say that spending money on anti-pollution devices may not really help the problem. At this time, industries in the United States are not required to install anti-pollution devices like scrubbers.

Those people against controls on sulfur content in air point to statistics that back them up. They say that in some instances sulfur content in air has gone down while acidity of rain has gone up. Many other factors, such as natural acidity of decayed forest vegetation, pesticides leaking into soil and water, and overfishing may have as much to do with the disappearance of fish as does acid rain.

Nitrogen oxides are not just released by industry. They come from car exhaust as well. Couldn't cars be contributing as much to acid rain problems as some industries? If so, why should industry take all the blame—and pay all of the bill?

The United States Environmental Protection Agency (EPA) estimates that the cost of repairing and replacing structures damaged by acid rain has been more than $5 billion. But that doesn't take into account environmental problems. And it doesn't take into account how this pollution could be affecting human health.

Should something be done now? If so, who should pay for it? If we wait, what will be the long-term effect?

Figure 3 shows industrial areas in North America. It also shows areas that are sensitive to damage by acid rain. The arrows show the main wind patterns and routes for the spread of acid rain.

APPLYING CRITICAL THINKING SKILLS

1. In North America, what country has the most industrial areas where sulfur and nitrogen oxides are produced?
2. What country has the most areas that are sensitive to acid rain?
3. How, do you think, does the acid rain situation affect relations between Canada and the United States?
4. Based on wind patterns, would acid rain be more of a problem in eastern Canada and the northeastern U.S. in summer or in winter? Why?
5. If scrubbers and other pollution-control devices are needed, who should pay for them? Explain your answer.
6. What kinds of industries are probably being hurt by acid rain?
7. In what other areas of the earth is acid rain likely to be a problem? Should the United States and Canada discuss the problem with other nations? Explain your answer.

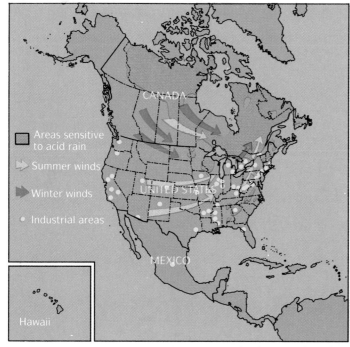

Figure 3

METEOROLOGY

*U*ntil now your study of the earth has concentrated on the solid portion of the earth. But as you know, there is also a gaseous part of the earth called the atmosphere. We are directly affected by the weather conditions of the atmosphere. Why is there so much change in the weather? How do meteorologists predict weather patterns? Why does weather change with the seasons? In this unit you will find the answers to these and other questions concerning the earth's atmosphere and weather. ■

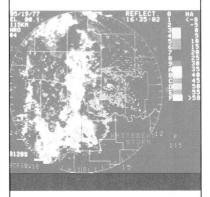

▲ *Meteorologists use radar to determine how weather systems are moving* (above).

◀ *A view of hurricane Elena photographed from Discovery on Sept. 2, 1985.*

▲ *Heat being emitted from buildings in a city has an effect on atmospheric conditions. White areas in the photograph above are areas giving off the most heat.*

◀ *A model of an old, pressure tube anemometer.*

▶ *Perils of Union Square, New York City, during the "Great Blizzard" of March 12–14, 1888.*

▲ *Lightning is the discharge of electricity from a thundercloud to the ground or to another cloud.*

THE ATMOSPHERE

These people are taking part in the sport called "hounds and fox." In this sport, one balloon is identified as the "fox." The other balloons, called the "hounds," try to catch the first balloon. The sport requires that the pilot of each balloon be a skilled balloonist.

Balloons were invented by two French papermakers in 1783. The men found that paper bags rose when filled with smoke. Soon, the first balloon to carry people made a 25-minute 91-m high flight. Balloons have since been used by the military, by scientists, and, of course, in sports such as "hounds and fox." A balloon has been flown to a height of over 34,000 m. Other balloons have been flown across North America, across the Atlantic Ocean, and across the Pacific Ocean.

- *How can balloons be used by scientists?*
- *How high can a balloon go? What, if anything, prevents a balloon from going into outer space?*
- *Why do hot-air balloons rise?*
- *How is the action of hot-air balloons similar to the movement of air in the atmosphere?*

17-1   THE ATMOSPHERE

COMPOSITION OF THE ATMOSPHERE

Have you ever considered that you live at the bottom of an ocean of air? In an ocean of water, some living things live on the bottom, and others swim at different levels above the bottom. In the ocean of air, some living things live on the ground, and others can fly through the air. As human beings, we spend most of our time close to the bottom of our ocean of air.

The ocean of air that surrounds the earth is called the **atmosphere**. The atmosphere is an invisible mixture of gases. If you were to analyze a sample of dry air collected within 80 km of the ground, you would find that it is made up of the gases listed in Table 17-1. Which two gases make up most of the atmosphere? If you took a sample from higher in the atmosphere, you would find that heavier

> After completing this section, you will be able to
> - **identify** the gases that make up the air.
> - **identify** the layers of the atmosphere.
> - **describe** each layer of the atmosphere.
>
> *The key terms in this section are*
> atmosphere   stratosphere
> exosphere   thermosphere
> ionosphere   troposphere
> mesosphere   weather

Table 17-1 *Gases in the Atmosphere*

Gas	Percent by Volume
nitrogen	78.08
oxygen	20.95
argon	0.93
carbon dioxide	0.03
neon	trace
helium	trace
methane	trace
krypton	trace
hydrogen	trace
xenon	trace
ozone	trace

gases, like nitrogen and oxygen, are not found high in the atmosphere. In fact, air in the upper part of the atmosphere contains only hydrogen.

In addition to the gases shown in Table 17-1, other materials can be found in the atmosphere. The amount of these materials varies from place to place and from time to time. Water vapor is one of these materials. Air over a desert has almost no water vapor in it. Air over a tropical rain forest, however, may consist of 4 percent water vapor. The amount of water vapor in the air over a particular place may vary from day to day. On a wet, rainy day there could be two to three times more water vapor in the air than there is on a dry day.

The amount of solid material in the air also varies. For example, salt is found in the air along a seashore. This occurs because breaking waves add salt particles to the air. Rock particles and dust may be thrown into the air by an erupting volcano or by wind. Some of these materials may stay in the air for many years. What other examples of materials in the air vary from place to place or from season to season?

ACTIVITY   How Much Oxygen Does the Air Contain?

OBJECTIVE
Determine the amount of oxygen in a sample of air.

MATERIALS
2 large test tubes, steel wool, deep pan, 2 test-tube clamps, ring stand, water, wax pencil, metric ruler

PROCEDURE
A. Wet a piece of steel wool and place it in the bottom of a large test tube.
B. Turn the test tube upside down in a deep pan of water so that the top (open end) of the test tube is just under the water. Clamp the test tube to a ring stand.
C. Repeat step **B** with an empty large test tube.
D. Every day, mark the level of the water in each test tube with a wax pencil. After the water level has not risen in either test tube for two straight days, remove the test tubes from the water.

E. Use a metric ruler to measure the length of the first test tube. Record this distance. Measure the distance from the top of the test tube to the water line closest to the bottom. Record this distance. Divide the second number by the first. Multiply the result by 100. This will tell you what percentage of the test tube had water in it. Record this percentage.
F. Repeat step **E** with the second test tube.

RESULTS AND CONCLUSIONS
1. Compare the percentages of water in the two test tubes. Explain this result.
2. The reaction in the first test tube used oxygen from the air in the test tube. As the oxygen was used up, water took its place. The reaction ended when there was no more oxygen in the test tube. The percentage of water in this test tube, then, should be equal to 21 percent. What percentage of your first test tube had water in it? Explain this result.

STRUCTURE OF THE ATMOSPHERE

The atmosphere can be divided into many layers. Identify these layers in Figure 17-1. The first layer is the troposphere (TROH puh sfihr). The **troposphere** extends from the earth to a height of between 7 km and 16 km. The temperature drops 6.5°C with every 1 km of altitude in this layer. The air pressure and the density of the air also decrease. Then the temperature levels off at the top of the troposphere. This region is called the tropopause, the boundary between the first two layers of the atmosphere. The temperature in the tropopause is about −55°C.

Above the tropopause is the stratosphere (STRAT uh-sfihr). The **stratosphere**, the second layer of the atmosphere, extends to a height of 50 km above the earth. The temperature remains around −55°C in the lower region of this layer. The upper region contains a form of oxygen called ozone (OH zohn). Ozone absorbs ultraviolet radiation from the sun and releases heat into the atmosphere.

stratus (spreading out)

sphaire (sphere)

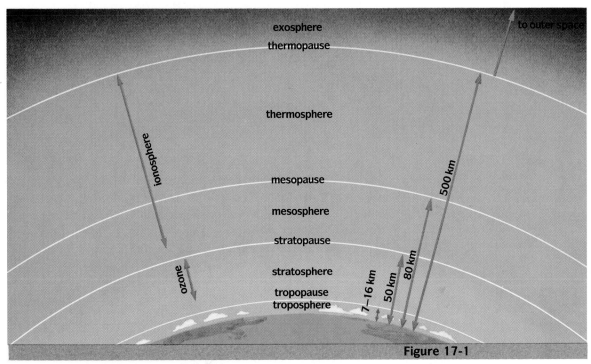

Figure 17-1

The layers of the atmosphere. What keeps the air from drifting into space?

As a result, the temperature at the top of the stratosphere is near 0°C. The ozone layer also prevents most of the ultraviolet radiation from the sun from reaching the surface of the earth. Few things could live on the earth without this protection. Some scientists are concerned that certain chemicals put into the air by people may be destroying the protective ozone layer.

Figure 17-2

Many satellites circle the earth in the exosphere.

mesos (middle)
therme (heat)

At the top of the stratosphere is another boundary, called the stratopause. Above this boundary is the third layer of the atmosphere, the mesosphere (MEHS uh sfihr). The **mesosphere** extends from the stratopause to a height of 80 km. Gases do not absorb much of the sun's radiation here. For this reason, this layer is cold, with temperatures near −100°C. Many "shooting stars," or meteors, burn up in this layer. The mesopause forms the boundary above the mesosphere.

Beyond the mesopause is the fourth layer of the atmosphere, the thermosphere (THER muh sfihr). The **thermosphere** extends to a height of about 500 km. Some spacecraft orbit the earth here. Molecules in the thermosphere absorb a tremendous amount of radiation. Because of the radiation, the temperature may reach 1000°C. Radiation also causes some molecules to become electrically charged. These electrically charged particles, or ions, are gathered and held in place by the earth's magnetic field. The region where these ions are found is called the **ionosphere** (ī AHN-uh sfihr). Radio signals can be reflected off the ionosphere and relayed around the earth.

The last layer of the atmosphere, called the **exosphere**, (EHK suh sfihr), extends into outer space. There is no exact end to this layer. Molecules are very far apart here. Some gases escape the earth's gravity and drift into space. This layer is where many satellites orbit the earth and where the Van Allen belts are found.

Since we spend almost our entire lives in the troposphere, it might be considered the most important layer of the atmosphere. One other important thing occurs in the troposphere—weather. **Weather** is the condition of the atmosphere in a particular place at a particular time. Temperature, air pressure, and wind are all factors of weather. In the next lesson you will learn about temperature and why it is important.

REVIEW

1. What are the major gases found in the atmosphere? What are some of the other materials found in the atmosphere?
2. List the five layers of the atmosphere in order, from the closest to the earth to the farthest from the earth. Which of the layers is the deepest? Which is the most shallow?
3. Describe two characteristics of each layer of the atmosphere.

CHALLENGE Why is it sensible to have satellites orbit in the exosphere rather than in the mesosphere?

17-2 TEMPERATURE AND THE ATMOSPHERE

Can you think of days in the summer when it feels too hot to move? On days like that you wonder if it will ever be cool again. Can you think of days in the winter that are so cold that you must wear sweaters, a hat, gloves, and a heavy coat? On cold days like that you wonder if it will ever be warm again. Temperature influences how you dress and how you act. But what is temperature?

Temperature is a measure of the energy of motion of the molecules in a material. When a material is heated, molecules that make up that material speed up and spread out. When a material cools, the molecules slow down and come closer together.

Heat is a measure of the total energy in a material. How is this different from temperature? To measure the heat of a particular object, you need to know both the temperature and the mass of the object. For example, think of a small glass of warm water that is the same temperature as a pail of warm water. The pail of water, which has more mass than the glass of water, will contain more heat than the glass of water. Which has a higher temperature—a burning match or a warm bath? Which has more heat?

Temperature is measured by using an instrument called a **thermometer**. A liquid thermometer is made of a sealed glass tube with a small bulb at one end. The tube and bulb contain either mercury or colored alcohol. As the temperature changes, the liquid in the tube expands or contracts accordingly. The tube is marked with a standard scale. Temperature is determined by reading the number on the scale next to the top of the liquid column. What is the temperature on the thermometer in Figure 17-3?

After completing this section, you will be able to

- define *temperature*.
- describe how a liquid thermometer works.
- explain the Celsius scale.
- describe how isotherms are useful to a meteorologist.

The key terms in this section are
isotherms   thermometer
temperature

Figure 17-3

A liquid bulb thermometer can be filled with alcohol or mercury.

A digital thermometer uses electronic circuits to show temperature. This type of thermometer contains a probe made of a material called a semiconductor. Electricity flows along the semiconductor. As the temperature around the probe changes, the temperature of the semiconductor changes. This changes the flow of electricity along the semiconductor. The semiconductor is connected to an electronic circuit. The electronic circuit changes electrical signals from the semiconductor into numbers, which are displayed on a small screen.

Figure 17-4

There are a variety of digital thermometers. There is one for measuring body temperature (*left*) and one for measuring air temperature (*right*).

In the metric system, temperature is measured in units called degrees Celsius (°C). On a Celsius thermometer, 0° represents the freezing point of water, and 100° represents the boiling point of water. The thermometer is marked with 100 equal spaces between these points. Therefore, a degree Celsius equals 1/100 of the temperature change between the freezing and boiling points of water. A comfortable room temperature is 21°C. The normal body temperature for most people is 37°C.

Each day, the National Weather Service collects data, including temperature readings, from weather stations around the world. Every three hours a map is printed that displays all of the collected information. Meteorologists (mee tee uh RAHL uh jihsts), or scientists who study weather, draw lines to connect stations reporting the same temperature. Lines drawn to connect stations that have the same temperature are called **isotherms** (ī suh thermz). Isotherms help to show patterns of air movement and are helpful in predicting temperatures for a given place. Study the isotherms in Figure 17-5. According to the map, what is the temperature in your region?

ACTIVITY   Isotherms in Your Classroom

OBJECTIVES

Construct a map with isotherms on it.

Predict warm regions and cool regions in the classroom.

MATERIALS

meterstick, metric ruler, sheet of graph paper, 5 thermometers

PROCEDURE

A. Using a meterstick and a metric ruler, make a map of your classroom on a sheet of graph paper. Label windows, doors, radiators, vents, and desks.

B. On your map, divide the width of your classroom into five equal sections. Divide the length of your classroom into five equal sections.

1. Predict which will be the warmest sections and which will be the coolest sections.

C. Use a thermometer to find the temperature in the center of each section of your classroom. Record each temperature reading in the correct place on your map.

D. Draw isotherms on your map by connecting identical temperature readings.

RESULTS AND CONCLUSIONS

1. Where, according to your map, are the warm areas of your classroom? Why are these areas warm?
2. Where are the cool areas? Why are these areas cool?
3. How do your results compare with your predictions?

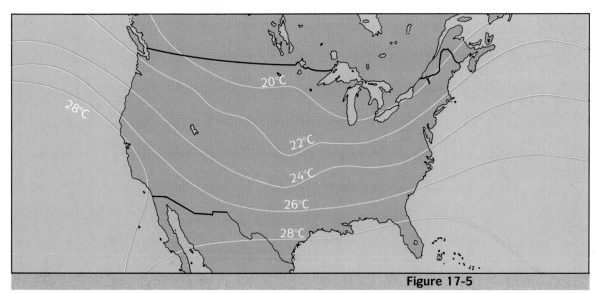

Figure 17-5

Isotherms connect places having the same temperature.

REVIEW

1. How is heat different from temperature?
2. How does a liquid thermometer measure temperature?
3. How is the scale on a Celsius thermometer set up?
4. How are isotherms useful to a meteorologist?

CHALLENGE Would it be possible to use water as the liquid in a thermometer? What advantages would there be to using water? What disadvantages would there be?

17-3 HEAT TRANSFER IN THE ATMOSPHERE

radians (ray, beam)

The earth and its atmosphere are heated by a process called radiation. **Radiation** is energy that travels in the form of waves. When these waves strike matter, they are either absorbed or reflected. Waves that are absorbed by matter warm the matter.

The source of the energy that warms the earth is the sun. The sun gives off radiant energy. **Radiant energy** includes forms of energy that travel as waves. Examples are gamma rays, X rays, ultraviolet rays, infrared rays, radio waves, and visible light. Ultraviolet rays cause sunburn. Infrared rays are felt as heat.

One way in which the various forms of radiant energy are different from one another can be seen in Figure 17-6. As you can see, the distance from the crest, or top, of one wave to the crest of the next wave is called the wavelength. Different forms of radiant energy have different wavelengths. Waves with short wavelengths have more energy than waves with long wavelengths.

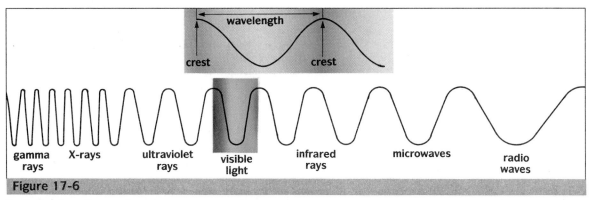

Figure 17-6

Radiation from the sun travels as waves. The different types of radiant energy vary in wavelength.

Look at Figure 17-7. Of the radiant energy that reaches the earth, about 30 percent is reflected back into space by the atmosphere, clouds, and the earth's surface. Only about 20 percent is absorbed by the atmosphere. The remaining 50 percent is absorbed by the surface of the earth.

As the earth absorbs radiant energy, the surface is warmed. As the surface cools, long waves of energy are given off. These long waves are easily absorbed by carbon dioxide and other gases in the atmosphere. As the atmosphere absorbs the long waves, it is warmed. The warming of the atmosphere due to the absorption of these long waves is called the **greenhouse effect**. Because of the greenhouse effect, the atmosphere acts like a blanket to keep the earth warm. You may have noticed that on clear

ACTIVITY
Testing the Greenhouse Effect with Different Materials

OBJECTIVE

Compare different materials for their ability to trap radiant energy.

MATERIALS

4 shoeboxes, 4 thermometers, cellophane tape, piece of wax paper, piece of clear plexiglass, piece of plastic wrap

PROCEDURE

A. Tape a thermometer in the center of the bottom of a shoebox. Repeat this with three other thermometers and shoeboxes.

B. Cover one box with a piece of wax paper, a second box with a piece of clear plexiglass, and a third box with a piece of plastic wrap. Leave the fourth box uncovered.

C. Set each shoebox in a sunlit area suggested by your teacher.

D. Check the temperature in each shoebox every minute for 20 minutes. Record the temperatures in a table.

RESULTS AND CONCLUSIONS

1. In which box did the temperature increase the fastest?
2. In which box did the temperature increase the slowest?
3. Which material most readily traps radiant energy?

EXTENSION

1. Make a graph that shows the results of your experiment.
2. Repeat the activity, using other materials, such as colored cellophane and heavy-duty plastic.

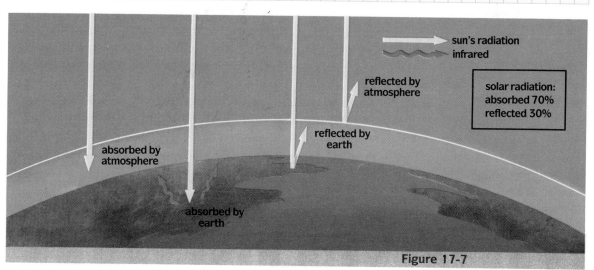

Figure 17-7

Some of the sun's radiant energy does not reach the earth's surface.

nights the air temperature drops more than it does on cloudy nights. This difference is because on cloudy nights there is more water vapor in the air to absorb energy radiated by the earth.

When radiant energy is absorbed by the earth or atmosphere, it moves from where it is concentrated to where it is less concentrated. One way this movement occurs is by conduction. **Conduction** is a process that occurs when heat energy moves from one object to another while the two objects are in direct contact. For example, air that touches a warm surface, like a hot asphalt road, receives warmth from that surface by conduction.

conductus (transmit)

Figure 17-8

Heat can be transferred throughout a room by convection.

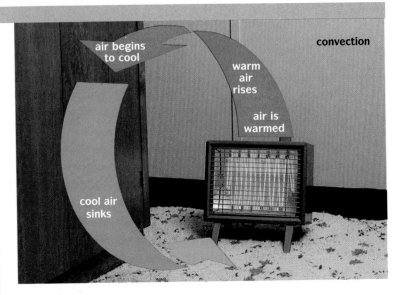

SCIENCE PUZZLER

This is a radiometer (ray dee-AHM uh tuhr). A radiometer consists of four crossed arms—each of which has a vane made of a piece of metal on its end—within a glass bulb from which most of the air has been removed. Each vane is black on one side and white on the other side. The colors face in the same direction on each vane. The arms are free to spin on a post.

When light shines on the radiometer, the arms spin. The stronger the light, the faster the arms spin. What do you think makes a radiometer work?

A second process by which heat energy moves is called convection. **Convection** is a process that occurs when heat energy is moved by a carrier, which is any material that collects energy and moves it to another place. For example, the air touching the hot asphalt road is heated by conduction; it expands and becomes less dense. Cooler, denser air sinks toward the road and pushes the warm air upward. The cooler air touches the road, is warmed, and is pushed upward. This continuing movement of air, which is shown in Figure 17-8, is called a convection current. In a convection current, air becomes a carrier of heat energy as the air begins to circulate.

Thus there are three processes involved in heating the earth and its atmosphere: radiation, conduction, and convection. You might think that these processes produce constant convection currents over an evenly heated earth. But this is not the case. The earth is not heated evenly at all. Different materials on the earth's surface absorb radiant energy differently. Dark-colored materials absorb radiant energy better than do light-colored materials. Solids absorb radiant energy faster than does water.

You might have noticed the uneven heating of the earth if you have been on a beach on a hot summer day. On such a day the sand is very hot, but the water feels cooler. This occurs even though the sand and the water receive the same amount of radiant energy for the same amount of time.

The uneven heating of the earth is an important idea in the study of weather. As you will see this uneven heating affects both wind and weather patterns.

ACTIVITY   Measuring the Uneven Heating of Materials

OBJECTIVE
Compare different materials for their ability to absorb radiant energy.

MATERIALS
5 plastic foam cups, 5 thermometers, scissors, water, dry sand, soil, 150-W light bulb, metric ruler, ring stand, string

PROCEDURE

A. Carefully cut the tops off 5 plastic foam cups about 3 cm from the bottom. Save the bottoms of the cups.
B. Fill the first cup bottom with water at room temperature. Fill the second cup with dry sand, the third with wet sand, and the fourth cup with soil. The last cup should remain empty. Arrange the cups in a circle beneath a ring stand.
C. Place a thermometer in each cup. Each thermometer should be covered with about 0.5 cm of material. Suspend the thermometers from the ring stand with string.

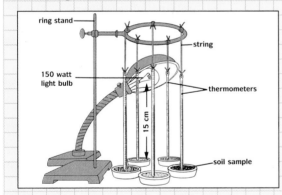

ring stand
string
150 watt light bulb
thermometers
15 cm
soil sample

D. Hang a 150-W light bulb on the ring stand 15 cm above the center of the circle. Do not turn the light bulb on.
E. Record the temperature of each material in a table.
   1. Predict which material will increase most in temperature.
   2. Predict which material will increase least in temperature.
F. Turn on the light bulb. Record the temperature of each thermometer every 2 minutes for 10 minutes.

RESULTS AND CONCLUSIONS
1. Which material increased in temperature the most?
2. Which material increased in temperature the least?
3. How do these results compare with the predictions you made?
4. Suppose you found a large area covered by the material that increased in temperature the most in this activity. Next to that large area was an equally large area made of the material that increased in temperature the least. In which direction do you think the air would move across these areas during the daytime?

EXTENSION
1. Make a graph that shows the results of this activity.
2. Use the same setup of 5 cups and repeat step **F**. After turning off the light, continue to record the temperatures every 2 minutes for 10 minutes. Which material cooled the slowest? Which material cooled the fastest?

REVIEW

1. Make a diagram that shows what happens to radiant energy that reaches the earth from the sun.
2. In what ways is the earth's atmosphere heated by solar radiation?
3. What is the greenhouse effect.
4. How are conduction, convection, and radiation similar? How are they different?

CHALLENGE What would happen to daily temperatures on the earth if the earth did not have an atmosphere?

17-4 AIR PRESSURE

Have you ever struggled to open a new jar of peanut butter? What holds a jar lid so tightly in place? Peanut butter and many other foods are bottled so that air presses on the lid harder from outside than from inside the jar. This extra pressure from outside the jar holds the lid tightly in place. The force that causes you to struggle with the lid of a jar, then, is caused by air. How can air produce so much pressure?

Air, like all types of matter, is affected by gravity. Because of this, air has weight. **Air pressure** is the force caused by the weight of air. The more air there is above a particular area, the greater the amount of air pressure on that area. For this reason, air pressure is lower at higher altitudes.

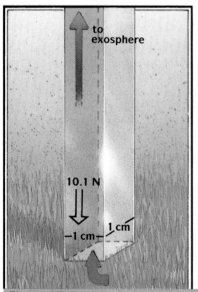

Figure 17-9

A column of air over a 1-cm square extending through the atmosphere weighs 10.1 N at sea level. Atmospheric pressure crushed this can after the air was pumped out of it.

It is hard to imagine how much the air weighs. One way is to think of a column of air such as the one shown in Figure 17-9. This column of air is 1 cm on each side and extends from the surface of the earth at sea level through the exosphere. What is the weight of this column of air? The pressure of the air at the bottom of this column is 10.1 N/cm^2, or 101,000 N/m^2. The unit that is equal to newton per square meter (N/m^2) is the pascal (PAS kuhl) (Pa). Therefore, average air pressure at sea level is 101,000 Pa, or 101 kPa. Meteorologists often use a unit called the millibar (mb) to measure air pressure. Since 1 mb equals 100 Pa, air pressure at sea level equals 1010 mb.

A **barometer** is an instrument that is used to measure air pressure. A *mercury barometer* consists of a glass tube that is sealed at one end. This tube is filled with mercury and temporarily capped. The tube is then inverted into a small pool of mercury and the cap is removed. Gravity causes the level of the mercury in the tube to lower, leaving a near vacuum in the space at the top of the tube. Air pressure on the pool of mercury holds the column in the tube at a certain height. Figure 17-10 illustrates a mercury barometer. When the pressure on the pool of mercury increases, the height of the column increases. When the pressure on the pool decreases, the height of the column also decreases.

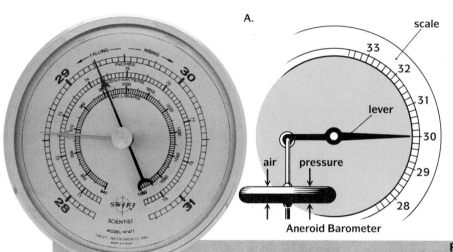
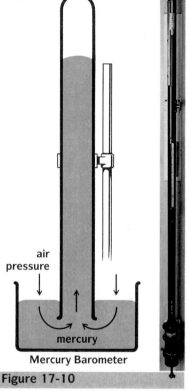

Aneroid Barometer

Mercury Barometer

Figure 17-10

A mercury barometer uses a column of mercury in a glass tube to measure air pressure. An aneroid barometer uses a sealed can to show changes in pressure.

Since mercury is such a toxic substance, you should not make a mercury barometer. A barometer that is easier to use is an aneroid (AN uh roid) barometer. An *aneroid barometer* is a barometer that consists of a sealed can, a spring, and a needle. The spring is placed inside the can, and the air in the can is removed. As air pressure increases, the sides of the can are pushed in. A decrease in pressure allows the spring to push the sides back out. A lever causes the needle to move back and forth across the scale.

REVIEW

1. What is air pressure?
2. Why does the air exert pressure on objects?
3. How is a mercury barometer different from an aneroid barometer?

CHALLENGE   How might a barometer be used to measure the altitude of an airplane?

17-5 PRESSURE BELTS

Measurements of air pressure are included in the information reported to the National Weather Service by weather stations around the world. These measurements are recorded on weather maps. Lines called **isobars** (ī suh bahrz) are drawn on the maps to connect places that have the same air pressure. Figure 17-11 shows a weather map with isobars drawn on it. You can think of isobars as being like contour lines on a topographic map. There is a difference of 4 mb between one isobar and the next on a weather map. Isobars that are far apart indicate a slow change in pressure. Isobars that are close together indicate a rapid change in pressure.

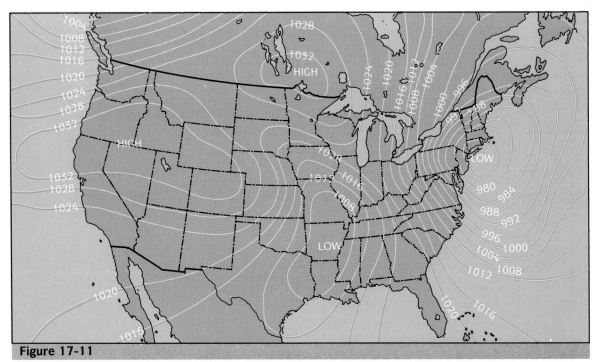

Figure 17-11

Isobars indicate places where air pressure is the same.

kyklon (move in a circle)

anti (opposite)

Look at the areas that are completely circled by isobars in Figure 17-11. Areas, such as these, that have higher air pressure than the surrounding areas are called high-pressure areas, or **highs** (H). Highs can be thought of as being like peaks of air. A high may also be called an *anticyclone* (an tee sī klohn). Areas that have lower air pressure than the surrounding areas are called low-pressure areas, or **lows** (L). Lows can be thought of as being like valleys of air. A low may also be called a *cyclone* (sī klohn).

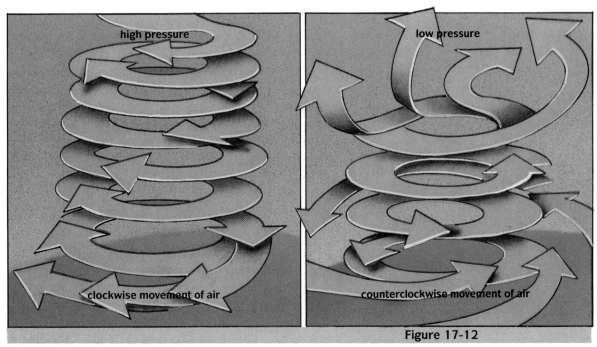

Figure 17-12

Air in a high spins clockwise. Air in a low spins counterclockwise.

Air in the center of a high is heavier than the air around it. This heavy air sinks toward the earth. As the air moves away from the center of a high in the Northern Hemisphere, it turns in a clockwise direction.

Air in the center of a low is lighter than the air around it. Unlike air in a high, the air in a low is lifted upward by denser air pushing in from around the low. Look at Figure 17-12. In what direction does the rising air turn?

The change in air pressure from one place to another is called the *pressure gradient*. The closer together the isobars are, the greater the pressure gradient is. Air moves from an area of higher pressure to an area of lower pressure. The greater the pressure gradient is, the faster the air moves. Therefore, one indication of the intensity of a storm is how close together the isobars are on a weather map. Which storm do you think would be more intense—a storm in which the isobars are close together or a storm in which the isobars are far apart?

Meteorologists have recorded air-pressure readings from around the earth for many years. By averaging the readings from each station, they have shown that there is a general pattern of high-pressure zones and low-pressure zones on the earth's surface. These zones are called pressure belts. A *pressure belt* is an area of constant high or low pressure that encircles the earth. At the equator, for example,

407

the air receives nearly direct rays from the sun all year long. The air at the equator is warmed more than the air in areas north and south of the equator. For this reason, there is a belt of low pressure surrounding the equator. Since the air at the equator is less dense than air around it, the air rises. As the air rising above the equator reaches the top of the troposphere, it spreads north and south toward the poles. By the time this air has reached latitudes 30° north and 30° south, it has cooled off. Since the air is then denser, it begins to sink back toward the earth. This forms belts of high pressure around latitudes 30° north and 30° south.

Figure 17-13 shows the major pressure belts and general circulation patterns of air across the earth's surface. Where are the major low-pressure belts on the earth? Where are the major high-pressure belts?

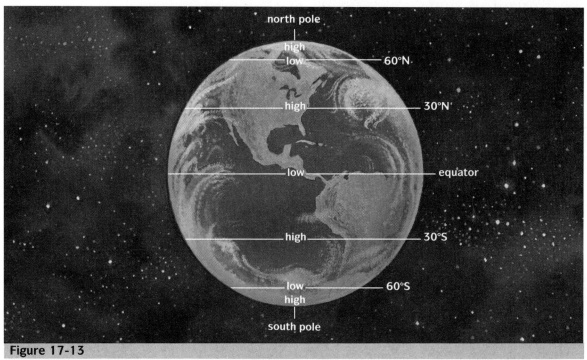

Figure 17-13

Belts of high pressure and low pressure circle the earth.

REVIEW

1. What is an isobar?
2. How are highs different from lows?
3. Where are the major pressure belts of the earth? What kind of pressure do you find at each one?

CHALLENGE How are isobars similar to isotherms? How are they different? What relationship would you expect between the temperature and pressure of an area?

17-6   WIND

Wind is moving air. Wind can make you feel comfortable on a hot summer day or make you feel cold on a winter day. Wind can be a gentle breeze that moves leaves across the street. It can be an 500-km/h wind during a tornado that can drive a piece of straw through a tree. Wind is a part of weather that you experience every day.

Wind is caused by differences in air pressure. As you have learned, these differences in air pressure are usually caused by the uneven heating of the earth. For example, areas near the equator are heated more than the areas near the poles. This uneven heating produces large global wind patterns. Land heats up more quickly than does water. This uneven heating produces local winds. By conduction, uneven heating of the earth causes the uneven heating of the air directly above the earth. This uneven heating of the air starts convection currents. The cool, denser air sinks under the warm, less dense air, lifting the warm air upward. The warm air cools as it rises. As it cools it becomes denser and sinks back toward the earth. The process continues as long as the uneven heating continues.

The terms *warm* and *cool* are relative terms. During the summer, a temperature of 20°C would be considered cool. During the winter, a temperature of 20°C would be considered warm. It is the difference in air temperature

After completing this section, you will be able to

- **describe** what causes wind.
- **illustrate** the movement of air in a convection current.
- **describe** how wind is measured.

The key terms in this section are
anemometer   wind vane
wind

Figure 17-14

When the differences in air pressure are great, the winds are strong. Strong winds can do damage to trees and buildings.

from one place to another that creates pressure differences which cause air to move. The greater the difference in temperature, the greater the difference in pressure, and the faster the wind.

Meteorologists are interested in both wind direction and wind speed. The instrument that measures the direction of the wind is called a **wind vane**, or weather vane. One end of the wind vane is larger than the other. When wind strikes the wind vane, there is more force on the large end than on the small end. As a result the large end is pushed away. The small end acts like a pointer, showing the direction from which the wind is coming. A wind is named by the direction from which it comes. For example, a north wind is a wind that comes from the north.

An **anemometer** (an uh MAHM uh tuhr) is an instrument that measures wind speed. A typical anemometer consists of three or four cup-shaped arms that are attached to a free-spinning axle. Wind from any direction will catch one of the arms and start it moving. As that arm is turned away, the next arm moves into place and is pushed by the wind. The faster the wind moves, the faster the anemometer spins. The axle of the anemometer is attached to a motor that produces an electrical current as the axle turns. This electrical current moves a needle on a gauge. The stronger the wind, the more electrical current is produced, and the farther the needle moves.

Winds in the upper atmosphere are measured with weather balloons. These balloons are released from the earth and tracked by meteorologists with telescopes and radar. The speed and direction of the balloons indicate the speed and direction of the winds. Winds in the upper atmosphere can be very different from surface winds. These lofty winds have fewer changes in direction and speed than the surface winds. They also tend to move faster than surface winds. A jet stream is one example of a wind in the upper atmosphere.

Figure 17-15

This weather station has a wind vane and an anemometer. Which one is which?

REVIEW

1. What is wind? How is wind produced?
2. Diagram the convection current that might form at a large asphalt parking lot next to an open field.
3. How is wind direction measured? How is a wind named?
4. How is wind speed measured?

CHALLENGE Wind vanes are often designed to represent animals, ships, or other objects. What must be true about the design of any wind vane if it is to work correctly?

17-7 TYPES OF WIND

LOCAL WINDS

You have learned that winds are caused by the uneven heating of the earth's surface. Some places on the earth vary little in temperature from day to day. The air in these places moves in the same direction most of the time. In other places, however, there are large daily or seasonal changes in temperature that cause special winds to occur. These daily or seasonal winds are called local winds.

As shown in Figure 17-16, a cycle of local winds occurs daily along the shoreline of a lake or ocean. During the day, even though the sun shines equally on the land and the water, the land warms up much more quickly than the water. In turn, the air over the land warms up more quickly also. The cooler, denser air over the water sinks under the air on the land and lifts the warm air upward.

> After completing this section, you will be able to
>
> - **distinguish** between four types of local winds.
> - **identify** and locate the global wind belts of the earth.
> - **describe** the Coriolis effect.
> - **describe** the jet streams.
>
> *The key terms of this section are*
> doldrums
> horse latitudes
> jet streams
> polar easterlies
> prevailing westerlies
> trade winds

sea breeze

cool sea   warm land

land breeze

warm sea   cool land

Figure 17-16

This cool breeze that moves from the body of water to the land during the day is called a *sea breeze*. During the evening, the land cools off faster than the water. At some point during the evening, the air over the land becomes cooler than the air over the water. The cool air from the land then moves over the water, forcing the warmer air upward and creating a *land breeze*. These breezes make the shoreline a very comfortable place to be in hot summer weather.

In the daytime the land warms up faster than does the water, causing a sea breeze. At night the land is cooler than the sea, causing a land breeze.

411

Another example of a daily wind cycle occurs in a mountain valley. During the day, the mountainside receives the sunlight first, and it warms up quickly. The valley, being shaded, remains cooler. The cool air over the valley sinks into the valley and pushes the warm air on the mountainside up the mountain, creating a *valley breeze*. At some point during the evening, however, the mountainside cools off but the valley tends to stay warm, so the breeze turns around. The cool mountain air falls down the mountain, pushing the warm valley air upward and creating a *mountain breeze*.

GLOBAL WINDS

In section 17-5 you learned about the major pressure belts. As you learned, air over the equator rises through the atmosphere, moves north and south, cools, and sinks back toward the earth. As it reaches the surface of the earth, some of the air moves toward the equator, where it is warmed again.

If the earth were not spinning, the air traveling back to the equator would move from north to south in the

SCIENCE & TECHNOLOGY

Altamont Pass, just east of San Francisco in California, is home to the world's largest collection of windmills. Row after row of 90-meter high windmills with blades up to 20 meters across capture the energy of the wind. The wind energy is turned into electricity and sold to local power companies. The project began in 1981 with just a few windmills. By 1983 some 2500 generators were producing electricity—enough to meet the needs of 50,000 households.

The success of the Altamont wind farm shows that wind energy can be an important renewable resource. Energy developers in other states are increasing efforts to develop wind power. New wind farms are being built in New Hampshire, Montana, Oregon, Kansas, and Hawaii. A wind farm as large as the one in California is being planned for the Catskills area of New York.

Other countries are also showing interest in wind energy. Many families and communities in Denmark own windmills, singly or in clusters. In island countries, energy costs are high. Experimental projects there have shown the economy of wind power.

The requirements for producing electricity from the wind are fairly constant winds and open spaces. Such conditions occur in many places in the United States. If interest in wind power continues, wind energy could supply 14% of the nation's electricity by the year 2000.

Northern Hemisphere. In the time it takes for the air to make the trip back to the equator, however, the earth has spun a distance on its axis. As a result, the air seems to curve to the west. This apparent change in direction, caused by the rotation of the earth, is called the *Coriolis* (kawr ee OH lihs) *effect*. The Coriolis effect explains why winds in the Northern Hemisphere are deflected to the right and why winds in the Southern Hemisphere are deflected to the left.

The air at the equator is generally rising. For this reason, there is little movement of air across the earth's surface in the region around the equator. The area around the equator is sometimes called the doldrums (DAHL druhmz). Locate the doldrums in Figure 17-17. The **doldrums** is an area of light, shifting winds at the equator.

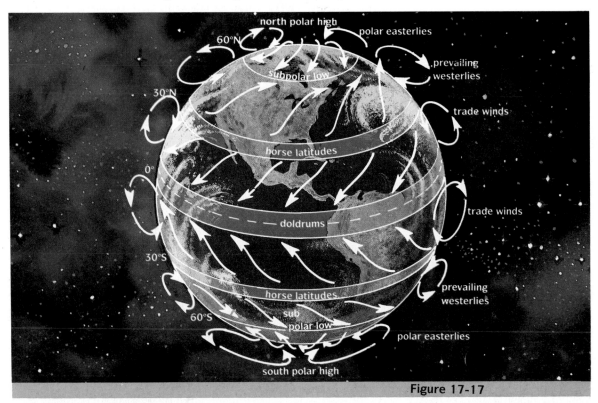

Figure 17-17

Global wind patterns are determined by the major wind belts of the earth.

Early sailors feared crossing the doldrums because there was always the possibility of being stranded there for long periods of time with no wind. Latitudes 30° north and 30° south are two other regions, called the **horse latitudes**, where there is no steady movement of air. At these latitudes the air is generally sinking toward the earth, and again there is little movement of air across the earth's surface.

Some of the air returning to the surface of the earth at the horse latitudes travels back to the equator across the earth's surface. The winds formed here, called the trade winds, deflect to the right because of the Coriolis effect. Northern Hemisphere **trade winds** are steady northeasterly winds between the doldrums and the horse latitudes. These winds came to be called the trade winds because they created a reliable route for trade with the New World. The rest of the air that sinks to the earth at the horse latitudes travels away from the equator. This air is deflected to the right by the Coriolis effect. These southwesterly winds between latitudes 30° and 60° north and south of the equator are called the **prevailing westerlies**. Much of the weather across North America is carried by the prevailing westerlies.

The air above the poles is cold and dense, and it sinks toward the earth. In the Northern Hemisphere this cold air spreads away from the poles and deflects to the right. These wind belts are called the **polar easterlies**.

JET STREAMS

Near the tropopause, at latitudes 30° north and 30° south are high-speed bands of wind called the **jet streams**. These narrow bands of wind move like waves through the atmosphere. The speeds, sizes, positions, and shapes of the jet streams vary from day to day and from season to season. During the summer in the Northern Hemisphere, for example, they tend to be weaker and farther north. The jet-stream winds travel as fast as 370 km/h. Knowing the position of the jet streams can also be very useful to those who forecast weather.

Figure 17-18

Jet streams can affect the travel time of airplanes.

REVIEW

1. How are a land breeze and a sea breeze similar to a mountain breeze and a valley breeze? How are they different?
2. Name the five major wind belts and describe where they are located.
3. How does the Coriolis effect alter the movement of air in the Northern Hemisphere?
4. Describe the jet streams.

CHALLENGE In what global wind belt do you live? In what direction does air move in that belt? Is wind in your area always from that direction? Explain why or why not.

CHAPTER SUMMARY

The main ideas in this chapter are listed below. Read these statements before you answer the Chapter Review questions.

- The atmosphere is a mixture of gases. (17-1)

- The atmosphere consists of layers, each having its own characteristics. (17-1)

- Temperature is measured with a thermometer in units called degrees Celsius. (17-2)

- Radiant energy from the sun heats the earth and the atmosphere. (17-3)

- Heat energy travels by the processes of conduction, convection, and radiation. (17-3)

- Air pressure can be measured with a barometer. (17-4)

- Lines that connect places on a weather map having identical air-pressure readings are called isobars. (17-5)

- Air moves from areas of higher air pressure to areas of lower air pressure. (17-5)

- Major zones of constant high or low pressure, or pressure belts, circle the earth. (17-5)

- Wind is caused by differences in air pressure. (17-6)

- Convection currents along shorelines produce land and sea breezes. Convection currents on mountains produce mountain and valley breezes. (17-7)

- The pressure belts produce global wind patterns, including the trade winds, prevailing westerlies, and polar easterlies. (17-7)

The key terms in this chapter are listed below. Use each term in a sentence that shows the meaning of the term.

air pressure	greenhouse effect	mesosphere	thermosphere
anemometer	highs	polar easterlies	trade winds
atmosphere	horse latitudes	prevailing westerlies	troposphere
barometer	ionosphere	radiant energy	weather
conduction	isobars	radiation	wind
convection	isotherms	stratosphere	wind vane
doldrums	jet streams	temperature	
exosphere	lows	thermometer	

Chapter Review

VOCABULARY

Use the key terms from this chapter to complete the following sentences correctly.

1. The _____ is the ocean of air that surrounds the earth.
2. The layer of the atmosphere in which you live is called the _____ .
3. The layer of the atmosphere that consists of electrically-charged particles that reflect radio waves is called the _____ .
4. _____ is a measure of the motion energy of the molecules in a material.
5. Radiant energy from the sun reaches the earth by the process of _____ .
6. A/an _____ is an instrument used to measure air pressure.
7. Lines on a weather map that connect places having the same air pressure are called _____ .
8. Wind speed is measured with an instrument called a/an _____ .
9. The process by which heat is transferred from one place to another by a carrier is called _____ .
10. The area of light, shifting winds at the equator is called the _____ .

CONCEPTS

1. Describe the materials that make up the atmosphere. (17-1)
2. Explain why certain materials found in the atmosphere vary from place to place and from time to time. Give an example of one such material. (17-1)
3. How is the ionosphere important? (17-1)
4. Distinguish between heat and temperature. (17-2)
5. Describe how a liquid thermometer works. (17-2)
6. What happens to radiant energy that reaches the earth's outer atmosphere? (17-3)
7. Explain the process of radiation. (17-3)
8. Describe the different forms of radiant energy. (17-3)
9. How is radiant energy related to the greenhouse effect? (17-3)
10. Describe the process of convection. (17-3)
11. What is air pressure? How is air pressure measured? (17-4)
12. Describe what would happen to an aneroid barometer if you moved it from sea level to the tropopause. (17-4)

13. How are isobars determined? (17-5)
14. Compare the movement of air in highs and lows. (17-5)
15. Distinguish between a cyclone and an anticyclone. (17-5)
16. What is pressure gradient? (17-5)
17. What are pressure belts? Describe the major pressure belts. (17-5)
18. What causes wind? (17-6)
19. How does an anemometer work? How does a wind vane work? (17-6)
20. Give three examples of local winds. Describe how each occurs. (17-7)
21. How does the Coriolis effect affect global winds? (17-7)
22. Name and describe three global winds. (17-7)
23. What are the jet streams? (17-7)

APPLICATION/ CRITICAL THINKING

1. Scientists are concerned about the amount of carbon dioxide in the atmosphere. What might happen to the earth if there was more carbon dioxide in the air? What might happen if there was less carbon dioxide?
2. Suppose you are given a liquid thermometer that does not have a temperature scale marked on it. Describe how you would find where the 50°C point on the thermometer is.
3. How would the jet stream affect air travel between New York and Miami, Florida? How would it affect air travel between New York and Los Angeles?

EXTENSION

1. Use reference books to find out about local and seasonal winds such as monsoons, chinooks, harmattan, foehn, mistral, simoom, and sirocco.
2. Use a barometer to measure the air pressure each day for two weeks. Record each reading. Also make notes about the type of weather you have each day. What types of weather follow a rising barometer? What types of weather follow a falling barometer? What type of weather occurs when the barometer remains unchanged?

READINGS

"Balloon-Borne Yo-yo Studies Atmosphere." *Science Digest,* May 1983, p. 27.

Linn, A. "Oh, What a Spin We're In, Thanks to the Coriolis Effect." *Smithsonian,* February 1983, p. 66.

Simon, C. "Global Study Probes Lower Atmosphere." *Science News,* September 17, 1983, p. 82.

WATER IN THE ATMOSPHERE

Has it rained in your town this week? Have you ever wished that rain would go away and not spoil your plans for a weekend? Or have you hoped for rain to cool you on a hot summer afternoon? Too much rain causes problems, but so does too little. To some people, rain is an inconvenience, yet to farmers who grow your food, it is a necessity. Rain is one example of water in the atmosphere that often affects us.

Water exists in the atmosphere in many forms. A rainbow is one sign that the air contains water vapor. Water droplets break sunlight into the colors of the rainbow.

- *How does water get into air?*
- *What makes it leave air?*
- *Is snow just frozen rain?*

18-1 THE WATER CYCLE

Water is one of the few materials that exists on the earth in all three states of matter: solid, liquid, and gas. Water in liquid form is found in oceans, lakes, streams, and as droplets in clouds. Water in solid form is called ice. It is found at the polar ice caps and in clouds as snowflakes. Water in gaseous form is called water vapor. Water vapor is present in air. The **water cycle** is the continuous movement of water between the earth and the air. Figure 18-1 illustrates the paths that water can follow and how water changes during the water cycle.

One change shown in the water cycle is evaporation (ee vap uh RAY shuhn). **Evaporation** is the process by which liquid water changes to water vapor. You know that puddles dry up and that wet clothes hung on a clothesline become dry. In both cases, the water evaporates.

Water is also added to the atmosphere by transpiration (tran spuh RAY shuhn). **Transpiration** is the process by which plants release water vapor into the atmosphere through their leaves. Much of the water that is collected by plant roots is lost into the air through transpiration.

> After completing this section, you will be able to
>
> - **define** *evaporation.*
> - **explain** the difference between condensation and precipitation.
> - **describe** the movement of water in the water cycle.
>
> *The key terms in this section are*
>
> | | |
> |---|---|
> | condensation | sublimation |
> | evaporation | transpiration |
> | precipitation | water cycle |

ex (out)
vapor (steam)

419

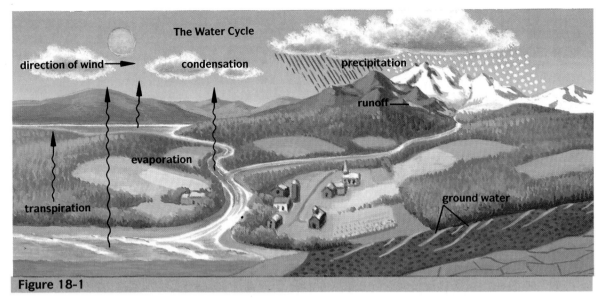

The Water Cycle

direction of wind→   condensation   precipitation

runoff—

evaporation

ground water

transpiration

Figure 18-1

The water cycle.

com (together)
densus (thick)

Once in the atmosphere, water vapor may become liquid water in the process called condensation (kahn den-SAY shuhn). **Condensation** occurs when water vapor changes into liquid water. The moisture that forms on a bathroom mirror after a hot shower and the water that collects on a cold drinking glass form by condensation. Many clouds form when water condenses in the atmosphere.

Sometimes, water vapor changes directly from gas to solid. This change occurs when vapor is forced out of the air at temperatures below freezing. It is in this way that snowflakes and the frost on a window form. The process in which vapor changes directly to a solid, or a solid changes directly to vapor, is called **sublimation** (suhb luh-MAY shuhn).

A cycle is a series of regularly occurring events. As you can see in Figure 18-1, a cycle has no beginning and no end. The driving force behind the water cycle is energy from the sun. What process in the water cycle is caused directly by the sun's energy? Most water vapor that enters the air evaporates from the oceans, which make up 70 percent of the earth's surface. The remaining water evaporates from streams, rivers, lakes, plants, animals, and industry. Each minute, millions of metric tons of water vapor are added to the air. The resulting water vapor is carried by wind into the atmosphere.

When air in the atmosphere cools, water vapor may condense into drops of liquid water or may sublimate to form ice crystals. The drops of liquid water or the ice crystals grow in size until they fall back to the earth. Water

Figure 18-2

Precipitation may occur as rain, snow, hail, or sleet.

that returns to the earth as rain, snow, sleet, or hail is called **precipitation** (prih sihp uh TAY shuhn). Identify the forms of precipitation in Figure 18-2. Precipitation falls on open water—lakes, streams, oceans—and on land. Water that falls on land may return to open water as surface runoff. Or it may soak into the ground and move underground to the open water. Water moving underground is called *ground water*. From the open water, water evaporates and the cycle repeats.

The water cycle is a balanced cycle. Over the entire earth, the amount of water that leaves the air equals the amount of water that enters it. In any place, however, the cycle may not be balanced. For example, the amount of evaporation and transpiration in a desert is much greater than the amount of precipitation. In a tropical rain forest, the amount of precipitation is much greater than the amount of evaporation and transpiration. At any time, a place may have more water coming in than leaving because of changes in seasons or weather. However, the water cycle for the entire earth is always balanced.

REVIEW

1. What is evaporation?
2. What is the difference between condensation and precipitation?
3. Make a diagram of the water cycle and label its parts.

CHALLENGE   How would producing rain by seeding clouds affect the water cycle?

18-2 AIR AND HUMIDITY

You already know that water evaporates from puddles and pools, but where does it go? When water evaporates, water molecules move into spaces between air molecules. **Humidity** (hyoo MIHD uh tee) is water vapor in air. Water vapor in air can vary from nearly 0 percent over a desert to almost 4 percent over a tropical rain forest. *Absolute humidity* is a measure of the amount of water vapor in air. Absolute humidity is measured in grams per cubic meter (g/m^3). For example, if 1 m^3 of air contained 15 g of water vapor, its absolute humidity would be expressed as 15 g/m^3.

Air's ability to hold water vapor depends on the temperature of the air. As temperature increases, air's capacity for water vapor increases. Figure 18-3 shows the relationship between temperature and air's capacity for water vapor. What is air's capacity for water vapor at 20°C? An increase in temperature causes molecules in air to spread, which creates more space for water molecules.

Meteorologists often compare the amount of water vapor in air with air's capacity for water vapor. The amount of water vapor in the air compared with the maximum amount of water vapor that air is able to hold at a given temperature is called the **relative humidity**. Relative humidity can be calculated using the following formula.

$$\text{Relative humidity} = \frac{\text{absolute humidity}}{\text{capacity}} \times 100$$

Relative humidity is measured in percent.

Figure 18-3

The capacity of air to hold water vapor increases with increasing temperature.

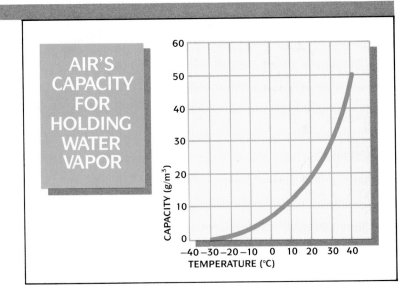

AIR'S CAPACITY FOR HOLDING WATER VAPOR

To show how this formula is used, look at Figure 18-4. At 10°C, air has a capacity of 11 g/m³. This means that a cubic meter of air at 10°C could hold a maximum of 11 g of water vapor. Assume that this cubic meter of air was actually holding only 5.5 g of water vapor. The absolute humidity of the air would be 5.5 g/m³. Using the formula, the relative humidity would be

$$\frac{5.5 \text{ g/m}^3}{11 \text{ g/m}^3} \times 100, \text{ or } 50\%$$

Relative humidity is affected by changes in absolute humidity. An increase in absolute humidity causes an increase in relative humidity because there is more water vapor in the air. Relative humidity is also affected by changes in temperature. For example, look at Figure 18-4. Notice that at 25°C the capacity of the air is 22 g/m³. If the same amount of water vapor that was present in air at 10°C (5.5 g/m³) was present in air at 25°C, the relative humidity would be

$$\frac{5.5 \text{ g/m}^3}{22 \text{ g/m}^3} \times 100, \text{ or } 25\%$$

Look at Figure 18-4, which shows how relative humidity changes as the temperature changes. Determine the relative humidity at 40°C. As you can see, as the temperature increases, the relative humidity decreases. This is why air indoors in the winter "feels" drier than in the summer. In the winter, cold outside air is brought indoors. Although the amount of moisture in the air does not change, the air becomes warmer. This lowers the relative humidity.

Figure 18-4

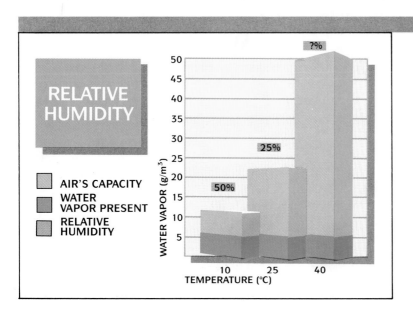

As temperature changes, relative humidity changes, even though the amount of water vapor in the air remains constant.

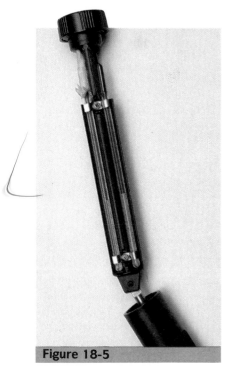

Figure 18-5

A psychrometer is used to measure relative humidity.

One instrument that measures relative humidity is a **psychrometer** (sī KRAHM uh tuhr). As you can see in Figure 18-5, a psychrometer contains two thermometers. The bulb of one thermometer is covered with a wet piece of cloth. This thermometer is called a wet-bulb thermometer. When water evaporates from the cloth, the wet-bulb thermometer shows a decrease in temperature. The other thermometer is called a dry-bulb thermometer. Since no evaporation takes place on the bulb of this thermometer, the dry-bulb thermometer's temperature does not change.

If the air is dry, water evaporates quickly from the wet-bulb thermometer and there is a large decrease in the wet-bulb temperature. This makes the difference in the temperatures of the two thermometers large. When the air is holding a large amount of water vapor, little water evaporates from the wet bulb. The difference in the temperatures of the two thermometers is small. If the air is saturated, no evaporation takes place from the wet-bulb thermometer. The two thermometers will show the same temperature. The difference in temperatures is an indication of the amount of water vapor in air.

Table 18-1 can be used to find the relative humidity from the temperature readings on a psychrometer. The numbers across the top of the table indicate differences between the wet- and dry-bulb readings in degrees Celsius. The numbers along the left side of the table list dry-bulb readings in degrees Celsius. The following procedure is used to determine relative humidity.

Table 18-1 *Relative Humidity* (%)

Dry-bulb temperature (°C)	Difference between wet-bulb and dry-bulb temperatures (°C)																	
	1	2	3	4	5	6	7	8	9	10	11	12	13	14	15	16	17	18
11	89	78	67	56	46	36	27	18	9									
12	89	78	68	58	48	39	29	21	12									
13	89	79	69	59	50	41	32	23	15	7								
14	90	79	70	60	51	42	34	26	18	10								
15	90	80	71	61	53	44	36	27	20	13	6							
16	90	81	71	63	54	46	38	30	23	15	8							
17	90	81	72	64	55	47	40	32	25	18	11							
18	91	82	73	65	57	49	41	34	27	20	14	7						
19	91	82	74	65	58	50	43	36	29	22	16	10						
20	91	83	74	66	59	51	44	37	31	24	18	12	6					
21	91	83	75	67	60	53	46	39	32	26	20	14	9					
22	92	83	76	68	61	54	47	40	34	28	22	17	11	6				
23	92	84	76	69	62	55	48	42	36	30	24	19	13	8				
24	92	84	77	69	62	56	49	43	37	31	26	20	15	10	5			
25	92	84	77	70	63	57	50	44	39	33	28	22	17	12	8			
26	92	85	78	71	64	58	51	46	40	34	29	24	19	14	10	5		
27	92	85	78	71	65	58	52	47	41	36	31	26	21	16	12	7		
28	93	85	78	72	65	59	53	48	42	37	32	27	22	18	13	9	5	
29	93	86	79	72	66	60	54	49	43	38	33	28	24	19	15	11	7	
30	93	86	79	73	67	61	55	50	44	39	35	30	25	21	17	13	9	5

ACTIVITY Relative Humidity

OBJECTIVE
Measure the relative humidity in several locations.

MATERIALS
15-cm × 30-cm piece of cardboard, 2 Celsius thermometers, clear tape, 4-cm piece of shoelace, cup of water, textbook, large index card

PROCEDURE
A. Place a 15-cm × 30-cm piece of cardboard in front of you. Place two thermometers side by side on the cardboard. Make sure that the bulb of each thermometer extends over the edge of the cardboard. Tape the thermometers to the cardboard.

B. Slide a piece of shoelace 4 cm long over the bulb of one thermometer. Dip the shoelace into the cup of water. This thermometer is called the wet-bulb thermometer. The other thermometer is called the dry-bulb thermometer.

C. Place the cardboard with the thermometers on a textbook so that the bulbs of the thermometers hang over the edge of the book.

D. While carefully watching the thermometers, fan the two bulbs with an index card. When the temperature reading on the wet bulb stays the same for one minute, read the wet-bulb thermometer. Then read the dry-bulb thermometer.
   1. What is the wet-bulb reading?
   2. What is the dry-bulb reading?

E. Calculate the difference between the readings.
   3. What is the difference?

F. Using Table 18-1, determine the relative humidity of your classroom.
   4. What is the relative humidity of your classroom?

G. With your teacher's permission, rewet the shoelace and repeat steps **C** through **E** outside your school.
   5. What is the relative humidity outside your school?
   6. In what rooms of your school would you expect to find high relative humidity? In what rooms would you expect to find low relative humidity?

H. With your teacher's permission, check your guesses by measuring the relative humidity in those places.

RESULTS AND CONCLUSIONS
1. Is the relative humidity today higher indoors or outdoors? Explain your answer.
2. Did you find different relative humidities for different parts of the school? Explain your answer.

1. Read the temperatures on a psychrometer.
2. Calculate the difference between the temperatures.
3. In the table find the dry-bulb temperature.
4. Find the column under the measured difference in the temperatures. Read the relative humidity.

What is the relative humidity when the temperature is 22°C and the difference in readings is 3°C?

REVIEW

1. What is humidity?
2. What is the difference between absolute and relative humidity?
3. What is the relative humidity when the temperature is 14°C and the difference between the two readings is 2°C?

CHALLENGE Why does air often seem more humid in summer than in winter?

18-3 CONDENSATION

After completing this section, you will be able to

- **describe** two ways in which air can become saturated with water vapor.
- **define** *dew point.*
- **explain** how dew and frost form.

The key terms in this section are
condensation nuclei
dew
dew point

For condensation to occur, air must become saturated with water vapor. Air can become saturated in two ways. It can become saturated as water evaporates from a body of water, such as a lake or an ocean. More often, however, air becomes saturated as its temperature decreases. The first box in Figure 18-6 represents air's capacity for water vapor at 20°C. The water in the box represents how much water is present in that air. If the temperature decreases to 10°C, the air's capacity for water also decreases. If the temperature decreases to 0°C, the capacity of the air in the middle box is reduced by one half. As the temperature of air falls, the capacity of air for water vapor decreases. The temperature to which air must be cooled to become saturated is called the **dew point**. In which box in Figure 18-6 has the air temperature reached the dew point?

When relative humidity is high, the dew point is close to the air's temperature. The temperature does not have to be lowered much for the air to become saturated, because the air is already nearly saturated. When the relative humidity is low, however, the dew point is much less than air temperature, because the air is dry. A large decrease in temperature is therefore needed to reduce air's capacity enough for it to become saturated.

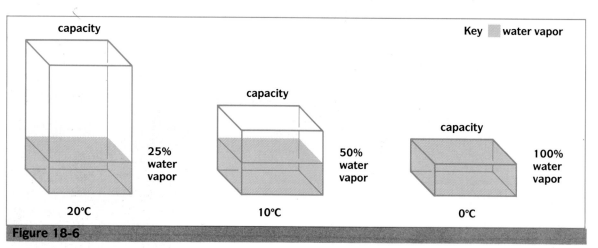

Figure 18-6

As temperature drops, air's capacity to hold water vapor decreases. Eventually, the air becomes saturated with water vapor.

When the temperature falls to the dew point, air becomes saturated. In order for water vapor to condense from air, however, it must have a surface to condense on. For example, **dew** is water vapor that condenses on cold surfaces, such as grass, plants, and automobiles, on cool mornings. Notice in Figure 18-7 that dew has formed on the pine needles.

ACTIVITY   Measuring the Dew Point

OBJECTIVES
Determine the dew point.
Estimate the altitude at which clouds form.

MATERIALS
Celsius thermometer, shiny can, stirring rod, water, ice

PROCEDURE
A. Using a thermometer, measure the temperature of the air. Record this in your notebook.
B. Half fill a shiny can with water. If condensation collects on the can, replace the water with warmer water. Dry the outside of the can. Repeat this procedure until no more condensation forms.
C. Place a piece of ice in the water. While carefully watching the outside of the can for moisture, use a stirring rod to slowly stir the ice and water. As soon as moisture appears on the can, remove the ice and measure the temperature of the water. Record this in your notebook.

D. Repeat steps **B** and **C** two more times and average your three readings. The average of these readings is the dew point.
E. Rising air decreases in temperature about 1°C for each 100 m of altitude through the troposphere. Subtract the dew point reading from the temperature reading. Multiply the difference by 100 m. This figure tells you at what altitude the temperature reaches the dew point. If air is pushed up to that height, clouds will form.

RESULTS AND CONCLUSIONS
1. What was the air temperature?
2. What was the dew point?
3. At what altitude would you expect clouds to form?
4. The dew point will decrease a small amount as altitude increases because of the changing pressure. In what way will this affect your prediction?

In air, water may also condense on dust, smoke, salt, and other small particles that are floating there. Small particles in air that water condenses on are called **condensation nuclei** (NOO klee ī). Condensation nuclei are always present in the air. Fog and clouds form when water condenses onto the condensation nuclei.

If the dew point is below freezing, water vapor does not condense and form drops of water. Instead, the water sublimates, or changes directly from water vapor to ice. This process forms the delicate crystal structure that you recognize in frost or snowflakes. Frost is ice that forms on objects when water vapor sublimates.

REVIEW

1. What are two ways in which air can become saturated with water vapor?
2. What happens to air when its temperature reaches the dew point?
3. What is the difference between dew and frost?

CHALLENGE The clouds that form behind jet airplanes are called *contrails,* short for "condensation trails." From where do the water vapor and condensation nuclei originate? Why does the water vapor condense?

Figure 18-7

Dew is the condensing of water vapor on surfaces.

18-4 CONDENSATION AND CLOUDS

HOW CLOUDS FORM

At any one time, about 50 percent of the earth is covered by clouds. A **cloud** is a collection of water droplets and/or pieces of ice floating in the atmosphere. Most clouds form in the troposphere. The shape and position of clouds are important clues to meteorologists when they prepare their forecasts. Clouds indicate the direction and speed of wind in an area as well as the amount of water vapor in the air.

In section 18-3, you learned that three conditions must exist in order for water to condense from air. First, air must contain water vapor. Second, air must contain condensation nuclei. Finally, the air temperature must drop to the dew point. Air generally has both water vapor and condensation nuclei. In what ways, then, does air cool to the dew point?

One way in which air can be cooled is by coming into contact with a cool surface. For example, air can be cooled if it moves over cooler water. This is why air that blows in from the ocean during the summer is cool.

Air also cools as heat radiates from it into space. For example, air cools more quickly on clear nights than on cloudy nights. This is because on cloudy nights the clouds trap heat that is radiating into space. Fogs often form in the early mornings after clear nights as the air temperature near the ground drops to the dew point. **Fog**, shown in Figure 18-8, is a cloud that forms close to the earth.

Figure 18-8

Fog is a cloud that forms close to the earth's surface (*left*). As air rises on a mountain, it cools, and clouds may form (*right*).

Air cools as it rises. Clouds form when rising air is cooled to the dew point. Clouds sometimes have flat bases, which indicate the altitude at which the dew point is reached. Air rises when it moves across a warm part of the earth's surface and is heated. As the air rises, the pressure around it decreases. This causes the rising air to expand. The temperature of any gas will decrease as the gas expands. Temperature changes that occur without heat being added or removed by outside sources are called *adiabatic* (ad ee uh BAT ihk) *changes*. Air also rises when it moves over a mountain. Very often the top of the mountain becomes cloud-covered when the temperature of the rising air drops to the dew point. When the air moves down the other side of the mountain, it is warmed. The clouds disappear as the water droplets evaporate.

KINDS OF CLOUDS

You probably have looked at clouds for signs of rain. But not all clouds bring rain. Some clouds indicate that cool, dry weather is on the way; other clouds can bring thunderstorms and tornadoes. Being able to "read" clouds is an important part of predicting weather. Clouds are named according to their shapes. The sky is usually a mixture of different kinds of clouds. Careful observation has shown that there are three basic shapes of clouds.

Cumulus (KYOO myuh luhs) **clouds**, shown in Figure 18-9, are heaped, fluffy clouds, often with flat bases, that form as warm air rises through the atmosphere. Cumulus clouds are found at all altitudes. Cumulus clouds generally

cumulus (heap)

Figure 18-9

Cumulus clouds usually indicate fair weather.

indicate fair weather. These clouds begin to form only when the temperature falls to the dew point. If the upward push of air is strong, these clouds may extend many kilometers into the atmosphere, forming a thunderhead. Another name for thunderhead is *cumulonimbus* (kyoo myuh loh NIHM buhs) *cloud.* When *-nimbus* or *nimbo-* is part of a cloud name, it means the cloud is precipitating. A cumulonimbus cloud may bring violent weather, including thunder, lightning, hail, and tornadoes.

stratus (spreading out)

Stratus (STRA tuhs) **clouds** are clouds that spread out in a layer where a large body of air is slowly lifted into the atmosphere. They usually indicate rainy weather. Look at the stratus clouds in Figure 18-10. Notice that these clouds are not as tall as cumulus clouds, but they cover a wider area. Stratus clouds may block the sun for many hours, even days, because it takes so long for them to pass. *Nimbostratus clouds* produce a light but steady rain or snow that can last for more than a day.

cirrus (curl)

Cirrus (SIHR uhs) **clouds** are thin, feathery clouds that are formed at high altitudes. The temperature at such altitudes is always well below freezing, so cirrus clouds are made of ice crystals. Notice in Figure 18-10 the shape of a cirrus cloud. Cirrus clouds are thin and wispy. This is because they form where the air is thin and the winds are strong. They are sometimes called mare's tails because of their appearance. Cirrus clouds are fair-weather clouds.

Figure 18-10

Stratus clouds occur in layers and bring precipitation (*left*). Cirrus clouds are high-altitude, fair-weather clouds (*right*).

Figure 18-11

The kinds of clouds.

Clouds can form at different altitudes. They are also named according to the altitudes where they form. Cumulus and stratus clouds that develop at altitudes between 2 km and 7 km are identified by the prefix *alto-*. A cumulus cloud at this altitude is called an *altocumulus cloud*. Cumulus and stratus clouds that develop at altitudes above

OBJECTIVE

Identify the conditions that lead to cloud formation.

MATERIALS

large clear plastic bottle with cap, graduate, cold and hot tap water, matches

PROCEDURE

A. Pour 50 mL of cold tap water into a clear plastic bottle and place a cap on it. Shake the bottle for 30 seconds and then set it on your table.

B. Squeeze the bottle and then release the pressure. Repeat this process several times.
   1. What changes do you see in the bottle?

C. Remove the cap from the bottle and light a match. Hold the match over the mouth of the bottle. Quickly squeeze the bottle to extinguish the match; then slowly release the pressure to draw smoke into the bottle. Replace and tighten the cap. Repeat procedure **B**.

   2. What changes do you now see in the bottle?
   3. Why is the result different this time?
   4. What are the smoke particles called in this situation?

D. Rinse the bottle thoroughly and pour 50 mL of hot tap water into it. Shake the bottle vigorously and place it on your table.

E. Repeat procedures **B** and **C**.
   5. How is this result different from your last result?

RESULTS AND CONCLUSIONS

1. What effect did increasing and then decreasing the pressure have on the temperature in the container? What effect did it have on the saturation of the air?
2. Which cloud was the thickest? Why, do you think, was it the thickest?

---

7 km are identified by the prefix *cirro-*. A stratus cloud at this altitude is called a *cirrostratus cloud*. At times, a halo, or ring, is visible around the sun or the moon. Such a halo or ring forms from light that is passing through cirrostratus clouds.

Clouds give helpful clues to changes in weather. For example, cirrus clouds followed by cirrostratus clouds often indicate that a rainy period and a temperature increase are on the way. Cumulus clouds followed by a cumulonimbus cloud generally precede a short period of heavy rain and a drop in temperature. You will learn more about why these clouds indicate these kinds of changes in the next chapter.

REVIEW

1. How do clouds form?
2. Compare the way fogs form with the way clouds form.
3. What are three basic shapes of clouds?
4. What type of weather is associated with each of the three basic shapes of clouds?

CHALLENGE Cumulus clouds usually form in the afternoon rather than in the morning. Provide an explanation to account for this.

18-5 PRECIPITATION

RAIN

Rain, the most common form of precipitation, is liquid water that falls to the earth. All clouds contain water, but not all clouds produce precipitation. As you know, clouds are made of cloud droplets that are either tiny droplets of liquid water or tiny pieces of ice. Figure 18-12 illustrates different sizes of cloud droplets compared with a raindrop. Notice how much larger the raindrop is than the other droplets. It takes about a million cloud droplets to make one raindrop.

Cloud droplets fall very slowly because of their small size, and the slightest upward movement of air can keep them afloat. Because of their small size, these droplets evaporate quickly as they fall through the warmer and drier air near the earth. For these reasons, the water in a cloud does not always reach the ground. To reach the ground the droplets must form large raindrops.

One way in which raindrops form is by cloud droplets colliding and joining. Scientists believe that cloud droplets of different sizes are more likely to join than are droplets of the same size. The large cloud droplets form on large condensation nuclei. They fall faster than the small cloud droplets and tend to collect smaller droplets along the way. Eventually, enough cloud droplets collect to form a raindrop. Some scientists also believe that the movement of cloud droplets creates electrical charges on them. These charges could speed the growth process by drawing droplets together.

After completing this section, you will be able to

- **compare** two ways in which rain forms.
- **list** two factors that affect the size of a raindrop.
- **describe** how snow and hail form.

The key terms in this section are

drizzle	rain gauge
glaze	sleet
hail	snow
rain	

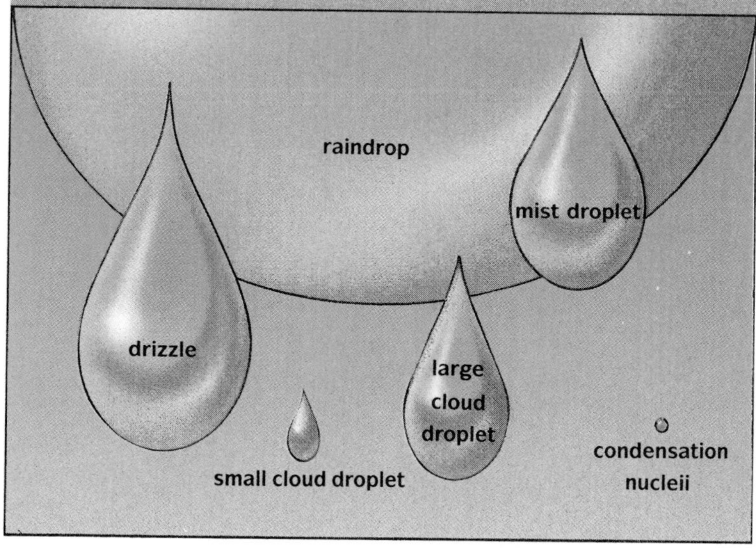

Figure 18-12

Comparative sizes of droplets and drops in a cloud.

raindrop

mist droplet

drizzle

large cloud droplet

small cloud droplet

condensation nucleii

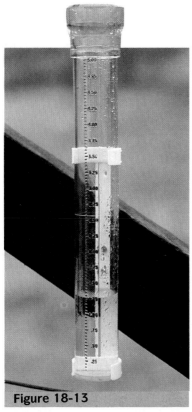

Figure 18-13

A rain gauge measures the amount of rainfall.

A second way in which raindrops form is by the melting of snowflakes. The tops of many high-altitude clouds are made up of ice crystals because the clouds are formed where temperatures are below freezing. During the winter months, even low-altitude clouds contain ice crystals. These ice crystals collect and grow to form snowflakes that fall through the clouds. As the snowflakes fall, they may reach parts of the clouds where the temperature is above freezing, so the snowflakes melt, forming raindrops.

Several factors influence how large the raindrops can become. One factor is how much water vapor the cloud contains. If the cloud has too little water vapor, then the raindrops do not grow large. A second factor is the vertical height of the cloud. A droplet that falls through a tall cloud can combine with many others and become much larger. A cumulonimbus cloud, for example, is very tall and can thus produce the heavy rain of a thunderstorm. In contrast, very small water droplets called **drizzle** form in thin stratus clouds. The droplets fall only a short distance through this type of cloud.

The amount of rainfall is measured with an instrument called a **rain gauge**. Notice in Figure 18-13 how the rain gauge is funnel-shaped at the top. This shape allows the gauge to collect rain from a large area and then direct it through a small tube to measure it. For example, 1 cm of rain may rise 5 cm in the tube. In this way, small differences in rainfall are easily detected. A rain gauge is placed in an open area to collect rain for a certain period of time.

SCIENCE PUZZLER

Manufactured snow is formed by snow-making machines that blow a mist of water into the air at temperatures below freezing. The snow forms when tiny water droplets in the mist freeze and fall to the ground. Is machine-made snow really snow? Explain your answer?

Packed snow on a slope contains many layers. If any one of the layers is too weak to hold the snow above it, an avalanche could occur. A sudden cold snap in early winter can create a weak layer of snow. The ground at that time may still be warm. Heat rising through the snow can change the structure of the crystals so that they do not stick to each other or to the snow above. The layer of snow becomes weak.

Snowflakes that are unable to stick to weak layers beneath them pull harder on snowflakes uphill. Eventually, the flakes pull apart and create a crack in the snow. The snow below the crack has nothing to cling to, and it dangles dangerously. An avalanche can be set off by a skier, pushing on the snow.

Attempts to predict avalanches have come a long way from the old method of poking holes in the snow. Snow guides now take instruments up the slope. With these instruments, they can measure characteristics of snow such as density and the tension between flakes.

Other information, including wind strength, wind direction, snow temperature, angle of the slope, and crystal type, is also gathered. The aim is to develop computer programs that will use this information to tell forecasters what conditions may lead to avalanches.

OTHER FORMS OF PRECIPITATION

You learned in section 18-3 that cloud droplets form when water vapor condenses on condensation nuclei. Snowflakes, however, form on *freezing nuclei* by the process of sublimation. Freezing nuclei are solid particles, such as ice crystals, that form when cloud droplets freeze. Unlike condensation nuclei, freezing nuclei are not very common in the atmosphere. This is because cloud droplets freeze at temperatures well below 0°C. In fact, tiny water droplets have been cooled to −40°C in laboratories before they froze. An ice crystal grows larger as water vapor sublimates on it. Eventually, the ice crystal grows large enough to fall through the cloud and combine with other ice crystals to form a snowflake.

Snow is the solid form of precipitation that occurs when snowflakes do not melt as they fall. They do not melt because the air temperature between the cloud and the ground remains below freezing. Snowflakes, like raindrops, also grow by colliding with and joining others as they fall. All snowflakes have six sides or points, but no two snowflakes seem to be exactly alike. Figure 18-14 shows several different kinds of snowflakes.

Figure 18-14

A snowflake is a solid form of precipitation.

Sleet, or freezing rain, forms when raindrops freeze after they leave the cloud, while falling to the earth. This form of precipitation may start as either rain or snow. If sleet starts as rain, the rain passes through a layer of below-freezing air near the ground, and some of the raindrops freeze. If sleet starts as snow, the snow falls through warmer air, changes to rain first, and then falls through freezing air below. Figure 18-15A illustrates a situation that would produce sleet. Why, do you think, is sleet often mixed with rain?

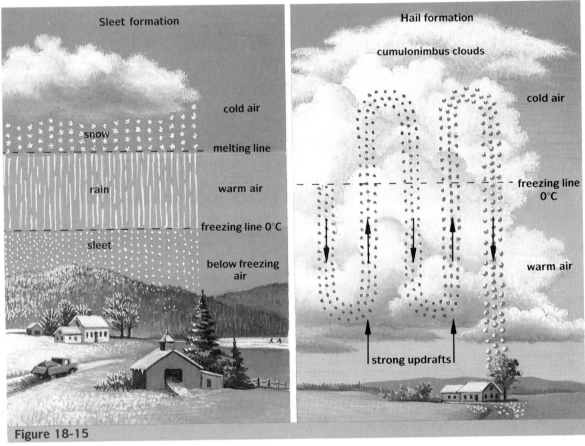

Figure 18-15

The formation of sleet (A). The formation of hail (B).

Hail is made of rounded pieces of ice formed by strong updrafts in cumulonimbus clouds. Hail begins as raindrops that are forced high into the cloud, above the freezing line, by the updrafts. The raindrops freeze and fall as ice pellets toward the earth. They pick up droplets as they fall. The pellets may also be caught in updrafts and sent high into the cloud, where the droplets freeze in a layer around them. This process can occur repeatedly before the pieces grow so large from each successive layer that they fall through the updrafts. Figure 18-15B illustrates this process. Hail can do tremendous damage to crops and has been known to break windows and damage other property as well.

Occasionally, objects on the surface of the earth have just cooled to below freezing when rain falls. When raindrops wet the freezing surfaces, a layer of ice forms. The layer of ice that forms from rain on objects whose temperatures are below freezing is called **glaze**. Glaze is actually an ice coating, not a form of precipitation.

REVIEW

1. Describe two ways in which rain forms in clouds.
2. Identify two factors that affect the sizes of raindrops.
3. Describe how snow forms.
4. How do large pieces of hail form?

CHALLENGE Explain why hail is unlikely to fall from stratus clouds.

CHAPTER SUMMARY

The main ideas in this chapter are listed below. Read these statements before you answer the Chapter Review questions.

- The water cycle shows the paths by which water enters and leaves the atmosphere. (18-1)

- The water vapor in the atmosphere can be measured in terms of absolute humidity and relative humidity. The absolute humidity is a measure of the amount of water vapor in the air. The relative humidity is a measure of the amount of water vapor in the air compared with the maximum that could be held at a given temperature. (18-2)

- In order for water vapor to condense, the air must become saturated and surfaces must be present for the water vapor to condense on. (18-3)

- Clouds form when rising air cools to the dew point. (18-4)

- Clouds are named according to their shapes and altitudes. (18-4)

- Precipitation forms when cloud droplets or snowflakes become large enough to fall. (18-5)

- Precipitation includes rain, snow, sleet, drizzle, and hail. (18-5)

The key terms in this chapter are listed below. Use each term in a sentence that shows the meaning of the term.

cirrus clouds	dew point	humidity	sleet
cloud	drizzle	precipitation	snow
condensation	evaporation	psychrometer	stratus clouds
condensation nuclei	fog	rain	sublimation
cumulus clouds	glaze	rain gauge	transpiration
dew	hail	relative humidity	water cycle

Chapter Review

Use the key terms from this chapter to complete the following sentences correctly.

1. The _____ is the exchange of water between the earth and the atmosphere.
2. _____ is the process in which liquid water changes to water vapor.
3. Water forms a solid directly from water vapor during _____.
4. Water vapor in the air is called _____.
5. Dew that collects on plants on cool mornings forms by the process of _____.
6. _____ forms when rain falls on objects whose temperatures are below freezing.
7. _____ is a cloud that forms close to the earth's surface.
8. Heaped, fluffy fair-weather clouds are _____ clouds.
9. _____ is made up of very small droplets of water that slowly fall to the ground.
10. Pellets of ice, sometimes created during thunderstorms, are called _____.

CONCEPTS

1. Give an example of each of the three states that water can exist in. (18-1)
2. What is the difference between evaporation and condensation? (18-1)
3. Describe the movement of water in the water cycle. (18-1)
4. How is humidity affected by temperature? (18-2)
5. How do changes in absolute humidity and temperature affect relative humidity? (18-2)
6. Use the graph shown in Figure 18-4 to answer the following questions. (18-2)
   a. What is the capacity of air at 30°C?
   b. What happens to the capacity of air as the temperature increases?
   c. If the absolute humidity of air at 30°C is 10 g/m³, what is the relative humidity?
7. What is the relationship between dew point and relative humidity? (18-3)
8. Give three examples of particles that can serve as condensation nuclei. (18-3)

9. What happens to water vapor when the dew point is below freezing? (18-3)
10. In what layer of the atmosphere do clouds form? (18-4)
11. Why does rising air cool? (18-4)
12. What causes the flat bases of some clouds? (18-4)
13. What are altocumulus and cirrostratus clouds? (18-4)
14. What are two processes that can cause cloud droplets to join? (18-5)
15. Do all raindrops reach the ground? Explain your answer. (18-5)
16. How does drizzle form? (18-5)
17. Compare the way snow forms with the way rain forms. (18-5)
18. Compare and contrast sleet and hail. (18-5)
19. How does glaze form? (18-5)

APPLICATION/ CRITICAL THINKING

1. Why is precipitation greater in areas near the equator than in areas near the poles?
2. Why does a high relative humidity on warm days cause you to feel uncomfortable?
3. Why does running a fan make you feel cooler?
4. If you blow up, seal, and release a balloon, will it rise more readily on a cold day or on a warm day?

EXTENSION

1. Using a pump, inflate a bicycle tube or basketball. Feel the temperature of the pump and notice whether it is hot or cool. Let the air out of the inflated tube or basketball and feel the air as it passes out of the stem. How does the temperature of the air compare with the temperature of the pump? How do you explain this?
2. Measure the amount of the next rainfall by doing this activity. Obtain a large juice can and a graduate. Fill the can with 1 cm of water. Pour this water into the graduate. Using a grease pencil, mark the level of the water as 1 cm. Mark off levels for 2 cm, 3 cm, 4 cm, depending on the amount of rainfall your area normally receives. Mark off fractions of these levels also. Place the can outside. After the next rainfall, pour the water collected in the can into the graduate to measure the amount of rainfall.

READINGS

Ivers, Pico. "The 'Great Dry' Drags On." *Time,* March 28, 1983, p. 41.

Schaefer, Vincent Jo, and John A. Day. *A Field Guide to the Atmosphere.* Boston: Houghton Mifflin Company, 1981.

THE CHANGING WEATHER

Look at the photograph on the opposite page. Do you recognize the kind of storm that is shown? Such storms, called tornadoes, occur with more frequency in the United States than in any other country. Although tornadoes are short-lived, they are powerful and destructive storms.

- *What conditions lead to the formation of tornadoes?*
- *What other major types of storms occur over the earth?*
- *What are some signs that indicate a change in weather?*

19-1 AIR MASSES

Large bodies of air are always moving through the atmosphere. These bodies of air are called air masses. An **air mass** is a large body of air that has about the same temperature and humidity throughout. People within one part of an air mass have nearly the same weather as people within another part. Air masses are high-pressure systems. The air in the center of the mass has the highest pressure and sinks toward the earth. The air spreads from the center along the earth's surface and, in the Northern Hemisphere, turns in a clockwise direction. Air masses can cover millions of square kilometers, yet are only 3 to 6 km deep.

Air masses form when air remains over a region long enough to take on the temperature and humidity characteristics of that region. It may take a week or more for an air mass to form. A region where air masses form is called a *source region.* Source regions have large uniform surfaces. A uniform surface is one that is nearly the same everywhere. For example, a large land area that is not broken up by mountains or divided by a large body of water would be a good source region.

After completing this section, you will be able to

- **define** the term *air mass*.
- **describe** how an air mass forms.
- **distinguish** between different types of air masses.
- **compare** the weather conditions associated with each kind of air mass.

The key terms in this section are
air mass
cold air mass
continental polar air mass
continental tropical air mass
maritime polar air mass
maritime tropical air mass
warm air mass

Source regions are found along the high-pressure belts of the earth. The air in these regions is sinking toward the earth and slowly spreading out. As the air moves across the surface, the type of surface helps to determine the characteristics of the air mass. For example, air over northern Canada becomes cool and dry, and air over the Gulf of Mexico becomes warm and humid. Which of these air masses is more likely to bring rain?

An air mass will eventually move away from its source region. As the air mass moves over the earth's surface, its temperature and humidity slowly change. Change occurs because an air mass is affected by the surface it covers. For example, a cold air mass will slowly warm as it moves over a warm surface. Air masses tend to move from west to east across North America, as shown in Figure 19-1.

maritimus (sea)

Air masses are classified by describing their source region. An air mass that forms over an ocean is called a *maritime* (MAR uh tīm) *air mass* (m). A maritime air mass tends to be humid. An air mass that forms over land is called a *continental* (kahn tuh NEHN tuhl) *air mass* (c). Such an air mass tends to be dry. An air mass that forms near the poles is called a *polar air mass* (P). Such air masses tend to be cold. An air mass that forms near the horse

Figure 19-1

Air masses move across the earth and carry their weather with them.

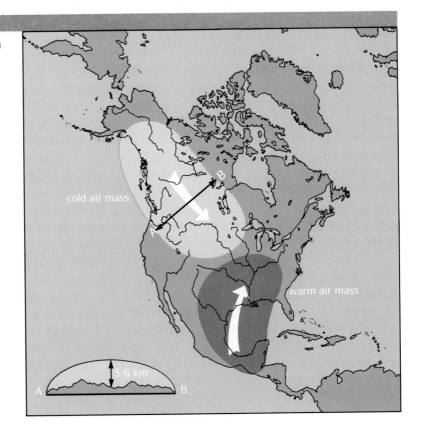

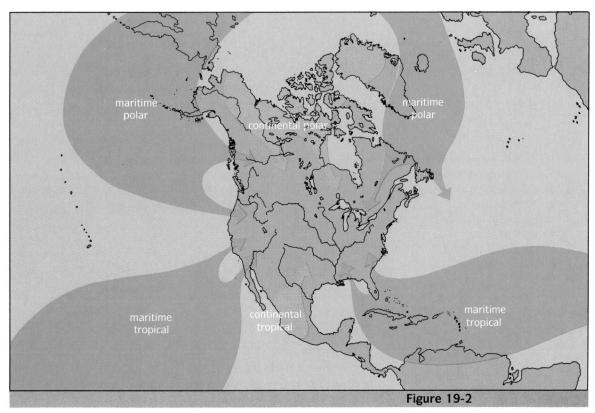

Figure 19-2

An air mass is named for the type of source region where it forms.

latitudes is called a *tropical air mass* (T). Such air masses tend to be warm. Figure 19-2 shows the major source regions that influence the weather in North America. Notice that each air mass is classified by describing two factors—humidity and temperature. For example, an air mass that forms over the northern Pacific Ocean is called a maritime polar air mass (mP). What do you call an air mass that forms over Mexico?

Each kind of air mass brings a different type of weather. A **maritime tropical air mass** (mT) is warm and humid. This air mass brings hot, humid weather in the summer. A **maritime polar air mass** (mP) is cold and humid. Maritime polar air masses carry the water that falls as snow on the Rocky Mountains. A **continental tropical air mass** (cT) is warm and dry. Continental tropical air masses bring warm, dry weather to the southwestern United States. A **continental polar air mass** (cP) is cold and dry. These air masses cause the cold spells that grip North America during the winter.

All air masses can be further classified into two groups. The grouping is based on the temperature of the air in the air mass. An air mass in which the temperature of the

443

OBJECTIVE

Determine the relationship between the movement of an air mass and weather changes.

MATERIALS

5 newspaper weather maps including national statistics for 5 consecutive days

PROCEDURE

A. Place the five weather maps in front of you, in chronological order.

B. Select a front that you can follow across the country on the five maps. Find listed in the statistics table a city that the front moves by on the second day.

C. List the high temperature, low temperature, and the weather for that city for each of the five days.

RESULTS AND CONCLUSIONS

1. How did the temperatures change as the front went by? What type of weather was reported as the front went by?

2. Where do you think the air mass originated? How would you classify it?

3. How did the temperatures change each day as the air mass continued to move? Explain these changes.

4. Did any precipitation occur? Why or why not?

5. How was the weather in the city that you chose determined by the air mass?

air is warm is called a **warm air mass**. An air mass in which the temperature of the air is cold is called a **cold air mass**. A warm air mass brings warmer weather, and a cold air mass brings cooler weather.

The movement of air masses is closely related to the position of the jet streams. During the summer, when the jet streams are near the United States-Canadian border, tropical air masses push farther north. Such air masses warm the United States and southern Canada. In the winter the jet streams move to the south. Cold polar air moves south with the jet streams and can affect places as far south as Florida. Meteorologists consider the position of the jet streams when they predict which direction an air mass will move.

REVIEW

1. What is an air mass?
2. How does an air mass form?
3. List the four types of air masses that influence the weather in North America.
4. Compare the weather conditions that are associated with each kind of air mass.

CHALLENGE   Suppose the path of the jet stream in a particular winter was along the United States-Canadian border. Predict the general weather pattern in each country.

19-2 AIR MASSES AND FRONTS

Different air masses have different densities because they have different temperatures and different amounts of moisture. Warm air masses are less dense than cold air masses, and humid air masses are less dense than dry air masses. Like oil and water, one air mass does not mix or blend with another. Where two air masses meet, a distinct boundary forms between the two air masses. The less dense air mass is lifted by the more dense air mass.

The boundary between two air masses is called a **front**. The shape of a front depends on the densities of the air masses and on their speeds. Figure 19-3 shows a front between two air masses. The warm air mass is pushing the cold air mass. Along the entire front, the less dense warmer air is slowly lifted by the more dense colder air mass. As the warmer air rises into the troposphere, the air cools. What will happen when the temperature of the rising air falls to its dew point? A line of clouds that mark a front can be seen in Figure 19-3. A line of clouds like these is a sign of a front.

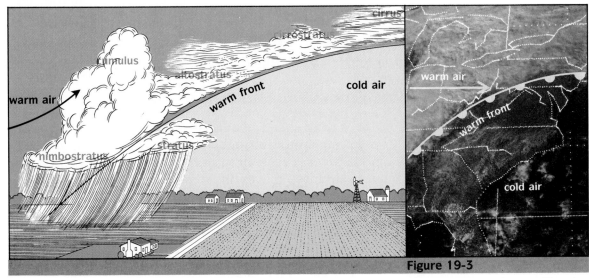

Figure 19-3

A warm front and a satellite photograph of a warm front.

Satellite photographs are helpful in locating fronts on the earth. However, there are also changes on the surface that indicate that a front is passing. One change that indicates a passing front is a falling barometer. Air masses are generally regions of high pressure, with the highest pressure at the center of the air mass and the lowest pressure along the edge. The air pressure falls when a front approaches, because the front is the edge of an air mass.

A second change that occurs as a front passes is a change in wind direction. Notice in Figure 19-4 how winds circulate in a clockwise direction around a high. Along the eastern edge of an air mass, the wind is from the north. From what direction will the wind along the western edge of an air mass blow? Since air masses tend to move from west to east, winds generally approach from the north when an air mass first moves in and from the south when an air mass leaves. A change in wind direction occurs as the front passes, because the front marks the western edge of one air mass and the eastern edge of another.

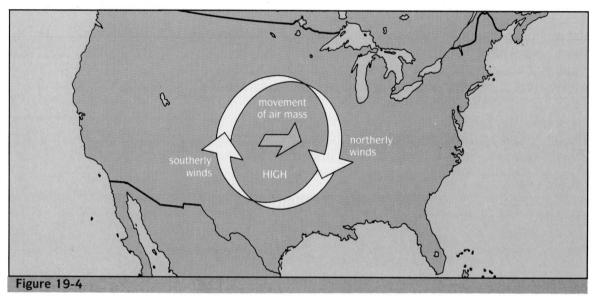

Figure 19-4

The movement of air around a high-pressure area.

A third change that is often measured as a front passes is a temperature change. A change in temperature takes place because each air mass has its own properties. As the new air mass moves in, it brings properties, including temperature, that are different.

Fronts are classified by determining whether the advancing air is warmer or colder than the retreating air. Figure 19-3 shows a warm front. A **warm front** forms when a warmer air mass replaces a cooler air mass. The warmer air is lifted far over the cooler air because the warmer air is less dense and meets little resistance. The clouds that form as the warm air rises may extend hundreds of kilometers ahead of the places where the front meets the ground. The clouds are thin and spread over large areas. It may take a day or more for the clouds to pass when a warm front moves by. If enough water condenses from air and if rain develops, it could rain off and on for a day or more before the front goes by.

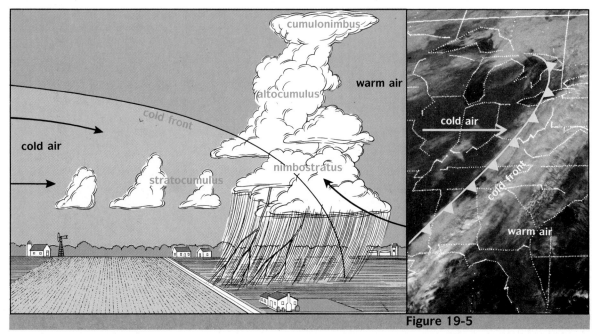

Figure 19-5

A cold front and a satellite photograph of a cold front.

A second type of front, called a cold front, is shown in Figure 19-5. A **cold front** forms when a cooler air mass replaces a warmer air mass. At a cold front the cooler air sinks under the warmer air ahead of it, and it pushes forward and upward. As you can see in Figure 19-5, the slope of a cold front is much steeper than the slope of a warm front. This occurs because the cold front moves much more rapidly than does the warm front. The cooler air moves underneath the warmer air, causing the warmer air mass to rise. The lifting of warmer air ahead of the front forms high clouds that do not extend far. When a cold front passes by, heavy rains and even a thunderstorm and hail can occur. These storms generally last for a much shorter time than do storms that are produced along warm fronts. A cold front is often followed by cooler, clear, and fair weather.

A third kind of front is called a stationary front. The word *stationary* means "standing still." A **stationary front** is a front that does not move for a time. This front forms when two air masses stop moving or move sideways so that the front between them does not move. A stationary front behaves like a warm front, regardless of whether the front was a warm front or a cold front before it stopped moving. What is happening to the warmer air mass along a stationary front? A stationary front brings overcast skies and rain to the area it covers, until the front finally moves.

stationarius (to stand)

Can You Locate a Low, Using the Direction of the Wind?

OBJECTIVE

Determine the location of a low by observing the wind.

MATERIALS

compass, newspaper weather map

PROCEDURE

A. With your teacher's permission, go to an open area outside of your school.

B. Stand and turn until the wind is blowing straight at your back. Now turn 40° to the right. Raise your left arm out to your side. Your left arm is now pointing toward the closest low-pressure area.

C. Determine the direction of the low, using the compass.
  1. In what direction is the nearest low?

D. Watch the clouds for several minutes.
  2. What kind of clouds do you see?
  3. In what direction are the clouds moving?
  4. Is the low moving toward you or away from you?

  5. What kind of cloud formations are associated with low pressure?
  6. What type of weather do these cloud formations bring?
  7. What kind of weather do you predict for the next 24 hours?

E. Read the newspaper weather map.
  8. Is there a low in the direction that you predicted?
  9. If yes, is there a front with the low? What kind of front is it?

RESULTS AND CONCLUSIONS

1. Based on your observations today, can you determine the location of a low by determining the wind direction?

2. What would your forecast for tomorrow be, now that you have seen the position of the highs, lows, and fronts on the newspaper map?

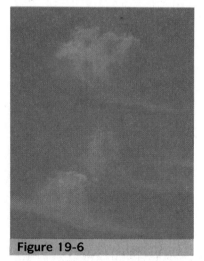

Figure 19-6

Cirrus clouds can indicate that the weather will change in about 24 hours.

You can use the clouds and your knowledge of fronts and air masses to make predictions about the weather. If you see a line of tall, dark cumulus clouds building on the horizon, then a cold front may be approaching. While the cold front is likely to reach you within a few hours, the storm that it brings probably will not last long.

Cirrus clouds are often the leading clouds of a warm front. When cirrus clouds are followed by cirrostratus clouds that appear to be getting lower and lower, a warm front is on the way. The rain from the warm front may not start for 24 hours or more after the cirrus clouds have passed. The warm front will probably bring overcast skies and a steady rain.

REVIEW

1. What is a front?
2. Describe the weather associated with the passing of a warm front, a cold front, and a stationary front.
3. How does the formation of a warm front differ from the formation of a cold front?
4. What cloud types are associated with a warm front?

CHALLENGE What kind of front is likely to form sleet?

19-3 FRONTS AND LOWS

There is a battle of air masses constantly being fought above you. Cold air masses from the poles move toward the equator. Warm air masses move toward the poles. These air masses are driven away from their source regions by the global winds. In the Northern Hemisphere the cold and warm air masses generally meet between 30° and 45° latitude. A more or less continuous front forms here, almost completely circling the earth. This front, where warm air from near the equator meets cold air from the poles, is called the **polar front**. Parts of the polar front may move to the north, and other parts move to the south. Notice in Figure 19-7 how the polar front resembles a wave across the earth.

Stormy areas often develop along the polar front. One kind of storm that forms is called a wave cyclone, or low. A wave cyclone involves the counterclockwise motion of air around an area of low pressure. Figure 19-8 shows how this storm develops. A counterclockwise motion of air is part of the early development of a wave cyclone.

As a wave cyclone forms, the polar front begins to fold. Notice in Figure 19-8 how the cold air pushes southward, producing a cold front. At the same time, the warm air pushes northward, producing a warm front. As you can see, the cold front moves faster than the warm front. Warm moist air is forced over the cold air mass, and many clouds form. A developing wave cyclone moves from west to east along the front.

After completing this section, you will be able to
- **describe** the polar front.
- **diagram** how fronts can form a wave cyclone.
- **describe** the characteristics of a wave cyclone.

The key terms in this section are
occluded front
polar front

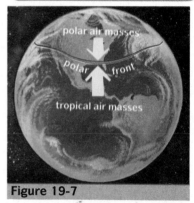

Figure 19-7

The polar front forms where tropical air meets polar air.

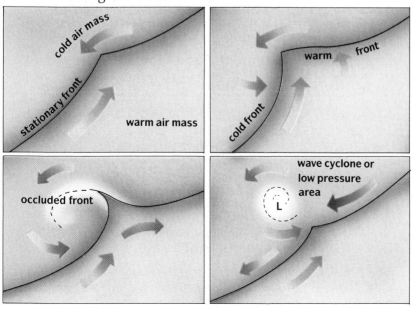

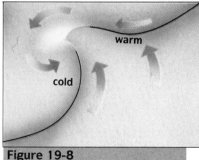

Figure 19-8

The formation of a wave cyclone.

Precipitation forms ahead of the warm front. A narrow zone of showers develops along the cold front. A developing wave cyclone moves from west to east along the front.

Wave cyclones can be very stormy when there is a large difference in temperature between the air masses at the polar front. As the wave cyclone moves, warm moist air continues to be lifted and the clouds continue to grow thicker. When the water condenses to form the clouds, heat is released. This causes air to become less dense. The lighter the air in the storm becomes, the faster the air entering the storm moves. In this way a wave cyclone can produce strong winds as well as heavy rains.

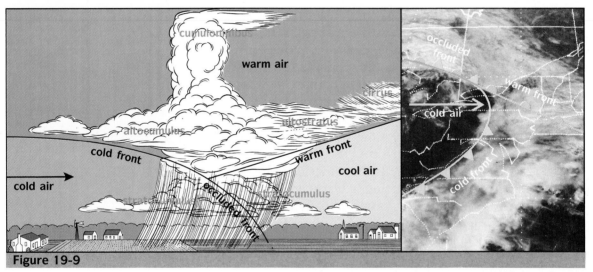

Figure 19-9

An occluded front and a satellite photograph of an occluded front.

A wave cyclone is fully developed when the cold front becomes occluded. An **occluded** (uh KLOO dihd) **front** forms when the cold front catches up to the warm front, as shown in Figure 19-9. The mass of warm air between the fronts is lifted completely off the ground. Occluded fronts signify the dying stage of a wave cyclone. In time the wave cyclone becomes surrounded by cold air and is cut off from the warm moist air that supplied its energy. About one week after developing the storm dries out.

REVIEW

1. What is the polar front?
2. Diagram how a wave cyclone forms.
3. Describe the characteristics of a wave cyclone.

CHALLENGE Why are most heavy snowfalls in New England formed by wave cyclones that pass to the south of New England?

19-4 THUNDERSTORMS

Another weather system that can form along fronts is a thunderstorm. Meteorologists have estimated that at any moment, roughly 2000 thunderstorms are taking place on the earth. In the United States alone, more than 120 people a year are killed by lightning from thunderstorms. Each year, hundreds of millions of dollars in property damage is caused by thunderstorms. What is this storm that affects the earth so much?

A **thunderstorm** is a violent weather system that produces tall cumulus clouds, strong winds, heavy rain, lightning, thunder, and, sometimes, hail and tornadoes. As you have learned, thunderstorms can form along cold fronts. At a cold front, warm air is pushed up by an advancing cold air mass. When the temperature of the rising warm air reaches its dew point, water condenses from the air, forming clouds and releasing heat into the atmosphere. This heat reduces the density of the air and causes the air to be pushed even higher. As more warm air is forced

Figure 19-10

A cumulonimbus cloud is also called a thunderhead.

upward, more water vapor condenses and more heat is released. As shown in Figure 19-10, a large cloud begins to build into the sky. As the storm moves, the growth of the cloud and the speed of the winds increase and a cumulonimbus cloud, or thunderhead, is formed.

Cumulonimbus clouds can reach a height of more than 12 km. At that altitude the high winds of the upper troposphere push the top of the cloud forward, forming the anvil-shaped top you see in Figure 19-10. When the

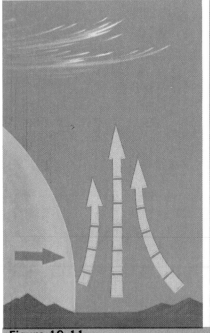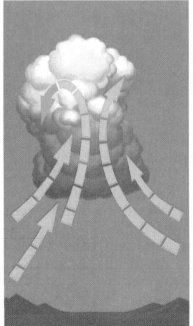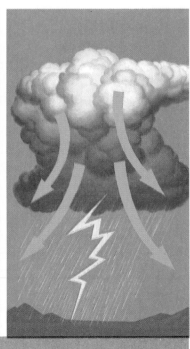

Figure 19-11

A thunderstorm begins as warm air is lifted by cooler air. As the temperature of the air reaches the dew point, a thunderhead forms. Precipitation indicates the mature stage of a thunderstorm.

storm matures, the cloud is filled with raindrops, snowflakes, and, possibly, hail.

The start of precipitation begins a new phase in the life of a thunderstorm. As shown in Figure 19-11, the falling precipitation creates downdrafts. Storm cells form within the cloud. A storm cell is a system of rising and falling air within a storm. A thunderstorm generally contains more than one storm cell. A storm cell lasts about 20 minutes, but may be replaced by others.

Figure 19-12

A squall line can form ahead of a rapidly moving cold front.

The thunderstorm is now in its mature stage. Thunder and lightning accompany the heavy rains. If the updrafts are strong enough, hail may form. The downdrafts in the storm cells, however, slow the movement of air up through the cloud. As the upward movement of air slows down, the air starts to dry. The storm then dies out.

Thunderstorms often form along a squall line. A **squall line** is a line of rapidly rising air that forms ahead of a cold front. A squall line includes clouds and storms produced by the rising air. The squall line may form as much as 130 km ahead of the front and may be many kilometers long. Squall lines are known to produce heavy hail, flash flooding, and tornadoes.

Thunderstorms are very active electrically. Meteorologists have found that there is always a difference in electrical charge between the ground and the atmosphere. Meteorologists disagree as to exactly how the charges in a thunderhead are created. However, it is clear that the top of a thunderhead has a positive charge, and its base is part negative and part positive. Look at Figure 19-13. How does the charge of the ground under the cloud differ from the charge at the base of the cloud? The charge on the ground gets stronger as the cloud's charge increases. When the difference between the charges on the base of the cloud and the charges on the ground or on another cloud become large enough, lightning occurs. **Lightning** is a large electrical discharge that occurs between clouds or between a cloud and the earth.

Figure 19-13

Different regions of a thunderhead have different charges. When there is a big difference in charge between cloud regions, or between the cloud and the ground, lightning occurs.

453

The loud crash that accompanies a flash of lightning is called **thunder**. Thunder occurs because the air around a lightning bolt is heated. The temperature of the air may reach between 8000°C and 33,000°C. The rapid expansion of the air caused by this heat creates a sound wave.

Thunderstorms can be very dangerous, and there are certain precautions that you should take. For example, do not stand near a tall object, such as a tree, during a thunderstorm. Lightning tends to strike the tallest object in an area. For this same reason, you should not stand in an open field. The best place to be during a thunderstorm is inside a building and away from exterior walls, windows, and electrical appliances. However, if you are in an open area when a thunderstorm approaches, stay low and move away from any friends you are with. It is also safe to stay inside a closed car. Do not go in or near open water during a thunderstorm because the water can conduct electricity. Do not talk on the telephone during a thunderstorm. People have been killed when a telephone pole was struck and the wires carried the charge to the phone.

REVIEW

1. What is a thunderstorm?
2. Make a sketch to show how a thunderstorm forms.
3. What kind of weather would you expect from a thunderstorm?
4. What causes lightning and thunder?
5. What precautions should you take when a thunderstorm approaches?

CHALLENGE Why would airline pilots want to avoid flying through a thunderhead?

19-5 TORNADOES

The most violent storm on the earth is a tornado. A **tornado** is a small funnel-shaped whirlwind that spins in a counterclockwise direction around an area of very low pressure. Notice the funnel shape in Figure 19-14. Tornadoes occur with thunderstorms and may produce wind speeds greater than 500 km/h. A tornado produces pressures so low that closed buildings explode as it goes by, because air cannot escape from them fast enough. More tornadoes develop in the United States than in any other country in the world. As many as 1000 tornadoes have occurred in the United States in one year.

Meteorologists do not yet fully understand the causes of tornadoes. Tornadoes develop within cumulonimbus clouds. The conditions needed for a tornado to form are a layer of warm moist air with cooler drier air above it. The warm air begins to rise, breaking through the cooler air. How the air begins to rotate and flow up is not understood. One hypothesis is that lightning may help to cause tornadoes by heating air, making it less dense. This low-density air would rise rapidly. Another hypothesis is that extreme differences in temperature between the air on the ground and the air in the upper troposphere are enough to start air rising.

Tornadoes most often form during spring and early summer in the middle section of the country. They travel toward the northeast, cutting a path anywhere from 50 m

After completing this section, you will be able to
- **define** the term *tornado*.
- **describe** the conditions under which tornadoes form.
- **contrast** a waterspout and tornado.
- **list** aspects of tornado safety.

The key terms in this section are
tornado   waterspout

Figure 19-14

More tornadoes form in the United States than in any other country.

ACTIVITY   How is Tornado Alley Determined?

OBJECTIVES
Analyze data on the average annual number of tornadoes, by state.
Draw conclusions about Tornado Alley.

MATERIALS
4 different colored pencils: 1 red, 1 yellow, 1 green, 1 blue

PROCEDURE
A. Trace the map on this page, or obtain one like it from your teacher.
B. Using the data in Table 19-1, copy the average number of tornadoes per year for each state onto the map.
C. Obtain the four different colored pencils. Color in the boxes on the key.
D. Color the states that correspond to the key. For instance, all of the states that have 25 or more tornadoes per year should be colored red.

RESULTS AND CONCLUSIONS
1. Where is Tornado Alley?
2. Which states in Tornado Alley have the greatest number of tornadoes per year?
3. Which state has a high occurrence of tornadoes but is not part of Tornado Alley?
4. The average number of tornadoes per 8000 sq km in Texas is 2.3 per year. The average number of tornadoes per 8000 sq km in Oklahoma is 3.9 per year. Which state has more tornadoes per area, per year?
5. Based on the data from this activity, what conclusions can you draw?

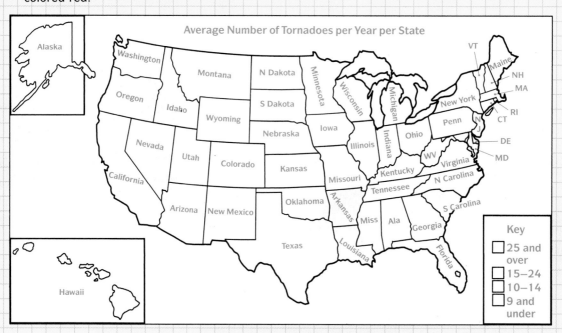

Average Number of Tornadoes per Year per State

Key
☐ 25 and over
☐ 15–24
☐ 10–14
☐ 9 and under

to 1500 m wide. They travel at speeds of from 30 km/h to 60 km/h, sometimes lifting off of the earth for a short time and then returning to it. Tornadoes seldom last more than a few minutes. But a tornado may move dozens of kilometers in its short lifetime.

A tornado that forms over a body of water is called a **waterspout**. A waterspout is shown in Figure 19-15.

Table 19-1 *Average Number of Tornadoes Per Year, Per State*

State		State		State		State	
Alabama	19	Indiana	22.9	Nebraska	34.0	Rhode island	.04
Alaska	0	Iowa	25.5	Nevada	.6	South Carolina	8.9
Arizona	3.8	Kansas	46.6	New Hampshire	2.5	South Dakota	22.6
Arkansas	18.4	Kentucky	7.8	New Jersey	1.6	Tennessee	11.0
California	2.9	Louisiana	18.8	New Mexico	8.5	Texas	124.2
Colorado	14.2	Maine	2.8	New York	3.4	Utah	1.36
Connecticut	1.7	Maryland	2.3	North Carolina	10.3	Vermont	1.0
Delaware	.85	Massachusetts	4.5	North Dakota	14.6	Virginia	5.24
Florida	36.3	Michigan	14.7	Ohio	13.0	Washington	1.0
Georgia	21.1	Minnesota	17.3	Oklahoma	55.3	West Virginia	1.9
Hawaii	.62	Mississippi	21.8	Oregon	.9	Wisconsin	17.3
Idaho	1.3	Missouri	29.5	Pennsylvania	6.6	Wyoming	6.7
Illinois	28.0	Montana	3.5				

What makes the waterspout visible as it moves over the surface? They have been known to pick up fish and drop them over land, as if it were raining fish. A waterspout may start over land and then move over water, or it may develop directly over a lake or ocean.

The National Weather Service issues a *tornado watch* for an area when the conditions are right for tornadoes to form. You should listen for weather forecasts and watch the clouds around you. When a *tornado warning* is issued, tornadoes have been seen in your area.

A good place to be when a tornado hits is under a stairway or under a strong table in a basement. If your home does not have a basement, a closet or small room at the center of the first floor is the next safest place to be. Kneel on the floor and cover your head. Most people killed by tornadoes die after being struck on the head by flying objects. In a public building, such as a school or a shopping center, you should move along a corridor in the middle of the first floor or go into a small room on the first floor. Such action will keep you away from the tornado's deadly winds.

Figure 19-15

A waterspout is a tornado that forms over water.

REVIEW

1. What is a tornado?
2. What are the conditions under which tornadoes form?
3. How is a waterspout different from a tornado?
4. How can you protect yourself when a tornado is approaching?

CHALLENGE Tornadoes form within cumulonimbus clouds. But not all thunderstorms produce tornadoes. Scientists have found that winds in the environment play a role in producing tornadoes. How might winds affect a thunderhead to produce a tornado?

19-6 HURRICANES

A **hurricane** is a large tropical cyclone that develops in the doldrums, usually during the late summer. Look at Figure 19-16. Over what type of surface do hurricanes form? These tropical cyclones go by other names in different parts of the world. In the western Pacific Ocean, they are called *typhoons*. In India they are called *cyclones*.

In some ways a hurricane is similar to a wave cyclone. For example, wave cyclones and hurricanes are both low-pressure systems that receive their energy from water vapor in the air. These storms differ, however, in that hurricanes do not form along fronts. Hurricanes form in areas where air is normally gently rising. They also cover a smaller area than wave cyclones, but are more powerful storms. Hurricanes, like other cyclones, form when warm air is forced upward through the atmosphere.

Figure 19-16

Hurricanes form over oceans in the doldrums.

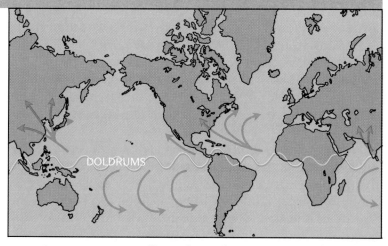

Scientists are still studying hurricanes to determine how they start. However, scientists have learned many things about these storms. They know that 70 percent of the hurricanes in the Atlantic Ocean form along the west coast of Africa during the late summer. At this time of the year, the ocean temperature is near 27°C and the air over the ocean is very warm and wet. Warm wet air is very light. Therefore, denser air from surrounding areas pushes in and lifts the light air upward. As the denser air moves in across the water, the Coriolis effect causes it to spin counterclockwise, as shown in Figure 19-17. This formation, where light air is lifted by denser air that spins counterclockwise toward the storm's center, is the beginning of a hurricane.

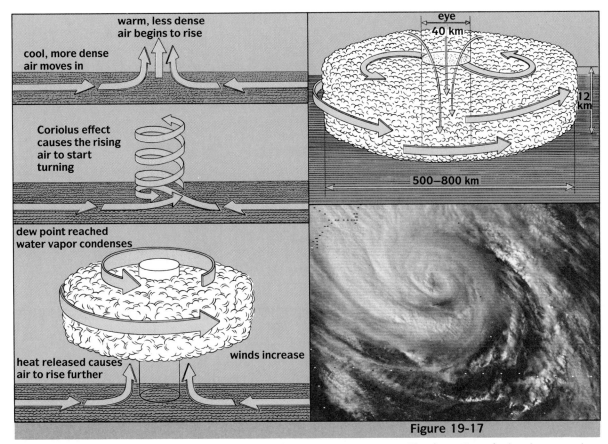

Figure 19-17

The formation of a hurricane, and a satellite photograph of Hurricane Gloria.

Water is the fuel that causes a hurricane to increase in speed and power. As shown in Figure 19-17, the air is pushed upward through the atmosphere. Its temperature falls and at some point reaches the dew point. When water vapor condenses from the rising air, heat is released and causes the air to become even less dense. As the air in the center becomes lighter, the surrounding air moves in faster. The faster the air moves over the ocean, the more water vapor it picks up. Finally, more water vapor in the air releases more heat into the atmosphere, increasing the winds further. The longer the storm stays over water, the more this cycle continues and the stronger the storm becomes. This cyclone becomes a tropical storm when its winds reach 63 km/h. It becomes a hurricane when its winds reach 119 km/h.

Hurricanes can reach a diameter of 800 km, and hurricane clouds may rise to 12 km above sea level. At the center of a hurricane is an area of calm called the eye. The eye is usually about 40 km in diameter. In the eye the air is slowly sinking and the sky is clear. As air in a hurricane

One year, a violent storm hit a recreation area a little north of Denver, Colorado. The storm was over in just 15 minutes, but it killed 139 people. Such storms develop quickly and move too fast to allow accurate predictions to be made about them.

But recently, a new approach has been developed to help predict how violent, short-lived storms will behave. The approach includes an updated radar system. This computer-controlled radar system collects data on such characteristics of a storm as wind speed, wind direction, and precipitation. It will detect the circular wind patterns that produce tornadoes.

In addition, a computer system is being developed to put together many kinds of data on such storms. The data include satellite images, cloud cover, locations of lightning strikes, and temperature and moisture readings at different altitudes. All of the data can be updated every five minutes. Such data may allow meteorologists to precisely pinpoint the locations and movement of small storms. For example, it may become possible to predict that a certain storm will hit the southwest area of a city in 30 minutes. Early warnings can save property — and lives.

moves toward the eye, the air accelerates. The fastest winds in a hurricane are found in a ring around the eye.

A hurricane is the earth's most powerful storm. Winds can exceed 300 km/h, and heavy rains, sometimes accompanied by lightning, thunder, and, even tornadoes, can cause great destruction. Even more dangerous than the heavy rain and wind, however, is the tidal surge that can occur with a hurricane. The tidal surge is a bulge in the ocean under the light air of the storm. The bulge is topped by large wind-driven waves. This surge may raise the level of the ocean by 8 m. Nine out of ten people who have lost their lives during hurricanes in this century have drowned in these stormy surges.

If you live along an ocean, special care must be taken as a hurricane approaches. Objects in the yard should be tied down so that winds will not blow them around. Boards can be placed over windows so that the windows will not be broken by flying objects. It is important to remember that most deaths caused by hurricanes are caused by water, not wind. Once your home and yard are secured, it is very important that you go inland until the storm is over.

Even if you live far from the ocean and the tidal surge will not reach your home, there are still precautions that you should take if a hurricane approaches. Candles or portable lights are helpful if your home loses electricity. A battery-powered radio can keep you in touch with the progress of the storm and where to find help.

REVIEW

1. What is a hurricane?
2. Describe how a hurricane forms.
3. How is a hurricane similar to a wave cyclone?
4. What should you do if a hurricane is forecast for your area?

CHALLENGE How will a hurricane change as it passes over a large island?

CHAPTER SUMMARY

The main ideas in this chapter are listed below. Read these statements before you answer the Chapter Review questions.

- Large bodies of air moving through the atmosphere are called air masses. (19-1)

- When air masses remain stationary, they take on the characteristics of the region. The region where an air mass forms is called the source region. (19-1)

- Air masses are classified by describing their source regions. (19-1)

- The boundary between two air masses is called a front. (19-2)

- Fronts are classified by determining whether the advancing air is warmer or colder than the retreating air. (19-2)

- Three types of fronts are: a warm, a cold, and a stationary front. (19-2)

- Different cloud types are associated with different fronts. (19-2)

- A polar front forms when air from the equator meets air from the poles. (19-3)

- The counterclockwise motion of air around a low-pressure area can cause a cyclone, or low. (19-3)

- An occluded front forms when a cold front catches up to a warm front. (19-3)

- A violent weather system associated with tall cumulus clouds, lightning, and thunder is called a thunderstorm. (19-4)

- Thunderstorms form where a cold front moves in on a warm front. (19-4)

- A line of rising air that forms ahead of a fast-moving cold front is a squall line. (19-4)

- Lightning is an electrical discharge. Thunder is the sound with lightning. (19-4)

- A tornado is a small funnel-shaped whirlwind that spins counterclockwise around a very low pressure area. (19-5)

- A tornado that forms over water is called a waterspout. (19-5)

- A tornado watch means conditions are right for tornadoes. A tornado warning means a tornado has been sighted. (19-5)

- A cyclone that develops in the doldrums, in late summer, is a hurricane. (19-6)

The key terms in this chapter are listed below. Use each term in a sentence that shows the meaning of the term.

air mass	front	occluded front	thunderstorm
cold air mass	hurricane	polar front	tornado
cold front	lightning	squall line	warm air mass
continental polar air mass	maritime polar air mass	stationary front	warm front
continental tropical air mass	maritime tropical air mass	thunder	waterspout

Chapter Review

VOCABULARY

Use the key terms from this chapter to complete the following sentences correctly.

1. An air mass that forms over warm oceans is a _____ .
2. The boundary between two air masses is called a/an _____.
3. A/An _____ forms when a cold air mass pushes a warm air mass away.
4. A front that nearly circles the earth and that is produced as warm air masses from the equator meet cold air masses from the poles is called the _____.
5. When a cold front catches a warm front, lifting the air mass between them upward, a/an _____ forms.
6. A large tropical cyclone, with winds faster than 120 km/h, that forms in the doldrums and over the ocean, is a/an _____.
7. A/An _____ is a violent weather system formed when warm air is pushed high into the atmosphere.
8. A series of thunderstorms that form ahead of a cold front is called a/an _____.
9. A small violent whirlwind formed in thunderstorms is a/an _____.
10. _____ is an electrical discharge that occurs when large differences in charge develop between a cloud and the earth.

CONCEPTS

1. Describe the characteristics of an air mass. (19-1)
2. What is the relationship between an air mass and a source region? (19-1)
3. Name the kinds of air masses. (19-1)
4. An air mass is classified by describing what two factors? (19-1)
5. What kind of weather would a maritime tropical air mass bring? (19-1)
6. What do meteorologists consider when they predict in which direction an air mass will move? (19-1)
7. Compare and contrast what happens when a warm front approaches and when a cold front approaches. (19-2)
8. Explain why a stationary front is so slow to move and what kind of weather to expect when such a front forms. (19-2)
9. Explain how a cold front, a warm front, and a stationary front form. (19-2)
10. With which front are high, local clouds associated? (19-2)
11. What weather would you expect if you saw a line of tall dark cumulus clouds approaching? (19-2)

12. What type of weather would cirrus clouds indicate? (19-2)

13. Describe where and how a polar front forms. (19-3)

14. Where and how do wave cyclones develop, and what conditions will cause a wave cyclone to be stronger than usual? (19-3)

15. What happens when a warm front catches a cold front? (19-3)

16. What is a thunderstorm and list the steps in its formation. (19-4)

17. Describe what happens to a thunderstorm after precipitation begins. (19-4)

18. Under what conditions does lightning occur? (19-4)

19. You are playing baseball, and a fast-moving, severe thunderstorm is approaching. Assuming that there is no shelter, what would you do? (19-4) What would you do if you saw a tornado? (19-5)

20. What is a tornado, and under what conditions do tornadoes form? (19-5)

21. Which is more dangerous, a tornado or a waterspout? (19-5)

22. Describe a hurricane and how it develops. (19-6)

23. In what ways is a hurricane similar to a wave cyclone? (19-6)

24. List the safety precautions you should take if a hurricane is approaching. (19-6)

APPLICATION/ CRITICAL THINKING

1. Describe what weather conditions would occur as a front approaches an area and as it leaves.

2. List at least 5 factors that meteorologists study and analyze to determine the change in weather.

3. Why do highs tend to have clear weather and lows tend to be cloudy?

EXTENSION

1. Set up your own weather station and, using what you learned, try to predict the weather. You will need a thermometer, anemometer, weather vane, and barometer.

2. Collect a series of weather maps from a newspaper for one week. Make observations about how the fronts are moving and the weather that you had.

READINGS

Funk, Ben. "Hurricane," *National Geographic*, September 1980, p. 346.

Jones, A. "Tracking a Killer Tornado." *Readers Digest*, November 1983, p. 139.

FORECASTING WEATHER

If you have plans for the next few days, how might the weather affect them? Your plans, and even what you decide to wear, may be determined, in part, by weather forecasts. At times, you have probably looked at the sky and made your own forecasts.

- *What forecast would you make based on the photograph on the opposite page?*
- *How do meteorologists make forecasts?*

20-1 MAKING LOCAL FORECASTS

As you have learned, day-to-day weather changes are caused by the passing of air masses, fronts, highs, and lows. You know that air-mass weather tends to be fair weather. You also know that fronts and lows are often marked by clouds and precipitation. Finally, weather systems, in general, move across North America from west to east. If you learn to recognize the signs that come with air masses, fronts, and lows, you can learn to predict the weather. A prediction about future weather is called a **forecast**.

One condition of the atmosphere that is measured when forecasting weather is air pressure. As you know, air pressure is measured with a barometer. Air masses are regions of high air pressure; fronts and lows are regions of low pressure. Therefore, if air pressure is rising, an air mass is moving over you, and the weather should be improving. If air pressure is falling, however, a front or a low is approaching. Falling pressure indicates a change in weather. Fronts separate different air masses, and fronts and lows often bring precipitation.

Another sign to consider when forecasting is the direction of the wind, as shown by a wind vane. You have learned that air in an air mass circulates outward from the center of the mass, in a clockwise direction. The winds in

> After completing this section, you will be able to
>
> - **predict** the weather, based on wind direction and changes in air pressure.
> - **determine** wind conditions, using the Beaufort wind scale.
> - **identify** conditions that make local forecasting more difficult.
>
> The key term in this section is **forecast**

fore (front)

465

566

FORECASTING WEATHER

Figure 20-1

From which direction will the winds approach as this air mass nears Washington, D.C.?

a low circulate inward, toward the center of the mass, in a counterclockwise direction. The direction of the wind around you indicates what part of the air mass or low is passing over you.

Figure 20-1 shows an air mass over the eastern United States. Imagine that the air mass is traveling directly east across the country. As the air mass from the west moves over New England, the pressure over New England begins to rise, and winds approach from the northwest. The same air mass would also pass over Georgia, and there too the pressure rises. But over Georgia the winds would approach from the northeast. By noting the changing pressure and wind direction, you can determine what part of the air mass or low is over you and then forecast the weather to follow.

Table 20-1 lists the weather indicated by different combinations of wind direction and air pressure in eastern North America. What type of weather is expected if winds are southwest to northwest and the barometer is 76.4 and rising rapidly?

Another important sign of future weather is the cloud cover. For example, wind from the southeast and falling air pressure indicate that a front is approaching. Figure 20-2 shows two different fronts approaching. If cirrus clouds are seen to the west, followed by cirrostratus and altostratus clouds, a warm front is approaching. Although the

Figure 20-2

Cirrus clouds and cirrostratus clouds (*top*) indicate an approaching warm front. Cirrus clouds followed by cumulonimbus clouds (*bottom*) indicate an approaching cold front.

466

Table 20-1 *Forecasting Weather*

Direction of Wind	Barometer Reading (cm of Mercury)	Weather Indicated
Variable	76.7 or above, steady	• Continued fair, with little temperature change.
SW to NW	76.7 or above, falling slowly	• Fair, slowly rising temperature for 2 days
SW to NW	76.2 to 76.7, steady	• Fair, with slight temperature changes for 1 to 2 days.
SW to NW	76.2 to 76.7, rising rapidly	• Fair and cooler, followed within 2 days by warmer weather and rain.
S to SE	76.2 to 76.7, falling slowly	• Rain within 24 hours and warmer.
S to SE	76.2 to 76.7, falling rapidly	• Wind increasing in force, rain within 12 to 24 hours, and warmer.
SE to NE	76.2 to 76.7, falling slowly	• Rain within 12 to 18 hours.
SE to NE	76.2 to 76.7, falling rapidly	• Increasing wind, rain within 12 hours.
SE to NE	76.2 or below, falling slowly	• Rain within 18 hours, continuing 1 to 2 days.
SE to NE	76.2 or below, falling rapidly	• Rain, with high wind, followed within 36 hours by clearing and, in winter, colder weather.
E to NE	76.2 or above, falling slowly	• In summer, with light wind, rain may not fall for several days. In winter, rain within 24 hours.
E to NE	76.2 or above, falling rapidly	• In summer, rain within 12 to 24 hours. In winter, rain or snow with increasing wind.
S to SW	76.2 or below, rising slowly	• Clearing within a few hours, fair and cooler for several days.
S to E	75.6 or below, falling rapidly	• Severe storm approaching, followed within 24 hours by clearing and, in winter, colder weather.
E to N	75.6 or below, falling rapidly	• Severe northeast wind and, in winter, heavy snow, followed by a cold wave.
Swinging to west	75.6 or below, rising rapidly	• Clearing and colder.

rain from the front is still far away, when it arrives it may rain for a long time. The clouds associated with a warm front extend many kilometers ahead of the front. If to the west cirrus clouds are seen, but they are followed by a tall, dark wall of cumulonimbus clouds, a cold front is approaching. This storm will arrive soon and could be violent. A storm resulting from a cold front usually does not last long, however. Fair weather will quickly follow as the front passes.

The direction from which the wind blows is useful in forecasting weather. One way to judge the strength of a weather system is to measure its wind speed. Around 1805, Admiral Francis Beaufort of the British navy developed a way to estimate wind speed without using an anemometer. This system, changed for use on land, is shown in Table 20-2. As you can see, the speed of the wind is estimated based on the wind's effects. For example, if wind is felt on the face and leaves rustle, the wind speed is 6-11 km/h. The wind is described as a light breeze. If whole trees moved in the wind and it was hard to walk, how fast would the wind be? What would the wind description be for this wind speed?

When using wind speed to predict weather, local geography must be considered. Mountains and large bodies of water can result in local winds. Such winds may differ in direction from winds resulting from large air masses. Large bodies of water add moisture to the air. Such factors make forecasting more difficult.

Table 20-2 *The Beaufort Scale of Wind Strength*

Description of Wind	Wind Speed (km/h)	Effect of Wind
Calm (0)	Less than 1	Air is still; smoke rises vertically.
Light air (1)	1 to 5	Wind direction shown by smoke drift; weather vanes inactive.
Light breeze (2)	6 to 11	Wind felt on face; leaves rustle.
Gentle breeze (3)	12 to 19	Leaves and small twigs move constantly; wind extends light flags.
Moderate breeze (4)	20 to 28	Wind raises dust and loose paper; moves twigs and thin branches.
Fresh breeze (5)	29 to 38	Small trees in leaf begin to sway.
Strong breeze (6)	39 to 49	Large branches move; telephone wires whistle; umbrellas difficult to control.
Moderate gale (7)	50 to 61	Whole trees sway; hard to walk.
Fresh gale (8)	62 to 74	Twigs break from trees; walking against wind very difficult.
Strong gale (9)	75 to 88	Slight damage to buildings.
Whole gale (10)	89 to 102	Trees uprooted; considerable damage to buildings.
Storm (11)	103 to 117	Widespread damage; rarely occurs inland.
Hurricane (12)	More than 117	Extreme destruction.

REVIEW

1. Suppose the winds are south to east and the barometer reading is 75.5 and falling rapidly. Predict the weather.
2. Using the Beaufort scale, estimate the wind speed outside.
3. Why are local conditions sometimes poor indicators of approaching weather?

CHALLENGE What is the scientific basis for the following saying: "Dark clouds in the west, stay indoors and get some rest"?

20-2 WEATHER MAPS AND FORECASTS

After completing this section, you will be able to

- **list** methods by which data is collected for weather forecasts.
- **describe** how a weather map is made.
- **interpret** a weather map.

The key terms in this section are

isobars · satellite · isotherms · weather maps

To plan a trip, information about possible routes, where to stay, and what to see is gathered. Before the National Weather Service (NWS) makes a forecast, it collects and organizes weather data from around the world. The NWS gathers data from almost 10,000 stations worldwide, nearly 2000 of them in the United States alone. From the information gathered, weather maps are produced. **Weather maps** are maps that provide an overall picture of weather activity across the earth. These maps help meteorologists as they study weather patterns and forecast the weather.

Weather maps are prepared from data collected around the country. Eight times a day, weather stations across the United States report local conditions to the NWS. These

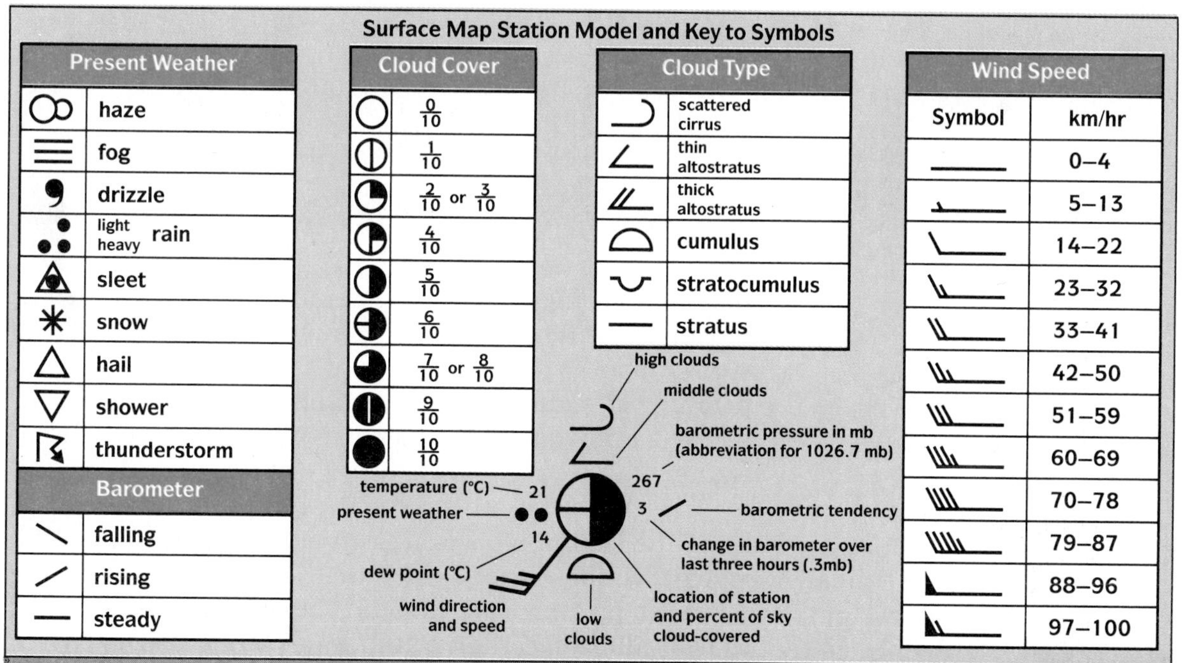

Figure 20-3

A station model consists of symbols that depict weather data.

conditions, measured from the ground, include temperature, air pressure, and the change in air pressure during the last three hours. Wind speed, wind direction, dew point, visibility, cloud cover, cloud types, and precipitation, if any, are also reported. These data are put together to produce a special map called a *surface map*.

An NWS surface map consists of many stations represented by groups of symbols. Each group of symbols is called a *station model* and describes the data collected at

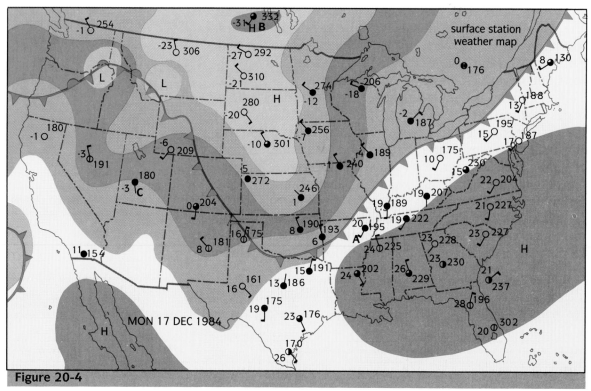

Figure 20-4

A National Weather Service surface map.

that station. Figure 20-3 shows an example of a station model and illustrates some common symbols. A NWS surface map is shown in Figure 20-4. What is the temperature at station *A*? How much of the sky is cloud-covered at station *B*? What does the barometer read at station *C*?

Several steps are taken to produce a surface map. First, the station models are printed on the map. Second, **isobars** (ī suh bahrz), lines that connect places having equal air pressure, are drawn. The air pressure, in units called millibars, is shown at the ends of the isobars. When the isobars are finished, some areas on the map may be completely circled by them. The circled areas that represent the lowest pressure are labeled *lows*. The smaller circled areas that represent the highest pressure are labeled *highs*. Occasionally, **isotherms** (ī suh thermz), lines that connect places having equal temperature, are also marked. Surface maps—including station models, isobars, and isotherms—are drawn today by computers. Finally, meteorologists analyze the map, mark the lines for the fronts, and shade the areas of precipitation. With a surface map, simple weather forecasts can be made.

iso- (equal)
baros (weight)

-therm (heat)

Weather forecasts can be improved by using a series of maps, since weather systems tend to move in straight lines. Figure 20-5 shows a way of forecasting weather by using a number of maps. Notice that both the warm front and the cold front are moving west to east across the country. When each of the maps is traced onto a single map, as shown, the pattern of movement is seen. This pattern of movement shows both the direction and the speed of the weather system. A forecast would be based on the predicted positions of the system. What would your forecast be for the state of Iowa on Thursday?

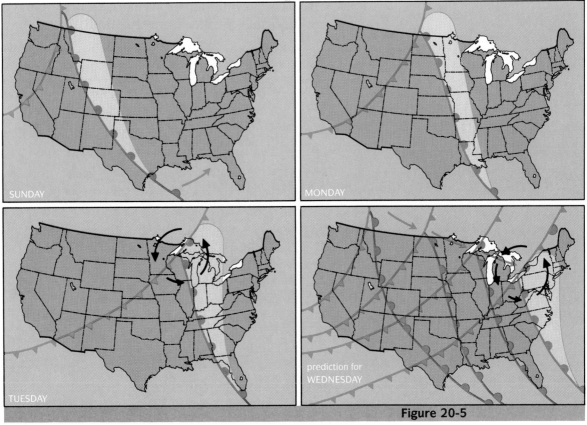

Figure 20-5

The movements of weather systems can be followed on a series of weather maps.

Even when a number of maps are used, a forecast is only accurate for about 12 hours. Beyond this time, other factors affect the weather pattern. For example, new air masses entering from north or south may change the movement of the air mass you are watching. Or a large air mass may stall, stopping everything behind it. Mountains can also change the paths of weather systems. Winds in the upper troposphere can cause a low to move north or south. To improve forecasts, more information is needed.

It is very important to know about weather patterns where people don't live as well as where people do live. A worldwide network for weather observation has been established to fill in the gaps. For example, spaced across the oceans are buoys that radio readings of the weather conditions around them. Ships, which depend on weather forecasts for their safety, also report conditions as they travel. Satellites (SAT uh līts), through the television and infrared cameras they carry, keep a constant watch on the surface of the earth. A **satellite** is an object placed in an orbit around a larger object. Figure 20-6 (*left*) is a satellite photograph of a section of the earth's surface. Notice the cloud patterns in the photograph. What areas of the United States are likely to experience precipitation?

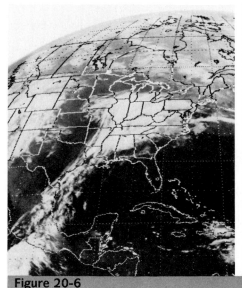
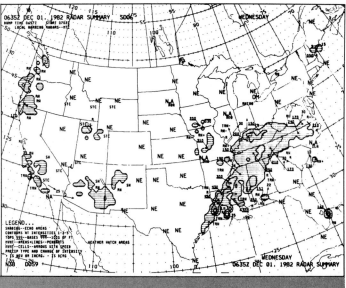

Figure 20-6

A satellite photograph of weather systems and a radar summary of the same systems.

One of the most difficult things to forecast is a small-scale storm, which can develop very quickly. An example is the heavy thunderstorm that can cause tornadoes and flash floods. Radar is used to study such storms. Radar measures the size and the number of rain droplets in the air. Radar waves pass through air unaffected, but they reflect from drops of water. The more drops in the air or the larger the drops in the air, the stronger the signal reflected to the station. Today, radar stations watch the entire United States for precipitation. Figure 20-6 (*right*) shows a radar summary chart of the United States. The shaded areas indicate where precipitation is occurring. Compare the radar summary and the satellite photo.

OBJECTIVE
Predict future weather by using weather maps for several days.

MATERIALS
3 newspaper weather maps, paper, 3 colored pencils, metric ruler

PROCEDURE
A. Save newspaper weather maps for three consecutive days. Today should be the third day. On a blank piece of paper, trace the outline of your country.
B. With a colored pencil, trace the main features (highs, lows, and fronts) of the first day's weather map onto your map outline. With a second color, trace the features of the second day's map onto your map. With a third color, trace the features of the third day's map onto your map.
C. Using a metric ruler, determine how far each low has traveled each day. Estimate the direction each low is traveling, and mark on your map where you expect each will be tomorrow.

D. Repeat step **C** for any highs on your map.
E. Mark the ends of each front and one point near the middle of each front on your map. Repeat step **C** for each of the fronts by following the movement of each marked point.
1. In general, in what direction did the formations move?
2. What, if any, formations occurred? Where did they occur?
3. What formations produced rain?
F. Study the movements of the highs, lows, and fronts for the three-day period.
4. Predict the weather for your area over the next 24 hours.

RESULTS AND CONCLUSIONS
1. How did the weather maps for the three days explain the weather that you experienced? (If it rained, why did it? If it was clear, why was it?)
2. How did your prediction compare with the actual weather?
3. Explain any differences between your prediction and the actual weather.

A newer kind of radar, Doppler radar, measures not only the rain but also the speed and direction of the winds within a storm. The wind patterns that produce a storm cell can be identified before the precipitation starts. Forecasts using Doppler radar are more accurate for predicting when the storms will start. Such forecasts also predict where the storms will strike and their severity.

Long-range forecasts are made based on winds in the upper troposphere and on seasonal averages of temperature and precipitation. The NWS issues 30-day and 90-day forecasts. But the long-term forecasts are very general. A long-term forecast might suggest that the following month will be warmer and drier than usual.

REVIEW

1. Describe some ways that data is collected for forecasts.
2. How is a weather map made?
3. In Figure 20-4, what type of front is approaching *A*? What is the air pressure near *B*? What is the cloud cover over *C*?

CHALLENGE   Local weather is likely to change more frequently in winter than in summer. Why is this so?

20-3 CLIMATE

There can be great differences in weather from day to day and season to season. Yet the records show that average seasonal patterns repeat themselves year after year. These repeating patterns make up the climate of a region. **Climate** is an average of the weather conditions in a region over a long period of time.

The two main conditions that determine climate are temperature and precipitation. The climate of a region is described by the averages, totals, and extremes of these conditions. For example, in a desert there is less than 25 cm of rain a year. Deserts have large daily changes in temperature. They warm quickly during the day and cool quickly during the night. How would you describe the climate of a tropical rain forest?

One important factor that influences climate is latitude. Figure 20-7 shows light rays from the sun hitting the surface of the earth. Notice that the light rays strike near the earth's equator very directly. During winter in

Figure 20-7

The amount of energy that the earth's surface receives varies with the angle at which sunlight strikes the surface.

the Northern Hemisphere, the light rays strike at an angle. Light rays striking the earth at an angle are spread out, covering a larger area than light rays striking directly. The earth's surface receives less energy when the rays are spread out. At the equator, where sunlight strikes more directly and is therefore more concentrated, the temperature is warm and varies little during the year. In places where sunlight is less direct and therefore less concentrated, the average temperature is cooler.

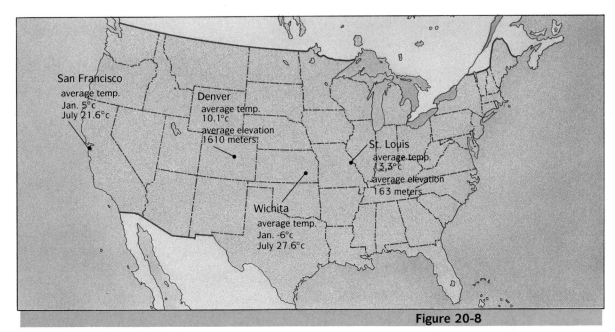

San Francisco
average temp.
Jan. 5°c
July 21.6°c

Denver
average temp.
10.1°c
average elevation
1610 meters

St. Louis
average temp.
13.3°c
average elevation
163 meters

Wichita
average temp.
Jan. -6°c
July 27.6°c

Figure 20-8

Nearness to large bodies of water and to mountains affects local weather patterns.

The tilt of the earth is partly responsible for seasonal changes in temperature. When a hemisphere is leaning toward the sun, the hemisphere is having summer. When it is leaning away from the sun, the hemisphere is having winter. Generally, climates are warmest near the equator and coolest near the poles.

Another factor that influences the climate of an area is altitude. As you know, the higher one travels into the troposphere, the colder the temperature is. Denver, Colorado, is sometimes called the mile-high city, because its altitude is 1610 m, or about one mile. The average yearly temperature in Denver is 10.1°C. Notice in Figure 20-8 that St. Louis, Missouri, is at about the same latitude as Denver, but its altitude is only 163 m. The yearly average temperature in St. Louis is 13.3°C. This difference in temperature is partially caused by the difference in altitude. The tops of many mountains are snow-covered year-round because their temperatures rarely rise above freezing.

Large bodies of water have two important effects on climate. First, as you know, air over a body of water picks up moisture. The climates of regions around large bodies of water tend to be more humid and have more precipitation. Second, water does not change temperature as quickly as does land. During the summer, the water heats more slowly than the land. During the winter, it cools more slowly than the land. The slowly changing water temperature cools the air on warm summer days and warms the air on cold winter days. The result is that air temperatures vary less near oceans and large lakes than in large inland areas. For example, in San Francisco, California, the normal low for January is 5°C, and the normal high for July is 21.6°C. In Wichita, Kansas, at about the same latitude, the normal January low is −6°C, and the normal July high is 27.6°C. What accounts for San Francisco's smaller variation in temperature?

Climate can also be influenced by the shape of the land. As an air mass moves up a mountain, the temperature of the air falls, very often to the dew point. When this happens, water vapor is released from the air. What happens to the air when it moves down the other side of the mountain, as shown in Figure 20-9? By the time the air has moved down the other side of the mountain, much of its water has been released. Therefore, the side of a mountain from which air approaches receives more precipitation than the opposite side. Winds blow over the Rocky Mountains from west to east. Which side of the Rocky Mountains is likely to be drier?

Figure 20-9

Air loses moisture as it moves over mountains.

REVIEW

1. What is climate?
2. What conditions determine the climate of a region?
3. Compare the influence of latitude with the influence of altitude on climate.
4. How do mountains affect climate?

CHALLENGE What, do you think, caused the "pea-soup" fogs that London, England, became famous for?

20-4 CLIMATE ZONES

Meteorologists have divided the earth into three major climate zones. These zones—tropical, temperate, and polar—are defined by their temperature ranges. Notice in Figure 20-10 that each zone is found both north and south of the equator. Although lines are drawn on maps to mark the boundaries of these zones, on the earth there are no definite boundaries. One climate blends into another.

The average yearly temperatures determine the climate zone. A **tropical climate** is found where the average temperature during the year stays above 18°C. The tropical climate zone is found between latitudes 30°N and 30°S. There the earth receives the most direct sunlight and the largest amount of heat.

A **polar climate** is found where the average temperature stays below 10°C during the year. The polar climate zones are found between the poles and latitudes 60°N and 60°S. In polar regions, sunlight hits the surface at an angle much of the time. For this reason, the land and air at the poles do not warm as much as they do at the equator.

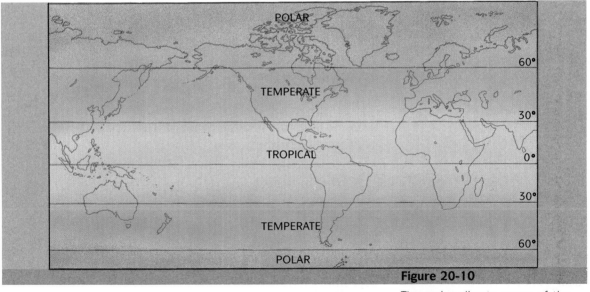

Figure 20-10

The major climate zones of the earth.

Between the regions of tropical climates and polar climates is a region where warm air meets cold air. The climate in this region is called a temperate climate. A **temperate climate** is found where the average summer temperature is above 18°C and the average winter temperature is below 10°C. The temperate climate zones are found both north and south of the equator.

Figure 20-11

The moisture zones of the earth.

wet and dry zones move south after June 21

wet and dry zones move north after December 21

dry zone

wet zone

SCIENCE PUZZLER

At times, the earth experiences ice ages. Glaciers cover much of the surface. Many scientists think that at least two factors play a role in causing ice ages: (1) The earth's orbit slowly changes from nearly circular to very elliptical, and back again; (2) The tilt of the earth's axis slowly changes from 22° to 25° and back again. How could these factors play a role in causing ice ages?

Temperature is an important factor in determining climate. But it is not the only one. As you have learned, precipitation is also important. For example, Houston, Texas, and Cairo, Egypt, have nearly the same temperature during the year. But their climates differ because Houston receives more rainfall. Just as there are zones defined by temperature, there are also zones defined by moisture. These zones are related to distance from the equator. Figure 20-11 shows the moisture zones.

These moisture zones move north and south with the seasons. During spring in the Northern Hemisphere, the zones move to the north. After summer starts, the zones begin slowly to move south until winter begins in the Northern Hemisphere. Then they again move back. Figure 20-11 shows these movements. Is the southeastern United States likely to receive more rain in the summer or in the winter?

You have learned that some regions of the earth are cold, some regions warm, some wet, and some dry. With this information you can begin to classify and name the climates of the earth. For example, tropical rain forests, such as those found in Hawaii, generally occur near the equator. There the temperature is always warm, and precipitation falls nearly every day. The total precipitation amounts to more than 150 cm per year. The name *tropical rain forest* describes the conditions of temperature and precipitation for the area. Many names for climatic regions are derived in this way.

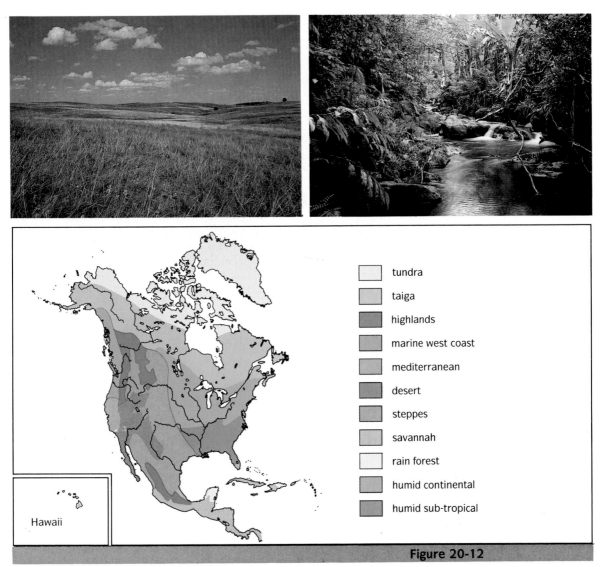

Figure 20-12

The climate regions of North America.

Legend:
- tundra
- taiga
- highlands
- marine west coast
- mediterranean
- desert
- steppes
- savannah
- rain forest
- humid continental
- humid sub-tropical

Hawaii

Figure 20-12 shows the climatic regions of North America. As you can see, North America extends from the tropical zone of Central America to the polar zone of northern Canada. The temperate zone is divided into many climatic regions because of the many variables that influence its weather. As you learned in Section 20-3, these variables include altitude, the land, nearness to bodies of water, and the prevailing movement of air masses. Most of the climatic regions on the earth can be found on North America.

The United States has many examples of temperate climates. The northwestern coast of the country receives moist air from the Pacific Ocean. This region receives 50 cm to 75 cm of precipitation a year, creating what is called

How Do Weather Conditions Compare in Different Climate Zones?

OBJECTIVES

Predict general weather conditions for places in different climate zones.

Compare weather data for places in different climate zones.

MATERIALS

globe or map of the world, almanac or other reference work

PROCEDURE

A. Using a globe or a map, select one city from each of the principal climate zones in North America.

B. Study the globe or map, noting the nearness of each city to large bodies of water, mountain ranges, and so on.

1. Predict the general weather pattern for summer and for winter in each city. Both temperature (warm, cool, cold) and precipitation (wet, dry) should be included in your predictions.

C. Using an almanac or other work, find out the general weather conditions in winter and summer for each city. Record the data.

RESULTS AND CONCLUSIONS

1. How do your general weather predictions compare with actual conditions as described by the data?

2. Referring again to the globe or map, try to explain why your predictions differ from the actual conditions.

---

a marine climate. Air along the California coast is dry in the summer, due to the moving moisture zones. This region, which receives about 25 cm of rain a year, has a Mediterranean climate. As the air passes over the mountains, it releases most of its water. The dry winds that flow down the eastern slopes create the temperate deserts of the Far West. These deserts have a cold winter and a hot summer. The dry air moving across these deserts interacts with moist air masses from the south to release precipitation on the Central Plains. This addition of water forms a climatic region called the temperate steppes (stehps), where grasslands flourish.

The eastern portion of the United States is divided into the humid continental and humid subtropical climates. The humid continental area is influenced more by cold polar air masses. Therefore, this area tends to have less precipitation and colder temperatures, particularly during the winter.

REVIEW

1. Where are the climate zones of the earth?
2. How do the major climate zones differ?
3. How does the humid subtropical climate compare with the humid continental climate?

CHALLENGE If the prevailing westerlies become easterlies, how would the climate of your area change?

20-5 ALTERING CLIMATE

There is no easy way to change the weather. But people have been successful in changing climates in very small areas. A climate in a small area is called a **microclimate**. Farmers, for example, may create microclimates to help their plants grow. Greenhouses extend the growing season by creating a warm, moist microclimate for seedlings before the warm weather arrives. Irrigation is used to add extra water to the soil. Rows of trees between the fields and the prevailing local winds form windbreaks that protect the plants and slow the evaporation of water from the soil.

The building of cities has created microclimates that differ from climates of surrounding areas. Very often you hear a meteorologist's weather forecast call for different conditions in a city and in a nearby suburb. These differences occur for many reasons. The concrete and asphalt that are used to build a city collect and store heat better than the fields and forests around the city. The buildings act like large windbreaks. For these reasons, a city is usually warmer than the areas around it.

In a city, precipitation does not soak into soil or sit on the surface and evaporate into the air. Instead, the water is collected in sewers and removed, leaving the city air drier than the air around the city. Smoke, car exhaust, and dust are more likely to be found in air over cities. The particles in such air act as condensation nuclei. The

> *After completing this section, you will be able to*
>
> - **give examples** of microclimates.
> - **explain** how cloud seeding is used to alter weather.
> - **identify** possible drawbacks to altering weather and climate.
>
> *The key terms in this section are*
>   cloud seeding
>   microclimate

micro (small)

SCIENCE & TECHNOLOGY

Africa is in the clutches of an extreme climate change. In 1968, after 10 years of wet weather, a drought began. It is still with Africa, centering on the Sahara Desert's southern border, and eastward across the continent to Ethiopia and Somalia.

Scientists are studying causes of the devastating drought. Some researchers at the National Meteorological Center in Maryland are getting close to an answer. They have found a link between droughts in southeast Africa and El Niños in the Pacific Ocean half a world away! El Niños are major warmings of the surface waters of the ocean. The scientists in Maryland found that in the past 110 years, 22 of 28 El Niños were accompanied by below normal rainfall in southern Africa. Links such as these are one step toward understanding what causes a drought.

481

ACTIVITY   How Do Microclimates Differ?

OBJECTIVES

Identify some microclimates in the vicinity of your school.
Collect data on each microclimate for comparison.

MATERIALS

pencil, paper, psychrometer, thermometer

PROCEDURE

A. Make a table to record temperature and humidity data for 5 days.
B. With your teacher's permission, choose two or three areas around your school to compare. Choose locations that are different. For example, you might choose the center of a ball field, under a shady tree, and alongside a building. Write the names of your locations in your table.

C. Measure the temperature and relative humidity at each location once a day for five days. Your measurements should be taken in the same place in each location each day. Record your results.
 1. What variable should you control to make sure your results are accurate?

RESULTS AND CONCLUSIONS

1. What was the average temperature for each location?
2. What was the average relative humidity for each location?
3. How did the areas that you measured compare?
4. How did the areas that you measured compare with different areas measured by your classmates?
5. How can you explain any differences?

Figure 20-13

Smog is a weather condition typical of cities.

rain that is produced by clouds that form from such nuclei can be acidic and may be causing serious damage to the environment of the entire earth.

People have also tried to alter the weather on a larger scale. In **cloud seeding**, for example, dry crystals are added to a cloud. The dry crystals act as condensation nuclei. Cloud seeding has been used to bring rain to areas that need it. Cloud seeding has also been used to force large storm systems to rain before they are ready and possibly reduce their power. Cloud seeding, however, has not been very effective in producing rain, and some scientists are concerned about its possible drawbacks. First, seeding a storm may make the storm more powerful. Second, scientists do not yet understand what effect the creating of rain in one place has on the climate of another place.

Climate change could result from damage to the ozone layer of the atmosphere. This layer protects living things from the sun's ultraviolet radiation. Some chemicals that people have released into the air have been shown to chemically react with ozone, changing it into new substances. If the ozone layer is being reduced, living things on the earth could develop health problems caused by increased exposure to ultraviolet radiation. A reduction in ozone might also cause the earth's climates to become warmer. Although it is very difficult to study these chemical changes high in the atmosphere, much work is now being done to determine if changes are taking place.

REVIEW

1. What is a microclimate?
2. How can a farmer alter the microclimate of his farmland to produce better food?
3. How is the climate within a city different from the climate around the city?
4. What is cloud seeding?
5. How might people have unknowingly changed the climate of the earth?

CHALLENGE Some years ago the route of a river was altered, shortening it by about 50 percent. The surrounding tropical land became drier, and plant and animal species began dying out. How might the change in the river have caused the altered climate in the area?

CHAPTER SUMMARY

The main ideas in this chapter are listed below. Read these statements before you answer the Chapter Review questions.

- Weather forecasts are based, in part, on changes in air pressure, wind speed and direction, and cloud cover. (20-1)

- Geographic conditions, such as nearness to large bodies of water and to mountains, can affect local weather. (20-1)

- Weather data gathered by weather stations, satellites, and automatic instruments are used to produce weather maps. (20-2)

- Weather maps are used to make long-range forecasts. (20-2)

- Temperature and precipitation are the main conditions that determine a region's climate. (20-3)

- Both latitude and altitude influence a region's climate. Nearness to large bodies of water and to mountains can influence a region's climate. (20-3)

- The three basic climate zones are the polar zone, the temperate zone, and the tropic zone. (20-4)

- Within each climate zone there are a variety of climate regions, based on conditions of temperature and precipitation. (20-4)

- Microclimates include farmed areas, greenhouses, and even cities. (20-5)

- Attempts to alter weather, such as by cloud seeding, have been largely unsuccessful and may have drawbacks. (20-5)

The key terms in this chapter are listed below. Use each term in a sentence that shows the meaning of the term.

climate	isotherms	temperate climate
cloud seeding	microclimate	tropical climate
forecast	polar climate	weather maps
isobars	satellite	

Chapter Review

Use the key terms from this chapter to complete the following sentences correctly.

1. Lines on a weather map that connect places having equal air pressure are called _____ .

2. Maps that provide overall pictures of weather activity across the earth are called _____ .

3. The climate that is found where average summer temperature is above 18°C and average winter temperature is below 10°C is the _____ .

4. A climate in a small area, such as in a greenhouse or in a city, is called a/an _____ .

5. A prediction about future weather is called a/an _____ .

6. Lines on a weather map that connect places having equal temperatures are called _____ .

7. An object placed in orbit around a larger object is called a/an _____ .

8. The climate that is found where the average temperature stays above 18°C all year is the _____ .

9. A technique involving the use of dry crystals to act as condensation nuclei to produce rain is _____ .

10. The climate that is found where the average temperature stays below 10°C all year is the _____ .

CONCEPTS

1. Suppose winds are from the south to southeast and the barometer is 76.4 and falling slowly. Use Table 20-1 to predict the weather. (20-1)

2. Suppose winds are from the south to southwest and the barometer is 76.0 and rising slowly. Use Table 20-1 to predict the weather. (20-1)

3. Suppose you notice that leaves are rustling and you can feel a wind on your face. Use Table 20-2 to estimate the wind speed. (20-1)

4. Suppose you notice that small trees are swaying in the wind. Use Table 20-2 to estimate the wind speed. (20-1)

5. Identify some geographic conditions that complicate the forecasting of local weather. (20-1)

6. List some of the kinds of data that a station model includes. (20-2)

7. What kind of information is included on a weather map? (20-2)

8. How is worldwide data on weather collected other than from weather stations? (20-2)

9. In Figure 20-5, what happens when the cold front meets the warm front on Tuesday? (20-2)

10. How does climate differ from weather? (20-3)

11. What are the two main conditions that determine a region's general climate? (20-3)

12. City *A* is located at latitude 15°N. City *B* is located at latitude 50°N. What general statement about the climate of each city can you make, based on this information? (20-3)

13. Both city *C* and city *D* are located at latitude 40°N. City *C* is at sea level. City *D* is at 2000 km in altitude. How will the difference affect their climates? (20-3)

14. How does nearness to the ocean affect a region's climate? (20-3)

15. Distinguish between the three major climate zones of the earth. (20-4)

16. What is the climate of the temperate steppes? (20-4)

17. Give two examples of microclimates. (20-5)

18. Describe how cloud seeding is used to alter weather. (20-5)

19. How might a reduction in the amount of ozone in the atmosphere affect the earth's climate? (20-5)

APPLICATION/
CRITICAL
THINKING

1. Identify the factors that determine the climate in your area.

2. Identify some ways in which your family controls the microclimate of your home.

3. Some satellites are placed in orbits that allow them to remain over the same place on the earth. What advantages would there be for having a weather satellite in such an orbit?

4. How might the presence of a large inland sea in central Canada affect the climate of North America?

EXTENSION

1. The earth's climate during the Mesozoic Era seems to have been very different from the climate on the earth today. What factors may have produced the climatic conditions of that time?

2. Using outside sources, prepare a map of the climatic regions of a continent other than North America.

3. Using an almanac or other source, look up some long-range weather forecasts. Follow up by checking the accuracy of these forecasts.

READINGS

Mann, C. "El Chichon." *Science Digest*, May 1983, p. 76.

———"The Weather Tamers." *Science Digest*, November 1983, p. 64.

"El Niño: Global Weather Disaster." *National Geographic*, February 1984, p. 144.

Science in Careers

As you know, air pollution can be a problem outdoors and indoors. The air on a busy street may contain dust and gas from car exhausts. And the air in an office building on the same street may contain dust, or gases from a leaky air conditioning system. However, recently it was discovered that some homes contain a different form of air pollution. The homes were found to contain radon gas, a radioactive gas formed inside the earth.

AIR ANALYST

An air analyst is a person who is involved in discovering and analyzing the forms of air pollution. He or she uses a device to take samples of air at different places. In a laboratory the samples are analyzed for pollutants.

The air analyst must know where to sample air. The job requires a high school diploma or junior college certificate. Most air analysts work for private companies. Courses in earth science, chemistry, and biology will benefit persons who are interested in this occupation. ■

Before weather predictions can be made, a vast amount of weather data must be gathered and analyzed. Much of this data is collected by thousands of weather observers around the country and the world.

Weather observers watch the sky, record cloud patterns, and take measurements using weather instruments. The observers send this information to weather stations by telephone and teletype.

Weather observers must have a high school diploma and may need one or two years of training at a trade school or junior college. Good observation and communication skills are helpful. Courses in earth science and geography will also be of benefit. ■

WEATHER OBSERVER

People in Science

One goal of meteorologists is to predict weather and climate accurately. U.S. Navy officer and meteorologist Dr. Florence van Straten has another goal — to control the weather. She has succeeded in developing ways to make rain through cloud seeding.

You may already know something about cloud seeding. Particles of dry ice or silver iodide are sent into cold rain clouds. Sometimes rain results.

Dr. van Straten thought of another way to seed clouds. She knew that clouds contain small

DR. FLORENCE VAN STRATEN, METEOROLOGIST

water droplets. But usually they were too small and light to fall as rain. She decided to seed clouds with small particles of carbon black. Water in the clouds condensed around the particles. Because the carbon is black, the particles absorbed heat and the water around them evaporated. It then condensed onto other water droplets in the cloud. These grew heavy and fell as rain. Dr. van Straten was successful because she used her knowledge of physics, chemistry and meteorology to solve a problem. ■

Issues and Technology

In the time it takes to read this article, over 20 hectares of tropical forest will be cut down. In a year's time that adds up to a deforested area the size of Pennsylvania. And the destruction doesn't show signs of stopping. People who are watching this situation are worried. There are many important reasons for cutting trees. But loss of the tropical forests could have negative effects scientists are just beginning to understand.

The tropical forests are home to two-thirds of the earth's 4.6 million plant and animal species. They contain a great many life forms that are not found anywhere else.

Compare the percent of tropical forests covering the land with the percent of temperate forests covering the land in Figure 1.

APPLYING CRITICAL THINKING SKILLS

1. What has happened to the amount of tropical forest land and temperate forest land between 1950 and now?
2. Why would you suppose the percent of land covered by temperate forests has remained constant?
3. What factors have caused a decline in the amount of land covered by tropical forests?

Loss of the tropical forest means loss of the habitat for all of its living things. And that could mean their disappearance from the earth forever.

Would this loss be important? Yes, in terms of what the tropical forests have already given the world. Many foods were first discovered in the tropical forests.

Such foods are now grown on farms around the world. They include the grains rice and maize (corn). These are important in the diets of millions of people. Botanists think that tropical forests hold many more undiscovered plants that could be important sources of food in the future.

Many medicines have also been developed from tropical plants. Forty-five percent of all prescription drugs contain ingredients that originated in the tropical forest. This includes the rosy periwinkle, which is a flower that produces medicines used to treat leukemia and Hodgkin's disease.

Only one-sixth of all tropical forest species that have been discovered have been identified so far. So scientists expect that cures for many diseases can still be discovered.

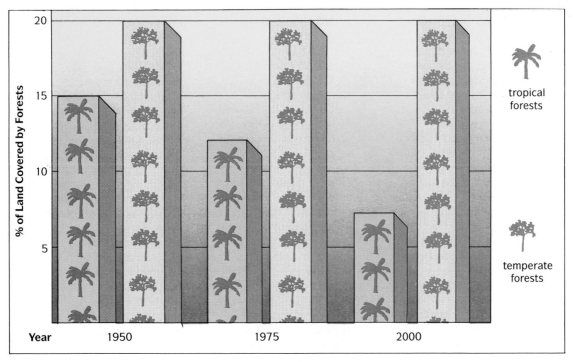

tropical forests

temperate forests

Figure 1

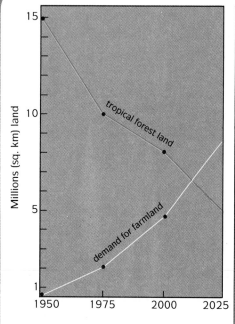

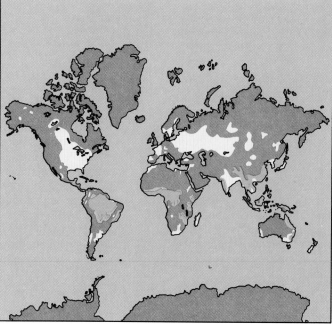

Main grain-producing areas

Tropical forests

Areas where forests are undergoing rapid depletion

Figure 2

The tropical forests also play a part in regulating earth's atmosphere by absorbing carbon dioxide. Too much carbon dioxide in the air could cause the earth to heat up. The trees play a part in the water cycle and they also help prevent soil erosion.

The population growth rate in the areas where these tropical forests are located is high. A higher population causes a demand for more food. This creates a need for more farmland, as shown in Figure 2. The tropical forests are being cut so that the land can be used for farms and pastures.

Figure 2 is a graph and a map. The figure shows the relationship between deforestation and the demand for farmland, and the earth's main areas of grain production.

APPLYING CRITICAL THINKING SKILLS

1. What has happened to the demand for farmland between 1950 and now? Will this trend continue?

2. What is the relationship between the drop in forest land and the rise in demand for farmland?

3. Aside from farmland, what else might contribute to the depletion of the forest?

4. Where are the main grain producing areas? Where are the largest areas of tropical forests? What can you conclude from this?

The lushness of the tropical forest suggests that this would make rich farmland. But this is not so. Most of the nutrients of the forest are in its plants, not in the soil. The soil is thin and easily overworked. Without its cover of trees it quickly breaks down and erodes.

Crop yields on this land are so poor that farms are abandoned after only a few years. The farmers then push farther into the forest and cut more trees.

Tropical forests are also being cut because of the need for wood. At present they have one half of the earth's supply. Wood is the primary fuel supply for one-third of the people on the earth. Most of these people live in poorer areas of the world. As population rises, more wood is needed for cooking and heating. Supplies are already running short. More than 100 million people don't have enough fuelwood. Nearly 1.2 billion are meeting their needs by chopping down forests.

A look around any American home will prove how important wood is even in developed nations. Wood is used to build homes and ships. It is used to make paper, cardboard, books, and cereal boxes. Tropical forest woods like teak and mahogany are in great demand for furniture.

The full impact of the disappearance of the tropical forest isn't totally known. But biologists suspect that climate patterns all over the earth would be changed.

Trees use up carbon dioxide. So the loss of tropical forests would raise the carbon dioxide level in the atmosphere. When an area of forest is cleared, it is usually burned down. This adds even more carbon dioxide to the air. So does increased burning of wood fuel. The oversupply of carbon dioxide in the atmosphere would cause it to hold in more heat. This warming is called the "greenhouse effect" and it would raise world temperatures. The warmer temperatures could melt polar icecaps, causing flooding in coastal cities.

Figure 3 illustrates another possible result that changes in the amount of carbon dioxide in the atmosphere could cause.

APPLYING CRITICAL THINKING SKILLS

1. According to the map, what factor of climate may be affected by a warmer earth?
2. How would climate in most of the United States change as a result of more carbon dioxide in the atmosphere?
3. How would much of the United States' grain-producing area be affected? Would this be a problem? Why or why not?
4. If the moisture patterns of the world are affected as the map suggests, which areas of the earth might become important grain producers?

If the clearing of tropical forests continues at the present rate, they will be gone by 2050.

There is some replanting going on now. But on the average just one hectare is replanted for every ten that are cleared.

The problem is a big one. And it has serious consequences for life on earth. Asking Americans to stop buying mahogany furniture is one thing. Mahogany furniture is not necessary for life. But how is it possible to tell people who need food that forests cannot be cut down to make farms? And what is to be done about the billions of people who depend on wood from tropical forests to cook? Can these people survive from day to day without using the resources of the tropical forest? Can the earth survive in the future if they do?

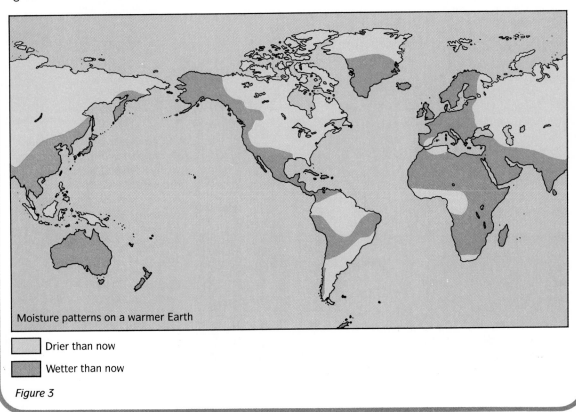

Moisture patterns on a warmer Earth

☐ Drier than now

■ Wetter than now

Figure 3

OCEANOGRAPHY

The earth consists of a solid portion, a gaseous portion, and also a water portion. The water of the earth is called the hydrosphere. The hydrosphere consists mostly of the oceans. But the hydrosphere also consists of fresh water lakes and streams. As you study this unit you will also find out about the hydrosphere and the resources that we obtain from it. ■

▲ *Ocean vents on the sea floor release chemical-rich sediments, which nourish these tube worms* (above). *Tube worms were discovered in 1977 by scientists aboard the submersible* Alvin *at 2500 meters. Oceanographers often scuba dive to study the sea* (left).

▲ Watercolor drawing of the HMS Challenger *from a journal of the voyage 1872–76. Insets show the naturalist's workroom* (top) *and the chemical laboratory*

▲ *Water flowing over falls can be used to generate electricity.*

EARTH'S FRESH WATER

*Caves are evidence of weathering beneath the earth's surface.
They usually begin as joints or cracks, in rock. Over many
thousands of years, the action of ground water can widen the
cracks into passages wider than interstate highways. The
photograph shows the descent of a caver in the Incredible Pit, a
134 m shaft in Ellison's Cave.*

- *What feature in the photograph shows how the cave may have formed?*
- *What do the layers in the rock tell about the type of rock that caves form in?*
- *How can caves be used to study the earth's past?*

21-1 WATER BUDGET

Every drop of water on the earth is part of the *water
cycle*. As part of the cycle, water is evaporated from the
ocean by heat from the sun and moved along in clouds
by wind. It can fall from the sky as rain, snow, sleet, or
hail. Once on the earth, water may be soaked up by the
gound, flow in rivers, or spend ages in ice sheets. Eventually, it returns to the oceans. As you can see, water takes
many different forms and travels many paths. However,
none of it is ever lost.

The earth's water supply is constantly circulated between the oceans, atmosphere, and land, in a process called
the water cycle. Each day more than a trillion metric tons
of water evaporate from the oceans and land. Each day
the same amount of water falls as precipitation. This amount
of water is more than enough to meet all present needs
for fresh water. For example, each day precipitation supplies the United States with almost ten times the amount
of water it uses.

However, precipitation does not fall evenly on the
earth. For example, Arizona, which has a desert climate,
only receives about 20 cm of rainfall each year. In contrast,
Florida receives about 140 cm. In addition, most of the

> *After completing this section, you will be able to*
>
> - **name** the parts of a water budget.
> - **relate** the water budget to an area's water supply.
> - **describe** several ways water can be supplied to areas of water deficit.
>
> *The key terms in this section are*
> deficit   water budget
> surplus

water that falls in Arizona evaporates almost immediately. Most of the water that falls in Florida soaks into the ground or runs off in rivers. The amount of precipitation and evaporation of water in an area determine an area's water supply.

The water supply of an area can be represented by a water budget. A **water budget** is a record of the amount of precipitation and evaporation for an area. The amount of precipitation is called the *income*. The amount of evaporation is called the *outgo*. Together, the income and outgo help make up an area's water supply.

The 1983 water budget for Yuma, Arizona is shown as a graph in Figure 21-1 (*left*). The graph shows the change in income and outgo throughout the year. When the amount of evaporation (outgo) is greater than the amount of precipitation (income) in an area, a **deficit** is said to occur. In what months does a deficit occur in Yuma? When the amount of precipitation is greater than the amount of evaporation in an area a **surplus** is said to occur. In what months does a surplus occur?

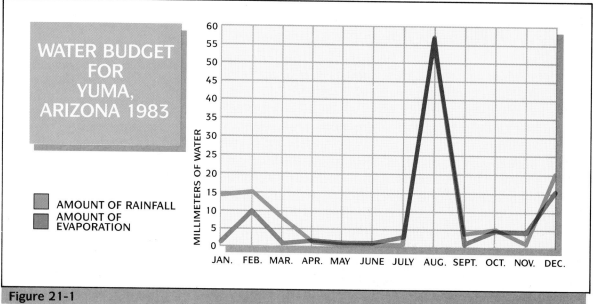

Figure 21-1

Water Budget, Yuma, Arizona

Figure 21-2 (*left*) shows the 1983 water budget for New Orleans, Louisiana. Notice that a surplus occurs for every month, except for one month. Which month does not show a surplus? When a surplus occurs for many months, the ground often becomes saturated with water. Precipitation does not enter the ground, but instead becomes surface runoff.

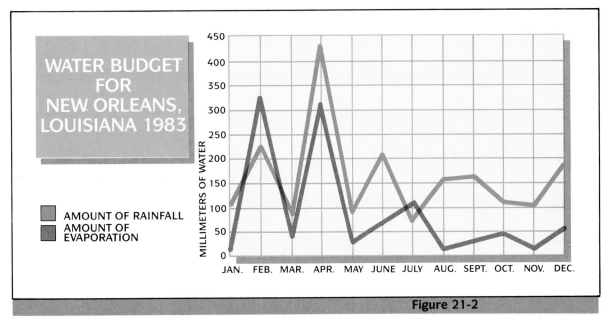

Figure 21-2

Water Budget, New Orleans, Louisiana

Areas of surplus can often supply water for areas of deficit. For example, areas in the southwestern United States often show deficits. In the spring and early summer, these areas receive surface runoff from melting snow in mountains located in the northwestern United States.

Surplus areas, especially in the western United States, cannot supply all the water needed in deficit areas. Water must also be supplied to deficit areas by diverting water from rivers. For example, water is often diverted from rivers to irrigate crops in these areas. In fact, the western United States uses 9 out of every 10 L of water for irrigation. In some areas along coasts, seawater is being changed to fresh water by a process called *desalination*. In desalination, salt is removed from seawater. The remaining water can then used for drinking or irrigation. Water shortages may be overcomed by *conservation*. Water can be conserved by using less and using it more efficiently.

REVIEW

1. What are the parts of a water budget?
2. What factors determine whether an area has a deficit or a surplus of water?
3. How can water be supplied to an area that has a water deficit?

CHALLENGE Explain why an area need not have a large amount of precipitation to be classified as humid.

495

21-2 GROUND WATER

After completing this section, you will be able to

- **compare** porosity and permeability.
- **explain** how water enters the earth's surface.
- **relate** the water table to springs and wells.
- **describe** two problems with overusing ground water.

The key terms in this section are

aquifer	porosity
geyser	water table
ground water	zone of aeration
permeability	zone of saturation

Beneath the earth's surface lies most of the world's fresh water. The amount of water stored under the surface is more than 30 times the amount stored in all rivers and lakes combined. More than half of the population of the United States depends on this water for drinking water.

When water is poured into the soil in a flower pot, the water sinks right in. This happens because there are many openings between the soil particles for the water to pass through. The open spaces between particles are called *pores*. The number of pores in a material compared with its volume is called **porosity**. Look at Figure 21-3 (*left*). What factor can affect a material's porosity?

Almost all materials on the earth's surface are porous or have pores. Soil, for example, is porous because it is made up of loose materials. Rocks can also be porous. Sandstone, for example, is porous because it has openings between its sand grains. As much as 25 percent of sandstone can be made up of pores.

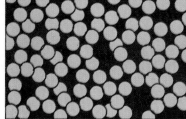

Figure 21-3

Loosely-packed particles have a higher porosity than tightly packed particles (*left*). Water flows easily through permeable materials, but not impermeable materials (*right*).

The ability of a material to transmit water, or **permeability**, depends on the size of the pores and how the pores are connected. Materials with high permeabilities, such as sand, have large pore spaces that are well connected. A material such as clay has a low permeability because it has small pore spaces that are not well connected. Look at Figure 21-3 (*right*). Which material is permeable?

496

Some rocks have a low porosity but are still permeable. As you can see in Figure 21-4, water can pass through a low-porosity rock if the rock has cracks running through it. Limestone is an example of a low-porosity rock that is permeable.

When rain falls on the earth's surface, some of it evaporates, some runs off, and some sinks into the ground. When rainfall is steady on a gentle slope, the land acts like a giant sponge, soaking up the water. The water passes through pores in the soil. Some water may be held by soil and used by plants. Most of it seeps downward until it is stopped by a layer of impermeable rock. The water then fills up the pore spaces above the impermeable layer. The area below the earth's surface filled with water is called the **zone of saturation**. The water in the zone of saturation is called **ground water**.

Above the level of the ground water, the pores contain mostly air. The area above the zone of saturation and below the surface is called the **zone of aeration**. The water in the zone of aeration supplies water for plants.

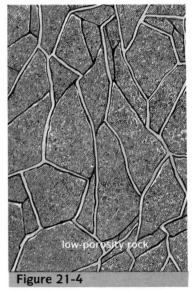

Figure 21-4

A low porosity rock can be permeable if its pores are well connected.

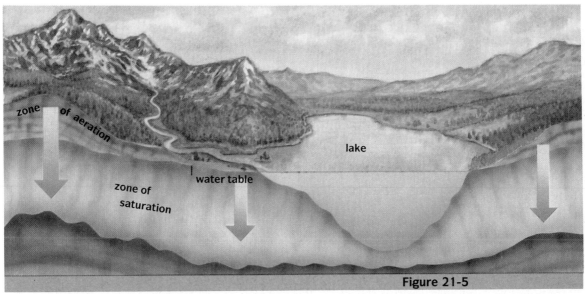

Figure 21-5

The water table follows the shape of the land surface.

The boundary between the zone of aeration and the zone of saturation is called the **water table**. The water table generally follows the shape of the land surface. Look at Figure 21-5. How does the shape of the water table follow the shape of hills and valleys?

The depth of the water table below the surface varies with rainfall and climate. In areas with a large amount of rain, the water table may be only a meter under the ground. In desert areas, it may be hundreds of meters down.

Ground water can flow in a rock layer called an aquifer (AK wuh fuhr). An **aquifer** is a layer of rock or rock material that holds water. Aquifers are usually made up of sandstone, limestone, or gravel.

Water in aquifers flows downhill due to the pull of gravity, just as rivers do. However, water in aquifers usually moves through pores rather than channels. Therefore, it travels much slower than water in rivers. It may take thousands of years to return to the surface.

Aquifers are important sources of water for drinking and for irrigation. An aquifer called the Ogallala (oh guh-LAHL uh) supplies water to irrigate more than 140 million hectares (ha) in the midwestern United States. The water is pumped from about 150,000 wells drilled into the aquifer. A *well* is a shaft sunk into the water table.

A well in which ground water rises naturally is called an *artesian* (ahr TEE zhuhn) *well*. The water in an artesian well comes from an aquifer. Look at Figure 21-6. What prevents the water in the aquifer from escaping? Pressure caused by water flowing downward in the aquifer causes water to rise in the artesian well.

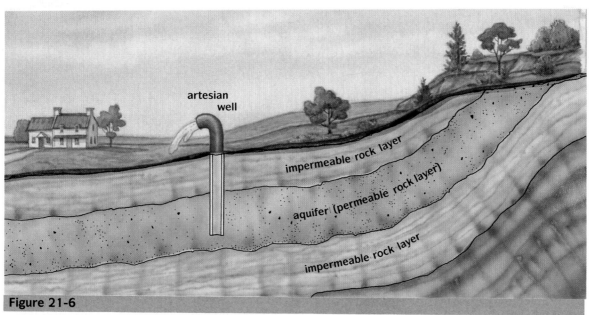

Figure 21-6

Ground water flows in porous rock layers called aquifers.

Water in an aquifer flows out onto the surface if the top of the aquifer, or the water table, reaches the surface. This may occur along a hillside. Water that comes naturally to the surface is called a *spring*. Springs can form swamps, streams, and lakes. As much as 30 percent of the water in rivers and lakes comes from springs.

DO YOU KNOW?

On a typical day over the United States, about 4.2 trillion gallons of rain or snow falls. Much of this water sinks into the ground and becomes ground water. It would seem to be enough water to keep the aquifers brimming. Yet aquifer supplies around the country are dwindling because people are using more water than can be replaced by rain.

One of the states being affected by low water supplies in aquifers is Texas. Texas obtains a lot of its water from the Ogallala Aquifer. This huge underground lake stretches from the edge of South Dakota through parts of Oklahoma, New Mexico, Kansas, Colorado, Nebraska, Wyoming, and into northern Texas. Much of the water from the Ogallala is used to irrigate land in Texas.

The high use of water in Texas is quickly draining the Ogallala. Some experts say that parts of the Ogallala will be dry by the next century.

Texans are looking for other water. Some Texans want to divert water from the Mississippi River. However, building aqueducts to transport the water would be very expensive, about $20 billion. Other people believe that water conservation would make a difference. Water conservation practices might include better irrigation methods and the use of new varieties of crops that flourish in a dry climate.

The problem has no easy solution. But as people continue to move to the southwestern states, the Texans will need to find one.

In some places where ground water moves deep in the earth, it becomes heated. If the heated water reaches the surface, it flows out as a hot spring. Often, minerals are deposited around the hot spring as the water cools.

Hot springs that erupt periodically are called **geysers**. Geysers form when ground water is heated to very high temperatures in underground chambers. The heating causes the water to expand and flow up to the surface. There it shoots out as hot water and steam.

The supply of ground water is limited. When water is removed from a well, the water table in the area is lowered until the water has been replaced. When ground water is used faster than it can be replaced, wells must be made deeper to reach the needed water. It may take many years before the table returns to its former level. In that time, many wells have become dry. This situation would mean disaster for farmers who depended on the well water for irrigation.

Another problem that can occur by removing too much ground water is subsidence (suhb SI duhns), or the sinking of land. In California's San Joaquin (san wah-KEEN) Valley, overpumping of well water for irrigation has caused the land to sink about 10 m since 1925. The sinking has caused the land to flood during heavy rains.

Figure 21-7

Old Faithful is a geyser that erupts about once every hour.

ACTIVITY   Permeability of Soil

OBJECTIVE
Determine how different soils affect the movement of water.

MATERIALS
3 large plastic foam cups, 3 coffee cans with plastic lids, 3 squares cheesecloth (large enough to cover bottoms of cups), 3 rubber bands, 3 soil samples (sand, clay, gravel), 100-mL graduate, water, pencil, watch or clock with second hand

PROCEDURE
A. Punch several holes in the bottoms and around the lower parts of three plastic foam cups. Be sure to punch the same size and number of holes in each cup.

B. Place a square of cheesecloth over the bottom of each cup. Be sure the cheesecloth covers all the holes. Secure the cheesecloth with rubber bands.

C. Cut a hole in each of three plastic lids of the coffee cans so that the lower half of a cup fits inside. Place the lids on the cans and fit the cups in the lids. Label the cups and cans A, B, and C.

D. Fill cup A half full of dry sand, cup B half full of clay, and cup C half full of a mixture of sand, clay, and gravel.

E. Using a graduate, measure 100 mL of water. Slowly pour the water into cup A, noting the time. Record the time in a table like the one below.

F. Note and record the time when water first drips out of the cup.

G. Repeat procedures in **E** and **F** for cups B and C.

H. Allow the water to drip in all three cans until it stops. Using the graduate, measure the amount of water in each can. Record each amount in your table.

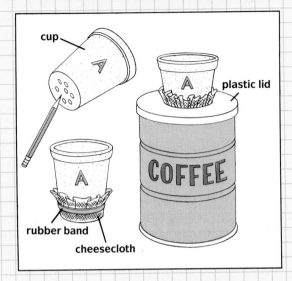

Cup	Time			Amount of Water in Can
	Water In	Water Out	Difference	
A				
B				
C				

RESULTS AND CONCLUSIONS
1. From the data in your table, answer the following questions.
   a. Which soil sample is most permeable?
   b. Which soil sample is least permeable?
2. Which kind of soil retained the most water? the least water?
3. Which kind of soil would allow ground water to build up quickly?
4. Which kind of soil would result in the most runoff?

REVIEW
1. How are porosity and permeability related?
2. How does water enter the earth's surface?
3. How are springs formed? How is the depth of a well determined by the water table?
4. What are two problems that can occur when too much water is pumped from wells?

CHALLENGE   Explain why the water table may not follow the shape of the land near wells.

21-3 THE WORK OF GROUND WATER

The rock below the surface in central Florida is slowly being dissolved by ground water. In some areas, ground water has carved out large caves under the ground. On May 8, 1981, in Winter Park, Florida, the earth over such a hole collapsed. A home, part of a highway, and part of a swimming pool fell into the cave-in.

The cave-in was caused by the lowering of the water table. As long as ground water remained in the caves below Winter Park, the ground could be supported by the water. But when more and more ground water was pumped out for the growing population in Winter Park, the water table dropped. In addition, the area had a *drought*, or a long period of below-normal rainfall, which caused the water table to drop further. Together, the overpumping of ground water and the drought caused the cavern to become empty of water. Without ground water supporting it, the ground sank almost 30 m, forming a huge circular hole or depression. A depression in the land caused by the dissolving of limestone or the collapse of a cave roof is called a **sinkhole**.

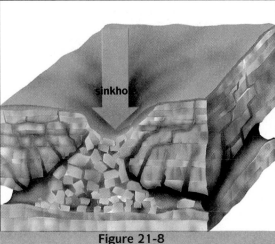

sinkhole

Figure 21-8

A cave forms when ground water dissolves rock below the earth's surface (*left*). In Winter Park, Florida, 1981, the roof of a cave fell in (*right*).

Pure water dissolves very little limestone. Ground water, however, contains carbon dioxide. The carbon dioxide comes from the air. The carbon dioxide is dissolved by rain water. The mixture of water and carbon dioxide forms carbonic acid. Carbonic acid can dissolve limestone.

Carbon dioxide can be added to water in another way. The decaying plant matter in soil produces carbon dioxide. As rain water seeps through the soil, it absorbs some of this carbon dioxide.

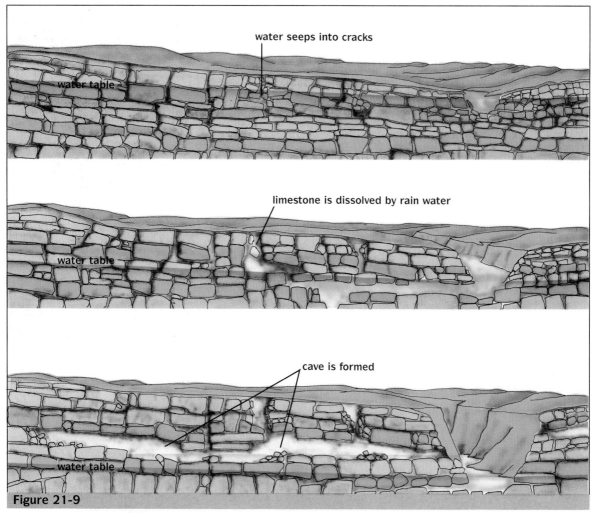

water seeps into cracks

water table

limestone is dissolved by rain water

water table

cave is formed

water table

Figure 21-9

Water enters limestone through cracks, enlarging them. The water then flows horizontally toward a river (*top*). As the river erodes its bed, the water table drops. The ground water seeps deeper into the limestone and carves a larger channel (*middle*). In time, as the water table drops, ground water drops to a lower level, leaving an empty cavern (*bottom*).

The erosion process begins when water enters small cracks or joints in limestone. As the water dissolves the rock, the cracks grow wider and longer. Eventually, the cracks reach the water table, allowing the acidic ground water to enter it.

The acidic ground water moves along the water table toward a body of water, such as a lake or river. As it moves, the water dissolves a horizontal channel in the limestone. Look at Figure 21-9. Over time, the water enlarges the channel and forms a cavern.

A **cavern** is a large underground chamber created by the action of ground water. It forms at or below the water table, in the zone of saturation. A cavern is filled with water until the water table drops. The water table may drop if the body of water that the ground water flows into is lowered. Look at Figure 21-9. What causes the river to become lower?

The lowering of the water table in a cavern causes the ground water to seep into lower cracks. In time, the cracks are enlarged and a new horizontal channel is carved out. The new channel is enlarged and becomes a cavern.

An area containing many caverns and sinkholes is called a **karst** region. Karst regions contain little surface water because most of it falls through sinkholes and enters underground rivers. A well-known karst region is Mammoth Cave in Kentucky, which extends for about 245 km. The region contains many underground rivers, including Echo River, which flows 100 m below the surface. Karst regions can also be found in central Florida, southern Indiana, and Tennessee.

Features called stalactites and stalagmites form in caverns above the water table. A **stalactite** is a formation of calcite that extends downward from the roof of a cave. It forms when water dripping from the roof of a limestone cave evaporates, leaving a deposit of calcite. Such deposits grow over many years, forming long fingers of calcite. Water dripping onto the floor of a cave forms a similar structure called a stalagmite. A **stalagmite** is a calcite structure that extends upward from the floor of a cave. Stalactites and stalagmites sometimes meet and form *columns*.

Most of the world's caverns were formed over hundreds of thousands of years by the dissolving of limestone by ground water. Caverns are found in various areas, including Kentucky, Florida, and New Mexico. These caverns are filled with deep chambers and long corridors.

Figure 12-10

Stalactites hang from the ceilings and stalagmites rise from the floor in Marengo Cave, Indiana.

SCIENCE PUZZLER

Trees made of stone? The photograph shows petrified wood, in Petrified Forest National Park, Arizona. The petrified wood was once part of living trees 180 million years ago. How did the wood of once-living trees become stone?

ACTIVITY   Water Hardness and Sudsing Action

OBJECTIVE
Determine the effects of water hardness on the sudsing action of soap.

MATERIALS
Graduate, four 1 L jars with lids, water, laundry detergent (liquid or powder), salt, masking tape, pencil

PROCEDURE
A. Using a graduate, add 500 mL of water to each of four jars. The jars should be about half full.
B. Add 10 mL of salt to one jar. Cap the jar and shake it for 15 seconds. Use a piece of masking tape to label the container, showing the amount of salt added.
C. Add 20 mL and 40 mL of salt respectively to two of the remaining jars. Cap the jars, label them to indicate the amount of salt you added, and shake them.
D. Do not add any salt to the last jar. Be sure to cap and label this jar.
E. Add 10 mL of laundry detergent to each of the jars. Vigorously shake each capped jar for 20 seconds. Observe the amount of suds present in each jar.

RESULTS AND CONCLUSIONS
1. What was the purpose of including water with no salt added in your activity?
2. How did the different concentrations of salt affect the sudsing action of the laundry detergent?
3. What effect do you think hard water, or water with a high concentration of dissolved minerals, has on washing clothes? On bathing? What is often done to water containing a large amount of dissolved minerals before it is used by people?

Formation of the Carlsbad Caverns in New Mexico began about 60 million years ago. It is believed that these caverns were carved out by seeping ground water. The ground water gradually withdrew as the water table lowered. About a million years ago, the first stalactites and stalagmites began to form. Today they are still growing.

REVIEW

1. How can ground water dissolve limestone?
2. What causes caverns to form?
3. Compare the ways stalactites and stalagmites form.

CHALLENGE   What effect does the burning of fuels, such as in factories and cars, have on erosion by ground water?

21-4 TWO GREAT RIVERS

The earliest civilizations began around rivers. Rivers supplied the people with fresh water for drinking and farming. Like the earliest civilizations, many cities and farms today depend on rivers for fresh water.

A river and all the tributary streams that flow into it are called a **river system**. Every river or river system has a watershed, or an area that the river or system drains. Each watershed is separated by a ridge, or divide. A **divide** is an area of high elevation that separates watersheds. A divide called the Continental Divide runs north and south through the Rocky Mountains. The Continental Divide separates the waters that flow toward the Pacific Ocean from those that flow toward the Atlantic Ocean or the Gulf of Mexico. The Mississippi River drains much of the area east of the Continental Divide, and the Colorado River drains much of the area west of the divide.

MISSISSIPPI RIVER

The Mississippi River is the major river of North America and the longest in the United States. This huge river flows 3780 km from its source in Minnesota to its various mouths in the Gulf of Mexico. The Mississippi and its tributaries have the largest watershed of any river system in North America. The watershed covers an area of more than 3 million square km. Altogether, the watershed of the Mississippi River system gathers water from 31 states and two Canadian provinces.

The Mississippi River is the main waterway in the United States. Ships use the river to transport agricultural goods, industrial products, and raw materials. Ships can travel almost 3000 km on the river, from Minnesota to the Gulf of Mexico.

Originating from Lake Itaska in Minnesota, the Mississippi River flows south, often through high limestone bluffs. In the north, the Mississippi is joined by tributaries such as the Minnesota, Des Moines, and Illinois rivers. A short distance north of St. Louis, the Missouri River flows into the Mississippi. Farther south, at Cairo, Illinois, the Ohio River joins the Mississippi.

Below Cairo, the Mississippi takes on all the characteristics of an old river. It flows through a broad flood plain, between 60 and 110 km wide. The river also contains numerous meanders and oxbow lakes, with many swamps nearby. At the Gulf of Mexico, the Mississippi has built up a huge delta area that grows and changes constantly.

Figure 21-11

Concrete slabs are placed along the banks of the Mississippi River to control flooding.

Each year, melting snows and spring rains raise the water level of the Mississippi, often causing the river to flood. The floods deposit silt on the flood plain. The silt fertilizes about 80,000 square km of farmland on the plain. Some of these floods have caused many deaths and enormous property damage. Over the years a number of steps have been taken to control the floods, such as erecting barriers along the river and deepening the channel. Another problem affecting the Mississippi is pollution. Parts of the river have been polluted by chemicals from factories, sewage from towns and cities, and erosion from farmland.

COLORADO RIVER

The Colorado River is the largest river in the Southwest. The river originates in northern Colorado, in the Rocky Mountains. The Colorado flows about 2250 km toward the Gulf of California. The river's watershed covers an area stretching over 600,000 square km. Look at Figure 21-12. What rivers join the Colorado River in Utah? Its watershed is about one fifth the size of the Mississippi's watershed. The Colorado River cuts through narrow valleys with steep cliffs.

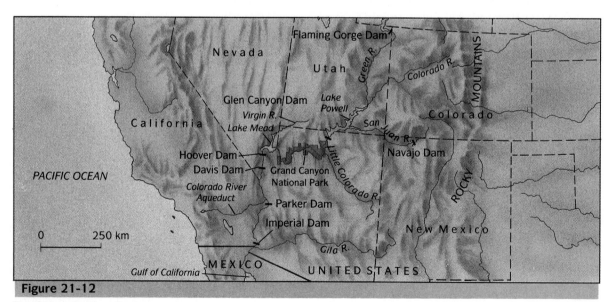

Figure 21-12

The Colorado River System.

The Colorado River is very important to the western United States. It supplies water for drinking and irrigation. It also serves as a source of electricity.

To help provide water and electricity for the western United States, several dams have been built along the Colorado. The dams block the river's flow of water. The water

ACTIVITY   Formation of a Delta

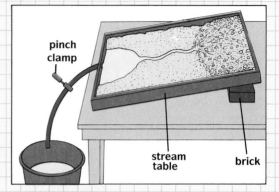

OBJECTIVE
Demonstrate the formation of a delta.

MATERIALS
stream table, water, 2 wood blocks, pail, pinch clamp, rock (flat) about 6 cm, fine sand, metric ruler, sprinkler can

PROCEDURE
A. The Mississippi River carries about 550 million t of material each year to the Gulf of Mexico. Seven deltas have formed and re-formed in this area during recent geologic time. Using a stream table, you can show how a delta forms. Set up a stream table as shown. Tighten the pinch clamp on the hose so that no water can escape.

B. Spread a layer of fine sand, at least 2 cm thick, over the bottom of the stream table. Place a flat rock on top of the sand at the upper level of the stream table.

C. Form a "lake" at the lower end of the stream table by scooping out some of the sand. With your finger, make a small channel ("river") about 1 cm deep from the upper level of the stream table to the lake.

D. *Gently* pour water over the flat rock at the upper end of the "river." Observe what forms in the "lake."

E. Now, alternately use more and then less water and note how this affects what forms in the lake.

RESULTS AND CONCLUSIONS
1. What formed in the lake after water was poured into the river?
2. What was the effect of using more water and then less water in the river?
3. How does this activity show what may have caused several deltas to form where the Mississippi joins the Gulf?

---

backs up into reservoirs. The reservoirs are used to hold supplies of water. The water is also released to run generators in hydroelectric plants. *Hydroelectric plants* use the energy of falling water to make electricity.

Withdrawing water from a river reduces its flow. Presently, California, Arizona, and six other western states draw water from the Colorado River. Because of this, the river no longer reaches its former mouth in the Gulf of California. The Colorado River, which begins powerfully at its headwaters in the Rockies, is reduced to a trickle some 50 km before it reaches the gulf.

REVIEW

1. Compare the Mississippi River system and the Colorado River system.
2. List several ways the Mississippi and Colorado rivers are important.

CHALLENGE   Why is it difficult for mapmakers to chart the course of the Mississippi in its flood plain region?

Figure 21-13

The Colorado River flows through the Grand Canyon.

21-5 LAKES AND PONDS

After completing this section, you will be able to

- **explain** how lakes and ponds are formed.
- **describe** two ways lakes and ponds are polluted.
- **discuss** the life cycle of lakes and ponds.

The key terms in this section are
eutrophication   pond
lake

Lakes are found in all parts of the world. They can be found high in the mountains and below sea level. Wherever large depressions form, they can be filled with water to form lakes.

A **lake** is a large water-filled depression in the earth's surface. Lakes are fed by rainfall, rivers, and springs. Most lakes contain fresh water; however, some, like the Great Salt Lake in Utah, have salty water. A **pond** forms from a smaller, shallower depression that fills with water. Unlike lakes, all areas of a pond are penetrated by sunlight and have plant growth.

Lakes and ponds develop in several different ways. One way a lake or pond can form is when a river is blocked. A landslide, for example, can dam a river, creating a lake. Another way is in karst regions, where sinkholes fill with water, producing lakes and ponds.

Many lakes and ponds were formed by the glaciers, or ice sheets, that covered a large part of North America thousands of years ago. The Great Lakes, for example, were formed when glaciers hollowed out lake basins from what had been large stream valleys. As the glaciers melted, the basins filled with water. The glaciers also left behind large deposits of material that often dammed up rivers. In New York, the glaciers widened and deepened river valleys and then left deposits that plugged both ends. The Finger Lakes in New York were formed in this way.

Figure 21-14

The Finger Lakes of New York State were once glacial valleys.

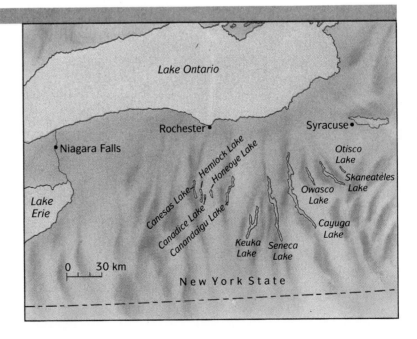

Humans create lakes and ponds too. When a dam is built, it forms an artificial lake, or reservoir. Reservoirs serve as vital sources of drinking water.

Ponds and lakes play important roles as sources of drinking water and as recreation areas. They also provide habitats for many species of plants and animals. Water lilies, bulrushes, and cattails can be found growing near the edges of ponds and lakes. Their water also provides homes for fish, like bass and bluegills.

Figure 21-15

As a lake ages, it becomes covered with algae and other plant life.

The addition of nutrients to a lake can increase the growth of water plants such as algae. Normally, the growth of algae is limited by the small amount of nutrients dissolved in the water. However, when the amount of nutrients increases—either naturally or by pollution— the algae grow rapidly. As the algae die, they become food for tiny organisms called *bacteria*. Bacteria consume oxygen and can deplete the supply of oxygen in a lake. A lack of oxygen causes fish to die and results in a lake covered by organic waste material. The adding of nutrients to a body of water which causes the quality of the water to decrease is called **eutrophication** (yoo troh fuh KAY-shuhn).

Eutrophication is a slow natural process in a lake. Through a series of stages, a lake or pond eventually disappears. The stages can be described as a life cycle. The three stages in the life cycle of a lake are youth, middle age, and old age. In its youth, a lake is rich in oxygen but poor in nutrients. Its water is clear, and it contains little plant and animal life.

At middle age, a lake has more nutrients flowing into it, and the nutrients begin collecting on the bottom. Plant life and large fish, such as trout and bass, exist.

In old age, a lake has abundant nutrients flowing into it, causing large amounts of algae and other plants to grow. The surface becomes covered with decaying plant matter. As the water is slowly depleted of oxygen, trout and bass die and are replaced by fish such as catfish. Silt, sand, and decaying plant matter slowly fill the lake. Eventually, the lake is filled with solid material and disappears.

Humans can speed up the process of eutrophication in a lake by polluting it. For example, the *nitrates* in fertilizers and the *phosphates* in detergents are nutrients often washed into lakes by streams.

Fish life can also be destroyed by pollution from the atmosphere. The pollution often comes from the burning of fossil fuels. The burning of fossil fuels produces gases such as nitrogen oxides and sulphur dioxide. These gases mix with rain to form acid rain. Acid rain can cause lakes to become so acidic that many kinds of fish cannot survive. For example, more than 200 lakes in the Adirondack Mountains in New York have been contaminated by acid rain. Some factories located in the Midwest burn fossil fuels and produce gases that are carried eastward by the wind. Eventually, the gases reach the Northeast and form acid rain or snow over lakes and ponds.

Figure 21-16

A lake destroyed by acid rain.

REVIEW

1. How are lakes and ponds formed?
2. What are two ways by which lakes and ponds are polluted?
3. Describe the three stages in the life cycle of a lake.

CHALLENGE In areas where stripmining has exposed coal seams, lakes have become polluted with acid. Explain why.

21-6 THE GREAT LAKES

The **Great Lakes** make up the largest region of fresh water in the world, covering an area over 256,000 square km. From east to west, this region includes Lake Ontario, Lake Erie, Lake Huron, Lake Michigan, and Lake Superior. Water in the lakes is supplied not by large rivers but by numerous small rivers and streams, which form a huge watershed.

Drainage from the Great Lakes follows an eastward course. Lake Superior and Lake Michigan drain into Lake Huron. Lake Huron flows into Lake Erie through the St. Clair River, Lake St. Clair, and the Detroit River. Lake Erie drains into Lake Ontario through the Niagara River, and Lake Ontario flows into the St. Lawrence River. Most of the drainage of the Great Lakes occurs at the St. Lawrence River.

The Great Lakes were formed by the large glaciers that once covered much of North America. These glaciers enlarged existing river systems and then dammed them, creating the lakes. At one time the Great Lakes drained southward through rivers that eventually ran into the Mississippi. As the glaciers melted, they left rock material that plugged up outlets to the south. The Great Lakes began to drain eastward through new outlets—the Susquehanna, Mohawk, Hudson, and St. Lawrence rivers. Eventually, the Great Lakes began to drain into the St. Lawrence.

> *After completing this section, you will be able to*
>
> - **describe** the physical characteristics of the Great Lakes.
> - **explain** the formation of the Great Lakes.
> - **predict** the effects of the Great Lakes on climate.
>
> *The key term in this section is*
> **Great Lakes**

Figure 21-17

Five lakes make up the Great Lakes.

511

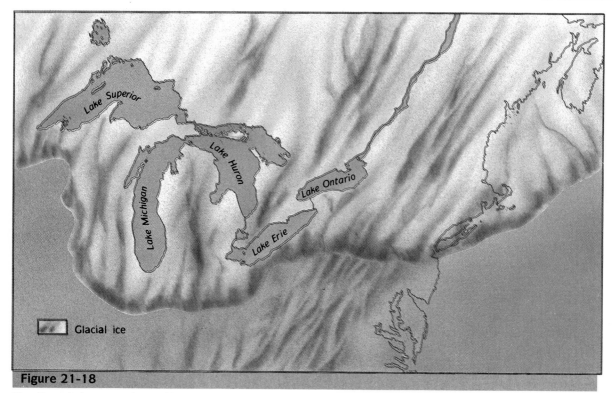

Figure 21-18

The Great Lakes were formed by glaciers that once covered North America.

Glacial ice

For centuries the Great Lakes have served as major commercial highways for the interior of the continent. Today, oceangoing ships enter the lakes from the St. Lawrence. Other vessels travel between the various ports along the lakes, carrying iron ore, agricultural produce, and oil products.

The Great Lakes are a major influence on local weather conditions. The lakes cause heavy snowfall on the eastern shore of Lake Erie. Air moving east across the lakes picks up moisture. When the air hits the cold landmass on the eastern shore, heavy snowstorms result. This area receives an average of 216 cm of snow per year. Like other large bodies of water, the lakes change temperature more slowly than do large continental areas. Thus the Great Lakes take longer to heat up in summer and longer to cool down in winter than do the land areas. This characteristic often means that summers and winters are milder for many areas around the Great Lakes than for areas farther from the water.

During this century, the Great Lakes have suffered from the same problem that affects many bodies of water: pollution. Lake Michigan has been polluted by industrial wastes from the city of Chicago, located on its shores. The mining industry has contributed pollutants to Lake Superior. The waters of Lake Erie have become a dumping site for sewage from cities such as Buffalo, Cleveland, and Detroit. Pollution has brought a decline in the large fishing industry on the lakes. Drinking water supplies from the Great Lakes have also been contaminated.

In recent years, Canada and the United States have undertaken a joint effort to clean up the Great Lakes. The water quality has greatly improved, but much work still remains to be done.

REVIEW

1. What are some physical characteristics of the Great Lakes?
2. How were the Great Lakes formed?
3. How would the Great Lakes affect the growing seasons of nearby farms?

CHALLENGE Why does eutrophication take a longer time in the Great Lakes than in smaller lakes?

CHAPTER SUMMARY

The main ideas in this chapter are listed below. Read these statements before you answer the Chapter Review questions.

- A water budget is a record of the amount of precipitation and evaporation of water for an area. (21-1)

- The amount of water that can enter the ground depends on the porosity and permeability of the soil and rock that make up the surface. (21-2)

- Ground water causes its greatest amount of erosion in areas where limestone exists under the surface. (21-3)

- The Continental Divide separates two large watershed areas in the United States. The watershed east of the Continental Divide is drained mainly by the Mississippi River system, and the watershed west of the Continental Divide is drained mainly by the Colorado River system. (21-4)

- Lakes and ponds form when water can collect in depressions in the earth. (21-5)

- The Great Lakes are the largest freshwater lakes in the world. (21-6)

The key terms in this chapter are listed below. Use each term in a sentence that shows the meaning of the term.

aquifer	Great Lakes	porosity	surplus
cavern	ground water	river system	water budget
deficit	karst	sinkhole	water table
divide	lake	stalactite	zone of aeration
eutrophication	permeability	stalagmite	zone of saturation
geyser	pond		

Chapter Review

VOCABULARY

Write the letter of the term that best matches the definition. Not all the terms will be used.

1. Number of pores compared with the volume
2. Area below the surface containing water and air in its pores
3. Large depression in earth's surface filled with water
4. A surface hole in limestone
5. Ability of substance to transmit water
6. Upper level of the zone of saturation
7. Small depression in earth's surface filled with water
8. Area that separates two watersheds
9. Water-bearing rock formation
10. Area below the surface containing only water in its pores

a. lake
b. permeability
c. water table
d. aquifer
e. zone of aeration
f. sinkhole
g. porosity
h. zone of saturation
i. ground water
j. pond
k. divide

Identify each statement as True or False. If a statement is false, replace the underlined term with a term that makes the statement true.

1. A record of the amount of precipitation and evaporation for an area is called the water table.
2. When the precipitation in an area is greater than the evaporation, the area has a deficit.
3. Stalactites are long calcite structures hanging from the ceiling of a cavern.
4. Water in the zone of saturation is called ground water.
5. As a lake or pond ages, the amount of nutrients in it increases in a process called eutrophication.

CONCEPTS

1. What is the source of water for a water budget? (21-1)
2. Under what conditions would a deficit occur? Under what conditions would a surplus occur? (21-1)
3. How can crops be grown in areas where the water budget usually shows a deficit? (21-1)
4. How is a material's permeability related to its porosity? (21-1)
5. Describe one condition in which runoff occurs. (21-2)

6. Describe one condition that would cause wells to dry up. (21-2)

7. What effect would ground water have on the water budget? (21-1, 21-2)

8. How does ground water become a weak acid? (21-3)

9. How are sinkholes formed? (21-3)

10. Why must caverns be above the water table in order for stalactites and stalagmites to form? (21-3)

11. Explain why ground water can dissolve more limestone than can pure water. (21-3)

12. Compare the watersheds of the Mississippi River and the Colorado River. (21-4)

13. Why are some lakes destroyed more by acid rain than by eutrophication? (21-5)

14. What factors can determine how fast a lake or pond goes through its life cycle? (21-5)

15. Describe the path that water takes as it drains out of the Great Lakes. (21-6)

16. How did glaciers change the drainage of the Great Lakes? (21-6)

17. What would be the effect on local climate if the Great Lakes disappeared? (21-6)

APPLICATION

1. Explain how plant cover on land could increase the supply of ground water.

2. Some detergents are advertised as "low phosphate." How would the use of these detergents affect the eutrophication of lakes?

3. Explain why lakes polluted by acid rain are usually crystal clear.

EXTENSION

1. Investigate the origins of a civilization that arose along a great river. An example is that of the Sumerians, who lived along the Tigris and Euphrates rivers in Mesopotamia.

2. Find out how the supplies of fresh water are obtained in your area. Does the water come from reservoirs? From wells? Contact a local water company or a municipal water department.

READINGS

Canby, Thomas Y. "Water: Our Most Precious Resource." *National Geographic*, August 1980, p. 144.

Jackson, Donald Dale. *Underground Worlds*. Alexandria, Va.: Time-Life Books Inc., 1982.

Pringle, Laurence. *Rivers and Lakes*. Alexandria, Va. Time- Life Books Inc., 1985.

EARTH'S OCEANS

The coastlines of the earth mark the meeting places of the oceans and continents. Anyone who has lived near the ocean knows that the shore is a place of constant change. In few other places on the earth do powerful forces change the landscape day to day. One example of a changing coastline is the coastline of New Zealand, shown in the photograph.

- *How many coastlines can you identify in the photograph?*
- *What factors can cause the shore to change?*
- *Do waves add sand to beaches or remove it?*

22-1 THE OCEAN FLOOR

On many maps and globes, the ocean is shown as a smooth blue surface. Yet beneath the ocean is a mountain taller than Mount Everest and a mountain chain that circles the entire earth. Valleys many times deeper than the Grand Canyon sink into the ocean floor. One of the most surprising discoveries about the ocean in recent years is that its floor is as rugged and varied as any place on the earth's land.

THE EARTH'S OCEANS

The oceans cover more of the earth's surface than the continents do—about 71 percent. However, the ocean water is not spread out evenly over the earth. Most of the Northern Hemisphere is land, and most of the Southern Hemisphere is water.

Most people think of oceans as separate bodies of water. However, the oceans are connected. The oceans actually form one great body of water in which the continents lie like huge islands.

After completing this section, you will be able to

- **describe** the four major oceans.
- **describe** the main features of the continental margins and the ocean basin.

The key terms in this section are
abyssal plains
continental rise
continental margins
continental shelf
continental slope
ocean basin
seamounts
submarine canyons
turbidity currents

517

Scientists divide the earth's great body of water into four major oceans: the Pacific Ocean, Atlantic Ocean, Indian Ocean, and Arctic Ocean. The Pacific Ocean is the largest and deepest of the oceans. It is equal in area to the Atlantic and Indian oceans combined, and it contains half of the water in the earth's oceans.

The Atlantic Ocean is next in size. It extends as far north and south as the Pacific Ocean does, but it is much narrower. Whereas the Pacific Ocean is about 20,000 km in width at its widest part, the Atlantic Ocean is only about 7000 km at its widest part.

The Indian Ocean is the third largest ocean. It is slightly smaller in area than the Atlantic Ocean. However, its average depth is between the depths of the Pacific Ocean and the Atlantic Ocean.

The smallest ocean is the Arctic Ocean. It is about one twentieth the size of the Pacific Ocean. At the center of the Arctic Ocean is the North Pole. Much of the Arctic Ocean is covered by ice all year round.

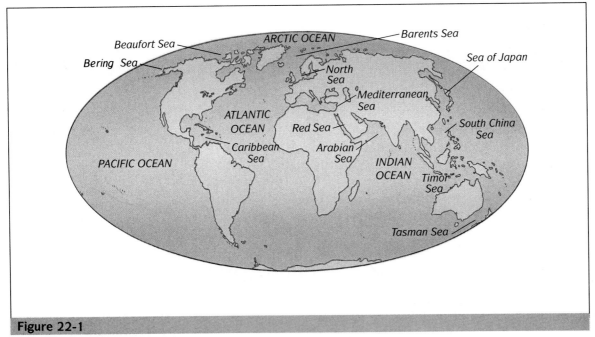

Figure 22-1

The oceans and some of the seas of the earth.

The earth also has bodies of water called seas, which are smaller than the oceans. A sea may be part of an ocean or separate from it. Notice in Figure 22-1, the Caribbean Sea is part of the Atlantic Ocean. The Mediterranean Sea, however, is separate from the Atlantic Ocean. Which sea is part of the Indian Ocean?

CONTINENTAL MARGINS

The **continental margins** are the underwater areas that border the continents. Each continental margin has three main parts: the continental shelf, the continental slope, and the continental rise.

The **continental shelf** is the gently sloping part of the continental margin that begins at the shoreline. It varies in width from almost nothing to about 1600 km, averaging about 65 km. It is widest where it borders gently sloping land. It is narrowest where it borders steep land. For example, the shelf is very narrow off the western coast of North America, which is mountainous. Compare the width of the continental shelf of North America to the continental shelf of South America. The continental shelf slopes gently, dropping an average of 0.1 m every 100 m. To the eye, the shelf would appear to be a flat surface.

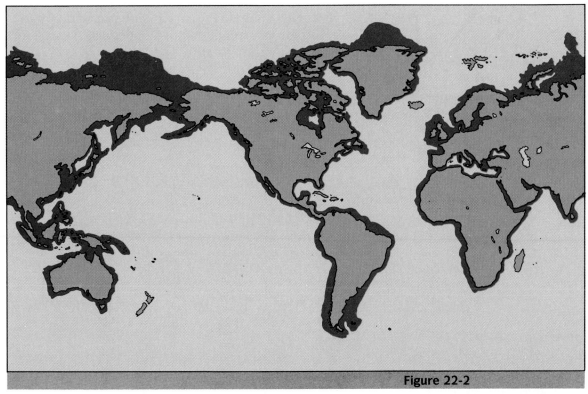

Figure 22-2

The continental shelves vary in width.

Scientists have studied the continental shelves in great detail. One reason is that the shelves are rich in resources. The shelves contain deposits of oil and natural gas. The water above the shelves is rich in nutrients. As a result, large quantities of sea life exist in these areas, making them the world's richest fishing grounds.

As a continental shelf extends out into the ocean, it gives way to a much steeper slope called the continental slope. The **continental slope** is the steep part of the continental margin. The slope drops off an average of about 70 m for each kilometer. It averages about 20 km in width.

sub (underneath)
maris (sea)

Among the main features of continental slopes are deep canyons that are cut into the surfaces and called **submarine canyons**. The canyons are similar to river valleys. They follow winding paths down the slopes, and are V-shaped. Submarine canyons can have a width across the top of 10 km and a depth of more than 300 m. One submarine canyon, the Monterey Canyon off central California, is as large as the Grand Canyon.

turbidus (turmoil)

Submarine canyons are believed to be formed by turbidity currents. **Turbidity currents** are currents caused by underwater landslides. Such landslides can be caused by earthquakes or volcanoes. As sediment slides down a slope, it mixes with the surrounding water, forming powerful currents. Currents moving up to 80 km/h can be produced. In 1929, turbidity currents snapped underwater telephone cables in the Atlantic Ocean.

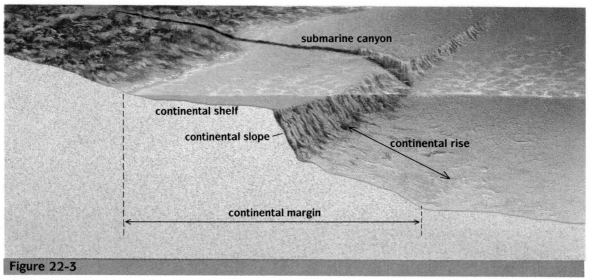

Figure 22-3

The continental slope is the steepest part of a continental margin. Submarine canyons can be found cut into the surface.

At the end of the continental slope, the ocean floor begins. Sediment that moves down the slope collects on the floor, at the foot of the slope, forming the continental rise. The **continental rise** is the part of the continental margin that begins at the continental slope and that is made of thick layers of sediment. The slope of the rise is gentle, decreasing about 6 m for each kilometer.

OCEAN BASIN FLOOR

At the lower end of each continental margin begins the ocean basin. The **ocean basin** is the deep depression that holds the surface waters of the earth. The main features of the ocean basin are the abyssal (uh BIHS uhl) plains, seamounts, and trenches.

Trenches are long, narrow features that are the deepest parts of the oceans. The bottom of the Mariana (mahr ee-AHN uh) Trench in the western Pacific Ocean is more than 11,000 m below sea level. If Mount Everest, the tallest mountain on land, were placed in this trench, there would still be over a kilometer of water above its peak.

Abyssal plains are the flat areas of the deep ocean floor. The abyssal plains are the most level areas of the earth's surface, more level than any plain on the earth's land. They are formed when sediment covers any rough or irregular parts of the ocean floor.

Seamounts are underwater volcanic mountains on the abyssal plains. Most seamounts are found in the Pacific Ocean. The largest seamount is the island of Hawaii. It rises more than 10 km above the ocean floor, making it the tallest mountain on the earth.

baccinum (vessel, bowl)

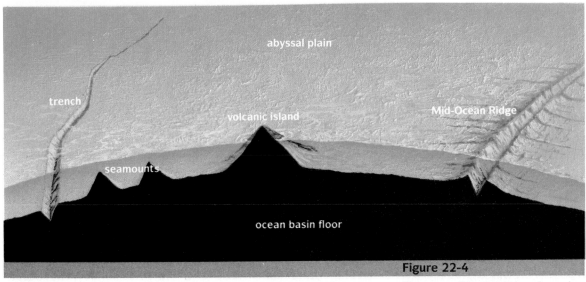

Figure 22-4

The ocean floor contains abyssal plains, seamounts, and trenches.

REVIEW

1. What are the names of the earth's four major oceans?
2. Make an outline of the main features of the continental margins and the ocean basins. Give a brief description of each feature.

CHALLENGE Explain the thick layer of sediments found at the end of submarine canyons.

22-2 OCEAN DEPOSITS

Unlike the land surface of the earth, the ocean floor has a nearly constant environment. Whereas rapid changes are common on land, they are rare beneath the ocean. Compared to the land, the ocean floor remains almost undisturbed.

OCEAN FLOOR SEDIMENT

Because the ocean floor can remain undisturbed for long periods of time, thick layers of sediment can collect. There are three sources of sediment on the ocean floor: the land, living things in the ocean, and ocean water.

One source of sediment on the ocean floor is the land. The sediment is formed by weathering and erosion of the land surface. Most of this sediment is carried from the land to the ocean by rivers.

Figure 22-5

The ocean bottom has a nearly constant environment.

Wind can also carry land sediment to the ocean. Fine particles of rock can be blown great distances out to the ocean, where they settle and become part of the ocean floor sediment. Ash and dust from volcanic eruptions can be carried by wind to the ocean. Such dust and ash can be found on almost all parts of the ocean floor.

A second source of sea-floor sediment is the remains of ocean animals and plants. This type of sediment is called **ooze** (ooz). Ooze is made up of the hard parts, such as shells and skeletons, that remain when tiny sea animals and plants die.

A third source of ocean floor sediments is sediment that comes from the minerals dissolved in ocean water. The minerals can form round objects on the ocean floor called *manganese nodules*. The nodules can contain valuable metals such as manganese, iron, copper, and nickel.

CORAL REEFS

In tropical or warm ocean waters, colorful deposits called coral reefs form where the water is shallow. **Coral reefs** are rocklike structures formed in shallow water by colonies of tiny sea animals called *corals*. Corals have soft bodies, but they form a hard shell-like material around their bodies. When they die, the hard material remains behind. Over time, the material collects, forming a reef.

There are three types of coral reefs: a fringing reef, a barrier reef, and an atoll. A *fringing reef* is a type of coral reef that forms around an island or along a coast. This is the most common type of coral reef. The reefs around the Florida Keys, for example, are fringing reefs.

Another type of coral reef is a barrier reef. A *barrier reef* is a coral reef that is separated from coastal land by water. The reef may be hundreds of kilometers long. The Great Barrier Reef is the largest coral reef on the earth. It lies off the northeastern coast of Australia.

Figure 22-6

A coral reef.

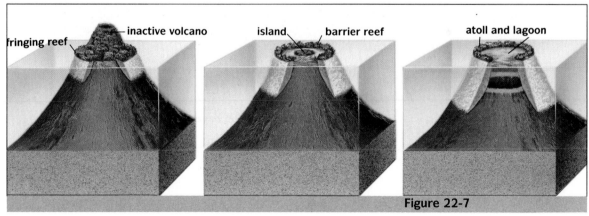

Figure 22-7

Three steps in the formation of an atoll: a fringing reef (*top*), a barrier reef (*middle*), and an atoll (*bottom*).

An **atoll** is a ring-shaped coral reef that surrounds a body of water. It does not appear to be connected to land, but it is actually attached to an underwater volcano. An atoll begins as a fringing reef around a seamount, or volcanic island. The island sinks at the same time it is worn away by waves. As the island sinks, the coral reef grows upward and forms a barrier reef. If the island sinks below the ocean surface, an atoll remains.

Reading a Seismic Sea Floor Profile

OBJECTIVE

Interpret information from a seismic sea-floor profile.

PROCEDURE

Echo sounding is a method in which sound waves are used to measure the depth of the ocean bottom. Sound waves are sent toward the ocean bottom by a ship. When the sound waves strike the bottom, the waves are reflected back to instruments on the ship. By measuring the amount of time it takes for the waves to return to the ship, the depth of the floor could be calculated. When enough measurements are made, a picture, or *seismic profile* of the ocean floor can be drawn. Study the seismic sea-floor profile of the ocean floor shown. Answer the questions below.

1. What is the length of the profile shown?
2. What is the depth of the ocean floor?
3. What is the highest elevation of the underwater mountain?
4. How deep is the deepest valley of the underwater mountain?
5. How can you tell that the underwater mountain is made of sediments?

RESULTS AND CONCLUSIONS

1. Describe the profile of the ocean floor.
2. Describe the profile of the abyssal plain.
3. What information can be read from a sea-floor profile?

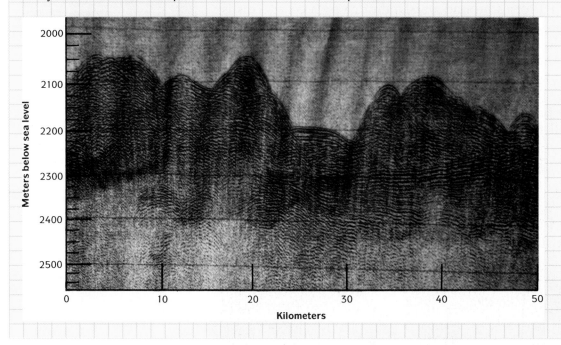

REVIEW

1. What are three sources of sediment on the ocean floor?
2. Name three kinds of coral reefs.
3. List the steps in the formation of an atoll.

CHALLENGE Where on the ocean floor would the finest sediment be found? Where would the coarsest sediment be found? Explain your answer.

22-3 OCEAN WAVES

Have you ever been to a beach and watched the ocean? If so, you probably noticed that the water was in constant motion. Most of this motion is in the form of waves.

Almost all water waves are caused by wind. When wind blows over the surface of water, it causes the water to flow with it. Because the water moves slower than the air, the water piles up, forming a wave. The wind can now push on the side of the wave, making it grow larger.

Look at the waves shown in Figure 22-8. How would you describe them? You might describe how high they are or how far apart they are from each other. These are two ways that all waves can be described.

Describing waves by how high they are refers to a characteristic of waves called the wave height. The **wave height** is the distance between the bottom part of a wave, called the *trough* (trawf), and the top part of a wave, called the *crest*. Describing waves by how far apart they are refers to a characteristic of waves called the wavelength. The **wavelength** is the distance from one crest to the next. All waves can be described by their height and wavelength.

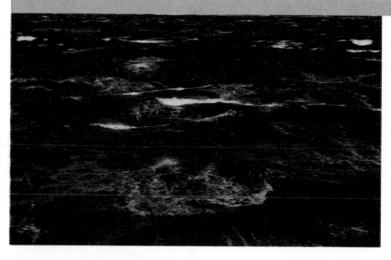

Figure 22-8

Waves can be described by their wave height and wavelength.

On a calm day, waves usually reach a height of about 3 m. However, the waves can reach a height of more than 30 m during a storm. The height of a wave depends on three factors: the speed of the wind, the length of time the wind has been blowing, and the amount of open water the wind blows across. The largest waves in the ocean form when the wind is strong and steady and blows across the ocean surface for hundreds of kilometers. The largest wave ever measured in the open ocean was 40 m in height.

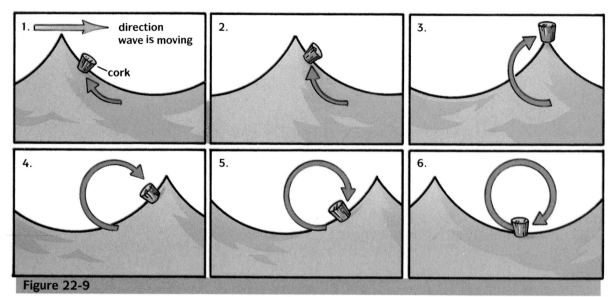

Figure 22-9

A cork floating in water illustrates how a wave moves without carrying water with it.

The motion of a water particle as a wave passes can be illustrated by a cork floating in water. As you can see in Figure 22-9, the cork is lifted up as the wave approaches. The cork is carried back and up to the crest of the wave. As the wave moves away, the cork moves down and forward to its original position. Describe the path of the cork as it rises and falls.

Figure 22-10 shows the movement of water particles as waves move through. As you can see, the particles move the way the cork moves, in circles. What happens to the size of the circles as the water becomes deeper?

Figure 22-10

Water particles move in circles in a wave

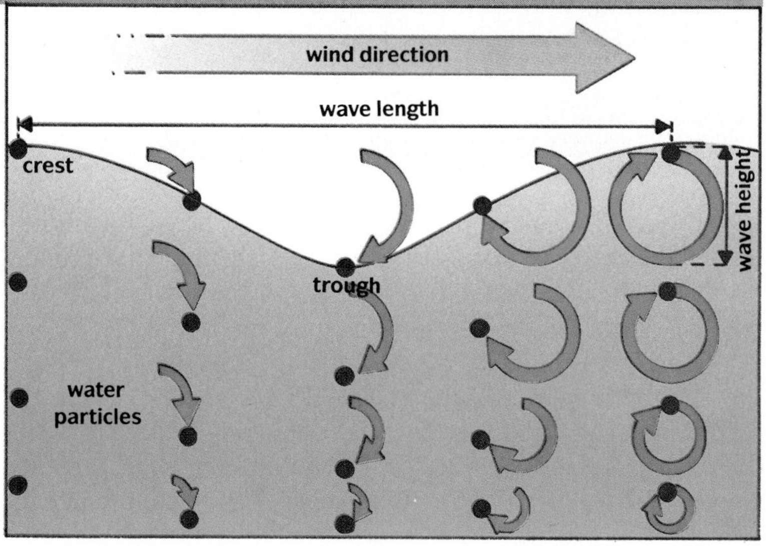

As a wave moves into shallow water near shore, the movement of the water changes. The motion of the water particles in a wave changes from a circle to an ellipse as the particles touch the bottom. This causes the water at the bottom of the wave to slow down. The wavelength shortens and the wave height increases.

When the wave height becomes too great, the crest breaks, and the water in it falls forward. A breaking wave is called a **breaker**. The water from a breaking wave is called the *surf*. The white foam produced in a breaker comes from the air that the water traps as it crashes down.

A wave can also break on the open sea if the wind is strong enough. A strong wind can blow the crest off a wave, forming a breaker called a *whitecap*. While ships can ride over waves without harm, they can be seriously damaged by large whitecaps.

The most destructive waves in the ocean are *tsunamis*. They are not formed by wind as are most other waves. They are caused by undersea volcanic explosions and earthquakes. The largest wave ever recorded was 64 m high, off the coast of Siberia in 1737. As they break and crash against the shore, tsunamis cause great destruction to buildings and houses near the shoreline.

Figure 22-11

A breaker.

REVIEW

1. What are two characteristics of waves?
2. What are three factors that determine the height of a wave?
3. How do water particles move in a wave.
4. How does a wave change its motion as it enters shallow water?

CHALLENGE Explain why large surface waves on the ocean grow larger but the small waves usually die out.

22-4 SHORELINE FEATURES

The most changing areas of the earth's surface are areas where the ocean meets land. On sandy beaches, ocean waves sweep sand along the shore or out to sea. Where ocean waves meet steep cliffs, the waves pound the faces of the cliff, wearing away huge slabs of rock.

BEACHES

The boundary between the land and sea is called the **shoreline**. Where the shoreline has not been eroded much, it is rocky and contains cliffs. The northwestern coast of North America, for example, contains many cliffs. Where cliffs have been eroded, large deposits of rock material, such as sand, gravel, and pebbles, form on the shore. A deposit of rock material along a shore is called a **beach**. Beaches cover much of the eastern shore of North America.

Figure 22-12

A pebble beach, California (*top*); a black sand beach, Hawaii (*top right*); a white sand beach, New Jersey (*bottom right*).

Not all the sand on beaches comes from the breaking up of cliffs and rocks that make up some shorelines. Rivers break up rocks inland, forming gravel and sand. The gravel and sand are carried to shorelines, where they are deposited. Beaches are usually thought of as having light-colored sand. However, many beaches do not have sand. Instead, they may be covered by pebbles or even rocks, like those shown in Figure 22-12. Some of the rocks on beaches can measure almost a meter across. The size and amount of

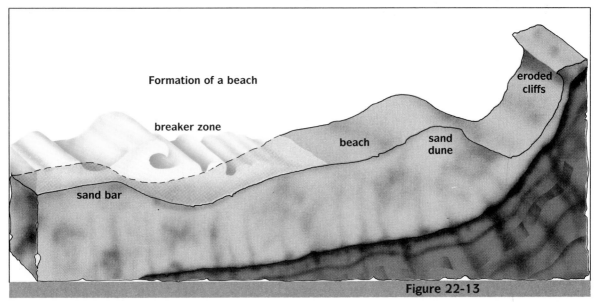

Formation of a beach

breaker zone

beach

sand dune

eroded cliffs

sand bar

Figure 22-13

A beach is made of sediment eroded from the land.

the material on a beach is determined by the age of the beach. The older the beach, the finer the material is, and the more material has collected. The western coast of North America, for example, is young and has very narrow beaches, with little sand. However, the eastern coast, being much older than the western coast, has wide beaches with large deposits of sand.

The color of the sand on a beach can vary greatly, depending on its origin. The beaches of the island of Hawaii, for example, are covered with black sand. The sand has formed from the weathering of lava flows. The light-colored sand on beaches of the eastern coast of North America comes from the weathering of granite. The white beach sand of southern Florida comes from the weathered remains of skeletons and shells of tiny sea animals.

A beach may vary between summer and winter. During the summer, the beach may be wide and contain sand. During the winter, the waves are larger and can wash away sand, leaving only gravel and reducing the width of the beach. The sand may be deposited offshore in a ridge called a *sand bar*. When the summer returns, gentle waves slowly return the sand to the beach.

Off the Gulf Coast and along much of the eastern shore of the United States, deposits of sand called barrier islands are found. A **barrier island** is a long ridge of sand in the ocean running parallel to the shoreline. Barrier islands may have once been sand dunes, or hills of sand, that became surrounded by the ocean.

Figure 22-14

A barrier island.

ROCKY SHORELINES

Some of the most unusual features of rocky shorelines are sea cliffs, sea caves, sea arches, and sea stacks. They form from headlands, or rocky points that extend out to sea from the land. As waves pound the rock, water and air are forced into cracks. This action eventually causes large slabs of rock to split off, forming a vertical cliff called a *sea cliff*.

The slabs of rock are further broken down into small pieces. The pieces of rock are picked up by the waves and help to abrade the wall of the cliff further. If the cliff contains soft rock, the waves hollow out the rock, forming a *sea cave*.

The waves may cut straight through a wall of the sea cave and form a sea arch. The *sea arch* is a kind of stone bridge that connects the land with one support in the sea. If the roof of the arch falls, the column of rock left standing in the water is called a *sea stack*. You can see sea cliffs, caves, arches, and stacks along the coasts of Oregon, Washington, California, and Maine.

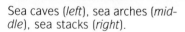

Sea caves (*left*), sea arches (*middle*), sea stacks (*right*).

LONGSHORE CURRENT

Ocean waves usually do not come straight into shore. Instead, they strike at an angle. As a result, water near the shore is pushed along the shoreline, forming a current called a longshore current. A **longshore current** is an ocean current that moves closely along the shore. Longshore currents can carry large amounts of sand along the shorelines. A longshore current can be compared to a conveyor belt. After sand is washed from a beach, it is transported by the longshore current.

In places where the shoreline changes direction, the longshore current slows down and deposits sand. In bays, for example, such a current leaves deposits of sand called spits. A *spit* is a deposit of sand that extends from land into the mouth of a bay. Look at Figure 22-16. In what direction is the longshore current moving?

If a longshore current is weak around a bay, it can deposit enough sand to completely cross the bay. A deposit of sand that completely crosses a bay is called a *baymouth bar*. A baymouth bar begins as a spit but eventually reaches across the entire bay.

Figure 22-16

A spit has formed from sand moved along the beach by a long-shore current.

OBJECTIVE

Demonstrate how cold and hot water mix.

MATERIALS

hot plate, 2 beakers, food coloring or ink, plastic straw

PROCEDURE

A. Fill a beaker with very cold water.
B. Fill another beaker with very hot water.
C. Add enough food coloring to the hot water so that the color is easily seen. Use a drinking straw to stir the mixture.
D. Use the straw to remove some of the colored water. Do this by inserting the straw into the colored water. Tightly cover the top of the straw with your finger. (*Do not use your mouth*.) With the top covered, lift the straw straight up out of the water.

E. Keeping the top covered, put the open end of the straw in the clear water near the bottom. Remove your finger from the top of the straw to release the colored water.
   1. What happens to the colored water?
F. Repeat steps D and E by putting some cold colored water into hot clear water.
   2. What happens to the cold water?

RESULTS AND CONCLUSIONS

What effect did the temperature have on the way the two liquids mixed?

EXTENSION

Try the experiment again, this time using hot and cold *salt* water. Are the results similar?

Figure 22-17

Jetties are placed on a beach to trap sand.

A longshore current also deposits sand around islands. As the current slows down around the islands, it may deposit enough sand to connect the islands or connect an island to a mainland. These deposits of sand are called *tombolos* (TAHM buh lohs).

Sand is also deposited by longshore currents around piers and similar human-made structures that extend out into the ocean. Sometimes such structures are built with the purpose of trapping sand for beaches. For example, walls called *groins* are built along open coasts. Piles of rocks called *jetties* are built on at the mouths of rivers to prevent erosion of beaches. Groins and jetties extend from the beaches into the ocean and trap sand that is carried by longshore currents. However, this causes longshore currents to become depleted of sand. Beaches farther down from the current lose their supply of sand and erode faster.

REVIEW

1. Why do materials on beaches vary?
2. How do the features on rocky shorelines compare with those on shorelines that have beaches.
3. What are three features produced by wave erosion?
4. What are three kinds of wave deposits?

CHALLENGE Explain why waves erode shorelines that have cliffs more quickly than they erode shorelines that have beaches.

22-5 OCEAN CURRENTS

As you have learned, wind can cause water at the surface of the ocean to move. When water flows in one direction, it is called a current. When wind blows over the surface of the ocean, surface water is moved, forming a surface current. Deeper water rises and replaces the surface water, forming a deep ocean current. Surface ocean currents and deep ocean currents are two ways in which water in the ocean is circulated.

SURFACE OCEAN CURRENTS

Wind blowing across the ocean causes the surface waters to begin moving in the same direction as the wind. However, currents do not continue moving in the same direction as the wind. Land can cause the currents to change direction by blocking their path. The earth's rotation causes the currents to bend to the right in the

After completing this section, you will be able to

- **describe** two major surface currents in the oceans.
- **explain** two ways that deep ocean currents can form.
- **explain** how cold, deep water can rise along coasts.

The key terms in this section are
gyres   upwelling

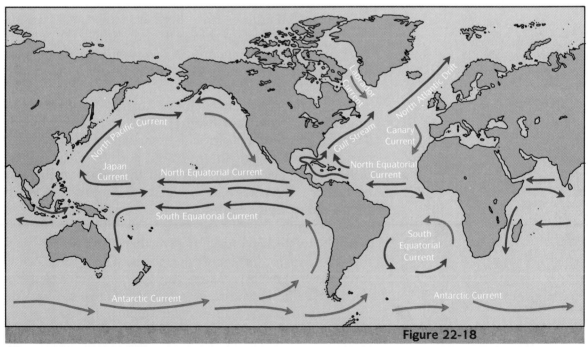

Figure 22-18

The major ocean surface currents.

Northern Hemisphere and to the left in the Southern Hemisphere. This bending of the current's path is called the *Coriolis effect.*

The Coriolis effect causes the currents to move in a circular pattern. The circular patterns of the major ocean currents are called **gyres** (jīrz). Figure 22-18 shows the circular patterns of the surface currents of the earth's oceans.

gyrus (circle)

Figure 22-19

This satellite image shows the Gulf Stream as purple.

In the Atlantic Ocean, there are two major currents flowing in circular patterns north and south of the equator. They are the *North Equatorial Current* and the *South Equatorial Current*. The energy for these currents comes from the trade winds blowing toward the equator. The Coriolis effect and the continent of South America force the North Equatorial Current northward. The current moves northwest to the Gulf of Mexico. Some of the water of the current flows toward the northern part of Cuba, and the other part of the current flows off the shores of the Gulf of Mexico. The parts come together again in the straits of Florida to form the Gulf Stream. Describe the path of the Gulf Stream.

The westerly winds of the Northern Hemisphere push the Gulf Stream farther to the north, where the Coriolis force pushes it east. When the Gulf Stream enters the northern Atlantic Ocean, it branches into two weaker currents. What are the names of these currents?

The currents that move the water in the North Atlantic circle an area in the center that has no major currents. This area of quiet waters is known as the *Sargasso Sea*, named for a brown seaweed, sargassum, that floats on the surface of the water.

The Pacific Ocean has currents similar to those in the Atlantic Ocean. In the Pacific Ocean, the North Equatorial Current travels west, where it meets barrier islands along the coast of Asia. The current turns north, forming the *Japan Current*. The current then travels northeast, across the Pacific Ocean, as the *North Pacific Current*. The current moves south along the west coast of North America, bringing cold water from the northern Pacific Ocean. Eventually, it joins the North Equatorial Current.

There are also currents in the Southern Hemisphere. The most powerful current here is the *Antarctic Current*. Since there are no land masses to block the current, it travels completely around Antarctica in a circle.

DEEP OCEAN CURRENTS

Surface currents may reach 100 m deep in the ocean. Other currents, called deep ocean currents, can occur several kilometers below the surface. They are caused by differences in density of the water.

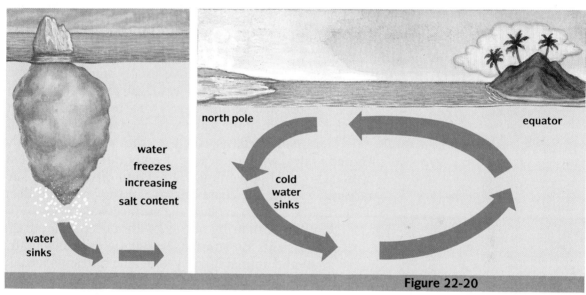

Figure 22-20

Deep ocean currents form from differences in the density of water (*left*) and in the temperature of water (*right*).

The density of water depends on its temperature and its salinity. When water at the surface cools, it becomes denser and sinks. Water also becomes denser when its salinity, or saltiness, increases. The forming of ice can increase the salinity of the remaining water. Freezing water, like evaporating it, leaves salt behind. Thus when water freezes, the salinity and density of the remaining water increases. This causes the water to sink.

As water sinks to the bottom, it pushes the water on the bottom outward in all directions. Some of the cold, deep water may mix with warmer water above, causing the combined waters to rise. The remaining deep water may continue to circulate on the bottom for as long as a thousand years.

The tides in the Bay of Fundy, in southeastern Canada, are the largest in the world, with a tidal range of more than 15 m.

An experimental power plant that harnesses the tide here can produce about 50 million kilowatt-hours of electric power a year. This is enough electricity for about 500 homes. The power plant uses a turbine that catches the energy of flowing water. This turbine generates electricity only when the tide flows out. When the tide comes in, gates to the turbine are opened, and the water flows into a holding pond. When the tide turns and begins to flow back out, the trapped tidal water rushes through the turbine. Electric power can be produced for about six hours.

A large-scale tidal plant with 128 turbines is presently under development in the bay. This plant will produce about 40 million kilowatt-hours per day, or enough electric power for about 40,000 homes. The tidal power planners believe that some of this power could also be used by United States power agencies. Many states would welcome power that is clean, renewable, and nonpolluting.

Deep ocean currents move much more slowly than surface currents. The sinking, cold, salty water at the poles usually takes 300 or more years to reach the equator. Describe the path of the water when it reaches the equator.

Along some coasts, such as the west coast of the United States, wind can cause deep ocean water to rise in a process called **upwelling**. Here, wind causes warm surface water along the coast to move out to sea. Cold deep water below rises to replace the surface water.

Upwelling can bring nutrients from deep water to the surface. Nutrients are substances that are used as food for some plant and animal life in water. The nutrients usually are washed into the ocean by rivers. Near the surface of the ocean, where the water is warm and sunlight reaches, plant life and tiny sea animals can deplete the supply of nutrients. However, the nutrients remain unused in deep ocean waters, where little sea life exists. Upwelling brings those nutrients to the surface. The nutrients can support tiny sea life, which attracts abundant fish.

REVIEW

1. Describe two major surface currents in the oceans.
2. Explain two causes of deep ocean currents.
3. What can cause cold, deep water to rise along coasts?

CHALLENGE Along the California coast, the wind blows parallel to the shore. Why does the surface water along the shore move out to sea instead of along the coast?

22-6 TIDES

For people living along the shore, tides can be as important as the weather. Tides can cause the water level to rise as much as 15 m, twice a day, covering large areas of the shore with water. Each day, changes occur in water level over the earth at every shoreline.

The periodic rise and fall in the level of the ocean is called the *tides*. Tides are caused by the pull of the sun's and moon's gravity. The moon, being much closer to the earth than the sun, has a much greater effect on the tides. On the side of the earth facing the moon, ocean water is pulled toward the moon and away from the earth. This forms a *tidal bulge*, or high tide.

A tidal bulge also occurs on the other side of the earth. Here, the solid earth is closer to the moon than the ocean is. As a result, the solid earth is pulled to the moon more than the water is. The water appears to be pulled from the earth in another tidal bulge. Thus at any time, there are two tidal bulges on the earth.

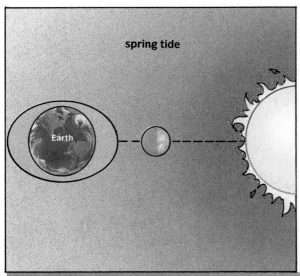
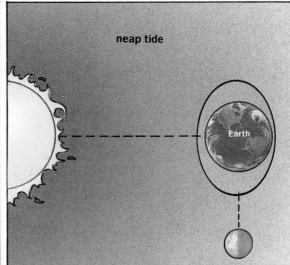

spring tide   neap tide

Earth   Earth

Figure 22-21

The greatest tidal range occurs during the spring tide, when the earth, moon, and sun are in line (*left*). A smaller tidal range occurs during the neap tide, when the sun and moon form a right angle with the earth (*right*).

The sun also causes two tidal bulges. Because the sun's pull of gravity on the ocean is much less than the moon's pull of gravity, the tidal bulges caused by the sun are very small. However, twice a month, the sun and moon are in the same line with the earth. Then the sun's pull is added to the moon's pull. Tides higher than usual, called **spring tides**, form. At the same time, the low tides are lower than normal. The tidal range is greatest during the spring tides.

The sun and moon can form a right angle with the earth. Then the moon's effect on the ocean is partly reduced by the sun's pull. There is little change in the level of water between high tide and low tide. These weaker tides are called **neap tides**. Using Figure 22-21, compare the tidal range during the spring tides and neap tides.

The two areas of ocean between the bulges supply water to fill the bulges. Here the water levels fall and form two low tides. The difference in the water level between low tide and high tide is called the *tidal range*.

The tidal bulges remain in place as the earth rotates. This causes many places on the earth to have two high tides and two low tides each day. However, because the moon is also moving in the same direction as the earth rotates, the tides occur about 50 minutes later each day.

Figure 22-22

Mount St. Michel at high tide (*left*) and at low tide (*right*).

The tidal range in the open ocean is less than a meter. Tidal ranges near coastal areas can change, depending on three factors. The factors are the shape of the ocean basin, the depth of the ocean basin, and the shape of the coastlines. In the Mediterranean Sea, the tides change by about a third of a meter. In the Bay of Fundy on the southeastern coast of Canada, the tidal range is about 15 m. In fact, the tide there rises about 3 m in 10 minutes!

At the mouth of a river or bay, the incoming tide can be channeled into the river or bay. Where the tidal range is large, the tide rushes in, forming waves called a *tidal bore*. The waves can move upstream for more than 10 km and at a speed up to 15 km/h. Some tidal bores can be used for surfing.

REVIEW

1. What causes tides?
2. How do the moon and sun together affect tides on the earth?
3. What are some factors that affect the change in tides in local areas?

CHALLENGE The moon travels in an elliptical path rather than a circular path around the earth. Explain how this would affect tides.

Figure 22-23

A tidal bore.

CHAPTER SUMMARY

The main ideas in this chapter are listed below. Read these statements before you answer the Chapter Review questions.

- The earth has four major oceans: the Pacific Ocean, the Atlantic Ocean, the Indian Ocean, and the Arctic Ocean. (22-1)

- The ocean floor has mountain ranges, underwater volcanoes, trenches, and vast plains. (22-1)

- Most of the sediment deposited on the ocean floor comes from weathering and erosion of the land surface. (22-2)

- In the tropical parts of oceans, deposits called coral reefs form around islands or near coastlines. (22-2)

- Almost all ocean waves are formed by wind blowing on the ocean surface. (22-3)

- Features such as beaches and cliffs, formed along shorelines, are the result of wave action. (22-4)

- Large amounts of sand are moved along beaches by longshore currents. (22-4)

- Surface currents are formed by wind, whereas deep-ocean currents are formed by differences in temperature and salinity. (22-5)

- The pull of gravity of the moon and the sun causes the level of the ocean to rise and fall periodically. (22-6)

The key terms in this chapter are listed below. Use each term in a sentence that shows the meaning of the term.

abyssal plains	continental shelf	neap tide	submarine canyon
atoll	continental slope	ooze	turbidity current
barrier island	coral reefs	seamounts	upwelling
breaker	gyres	shoreline	waveheight
continental margin	longshore current	spring tide	wavelength
continental rise			

Chapter Review

VOCABULARY

Write the letter of the term that best matches the definition. Not all the terms will be used.

1. Deepest part of the ocean
2. Part of the continent underwater
3. Highest high tide
4. Current carrying sediment
5. Valley on continental slope
6. Volcanoes on the ocean floor
7. Deep current that rises to ocean
8. When a wave crest falls foward
9. Shell-like material deposited
10. Flows parallel to the shore
11. Flat area of the ocean floor
12. Steepest part of the continental margin

a. turbidity current
b. coral reef
c. upwelling
d. submarine canyon
e. longshore current
f. spring tide
g. breaker
h. gyre
i. continental slope
j. trench
k. neap tide
l. continental shelf
m. seamounts
n. continental rise
o. abyssal plain

CONCEPTS

1. List, in order of size, the major oceans of the earth. (22-1)
2. Explain how submarine canyons form. (22-1)
3. Compare the topographies of the continental margins and ocean basins. (22-1)
4. Explain how most sediment reaches the ocean floor. (22-2)
5. Describe three kinds of coral reefs. (22-2)
6. How are atolls related to seamounts? (22-2)
7. What is the difference between the wave height and wavelength of a wave? (22-3)
8. How does a large wave form in the ocean? (22-3)
9. Compare the motion of a water particle in a wave with a cork floating on a water wave. (22-3)
10. How does the cause of a wave breaking on shore compare with the cause of a wave breaking on the open ocean? (22-3)
11. Why do beach materials differ in size and color? (22-4)
12. Why do rocky shorelines erode more quickly than shorelines with beaches? (22-4)
13. List the steps in the formation of a sea stack from a sea cliff. (22-4)
14. Explain how a longshore current forms. (22-4)
15. Describe the path of the Gulf Stream. (22-5)

16. Why is fishing concentrated in areas of upwelling? (22-5)

17. Explain how deep ocean water circulates. (22-5)

18. Compare the way tides are caused on the side of the earth facing the moon with the way they are caused on the side of the earth facing away. (22-6)

19. Compare the effect of the sun on tides to the moon's effect on tides. (22-6)

20. Why don't all areas have the same rise and fall of water level during tides? (22-6)

APPLICATION/
CRITICAL
THINKING

1. How might the thickness of sediment on the continental shelves be used to determine the age of the earth?

2. What causes driftwood to wash up onto the beach?

3. Think about the various parts of a wave. Where would a submarine have to go to escape the motion of surface waves?

4. The climate of southern Florida is affected by the Gulf Stream. How does this explain the fact that the climate in southern Florida is warmer than that in northern Florida?

5. Winds north of the Sargasso Sea in the North Atlantic Ocean blow toward the east while winds south of the sea blow toward the west. Explain why seaweed in the Sargasso Sea is pushed toward the center.

6. Explain why the water off the beaches in southern California is much colder than the water off the beaches in southern Florida.

EXTENSION

1. Go to the library to get information about guyots. What is the origin of the name?

2. Find out why the cliff divers at Acapulco, Mexico, must jump at the right moment if they are to dive safely.

3. There are certain places on earth that are ideal for surfing. Find out where those places are and why the special breaking waves occur there.

4. Go to the library and find out how the salinities of the Red Sea, the Black Sea, the Mediterranean Sea, and the Great Salt Lake compare.

READINGS

Asimov, Isaac. *How Did We Find Out About Life in the Deep Sea?* New York, Walker. 1982.

"El Niña." *National Geographic.* February 1984, p. 144.

Sacjett, Russell. *Edge of the Sea.* Alexandria, Va.: Time-Life, Inc., 1983.

"A Walk in the Deep." *National Geographic.* May 1980, p. 624.

OCEAN RESOURCES

Have you ever been in a forest such as the one shown in this photograph? The plants shown here are called kelps. Kelps are a type of seaweed. Seaweed is used for food in many parts of the world. Some people have suggested that kelps could be used to produce methane gas.

- *What other kinds of food do the oceans supply?*
- *What other types of resources are obtained from the oceans?*
- *How do the activities of humans endanger the oceans?*

23-1 COMPOSITION OF SEAWATER

How is seawater different from lake water? Of course, seawater is salty. Samples of seawater collected from around the earth have been studied. Seawater is a complex solution. It contains most of the elements that are found on the earth. On the average, seawater is 96.5 percent water. Only 3.5 percent is salts, along with very small amounts of other compounds and elements. The salts give seawater its salty taste.

The **salinity** (suh LIHN uh tee), or saltiness, of seawater is defined as the number of grams of dissolved salt in a kilogram of seawater. If a kilogram of seawater is left to evaporate, about 35 g of matter remains. Thus the average salinity of seawater is 35 g/kg.

The salinity of the ocean varies from place to place. Near the mouth of a river the salinity of the ocean is lower. In places where evaporation is rapid or where freezing occurs, the salinity is higher than average. Why would salinity be higher under such conditions? Although salinity varies, it is seldom less than 33 g/kg or more than 38 g/kg. In deep water, there is even less variation.

> *After completing this section, you will be able to*
>
> - **list** the major components of seawater.
> - **describe** a hypothesis that explains why the oceans are salty.
> - **identify** factors that affect the composition of seawater.
>
> *The key terms in this section are*
> degassing   salinity

salis (salt)

543

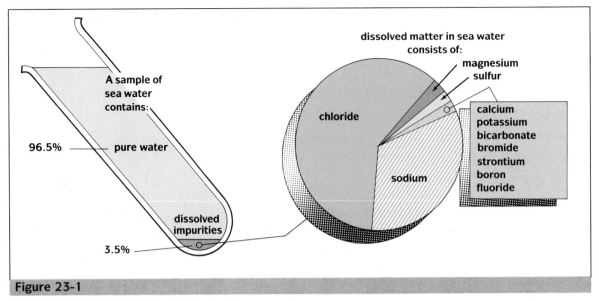

Figure 23-1

Dissolved minerals make up about 3.5 percent of seawater.

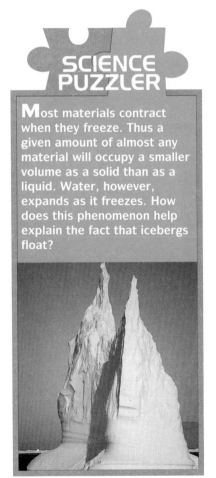

SCIENCE PUZZLER

Most materials contract when they freeze. Thus a given amount of almost any material will occupy a smaller volume as a solid than as a liquid. Water, however, expands as it freezes. How does this phenomenon help explain the fact that icebergs float?

Although the salinity of the ocean varies, the ratio of the most abundant salts to each other does not change. When water evaporates from the ocean or is added to the ocean, the salts are not affected. So the ratio of salts does not vary. The fact that the ratio does not vary indicates that the ocean is well mixed. Currents carry water throughout the ocean. Cold water sinks and warm water rises. The major oceans are continuous around Antarctica. The constant movement of water within each ocean and among the oceans causes the salts to mix.

Figure 23-1 lists the most common materials in seawater. What two materials make up most of the dissolved matter? What familiar substance do these two materials make up?

How did seawater come to contain so much dissolved material? Early in its history, the earth was a much hotter place. Much of the original gases probably escaped the earth's gravity. Liquid water could not collect on the earth's surface because the surface was too hot. Volcanic activity constantly released more gases. The process in which gases are released by volcanic activity is called **degassing**. Only when the earth cooled enough could gravity hold the degassed matter and could rain water collect on its surface. This rain water carried with it degassed matter from the early atmosphere. The matter contained salts. It is likely that when the first ocean formed on the earth, it contained these salts also.

As water evaporated from the early ocean, the salts were left behind. In time, rain water washed more salts

Salts added from rivers, volcanic activity, and mid-ocean ridges.

Gases added from atmosphere (nitrogen oxygen, carbon dioxide) and plants (oxygen).

Salts removed by living things and sediment formation.

Gases removed by living things (oxygen, carbon dioxide) and a rise in ocean temperature.

Figure 23-2

Gases and salts are constantly being added to and removed from the sea.

from the air and also from rocks on the earth. These materials, too, were added to the seawater. Finally, the ocean became as salty as it is today.

There is a constant cycling of salts to and from the ocean. Salts are added at the Mid-Ocean Ridges by volcanoes. Salts are also added by rivers that empty into the ocean. At the same time, living things remove salts from the water. And salts become buried in the ocean floor. These processes balance each other, since the ocean's salt content does not seem to be changing today.

Although the salt content of seawater is very stable, the amounts of gases found in seawater vary. There are more gases in surface water because this water interacts with air. Carbon dioxide, nitrogen, and oxygen are added to seawater from the air. These are seawater's most abundant gases. Living things change the amounts of the gases in seawater. For example, plants in the upper layers of the ocean, which are reached by sunlight, add oxygen through photosynthesis. Living things also remove oxygen and add carbon dioxide to the ocean. Another factor affecting the amounts of dissolved gases in seawater is temperature. Cold water can hold more dissolved gas than can warm water. When cold surface water sinks below warmer water, it carries with it a rich supply of gases. For this reason, animals are able to live in cold water deep in the ocean.

ACTIVITY   Salinity Affects Floating Objects

OBJECTIVE
Determine the effect of salinity on floating objects.

MATERIALS
scissors, ruler, masking tape, metric scale, pen or pencil, plastic drinking straw, modeling clay, 2-L container, tap water, 1-L graduate, balance, table salt, glass stirring rod

PROCEDURE
A. Copy the table.

B. Cut a 10-cm length of masking tape with scissors. Draw a line 8 cm long down the center of the tape. Mark a scale on the line by placing lines at 1- mm intervals. Make the first line and every fifth line longer than the others.

C. Attach the tape to the straw, as shown in the drawing. The zero end of the scale should be even with the end of the straw.

D. Make a small ball of clay (about 2 cm in diameter). Push the clay onto the end of the straw away from the scale.

E. Add 1 L of water to the 2-L container. Carefully place the straw into the container with the clay end down. If the straw does not float upright, clay can be added or taken away until it does. In the table, record under "0 g" the number from the scale at the water's surface.

F. Carefully remove the straw from the container. Measure 10 g of table salt on a balance and stir it into the water with a stirring rod. Carefully replace the straw into the water and record the number at the water's surface.

   1. Does the straw float higher or lower in the salt solution?

G. Repeat step **F** four more times. Record the number from the scale each time.

H. Graph your data. Show the grams of salt on the x-axis and the scale readings on the y-axis.

   2. Does the straw change position each time you add more salt?

   3. Does the straw change position by the same amount each time you add salt?

RESULTS AND CONCLUSIONS
1. Do objects float easier in salt water than in fresh water?
2. The salinity of the Great Salt Lake, in Utah, is about 6 times greater than that of seawater. How would this amount affect the way objects float in the lake?
3. How could an instrument like the floating straw be used to measure the salinity of seawater?

Table

Salt Content (g)	0	10	20	30	40	50
Reading on straw						

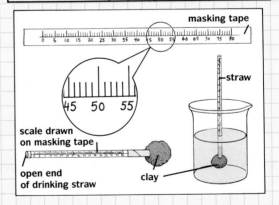

REVIEW

1. What are the most common substances in seawater?
2. How do scientists think that the oceans became salty?
3. What factors affect the amounts of dissolved gases found in seawater?

CHALLENGE What effect would the formation of a new volcanic island in the Hawaiian chain have on the composition of the ocean around Hawaii? Would any change be permanent? Explain your answers.

23-2 OCEAN LIFE

The ocean is a very stable environment. Most chemical and physical properties of seawater change little from one place to another. However, pressure changes greatly with depth. Pressure increases at a rate of one atmosphere, the atmospheric pressure at sea level, for each 10 m of depth. At 100 m the pressure of the water equals the pressure of 10 atmospheres. At any particular depth, however, the pressure is constant. Different living things are adapted to different depths or pressures in the ocean.

Living things in the ocean are divided into three groups, based on where they live and their habits. **Plankton** (PLANGK-tuhn) are microscopic plants and animals that float near the surface. Plankton make up the largest group of living things in the ocean. Figure 23-3 shows a sample of the many microscopic creatures that make up plankton. Many kinds of plankton cannot swim. Rather, they float with the ocean currents in the surface waters. The simple plants and plantlike organisms in plankton are called *phytoplankton*. Phytoplankton produce 80 percent of the atmosphere's oxygen through photosynthesis.

plankton (drifting)

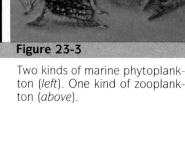

Figure 23-3

Two kinds of marine phytoplankton (*left*). One kind of zooplankton (*above*).

Phytoplankton are the primary producers in the ocean food web. A *food web* describes how energy flows from organism to organism in an environment. Figure 23-4 shows an ocean food web. *Zooplankton,* the tiny animals in plankton, get their energy by feeding on phytoplankton. Small shrimp, small fish, and other organisms feed on plankton. Larger animals feed on these shrimp and fish. In this way, energy moves from the producers to other organisms in the food web. Finally, scavengers and bac-

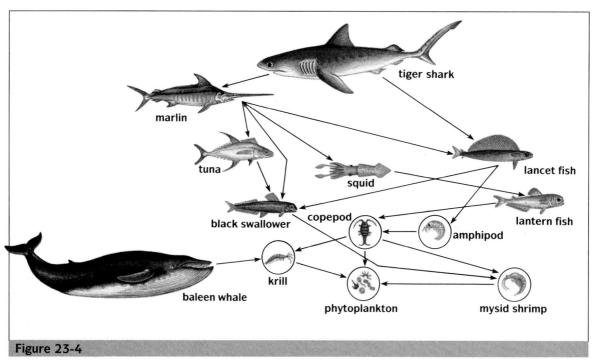

Figure 23-4

An ocean food web.

nekton (to swim)

benthos (depth of the sea)

teria feed on dead and dying creatures. Breaking down the remains of once-living creatures returns nutrients to the water. Plankton are abundant on the continental shelf areas and where upwelling brings nutrients to the surface.

A second group of living things in the ocean is called nekton (NEHK tahn). **Nekton** are living things that swim through the water. Swimming enables these creatures to search for food and to escape predators. Fish, whales, and squid belong to this group. Nekton are found throughout the oceans. What are some nekton in Figure 23-5?

A third group of living things within the ocean is called benthos (BEHN thahs). **Benthos** are plants and animals that live on the ocean floor. Most benthic plants are found in continental shelf areas where the water is less than 30 m deep. Why are benthic plants found in fairly shallow water?

There are many kinds of benthic animals, including crabs, clams, and starfish. Such benthic animals as barnacles and sea anemones attach themselves to the ocean floor. Corals not only attach to the ocean floor, but to the shells of old corals as well. In this way, these animals build coral reefs. A few benthic animals live in the deepest parts of the oceans. Identify some benthos in Figure 23-5.

Although conditions in the ocean are stable, there are different environments that can be described within the ocean. Figure 23-5 shows these zones. The **shore zone,** the harshest ocean zone, is the area between the high-tide line and the low-tide line. Clams, crabs, seaweeds, and marine worms are examples of life forms that are found in the shore zone.

The **neritic** (nih RIHT ihk) **zone** extends from the low-tide line to the edges of the continental shelves. In this zone, the temperature is stable. Sunlight reaches the bottom. Because sunlight penetrates this area, many photosynthetic organisms are found in this zone. Seaweed and plankton are the main producers. Many fish, as well as lobsters and porpoises, live in the neritic zone.

The **oceanic zone** is the ocean area beyond the continental shelves. The oceanic zone is divided into three regions. The top 200 m is the *light region*. Plankton and nekton are found in this zone. The *bathyal* (BATH ee uhl) *region* extends from 200 m to a depth of 2000 m. Many kinds of nekton, including octopuses and sharks, live in the bathyal region. The *abyssal* (uh BIHS uhl) region extends from 2000 m to the ocean floor. In the abyssal region there is no sunlight, little food, very low temperatures, and extremely high pressures. Yet some animals live there. What adaptations does the angler fish in Figure 23-5 have that helps it to attract food?

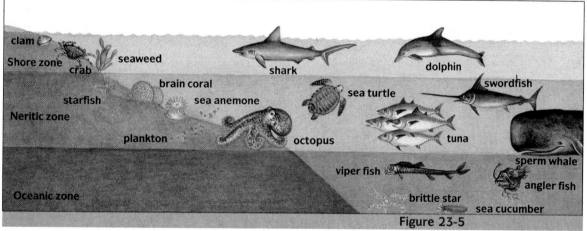

Figure 23-5

The three levels of the ocean support various types of organisms. The angular fish has adapted to life in the deep sea (*top*).

REVIEW

1. Give two examples of nekton and two examples of benthos.
2. What is the role of phytoplankton in an ocean food web?
3. Compare the shore zone with the neritic zone.

CHALLENGE A species of seaweed is found to have holdfasts, which are adaptations for clinging to material. In which zone are such seaweed likely to live? Why?

23-3 RESOURCES FROM THE SEA

The oceans have been used by people throughout history as a source of food and a means of travel. Oceans were a trade link between early nations. Today, the population of the earth is rapidly increasing. More and more, people are looking toward the ocean as a source of food, fresh water, energy, raw materials, and perhaps as a place to live.

The ocean is already an important source of food. Fishing vessels equipped with sonar locate and gather large schools of fish. Some fish are sold fresh in seacoast areas. Many large fishing vessels have complete processing plants to preserve the catch. These ships either freeze or can the fish as it is brought in. The fishing industry takes more than 60 million tons of food from the ocean each year. About 90 percent of this food is fish such as herring, cod, and salmon. The remaining 10 percent includes animals like lobsters, clams, and shrimp.

Figure 23-6

A modern fishing vessel off the coast of California (*left*). A commercial shrimp-fishing vessel in Alabama (*right*).

Seaweed is also harvested as a source of food. In some countries, seaweed is used in salads, soups, and other recipes. Seaweed is also used in the production of foods. For example, seaweed products are used when making ice cream and creamy salad dressings.

Many scientists think the ocean can produce more food. One species that is a potential food source is krill, shown in Figure 23-7. **Krill** are shrimplike creatures that live in the cold waters around Antarctica. Scientists think that krill can be gathered in large quantities without damaging the food web. Krill can be prepared and eaten like shrimp or used in other food products.

Another way to increase the productivity of the sea is by setting up sea farms. People already farm seaweed in shallow water. Shellfish such as clams and oysters are farmed on lines that hang into the water. The shellfish can then be easily collected. The farming of fish may require fencing in large areas of ocean and forcing mineral-rich waters through the fenced areas. Scientists are studying the possibility of fish farms. But it may be some time before they become a reality.

Seawater may also become an important source of fresh water in the future. Fresh water is needed by many kinds of living things. But 97 percent of the earth's water is seawater. As the population of the earth increases, the need for fresh water grows.

The process of removing salts from seawater is called **desalination** (dee sal uh NAY shuhn). Figure 23-8 shows a simple desalination device. Notice that the sun causes water to evaporate. The water vapor then condenses on the clear panels at the top. It runs down the panels and drops into the center channel. Though this simple device is not costly, it produces only small amounts of fresh water. Large desalination plants use much energy to increase the production of fresh water. The cost of building a plant and the cost of the energy make desalinated water very expensive. New ways of removing salts from seawater,

Figure 23-7

Krill may be the protein source of the future.

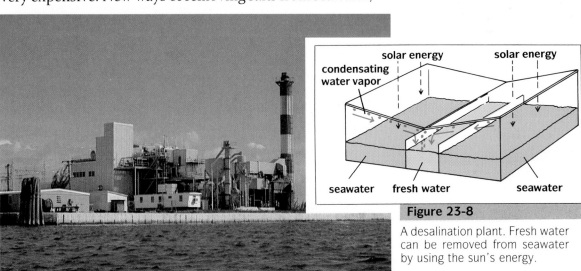

Figure 23-8

A desalination plant. Fresh water can be removed from seawater by using the sun's energy.

such as special filters that let pure water pass through, are being tested. In the future, scientists hope to be able to remove the salts from seawater cheaply.

The ocean is being considered as a source of energy. Large quantities of oil and natural gas have been found beneath the ocean. Tidal power is used to produce electrical energy in certain bays.

The ocean is also a source of minerals. Minerals are added to the oceans by rivers, sea-floor spreading, volcanic activity, and winds that carry matter from the land. Some of these minerals remain dissolved in the water. Table salt, bromine, and magnesium are removed from seawater by evaporating the water and collecting the dried matter. Other materials settle in various places in the ocean and must be collected from the ocean floor.

Near the shores are deposits of heavy minerals called placers. Placers settle quickly when they wash into the ocean from land areas. Placers that contain sulfur and placers that contain phosphorus have been found. Sand and gravel are also taken from deposits near the shores. Tin can be removed from such deposits.

SCIENCE & TECHNOLOGY

Hot water vents on the ocean floor may be new commercial sources of metals. One of the first discoveries of these vents was made in the Red Sea. Oceanographers found very salty, metal-rich pools in several basins along the sea floor. The metals found were copper, lead, manganese, and zinc. Researchers believe that the vents are formed when seawater penetrates cracks in the seafloor. As it flows through hot rock, the seawater dissolves metals from the rock. When the salty, metal-laden water rises again, the metals come out of solution, and are deposited in the sediment, or they collect in pools on the sea floor.

A second type of hot water vent containing rich metal deposits has also been found. Rather than pools, oceanographers found tall mounds of sulfides, compounds of sulfur and metals. The metals found in these mounds included copper, iron, and zinc. Some of the metal mounds were 30m tall and were topped by chimneylike vents. Very hot fluid, up to 325°C, flowed out of the vents. Scientists believe that the metals built up the mounds around vents.

Hot water vents may become economically important sources of metals. Studying such sea floor deposits will also help scientists learn how metal deposits are formed.

ACTIVITY   Desalinating Seawater

OBJECTIVE
Prepare a sample of fresh water from artificial seawater.

MATERIALS
safety goggles, artificial seawater, graduate, flask, 250-mL beaker, large test tube, tap water, ice, one-hole stopper, 2 pieces of glass tubing, rubber hose, burner stand, Bunsen burner

PROCEDURE
A. Put on safety goggles. Be sure that all glassware is clean. Measure 50 mL of artificial seawater (colored salt water) with a graduate. Pour the seawater into a flask.

B. Set up the equipment as shown in the drawing. **Caution:** Use care when inserting the glass tubing into the one-hole stopper. The beaker should be three-fourths full of ice and cold water. The second piece of glass tubing connects to one end of the rubber hose. This piece of glass tubing goes into the test tube. Notice that the rubber hose is connected to the glass tubing in the stopper.

1. How has the color of the seawater changed?
2. What do you think the liquid in the test tube is?

D. Be very careful with the hot equipment! Remove the test tube from the beaker.
E. Use the graduate to measure the liquid that collected in the test tube.
   3. How much water collected in the test tube?
   4. How does this amount compare with the amount of seawater that you started with? Explain any difference that you find.
F. Before doing the next part, be sure that the flask is cool. Remove the stopper from the flask. Examine the material that remains in the flask.
   5. Describe the material.
   6. Where did this material come from?
G. Add some tap water to the flask. Swirl the water in the flask.
   7. What happened to the material in the flask?

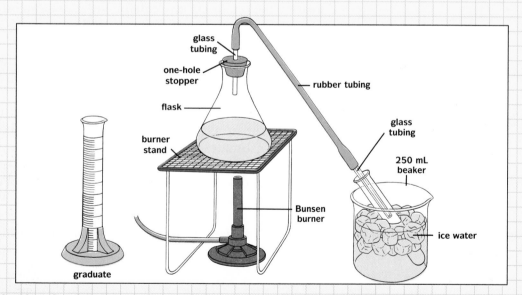

glass tubing

one-hole stopper

flask

burner stand

graduate

rubber tubing

glass tubing

250 mL beaker

Bunsen burner

ice water

C. **Caution:** Carefully light the burner and bring the seawater to a slow boil. Continue boiling until the solution is almost boiled away. As soon as the flask begins to dry or solids begin to form, put out the burner. **Caution:** Never completely boil away a liquid in a beaker.

RESULTS AND CONCLUSIONS
1. What physical changes does water go through during the process of desalination?
2. Is this method of removing salt from seawater practical for home use? Why or why not?
3. How is this process like the water cycle?

Figure 23-9

Ships can mine the oceans for minerals found in nodules like those in the photograph.

nodules (knot)

On the ocean floor are sediments that contain small lumps of matter. These lumps of matter are called **manganese nodules** because they are about 35 percent manganese. These lumps also contain iron, copper, nickel, and cobalt. Some scientists think that there is more manganese and iron in the ocean than can dissolve. So some of the metals may collect together and settle to the bottom. Many nodules appear to have formed around things such as shark teeth and small pieces of bone. Scientists think that manganese and iron may have electrical charges that cause them to attract other metals as they drift down. It is also possible that the manganese came from volcanoes beneath the ocean. Estimates show that 1.5 trillion t of manganese nodules may exist on the Pacific Ocean floor alone.

Several methods are being investigated for collecting these nodules. Submarines could be used to collect them from the ocean floor. Perhaps a rakelike device or a large vacuum system could be built to collect them.

REVIEW

1. What are some resources that can be taken from the ocean?
2. Describe some methods for gathering mineral resources from the oceans.

CHALLENGE Desalination could supply fresh water. Why would the waste products of the process be considered useful?

23-4 EARLY EXPLORATIONS

Oceanography, the study of the ocean, is a combination of many sciences. Chemists study the composition of seawater. Biologists study plants and animals in the ocean. Geologists learn about the ocean floor. Meteorologists study how the ocean affects weather. These scientists and others study the ocean today. But even before recorded history, oceans were an important part of people's lives.

Explorations of the ocean have been continuous since the eighteenth century. Between 1768 and 1778, James Cook, a British explorer, made three long voyages. These voyages, each lasting about three years, are important because their main purpose was to study the oceans of the world.

The voyage of H.M.S. *Challenger* was one of the most important ocean expeditions of all time. With the royal order to "learn everything about the sea," John Murray and Charles Wyville Thomson, two British oceanographers, set sail in 1872. Their expedition lasted four years. During that time, thousands of samples and measurements were taken and analyzed.

Figure 23-10

The H.M.S. *Challenger* among ice near Antarctica.

The oceanographers on H.M.S. *Challenger* used a special sounding device to measure the depth of the ocean in many places and to return samples of the ocean floor to the surface. Each sample of the ocean floor was analyzed to find the kinds of living things present, the number of each species present, and the mineral content. Manganese nodules on the ocean floor were first discovered during this voyage.

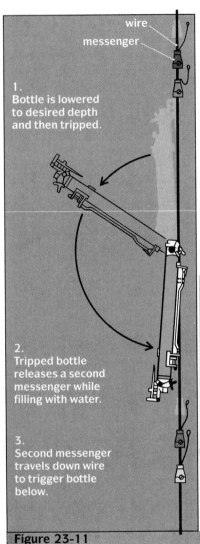

1.
Bottle is lowered to desired depth and then tripped.

2.
Tripped bottle releases a second messenger while filling with water.

3.
Second messenger travels down wire to trigger bottle below.

Figure 23-11

The Nansen bottle is still used today.

The **Nansen bottle**, first used around the turn of this century, is a special device used to collect and measure samples of seawater. Nansen bottles are attached to a cable at regular intervals and lowered into the ocean. Each bottle is designed to collect one to two liters of water, and it contains instruments that measure temperature and pressure. When the bottles are in position, a mechanical messenger is sent down the cable. Notice in Figure 23-11 how the bottle turns over when struck by the messenger. This causes the bottle to collect a sample of seawater and fixes the instrument readings. How is the next bottle set off? The bottles are then collected and their samples and readings are analyzed. A profile of the ocean at that location is produced.

Exploration and research continued into the 1900s. The German research vessel *Meteor*, using echo sounders, measured the depth of the ocean. Echo depth sounders were much more accurate than using weighted lines. Echo depth sounders allowed oceanographers to measure the ocean floor in detail, forming a more complete picture.

In 1934, the Americans William Beebe and Otis Barton descended nearly 1 km below the surface in a vessel that looked like a steel ball hanging from a cable. The total weight of the water on their vessel reached 7 tons. While cramped inside this small sphere, less than 2 m across, they viewed what no person had seen before. Through thick plexiglass windows, they peered into a world lit only by the vessel's searchlight and the passing of an animal that produced its own light.

ACTIVITY — Depth Sounding

OBJECTIVE
Draw a map of a simulated ocean floor using depth sounding.

MATERIALS
2 sheets of graph paper, cardboard box, tape, knitting needle, metric scale, wax marker, ruler

PROCEDURE

A. Place one sheet of graph paper on the table in front of you. Starting from the space in the top left hand corner, count across three spaces and then down three spaces. Mark a small "x" in that space, as shown in the drawing. Label this "x" *1*. Starting from this "x," mark a small "x" in every third space *across* your paper. Then, starting from each "x" in that row, mark every third space *down* the paper.

B. Repeat step **A** with the second sheet of graph paper.

C. Place a cardboard box on its side in front of you. The largest sides should be the top and bottom. Tape one sheet of graph paper securely to the top of the box.

D. Use a knitting needle to poke a hole through each "x" on the graph paper.

E. Take the box to your teacher, who will place an object inside. *Do not look inside*.

F. The knitting needle will now become your sounding line. The bottom of the box is the bottom of the ocean. Carefully place the needle, straight up and down, into the hole labeled *1*. When the needle touches the bottom, mark the needle with the wax marker where it touches the top of the box. Remove the needle and measure, with a metric ruler, from the point of the needle to the mark. Record that distance, to the nearest 0.5 cm, next to the "x" labeled *1*

on the other sheet of graph paper. Wipe the wax mark from the needle.

1. Why is it important to be sure that the knitting needle is straight up and down?

G. Repeat step **F** for each of the other holes.
2. How far down is the bottom of the box?
3. How high is the tallest peak within the box?

H. Draw a contour map on the sheet of graph paper that shows your depth soundings.

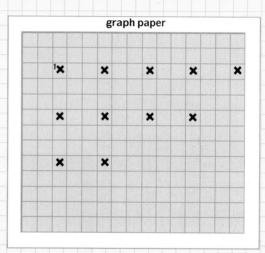

graph paper

RESULTS AND CONCLUSIONS
1. What are the problems with this system of determining the shape of the ocean floor?
2. How could your map be improved?
3. What do you predict is inside the box? With your teacher's permission, check your prediction.

REVIEW

1. Describe two kinds of scientific investigations that could be part of oceanography.
2. What kind of information was obtained by the voyage of H.M.S. *Challenger*?

CHALLENGE Measurements of ocean depths taken by echo sounding differed most from measurements taken by lines in areas where currents are strong. Explain why there would be such differences.

23-5 EXPLORATIONS TODAY

After completing this section, you will be able to

- **describe** current methods and techniques for studying the ocean.
- **explain** how pollution of the ocean threatens ocean resources.

The key term in this section is **bathyscaph**

Many of the methods used by modern oceanographers are similar to those used by early oceanographers. Research vessels drill into the sea floor and remove samples for study. Oceanographers collect and analyze samples of seawater and observe life within the sea. Modern techniques, however, are more accurate and give more information than early techniques.

One advantage that modern oceanographers have is the ability to go below the ocean surface for long periods of time. Scuba (self-contained underwater breathing apparatus) equipment allows oceanographers to work underwater to a depth of about 100 m. They can move freely and observe the underwater environment in detail. They are not restricted to studying what a dredging device happens to collect. Beyond 100 m, the pressure is so great that oceanographers must wear pressure-controlled diving

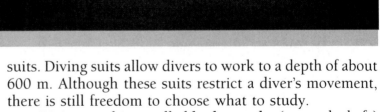

Figure 23-12

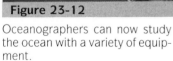

Oceanographers can now study the ocean with a variety of equipment.

bathys (deep)

skaphe (a tub)

suits. Diving suits allow divers to work to a depth of about 600 m. Although these suits restrict a diver's movement, there is still freedom to choose what to study.

Diving machines called **bathyscaphs** (BATH uh skafs) allow scientists to reach to the deepest parts of the ocean. The bathyscaph *Alvin*, shown in Figure 23-12 (*right*), has been used in many studies. During the early 1970s, *Alvin* was used to study the Mid-Atlantic Ridge. In 1979, sci-

Figure 23-13

Deep-sea ocean vents are rich sources of new minerals from the oceans.

entists in *Alvin* found places along the Pacific Ridge where minerals were flowing from hot vents in the ridge. The temperature within these vents is thought to be about 350°C. These vents, shown in Figure 23-13, are called "smokers" because of their appearance. Special lights and high-speed films allow scientists to take pictures of these vents as well as large areas of the sea floor.

Exploration also continues from research vessels on the surface. These floating laboratories are equipped with side-scan sonar. Such sonar can produce three-dimensional pictures of the ocean floor. Side-scan sonar is towed below the surface and produces sound waves that travel through the water. Sensitive microphones listen for returning echoes. Computers interpret the echoes and determine the depth and shape of the sea floor.

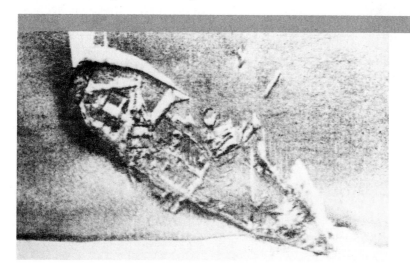

Figure 23-14

Side-scan sonar image of a sunken ship.

Figure 23-15

The *Glomar Challenger* can drill into the ocean floor.

The *Glomar Challenger*, shown in Figure 23-15, is a specially designed drilling ship. It was used to do much of the work for the Deep Sea Drilling Project. This project made many interesting discoveries. For example, the oldest sample of sea floor that was collected is only 200 million years old. The sea-floor samples also indicate that some sea-floor segments have moved thousands of miles. This is strong evidence that the sea floor spreads.

One of the biggest problems affecting the ocean today is pollution. People used to believe that the ocean could absorb any amount of waste placed in it because the world's ocean is so large. Oceanographers now realize that the ocean is a fragile system that must be protected. There is a limit to what the ocean can absorb. Some materials do not break down. Oceanographers also know that because

Figure 23-16

Sea-floor samples are used to study the earth's geology and history.

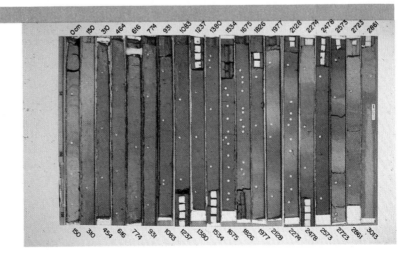

the oceans mix, polluting one ocean pollutes them all. Organisms in the ocean supply 80 percent of the oxygen that people breathe. The ocean is a source of food and may become a source of fresh water. Polluting the ocean could reduce these supplies of food and water. Wise use of ocean resources is needed. Perhaps someday you will live upon or below the ocean. You may eat food from fish farms, drink desalinated seawater, and use ocean water as a major source of energy.

REVIEW

1. What techniques are used for a direct study of the ocean below the surface?
2. Why is pollution in the ocean such a serious problem?

CHALLENGE Early attempts to bring living things back from great depths were usually failures. The organisms seemed to explode. Can you explain why this occurred?

CHAPTER SUMMARY

The main ideas in this chapter are listed below. Read these statements before you answer the Chapter Review questions.

- Seawater is a complex solution that contains salts, minerals, and gases dissolved in water. (23-1)

- The salt content of seawater is relatively constant throughout the ocean. Temperature and depth affect the amount of gases dissolved in seawater. (23-1)

- The three groups of living things in the ocean are plankton, nekton, and benthos. (23-2)

- The ocean is divided into three zones of living things, the shore zone, the neritic zone, and the oceanic zone. (23-2)

- Many natural resources, including food, fresh water, minerals, and energy, can be taken from the ocean. (23-3)

- Oceanography, the study of the ocean, is a combination of many sciences. (23-4)

- The ocean has been explored for many years. Expeditions in the past gathered data on currents, the depth of the ocean, the life forms found at different depths, and the minerals present. (23-4)

- Modern oceanographers use surface ships to probe the ocean. They also study the depths of the ocean using specialized devices. (23-5)

- Pollution of the ocean may become a serious problem for life on the earth. (23-5)

The key terms in this chapter are listed below. Use each term in a sentence that shows the meaning of the term.

bathyscaph	krill	neritic zone	plankton
benthos	manganese nodules	oceanic zone	salinity
degassing	Nansen bottle	oceanography	shore zone
desalination	nekton		

Chapter Review

1. Microscopic plants and animals that float near the surface of the ocean are called _____ .

2. Shrimplike creatures that live in the cold water around the Antarctica are called _____ .

3. Lumps of matter found on the ocean floor that are a potential source of minerals are called _____ .

4. The number of grams of dissolved salt in a kilogram of seawater is known as the water's _____ .

5. Plants and animals that live on the ocean floor belong to a group of ocean life called _____ .

6. The process in which gases are released by volcanic activity is called _____ .

7. The ocean zone between the high-tide line and the low-tide line is called the _____ .

8. The process of removing salts from seawater is _____ .

9. A device that allows oceanographers to descend into the ocean depths is the _____ .

10. The ocean zone from the low-tide line to the edge of the continental shelf is the _____ .

CONCEPTS

1. List the ten major substances that are found in seawater. Include the amount of each component found in a kilogram of seawater. (23-1)

2. What role do scientists think volcanoes had in making the ocean salty? (23-1)

3. Describe the cycling of salts to and from seawater. (23-1)

4. How do temperature, depth, and living things affect the amounts of gases dissolved in seawater? (23-1)

5. Compare the three groups of living things in the ocean. Give examples from each group. (23-2)

6. Compare the three different zones of life in the ocean. What factors are important in determining the nature of each zone? (23-2)

7. Describe a shore-zone food web. (23-2)

8. What resources are people already taking from the ocean? What resources may be taken from the ocean at some time in the future? (23-3)

9. Explain how people could improve food production from the ocean. (23-3)

10. Describe one method for desalinating ocean water. Why is desalination not a common procedure for producing fresh water? (23-3)

11. What is oceanography? What are some of the sciences that oceanography includes? (23-4)

12. What kinds of information about the oceans is obtained by using a Nansen bottle? (23-4)

13. What information about the ocean was improved through the use of echo sounding? (23-4)

14. What types of data are collected by modern surface ships used in oceanographic research? (23-5)

15. Compare the advantages and disadvantages of diving with scuba equipment and diving in bathyscaphs for underwater research. (23-5)

16. What effect may pollution of the ocean have on the ocean as a natural resource? (23-5)

APPLICATION/ CRITICAL THINKING

1. What might happen to the food web in an ocean area if an oil spill destroyed the plankton living there?

2. During an ice age, much of the earth's water is locked up in glaciers. How would sea level be affected? How would the salinity of the ocean be affected?

3. Some birds, such as gulls and terns, have special salt glands. These glands excrete highly concentrated solutions of salt. How are such glands related to the life style of the birds?

EXTENSION

1. Animals that live in the oceanic zone produce their own light. The phenomenon is called bioluminescence. Prepare a report on bioluminescence among deep-sea creatures.

2. Prepare a report on an eighteenth-century or nineteenth-century voyage of exploration of the oceans. Include information on what was learned from the voyage.

3. Find out how long people have been able to live in artificial enclosures under the sea? What do such experiments indicate about the future?

READINGS

Matthews, Samuel W. "New World of the Ocean." *National Geographic*, December 1981, p. 792.

Trefil, James G. *A Scientist at the Seashore.* New York: Charles Scribner's Sons, 1984.

Whipple, A.B.C. *Restless Oceans.* Alexandria, Va.: Time-Life Books Inc.

People have fished for thousands of years. Today the fishing industry provides us with a large part of our food supply. Although many old methods of fishing are still used, modern fishers depend more and more on scientific ways to increase their catches.

Fishers spend much of their time on boats at sea, where most fishing occurs. Small fishing boats usually stay within several

FISHER

kilometers of shore. However, large factory fishing ships can travel anywhere in the open sea. Fish that are caught may be sold at local markets. Or they may be processed and frozen on board for shipment to distant markets.

Fishers may use sonar, radar, electronic devices, and information from satellites to help them find fish. The weather is sometimes harsh, and the work is hard. If you are interested in a life at sea, you should take courses in biology and oceanography. You may also be able to tour a fishing boat. ∎

Have you every wondered why a stream or river follows the same course year after year? Did you know that water in the air conditioning systems of large office buildings must be carefully checked for disease organisms and wastes? People who think about these things — about fresh water, its sources, and ways it is used — are called hydrologists.

HYDROLOGIST

A hydrologist may work on an irrigation system or study a river. Hydrologists sample ground water and surface water for pollutants. Others work in waste treatment plants where water is recycled.

Hydrologists must have a college degree. Some go on to receive master's and doctor's degrees. Courses in geology, chemistry, biology, and math will benefit those who are interested in this career. ∎

DR. YASUO ONISHI, HYDROLOGIST

You have learned about ocean and freshwater pollution. In the past, people thought that dumping garbage and wastes into bodies of water was not harmful. But Dr. Yasuo Onishi takes a different view.

He is a research engineer who works in the field of hydrodynamics — the study of the physical properties of bodies of water. Dr. Onishi knows that many pollutants settle to the ocean and river bottoms. He also knows that the pollutants do not always remain there.

His work involves studying how marine and river sediments move. He has contributed to knowledge about currents, tides, waves, and sediment movements. For example, ocean currents and waves carry polluted sediment from the ocean floor upward to the surface.

Dr. Onishi is concerned about how water and sediment movements on ocean and river bottoms affect pollution. His work has taught us about some of the causes of water pollution and has suggested ways of avoiding it. ∎

Issues and Technology

Who owns the sea and its resources? And who is responsible for seeing that it is used wisely? For centuries the sea was a place that no nation controlled. So nations and individuals did what they pleased.

The nations of the world are taking a critical look at this practice now. The sea has many resources and it is the source of much of our food. How should the resources from the seas be shared? Who should be responsible for environmental problems at sea? Many nations are now trying to come up with a way to work together on these issues.

The latest attempt to work together was the Third Conference on the Laws of the Sea (UNCLOS III). It lasted from 1973 until 1982 and over 150 nations took part. These nations tried to come up with a way to work together to protect the sea and share its resources. The conference pro-duced a Law of the Sea treaty. However, this treaty is not widely supported. As of 1984, 134 nations had signed the treaty. That means that they agree with it in principle. But they are not bound by the treaty until their governments ratify it. Less than ten nations have ratified. Twenty-five other nations have refused to even sign the treaty. The United States is one of those nations, as shown in Figure 1.

The map in Figure 1 uses color to show which countries have agreed to abide by the Law of the Sea and have ratified the treaty and which countries rejected the Law of the Sea.

APPLYING CRITICAL THINKING SKILLS

1. Many of the rich and powerful countries in North America and Europe have not ratified the treaty. Explain why.

2. Why might nations with large coastlines be reluctant to sign a treaty involving the sharing of resources?

3. Most nations have signed the treaty but have not ratified it. What does that suggest?

4. All of the nations that have ratified the treaty are poor and underdeveloped. Why do you think it would be a good idea for such nations to agree to the treaty?

5. The larger and more influential nations, such as the United States, the Soviet Union, the United Kingdom, Japan, France, West Germany, and Italy, have not ratified the treaty. They have each set up their own agencies to control mining minerals in the sea. What do you think of this? What will this mean for the Law of the Sea treaty? How might this affect nations without coastlines?

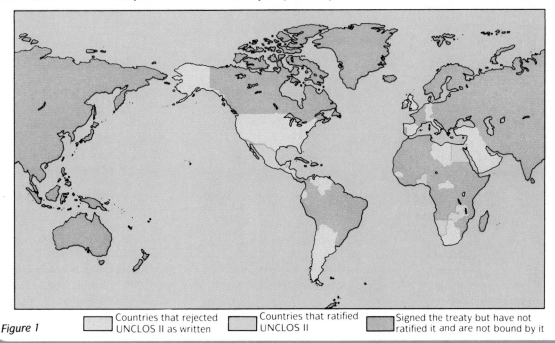

Figure 1

☐ Countries that rejected UNCLOS II as written   ☐ Countries that ratified UNCLOS II   ▨ Signed the treaty but have not ratified it and are not bound by it

565

The biggest problem for nations like the United States concerns the way the treaty handles the ocean's resources. The most important resource is probably manganese nodules. Manganese nodules are small, potato-shaped hunks of mineral that may contain manganese, nickel, copper, cobalt, and other minerals. If they can be mined and the minerals extracted, they could prove very valuable.

Minerals have also been found in the sediments at the bottom of the Red Sea, along the continental shelves, and in seawater itself.

The Law of the Sea would give control over the ocean's minerals to an international agency called the International Seabed Authority (ISA). Technology developed by any one nation or company to mine and extract minerals would have to be shared with the agency. The agency would then make it available worldwide.

Many developing nations that don't have the money or technology to exploit the ocean's resources favor this treaty. They can share the wealth with little or no investment.

Figure 2 shows where most of the valuable manganese nodules are located. It also shows where the metal-rich sediments and the industrial plants are located that extract minerals from the sea. The red lines enclose what the treaty calls Extended Economic Zones (EEZs). These are areas where coastal nations have special economic rights. And finally, the figure shows which countries have spent money on research to develop technology to extract resources from the sea.

APPLYING CRITICAL THINKING SKILLS

1. Are most of the manganese nodules under control of any one nation? What part of the ocean are they in? What would this mean under the Law of the Sea treaty?

2. Presently there are many industrial plants extracting minerals from seawater. What does this mean for land-locked countries? Is this fair? What do you propose should be done?

3. Which countries are spending money extracting minerals from the sea? Why do you suppose there are so few countries developing this technology?

4. Which countries are probably the most upset by the Law of the Sea treaty? Why?

5. How would you suggest that the wealth of the sea be shared wisely and fairly?

The United States and some other nations that have not signed the treaty have developed much of the technology that would be used. They feel that it would be unfair to share all they have learned with countries that have invested nothing.

Unfortunately, the treaty must be accepted whole or not at all. So the United States has refused to sign unless changes are made in some of the sections.

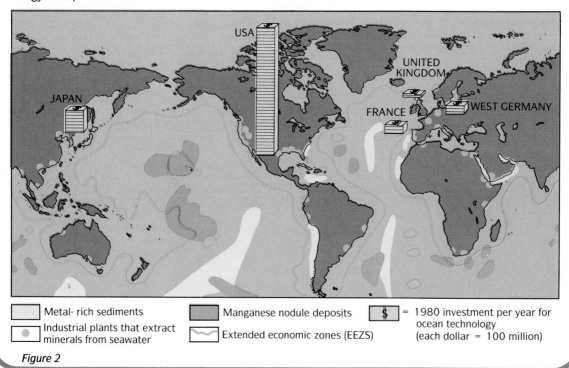

Metal-rich sediments
Industrial plants that extract minerals from seawater
Manganese nodule deposits
Extended economic zones (EEZS)
$ = 1980 investment per year for ocean technology (each dollar = 100 million)

Figure 2

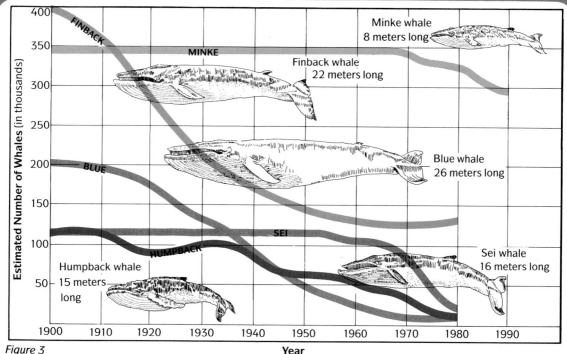

Figure 3

But sharing the resources of the sea is only one part of the treaty. For example, the treaty also helps regulate ocean resources like fish. Many people depend on fish for a large part of the protein in their diets. Many varieties of fish are becoming scarce due to overfishing. The nations of the world need a way to work together to preserve the fish they use for food.

Ocean pollution is another problem that all nations could work on together. The oceans receive great amounts of waste that runs off the land. Toxic chemicals are dumped into the sea. The toxic chemicals circulate around the world with ocean currents. They get into ocean food chains. They kill some creatures and contaminate some fish people eat. The treaty has provisions to make all nations reduce pollution of the sea.

The treaty guarantees freedom of movement for all ships at sea as well. Nations would not be permitted to block foreign ships because of disputes.

The Law of the Sea would also protect endangered sea mammals. This is good news for whales. Whale hunting has almost wiped out these giant creatures in some areas. Today, the whale is an endangered species.

Figure 3 shows what has happened to five whale populations. Whales have been hunted for hundreds of years. Their bones were used for corsets and jewelry. The rest of the whale was, and still is, used for things like oil, meat, and soap. Many whales are now endangered and need protection.

APPLYING CRITICAL THINKING SKILLS

1. What type of whale had the largest population in 1980? What was the population?
2. What type of whale had the smallest population in 1900? What was the population?
3. In what direction have all of these whale populations gone between 1900 and 1980? Why?
4. What type of whale had the lowest population in 1980?
5. What would probably have to happen to make the population curves go up again? Can we live without whale products? Why is it important not to wipe out a species of animal?
6. The Law of the Sea would make all nations protect the whales. Why is it necessary for nations to do this together?

The treaty does have problems. But is it wise to disregard the entire treaty because of problems with only parts? Some people feel that if countries cooperate on using the sea they will learn to cooperate on other things, too.

Should the Law of the Sea treaty be changed to make sharing of the ocean's wealth more fair — or is it fair enough already? Is sharing the ocean's wealth really as important as other parts of the treaty? Should nations that don't like one part of the treaty just give up on it?

APPENDIX 1. *Properties of Some Minerals by Family Groups*

MINERAL	HARDNESS	FRACTURE OR CLEAVAGE	COLOR	STREAK	CHEMICAL SYMBOL
Metals and non-metals					
gold	2.5–3	none	rich yellow	yellow	Au
silver	2.5–3	none	white	white	Ag
iron	4–5	cubic	steel-gray	gray	Fe
sulfur	2	conchoidal	light yellow	white to yellow	S
graphite	1–2	1 direction	black	black	C
Sulfides					
galena	2.5–2.7	cubic	lead-gray	bluish gray	PbS
sphalerite	3.5–4	4 directions	colorless to yellow-black	yellowish	ZnS
chalcopyrite	3.5–4	none	golden	greenish black	$CuFeS_2$
pyrite	6–6.5	conchoidal	rich yellow	greenish black	FeS_2
Oxides					
cuprite	3.5–4	4 directions	red	red	Cu_2O
corundum	9	conchoidal/ uneven	variety of colors	colorless	$A1_2O_3$
bauxite	1–3	poor	white to red-brown	white to red-brown	$A1(OH)_3$
magnetite	6	none	black	black	Fe_3O_4
Halides					
halite	2.5	cubic	colorless	colorless	NaC1
fluorite	4	4 directions	variety of colors	colorless	CaF_2

MINERAL	HARDNESS	FRACTURE OR CLEAVAGE	COLOR	STREAK	CHEMICAL SYMBOL
Carbonates					
calcite	3	3 directions, not 90°	variety of colors	colorless	$Ca(CO_3)_2$
dolomite	3.5–4	3 directions, not 90°	variety of colors	colorless	$CaMg(CO_3)_2$
Sulfates					
anhydrite	3–3.5	2 directions	colorless, white, gray	colorless	$CaSO_4$
gypsum	2	2 directions	white	white	$CaSO_4 \cdot 2H_2O$
Phosphates					
apatite	5	none	variety of colors	white	$Ca_5(Cl, F)(PO_4)_3$
Silicates					
quartz	7	3 directions	variety of colors	colorless	SiO_2
kaolin	2–2.5	none	white	colorless	$Al_2Si_2O_5(OH)_4$
talc	1	1 direction	white, greenish gray	colorless	$Mg_3Si_4O_{10}(OH)_2$
serpentine	2–5	none	greenish	colorless	$Mg_3Si_2O_5(OH)_4$
chlorite	2–2.5	none	variety of colors	colorless	complex structure
mica (muscovite)	2–2.5	1 direction	white to dark	colorless	complex structure
hornblende	5–6	2 directions	blue-green to black	blue-green to black	complex structure
olivine	6.5–7	conchoidal	green to light gray	white	$(Mg, Fe)_2SiO_4$
orthoclase	6	2 directions, 90°	white, pink, yellow	colorless	$KAlSi_3O_8$
topaz	8	3 directions	variety of colors	colorless	complex structure

APPENDIX 2. *Periodic Table of Elements*

1 **1** 1.0 **H** Hydrogen								

KEY

Atomic Mass →

Atomic Number → **6**   12.0

C ← Symbol of Element

Element Name → **Carbon**

2	**3** 6.9 **Li** Lithium	**4** 9.0 **Be** Beryllium
3	**11** 22.9 **Na** Sodium	**12** 24.3 **Mg** Magnesium

4	**19** 39.1 **K** Potassium	**20** 40.0 **Ca** Calcium	**21** 44.9 **Sc** Scandium	**22** 47.9 **Ti** Titanium	**23** 50.9 **V** Vanadium	**24** 51.9 **Cr** Chromium	**25** 54.9 **Mn** Manganese	**26** 55.8 **Fe** Iron
5	**37** 85.4 **Rb** Rubidium	**38** 87.6 **Sr** Strontium	**39** 88.9 **Y** Yttrium	**40** 91.2 **Zr** Zirconium	**41** 92.9 **Nb** Niobium	**42** 95.9 **Mo** Molybdenum	**43** (99)* **Tc** Technetium	**44** 101.0 **Ru** Ruthenium

Row 4 continued: **27**   58.9 **Co** Cobalt

Row 5 continued: **45**   102.9 **Rh** Rhodium

6	**55** 132.9 **Cs** Cesium	**56** 137.3 **Ba** Barium	Lanthanide Series†	**72** 178.4 **Hf** Hafnium	**73** 180.9 **Ta** Tantalum	**74** 183.8 **W** Tungsten	**75** 186.2 **Re** Rhenium	**76** 190.2 **Os** Osmium
7	**87** (223)* **Fr** Francium	**88** (226)* **Ra** Radium	Actinide Series‡	**104** (259)* **Unq** Unnilquadium	**105** **Unp** Unnilpentium	**106** **Unh** Unnilhexium		

Row 6 continued: **77**   192.2 **Ir** Iridium

† **LANTHANIDE SERIES**

57 138.9 **La** Lanthanum	**58** 140.1 **Ce** Cerium	**59** 140.9 **Pr** Praseodymium	**60** 144.2 **Nd** Neodymium	**61** (147)* **Pm** Promethium	**62** 150.3 **Sm** Samarium	**63** 151.9 **Eu** Europium

‡ **ACTINIDE SERIES**

89 (227)* **Ac** Actinium	**90** 232.0 **Th** Thorium	**91** (231)* **Pa** Protactinium	**92** 238.0 **U** Uranium	**93** (237)* **Np** Neptunium	**94** (242)* **Pu** Plutonium	**95** (243)* **Am** Americium

*Atomic masses appearing in parentheses are those of the most stable known isotopes.

■ **Metals**   □ **Nonmetals**

					2　4.0 **He** Helium

5　10.8 **B** Boron	6　12.0 **C** Carbon	7　14.0 **N** Nitrogen	8　15.9 **O** Oxygen	9　18.9 **F** Fluorine	10　20.1 **Ne** Neon
13　26.9 **Al** Aluminum	14　28.0 **Si** Silicon	15　30.9 **P** Phosphorus	16　32.0 **S** Sulfur	17　35.4 **Cl** Chlorine	18　39.9 **Ar** Argon

28　58.7 **Ni** Nickel	29　63.5 **Cu** Copper	30　65.3 **Zn** Zinc	31　69.7 **Ga** Gallium	32　72.5 **Ge** Germanium	33　74.9 **As** Arsenic	34　78.9 **Se** Selenium	35　79.9 **Br** Bromine	36　83.8 **Kr** Krypton
46　106.4 **Pd** Palladium	47　107.8 **Ag** Silver	48　112.4 **Cd** Cadmium	49　114.8 **In** Indium	50　118.6 **Sn** Tin	51　121.7 **Sb** Antimony	52　127.6 **Te** Tellurium	53　126.9 **I** Iodine	54　131.3 **Xe** Xenon
78　195.0 **Pt** Platinum	79　196.9 **Au** Gold	80　200.5 **Hg** Mercury	81　204.3 **Tl** Thallium	82　207.1 **Pb** Lead	83　208.9 **Bi** Bismuth	84　(210)* **Po** Polonium	85　(210)* **At** Astatine	86　(222)* **Rn** Radon

64　157.2 **Gd** Gadolinium	65　158.9 **Tb** Terbium	66　162.5 **Dy** Dysprosium	67　164.9 **Ho** Holmium	68　167.2 **Er** Erbium	69　168.9 **Tm** Thulium	70　173.0 **Yb** Ytterbium	71　174.9 **Lu** Lutetium
96　(247)* **Cm** Curium	97　(247)* **Bk** Berkelium	98　(251)* **Cf** Californium	99　(254)* **Es** Einsteinium	100　(257)* **Fm** Fermium	101　(258)* **Md** Mendelevium	102　(255)* **No** Nobelium	103　(256)* **Lr** Lawrencium

Atomic masses based on C-12 = 12.0000

APPENDIX 3. Safety Symbols

Within certain activities, safety symbols are included next to the heading PROCEDURE. These safety symbols alert you to specific hazards in the procedure and to safety measures to prevent accidents. Six safety symbols are used throughout the text. In any given activity you will see no more than three or four of these symbols. The symbols are as follows:

Electrical Safety

Body Protection

Eye Safety

Hand Safety

Poison

Fire

APPENDIX 4. Weather Map Symbols

Symbol	Wind Speed km/hr
◎	Calm
—	0-4
↘	5-13
↘	14-22
↘	23-32
↘	33-41
↘	42-50
↘	51-59
↘	60-69
↘	70-78
↘	79-87
↘	88-96
↘	97-100
↘	101-105

Location of Weather Station

Type of high clouds
Type of middle clouds
Temperature (°F) — 55
Type of precipitation — **
Wind speed and direction
Dew point temperature — 54°

Barometric pressure (in millibars) — 257
Change in barometric pressure in last 3 hours — +28
Total percent of sky covered by clouds
Type of low clouds

Fronts and Pressure Systems

Ⓗ Center of high or
Ⓛ low pressure system

▲▲▲ Cold front

●●● Warm front

▲●▲ Occluded front

●▼●▼ Stationary front

Symbols Showing Percentage of Cloudiness

0	1/10	2/10	3/10	4/10	5/10	6/10	7/10	8/10	9/10	10/10
○	①	◔	◔	◑	◑	◕	◕	◕	◑	●

Symbols Showing Precipitation

drizzle	rain	shower	snow	sleet	fog	hail	thunderstorm
,	●	▽	*	△	≡	⏚	⏀

Clouds

High Clouds
→ Scattered cirrus
⌒→ Dense cirrus
⌐ᶜ Veil of cirrus covering entire sky
ᴄ Cirrus not covering entire sky

Middle Clouds
⟋ Thin altostratus
⟋⟋ Thick altostratus
⌒ Thin altostratus in patches
ᵔᵔ Thin altostratus in bands

Low Clouds
⌒ Cumulus fair weather
ᴗ Stratocumulus
- - - Fractocumulus bad weather
— Stratus fair weather

Silver Burdett
EARTH SCIENCE SKILLS HANDBOOK

The Earth Science Skills Handbook provides an additional opportunity to develop skills that are useful in earth science. Each of the eight lessons is tied to a specific unit in the text. A given lesson may provide an in-depth extension of the text material, or it may explore an additional topic.

The theme of this handbook is mapping. Beginning with the familiar political/physical map of the world, you will read and interpret data presented in map form. You can then work with maps of the sky, the oceans, and the earth's surface, as well as weather maps and climate maps.

Each lesson consists of a visual display, a brief explanation, and a series of questions. Rather than asking you to simply recall information, the questions require you to compare, predict, infer, and identify cause and effect, as well as interpret data.

CONTENTS

Arctic Ocean

Greenland

NORTH AMERICA

Hudson Bay

Great Lakes

ROCKY MOUNTAINS

Mississippi River

Appalachian Mountains

NORTH ATLANTIC OCEAN

Great Plains

Sonoran Desert

Gulf of Mexico

Caribbean Sea

TO SCALE WITH ABOVE MAP

SOUTH ATLANTIC OCEAN

0°

Weddell Sea

60°

ANTARCTICA

SOUTH

PACIFIC

OCEAN

180°

INDIAN OCEAN

Amazon River

ANDES

Amazon Basin

SOUTH PACIFIC OCEAN

SOUTH AMERICA

SOUTH ATLANTIC OCEAN

THE EARTH AT A GLANCE

Maps can help you view large areas of the earth, or even the entire world, at one time. This, in turn, can help you better understand the world around you. The map above is a political/physical map This kind of map is designed to show the continents, or major land masses, and the countries of the world. It also shows major physical features, such as mountains.

The map also shows that there is more to the earth than just continents. Surrounding these land masses are oceans. In fact, if you were to view the earth from space or by using a globe, you would notice that about three fourths of the earth is covered by water!

Questions

1. How many continents can you find? Name the continents.
2. Locate the United States, giving the latitude range and longitude range.
3. Find the location of your state or province and give the approximate latitude and longitude.
4. State the continents whose eastern and western borders touch oceans, and name

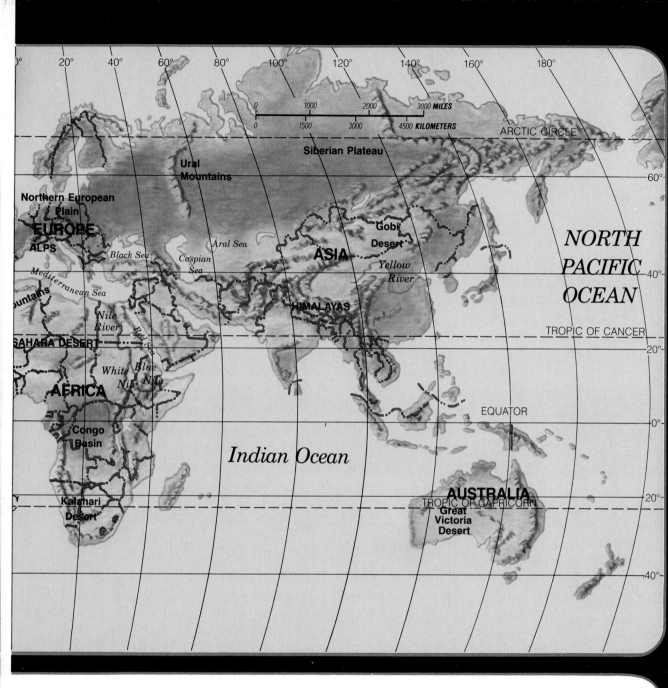

the oceans they touch.

5. Is the land evenly scattered over the earth? Describe the general placement of the continents.

6. Why do you suppose this map does not show the true proportions of land to water?

7. Glaciers once covered a large part of North America. What evidence of this can be found on the map?

8. What do the Hudson Bay, the Mediterranean Sea, and the Red Sea have in common? Explain your answer.

9. What physical feature extends in a north-south direction in western North America? In western South America? What physical feature dominates the continent of Africa?

10. Look along the borders of all the continents. What physical feature is most commonly found?

11. What is the latitude of the Sahara Desert? The Gobi Desert? The Sonoran Desert? The Great Victoria Desert?

12. What are some other kinds of physical features shown on this map?

THE AUTUMN STAR MAP

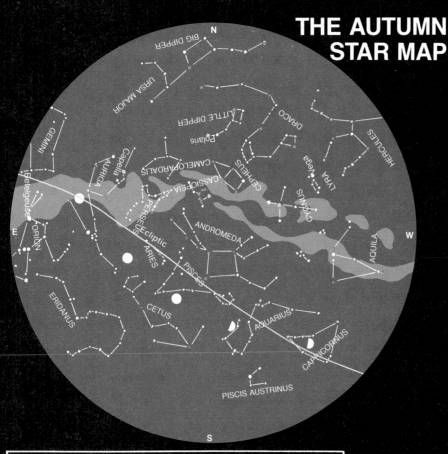

THE CHANGING NIGHT SKY

The star maps on these pages show you the positions of the stars for each season in the Northern Hemisphere. The view is from mid-latitudes, during the evening hours. The lines connecting certain stars form constellations, or star groups.

Choose a constellation and follow it through the sky for each season. Note any changes in the position of the constellation. Identify the brightest stars in the constellation. See if the stars change position with respect to one another. You may want to mark the position of the stars on tracing paper to keep track of them. Do this for some of the other constellations.

Notice the streak of white across the sky. This, of course, is the Milky Way. Notice also the ecliptic, which is an imaginary line that marks the approximate path of the sun, the moon, and the planets across the sky.

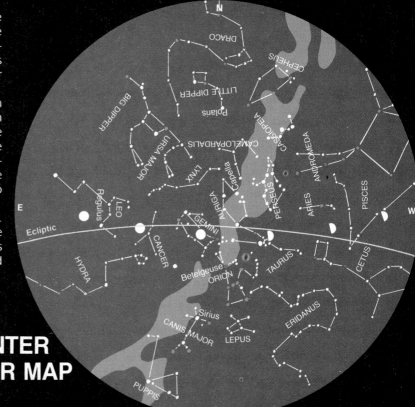

THE WINTER STAR MAP

THE SUMMER STAR MAP

STAR TEMPERATURES

- 3500°C.
- 5500°C.
- 6500°C.
- 8000°C.
- 11,000°C.

THE SPRING STAR MAP

Questions

1. Why do the constellations change position in the sky?
2. Which constellations are visible throughout the year?
3. Why do the stars in the constellations appear in various colors?
4. Name the constellation each of the following stars is in: Polaris, Vega, Betelgeuse, Sirius, Regulus, Capella.
5. What constellations would be useful for navigation? Give a reason for your answer.
6. Identify the following constellations as best seen during winter, spring, summer, or fall: Orion, Scorpius, Pegasus, Canis Major, Virgo, Sagittarius, Cetus, Bootes.
7. Find the ecliptic on each map. Planets can be found in constellations through which the ecliptic passes. Identify these constellations.
8. Due to the earth's rotation, the constellations move westward continuously through the night. Thus, new constellations rise in the east as others set in the west. What would be the best time to look for spring constellations on January 1?
9. Look at any one of the star maps. Due to the earth's rotation, the stars appear to revolve around Polaris. Do they revolve in a clockwise or counterclockwise direction?

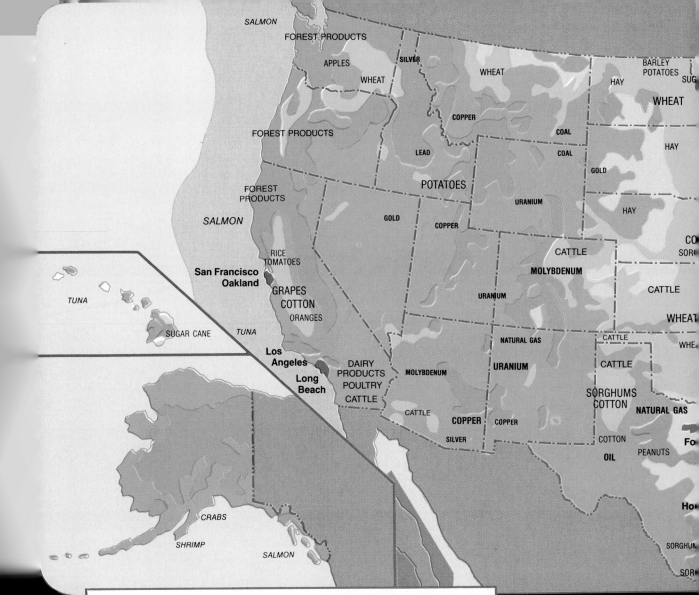

SALMON
FOREST PRODUCTS
APPLES
SILVER
WHEAT
WHEAT
HAY
BARLEY
POTATOES
SUG
WHEAT
COPPER
COAL
HAY
FOREST PRODUCTS
LEAD
COAL
GOLD
POTATOES
URANIUM
HAY
FOREST PRODUCTS
SALMON
GOLD
COPPER
CATTLE
CO
SOR
MOLYBDENUM
RICE
TOMATOES
URANIUM
CATTLE
San Francisco
Oakland
GRAPES
COTTON
ORANGES
WHEAT
TUNA
SUGAR CANE
TUNA
NATURAL GAS
CATTLE
WHE
Los
Angeles
DAIRY
PRODUCTS
POULTRY
CATTLE
MOLYBDENUM
URANIUM
CATTLE
Long
Beach
SORGHUMS
COTTON
NATURAL GAS
CATTLE
COPPER
COPPER
COTTON
Fo
SILVER
PEANUTS
CRABS
OIL
SHRIMP
Ho
SALMON
SORGHU
SOR

THE MANY USES OF OUR LAND

Fertile soil is one of America's most valuable resources. The flat plains and rich soil east of the Rocky Mountains have developed into some of the best farmlands in the world. As the prevailing westerlies roll over the Rocky Mountains, rain falls and nourishes the soil. Because of our fertile farmlands and temperate climate, American farmers lead the world in agricultural production.

Forests flourish on America's rich soil. Forests provide the raw materials for lumber, paper, and other products manufactured in the United States. They also provide homes for many types of plants and animals. People use forests as well. Hiking, camping, and hunting are activities enjoyed by many of us in forests.

Because soil is a natural resource, we must use it wisely. Forest management and proper farming and mining methods all help to conserve the land. Land misuse can increase erosion, leaving rich and fertile areas barren.

The map shown here illustrates how land is used in the United States today. Labels on the map show the chief products of various areas.

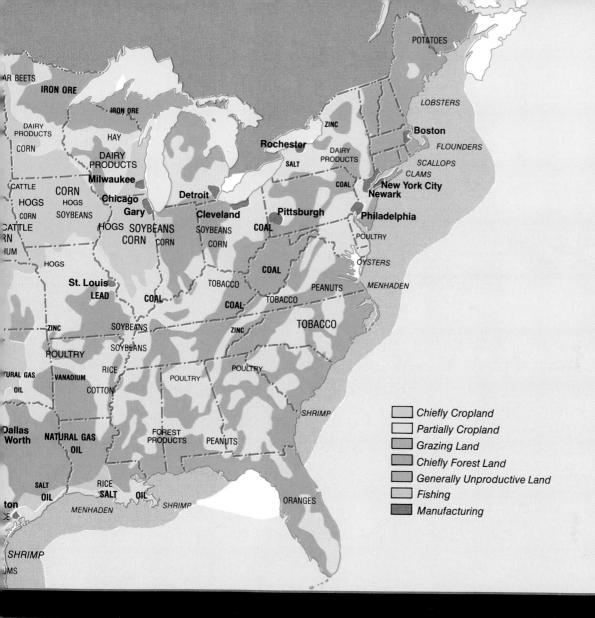

The size of the label indicates the importance of the product. Notice that areas of manufacturing are labeled in red.

Questions

1. What are the chief products of your state?
2. How is land mainly used in your state?
3. Where are most grazing lands located?
4. Why are most American farms located east of the Rocky Mountains?
5. What areas of the United States are mostly forest?
6. Name at least five states in which cattle are raised.
7. Where in the United States would you expect to find the most mines?
8. What areas in the United States are unproductive for farming? Why?
9. Why might some people object to clearing forests to build houses?
10. Why should paper be recycled?
11. Notice on the map that manufacturing centers are often near sources of water. What do you think is the relationship between water and industry?

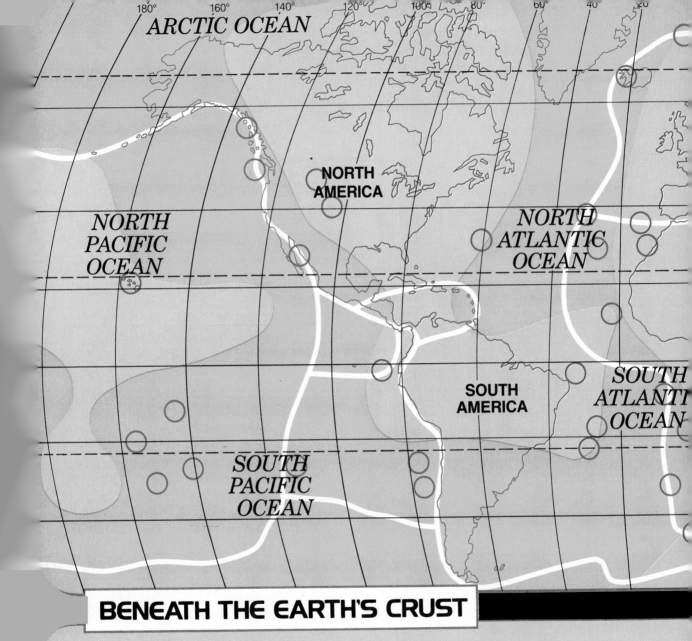

BENEATH THE EARTH'S CRUST

Many scientists who study the earth believe that its crust is broken up into huge pieces called plates. These plates move over hot, molten rock beneath the crust much as ice moves over water. The plates may move as little as a few centimeters or as much as 20 cm in a year. Two scientists, John Woodhouse and Adam Dziewonski, have mapped the interior of the earth, showing temperatures 37.2 km beneath its crust. Cool regions under the continents are pictured in blue. Hotter regions near the edges of plates are shown in orange. Areas of rising molten rock appear as red circles.

The map was made by interpreting 2,000 siesmograms from 53 earthquakes. Earthquake waves move faster through cool, rigid rock than through hot, molten rock. So by charting the speed of the waves, a map could be created. Before this, scientists could only guess about the earth's structures from core samples and land features. As you can see, much has yet to be learned about the earth's interior.

Questions

1. Why are temperatures hottest at plate boundaries?
2. Where would you expect to find earthquakes and volcanoes? Explain your answer.
3. Find the border of North America that coincides with a plate boundary. Notice the temperatures beneath the surface. Why is there much volcanic activity and many earthquakes in this region?
4. Would you expect to find evidence of volcanoes in Africa? Explain your answer.
5. Look carefully at the blue region beneath South America. Below what other continent can you find this region?
6. What does this show about the position of the two continents at some time in the past?
7. What is occurring at the boundary between these continents?
8. Using your answers to questions 7 and 8, what can you conclude about the present motion of these two continents?

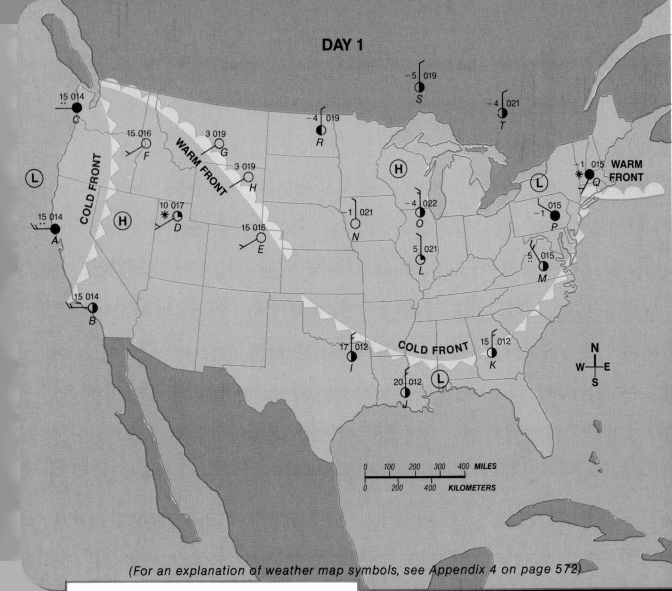

DAY 1

(For an explanation of weather map symbols, see Appendix 4 on page 572)

PREDICTING WEATHER

Reading and understanding weather maps can help you predict weather patterns. The two weather maps show the weather for two consecutive days in January, as plotted at various stations throughout the United States. To understand developing weather patterns, read each station's report. Notice wind speed and direction. Remember that winds are plotted in the direction from which they come. Check each station's air pressure and temperature and check if any precipitation has been reported.

Compare each station's weather for both days. Remember to compare the location of weather fronts and air masses on both maps. After carefully examining all the weather data on both maps, you should be able to predict the next day's weather.

Questions

1. Give the location, type, and direction of movement of each front shown on the map for day 1.

2. What stations are reporting precipitation on day 1?

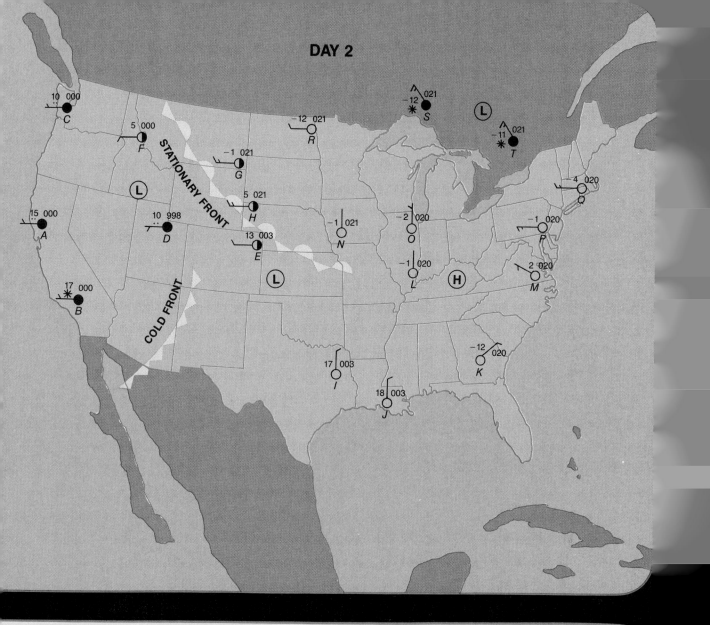

DAY 2

3. In what directions are the winds coming from for stations E, D, F, G, and H on day 1?
4. In what direction are winds in the high moving over stations L, N, R, S, and T: clockwise or counterclockwise?
5. How do you account for the formation of a stationary front on day 2? Support your answer with data.
6. On day 2, what happened to the front that had covered most of the south and southeast on day 1? Give evidence for your answer.
7. Describe the movement of each of the high-pressure air masses over the two days.
8. Predict the weather at station M for day 3.
9. Notice the wind speeds around the stationary front. What do you predict will happen to the front? Give a reason for your answer.
10. Suppose you were to draw isobars on each map. State what stations would be connected to each other and give the type of air mass they are in.
11. Predict the weather for stations I and J. Give a reason for your answer.

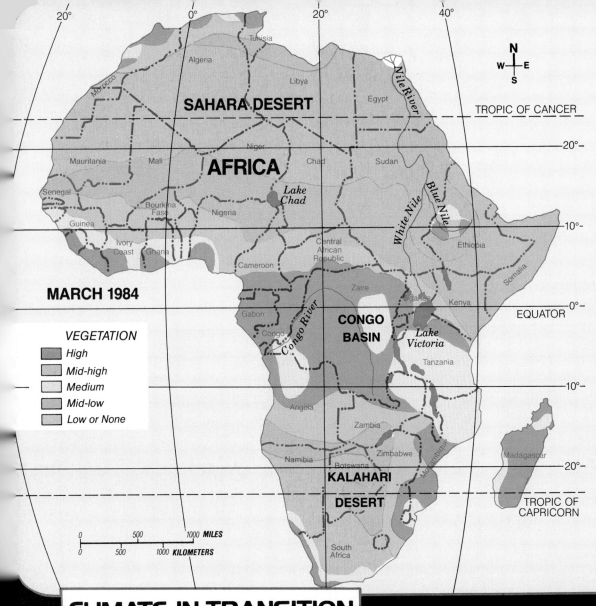

VEGETATION
- High
- Mid-high
- Medium
- Mid-low
- Low or None

MARCH 1984

CLIMATE IN TRANSITION

Africa is experiencing its worst drought in this century. Farmers have not had a good harvest in ten years. What is causing the drought? Are the deserts in Africa advancing? Which areas are showing a steady decline in rainfall? These and many other questions about Africa's drought remain unanswered.

By using weather satellites, scientists have been able to map the vegetation of Africa each day. The satellites measure reflected sunlight. First, researchers found out what wavelengths were reflected by various regions on the earth's surface. Then, they recorded vegetation patterns throughout Africa and determined the amount of plant life on sample areas of land. These observations helped them to interpret the satellites' data. By comparing satellite readings, certain patterns emerged. For example, the total mass of vegetation per hectare in 1984 was less than one-twentieth of what it was in 1981.

The two maps shown here compare the vegetation patterns of Africa for March, 1984 (left) and September, 1984 (right). Vegetation is

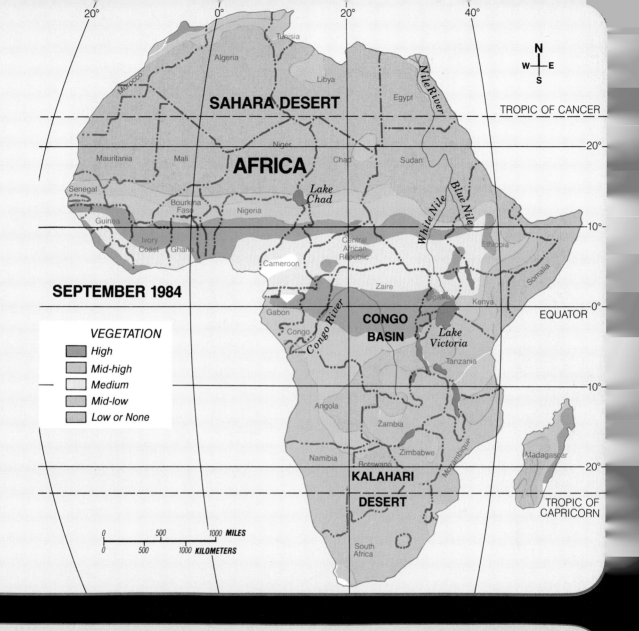

VEGETATION
- High
- Mid-high
- Medium
- Mid-low
- Low or None

SAHARA DESERT

AFRICA

SEPTEMBER 1984

CONGO BASIN

KALAHARI DESERT

TROPIC OF CANCER

20°

10°

EQUATOR

10°

20°

TROPIC OF CAPRICORN

N
W E
S

| 0 | 500 | 1000 MILES |
| 0 | 500 | 1000 KILOMETERS |

shown in shades of green. Notice that in March, vegetation bloomed in southern Africa during their rainy season. Normally the rains move north in September. But the satellite image for September shows that vegetation did not move very far north. In fact, it is 322.6 kilometers south of its normal position.

Questions

1. Using the map key, point out which countries experienced a drought in September, 1984. If aridity became a permanent condition in some parts of north-central Africa, what natural feature would probably increase in size?

2. Some scientists believe that one reason for Africa's drought is overpopulation and overgrazing of grasslands. How might these two conditions contribute to drought?

3. If rainfall increased in the region, how would the satellite image of the region change? How would it change if rainfall decreased?

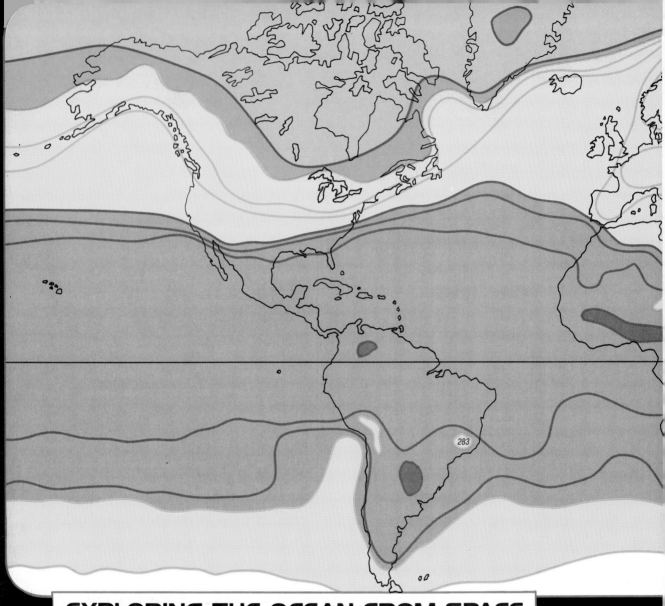

EXPLORING THE OCEAN FROM SPACE

Understanding the earth's vast oceans is an enormous task. Until recently, scientists could only gather data from specially equipped ships. Today, satellites in space provide oceanographers with a wealth of information. For instance, satellites have provided information about the topography of the ocean floor, global wave patterns, and global temperature patterns.

The map on these pages shows global sea- and land-surface temperatures in degrees Kelvin (°K). In order to get this satellite-generated image, infrared and microwave radiation of sea and land surfaces were measured during January, 1979. The key below the map shows the temperature changes for every 10°K. To better understand this temperature scale, remember that pure water freezes at 273°K.

Notice that, generally, the land-surface temperatures tend to be similar to the sea-surface temperatures. Note, too, that the warmest waters are nearest the equator. Similarly, the coldest waters are closest to the poles.

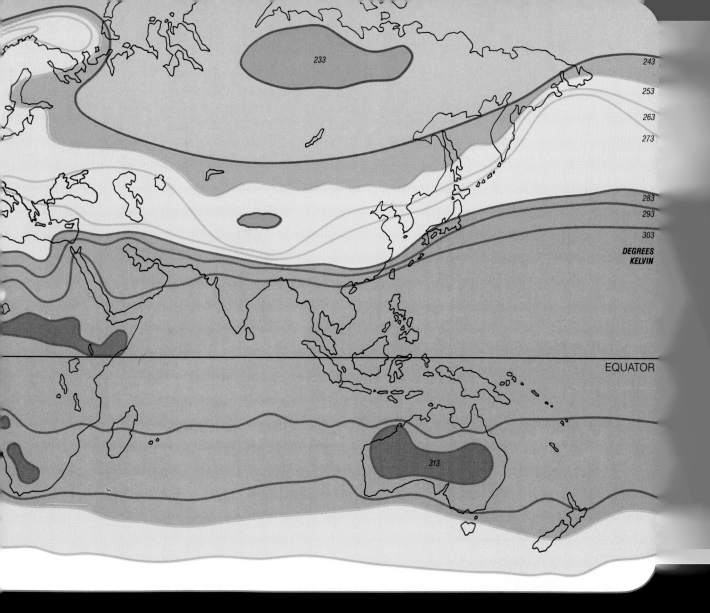

233

243
253
263
273

283
293
303

DEGREES KELVIN

EQUATOR

313

Questions

1. Look at the water temperatures near the poles. Temperatures there range from 230°K to 260°K, well below the freezing point of pure water. Why don't these polar waters freeze?

2. The Gulf Stream moves across the North Atlantic Ocean. On the map shown here, find the water temperatures of the Gulf of Mexico and of the water near England and Alaska. How can you account for the difference in water temperatures of England and Alaska, even though they lie on a similar line of latitude?

3. During the time of year this map was made, where is the air warmest: over the continent of Australia or over the waters surrounding it? Give a reason for your answer.

4. Compare the temperatures of the west coast of the United States to those of the east coast.

5. Explain the difference in the temperatures of the west coast and east coast of the United States.

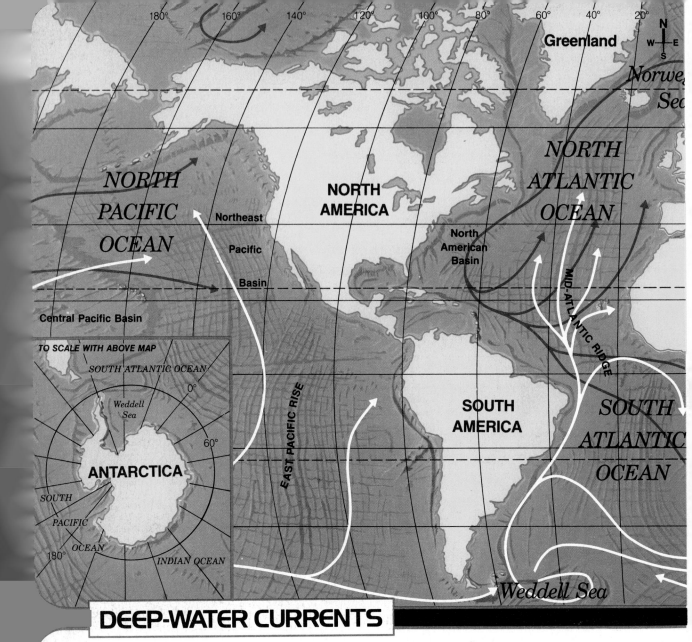

DEEP-WATER CURRENTS

Ocean waters deep beneath the surface are constantly moving. These abyssal, or deep-water, currents begin at areas near the poles.

Water at the poles is very dense due to cold temperatures and high salinity. Near the coast of Antarctica, in the Weddell Sea, cold, dense water sinks to the ocean floor and moves north. In the North Atlantic Ocean, between Greenland and Norway, the frigid waters of the Norwegian Sea sink and move south. Together, these two seas represent the two major areas where cold, dense water is formed.

The path these currents take is determined by the earth's rotation and the topography of the ocean floor. The currents move so slowly that it takes hundreds of years for them to circulate.

The map shows the path of these abyssal currents. White arrows depict the path of water from the Weddell Sea. The path of water from the Norwegian Sea is shown in red.

Questions

1. Why is water at the poles denser than in most other ocean areas?

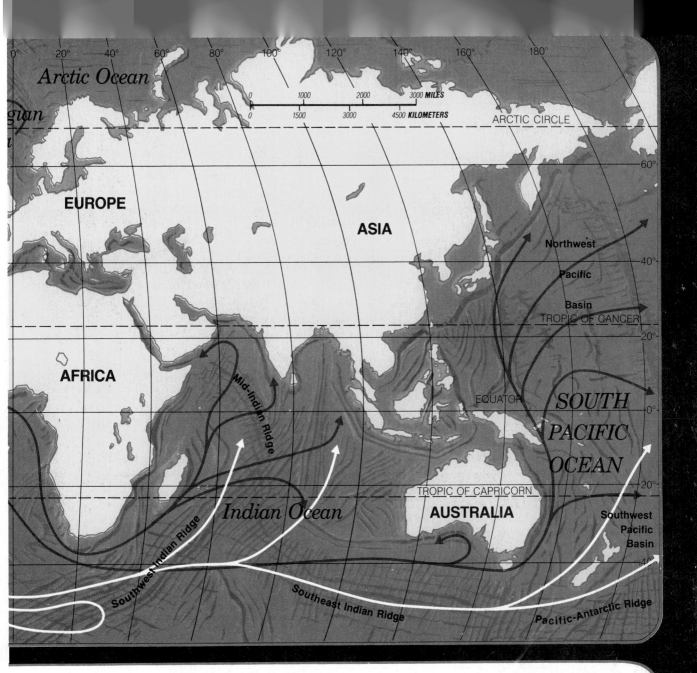

2. What climatic conditions exist to form such cold, dense waters as those of the Norwegian and Weddell seas?

3. There is less ice floating in arctic water than in antarctic water. How does this affect the salinity and density of the arctic waters versus antarctic waters? Why?

4. Look at the map of sea and land surface temperatures on pages 586–587. Compare the surface temperature of the Norwegian Sea to that of the Weddell Sea. Which sea's water do you think is denser? Why?

5. During which season of the year would arctic water have its lowest salinity? Why?

6. Why is the Pacific Ocean more dominated by the abyssal currents from the antarctic waters than from the arctic waters?

7. The earth rotates on its axis from west to east. How does this affect abyssal currents?

8. How do land masses affect the path of abyssal currents?

9. How would the topography of the ocean floor affect the path of abyssal currents?

GLOSSARY

abrasion A process in which rock is worn away by rock materials carried by an erosional agent.

absolute age Actual age, of a body such as the earth, in years.

absolute magnitude A description of how bright a star would be if it were placed a certain distance from the earth.

abyssal plains The flat areas, or plains, that form the main part of the ocean floor.

acid rain An acid formed when sulfur dioxide in the air is dissolved by rain.

aftershocks Smaller, less intense earthquakes that follow a major earthquake.

air mass A large body of air that has about the same temperature and humidity throughout.

air pressure The force caused by the weight of air.

anemometer (an uh MAHM uh tuhr) An instrument that measures wind speed.

annular eclipse An eclipse of the sun that occurs when the moon's umbra does not reach the earth.

aquifer (AK wuh fuhr) A layer of rock or rock material that holds water.

ash Rock fragments, about the size of sand particles, that are thrown out by volcanoes.

ash flows Deposits of volcanic ash that come out of fissures.

asteroids Rocky objects of various sizes moving around the sun.

asthenosphere (as THEHN uh sfihr) A zone in the upper mantle on which the plates float.

astronomical unit (AU) A unit of length that is equal to the average distance from the sun to the earth.

atmosphere (AT muh sfihr) The ocean of air that surrounds the earth.

atoll A type of coral reef that surrounds a body of water.

aurora Light that is released when charged particles from the solar wind collide with gases within the earth's atmosphere.

autumnal equinox (aw TUHM nuhl   EE kwuh nahks) A point in the sky through which the sun passes on the first day of fall in the Northern Hemisphere.

barometer An instrument that is used to measure air pressure.

barrier island A long ridge of sand in the ocean that is parallel to the shoreline.

batholith A large mass of igneous rock below the earth's surface.

bathyscaphs (BATH uh skafs) Diving machines that allow oceanographers to descend to the deepest parts of the ocean.

beach A deposit of rock material along a shore.

bedrock Underlying, unweathered rock.

bench marks Marks on a topographic map that show the elevations of specific points that are not located on contour lines.

benthos (BEHN thahs) Plants and animals that live on the ocean floor.

big bang theory The idea that the universe began as a tremendous explosion.

biomass energy Energy obtained from plant material.

black hole An object, formed from a collapsed star, whose gravity is so strong that not even light escapes it.

bombs Large rocks measuring up to 1 m across that are thrown out by volcanoes.

breaker A breaking wave.

caldera (kal DIHR uh) A very large crater located at the top of a volcano.

carbonation The reaction of carbonic acid with other substances.

cartography (kahr TAHG ruh fee) The science of mapmaking.

cast A fossil that has the same outer shape as the original object.

cavern A large underground chamber created by the action of ground water.

cementation (see muhn TAY shuhn) A process in which minerals act like cement to hold sediments together.

Cenozoic Era The most recent era in geologic time.

chart A map used for air or ocean travel.

chemical property A property that describes how the particles of matter will react and change with other kinds of matter.

chemical rocks Sedimentary rocks made up of chemical sediments.

chemical weathering A process that forms new substances from elements in a rock.

chromosphere (KROH muh sfihr) The first layer of the sun's atmosphere.

cinder cone A pile of ash and cinders around a volcanic opening.

cinders Rock particles that are sent out by an eruption and that are several centimeters across.

cirrus (SIHR uhs) **clouds** Thin, feathery clouds that are formed at high altitudes.

clastic rocks Sedimentary rocks that form from pieces of other rock.

clay A type of soil that is made up of very small particles produced by the chemical weathering of feldspar and other minerals.

cleavage A property that describes how a mineral splits apart along one or more smooth surfaces.

climate An average of the weather conditions over a long period of time.

cloud A collection of water droplets and/or pieces of ice floating in the atmosphere.

cloud seeding The process in which dry crystals are added to a cloud in order to create a thicker cloud and possibly cause rain.

coal A fossil fuel formed from the remains of plants.

cold air mass An air mass in which the temperature of the air is cold.

cold front A front that forms when a cooler air mass replaces a warmer air mass.

collision hypothesis The idea that the planets were formed as a result of a star pulling matter from the sun.

color A physical property, related to reflected light, that helps to describe a mineral.

comets Large chunks of ice, frozen gases, dust and rock that move through space.

compaction (kuhm PAK shuhn) A squeezing process that causes pieces of rock to hold together.

composite cone A volcanic cone that is formed from alternating layers of lava and rocks.

compound The chemical combination of atoms of two or more elements.

conclusion A statement of whether or not the evidence supports the hypothesis in an experiment.

concretion (kahn KREE shuhn) A ball-shaped rock.

condensation nuclei (NOO klee ī) Small particles in air that water condenses on.

conduction A process that occurs when heat energy moves from one object to another while the two objects are in direct contact.

conservation A method of saving resources by controlling how they are used.

constellation A group of stars that form a pattern, or picture, in the sky.

contact metamorphism The process by which solid rocks come into contact with molten rock.

continential glacier An ice sheet that covers a large area of the earth's surface.

continental margins The underwater areas that border the continents.

continental polar air mass (cP) A cold air mass that forms over land in polar regions.

continental rise The part of the continental margin that begins at the continental slope and is made of thick layers of sediment.

continental shelf The gently sloping part of the continental margin that begins at the shoreline.

continental slope The steep part of the continental margin that begins at the continental shelf.

continental tropical air mass (cT) A warm air mass that forms over land in tropical regions.

contour interval The difference in elevation between one contour line and the next.

contour line A line that connects points of the same elevation on a topographic map.

convection A process that occurs when heat energy is moved by a carrier.

convection zone The layer of the sun in which energy is transferred from the radiation zone to the sun's surface.

convergent boundary A place where two plates come together.

core The center of the sun. The innermost layer of the earth.

corona The outer layer of the sun's atmosphere.

correlation The process of matching rocks of the same age but from different areas.

crater A bowl-shaped depression located at the top of most volcanic cones. A circular depression on the moon's surface.

creep A slow form of mass movement that occurs on gentle slopes.

crust The outermost layer of the earth.

crystal A solid with a regular shape and flat sides.

cumulus (KYOO myuh luhs) **clouds** Heaped, fluffy clouds, often with flat bases, that form as warm air rises through the atmosphere.

deficit A condition that occurs when the amount of evaporation is greater than the amount of precipitation in an area.

deflation The lifting and carrying away of loose rock material by wind.

degassing The process in which gases are released by volcanic activity.

degree Celsius (°C) A unit for measuring temperature.

deposition The settling of material.

desalination (dee sal uh NAY shuhn) The process of removing salts from seawater.

dew Water vapor that condenses on cold surfaces, such as grass, plants, and automobiles, on cool mornings.

dew point The temperature to which air must be cooled to become saturated.

dike A structure formed if magma fills and hardens in a vertical crack in rock.

divergent boundary The place where two plates move apart.

divide An area of high elevation that separates watersheds.

doldrums (DAHL druhmz) An area of light, shifting winds at the equator.

drift The deposit from a glacier.

drizzle Very small water droplets.

dune A hill of sand.

earth science The branch of science that studies the earth and space.

earth-centered model A model of the universe in which all other heavenly bodies revolve around the earth.

earthquake The sudden movement of rock in the earth.

echo sounding A method in which sound waves are used to measure the depth of the ocean.

electromagnetic spectrum The different kinds of electromagnetic waves.

electron A particle with a negative charge that moves around outside the nucleus of an atom.

element A material that cannot be changed by chemical means into a simpler material.

ellipse A slightly flattened circle.

epicenter The place on the surface of the earth directly above the focus of an earthquake.

epicycle A small circle that is carried around in a larger circle.

epoch (EP uhk) A time interval into which periods of geologic time are divided.

equal-area projection A map projection that shows land and sea areas in their true shapes and relative sizes.

equator An imaginary line that circles the earth halfway between the North Pole and South Pole.

era A unit of geologic time.

erosion The wearing away and moving of rock materials by natural agents.

eutrophication (yoo troh fuh KAY shuhn) The adding of nutrients to a body of water, which causes the quality of the water to decrease.

evaporation (ee vap uh RAY shuhn) The process by which liquid water changes to water vapor.

evaporite A chemical rock that has formed from mineral deposits left after a body of water has evaporated.

evolution The process of change that produces new species from existing species.

exfoliation The peeling off of slablike sheets of rock.

exosphere (EHK suh sfihr) The top layer of the atmosphere.

experiment A test of a hypothesis.

extrusive (ek STROO sihv) **rocks** Igneous rocks that form from lava.

extrusive volcanism Volcanic activity that occurs on the earth's surface.

fault A place where rock has moved on one or both sides of a crack.

felsite A light-colored igneous rock with crystals that cannot be seen with the naked eye.

flood basalts Extremely thin lava flows that come out of cracks in the earth.

fog A cloud that forms close to the earth.

foliated (FOH lee ayt uhd) **rocks** Metamorphic rocks that have minerals arranged in bands or that are made up of layers.

forecast A prediction about future weather.

fossil fuels Fuels that form from the remains of plants and animals.

fossils The preserved remains or traces of living things of the past.

fracture A break along an irregular surface.

front The boundary between two air masses.

galaxy A large system of stars.

gem A mineral crystal that is unusually colorful and that reflects much light.

geode (JEE ohd) A hollow rock with mineral crystals lining the inside surface.

geologic column A diagram of the sequence of rock layers in an area in order of age.

geologic time scale The division of the earth's history into units of time based on geologic changes and changes in forms of life.

geothermal energy Energy that comes from heat produced within the earth's crust.

geysers Hot springs that erupt periodically.

glacier A large mass of moving ice.

glaze The layer of ice that forms from rain on objects whose temperatures are below freezing.

Gondwanaland The southern continent formed when Pangaea split apart.

Great Lakes Five lakes making up the largest region of fresh water in the world.

greenhouse effect The process in which the surface of the earth radiates waves that warm the atmosphere.

ground water The water in the zone of saturation.

hail Rounded pieces of ice formed by strong updrafts in cumulonimbus clouds.

half-life The length of time it takes for one half of an element's atoms to decay.

hardness The ability of a mineral to be scratched.

heft The relative weight of a mineral.

highs (H) Areas of atmosphere that have higher air pressure than the surrounding areas.

horizons Layers of soil that make up the soil profile.

horse latitudes Two regions, found at latitudes 30° north and 30° south of the equator, where there is no steady movement of air.

humidity (hyoo MIHD uh tee) Water vapor in air.

hurricane A large tropical cyclone that develops in the doldrums, usually during the late summer.

hydration A process that occurs when water combines with minerals.

hydroelectric energy Energy that comes from water flowing downward.

hydrosphere (HĪ druh sfihr) The earth's water.

hypothesis (hī PAHTH uh sihs) A proposed answer to a question about nature that is being investigated.

ice age A cool period in the earth's history during which ice sheets advanced.

igneous (IHG nee uhs) **rocks** Rocks formed from molten rock material that cools and hardens.

index contour A dark contour line.

index fossil A guide fossil that can tell the relative age of the rock in which it is found.

inner core The inner layer of the core of the earth.

inner planets The four planets closest to the sun: Mercury, Venus, Earth, and Mars.

International Date Line The place where one calendar day ends and the next begins.

intrusive (ihn TROO sihv) **rocks** Igneous rocks that form from magma.

intrusive volcanism Volcanic activity below the earth's surface.

invertebrate (in VER tuh brayt) An animal that does not have a bony skeleton.

ionosphere (ī AHN uh sfihr) The region of the atmosphere where ions are held in place by the earth's magnetic field.

isobars (ī suh bahrz) Lines drawn on weather maps to connect places that have the same air pressure.

isotherms (ī suh thermz) Lines drawn on weather maps to connect stations that have the same temperature.

jet streams High-speed bands of wind.

Jupiter The fifth planet from the sun.

karst An area containing many caverns and sinkholes.

kilogram (kg) The SI unit for measuring mass.

krill Shrimplike creatures that live in the waters around Antarctica.

laccolith A mass of intrusive igneous rock that is dome-shaped.

lake A large water-filled depression in the earth's surface.

Landsat A satellite that photographs the earth's surface and helps identify resources.

landslide A rapid movement of rock and other earth materials down a slope.

latitude The distance north or south of the equator.

Laurasia The northern continent formed when Pangaea split apart.

law of cross-cutting relationships The principle that younger features in rock formations cut across older features.

law of superposition The principle that each layer in an undisturbed section of sedimentary rock is older than layers above it and younger than those below it.

legend A list that explains the meaning of each symbol and color on a map.

lightning A large electrical discharge that occurs between clouds or between a cloud and the earth.

light-year (ly) A unit equal to the distance light can travel in one year.

liter (L) A unit of volume.

lithosphere (LIHTH uh sfihr) The crust and upper mantle of the earth.

loam A combination of sand, clay, and pieces of sedimentary rock called silt.

loess (LOH ihs) Deposits of windblown silt.

longitude The distance east or west of the prime meridian.

longshore current An ocean current that moves closely along a shore.

lows (L) Areas of the atmosphere that have lower air pressure than the surrounding areas.

lunar eclipse A phenomenon that occurs when the moon passes through the shadow of the earth.

luster A physical property that describes the way the surface of a mineral reflects light.

magnetosphere (mag NEE tuh sfihr) The magnetic field of the earth.

magnitude A measure of the total amount of energy released by an earthquake.

main-sequence stars Stars that appear on the main sequence of the H-R diagram.

manganese nodules Round objects on the ocean floor formed from minerals in ocean water.

mantle The layer within the earth that surrounds the core and that is located below the crust.

map A model of the earth's surface.

map projection A drawing that shows the curved surface of the earth on a flat surface.

mare (MAHR ee) A flat area on the moon's surface.

maritime polar air mass (mP) A cold air mass that forms over water in polar regions.

maritime tropical air mass (mT) A warm air mass that forms over water in tropical regions.

Mars The fourth planet from the sun.

mass A measure of the amount of matter in an object.

mass movement The movement of a large amount of weathered rock and other earth materials down a slope.

matter Anything that has mass and takes up space.

mechanical weathering A process that breaks large rocks into smaller rocks.

Mercator projection A map projection in which the grid consists of straight lines.

Mercury The closest planet to the sun.

mesosphere (MEHS uh sfihr) The third layer of the atmosphere.

Mesozoic Era The era following the Paleozoic Era, and during which reptiles were dominant.

metamorphic (meht uh MAWR fihk) **rocks** Rocks that have been changed by heat or pressure.

meteorite impact hypothesis The theory that the extinction of the dinosaurs was caused by a meteorite or comet.

meteoroids Small bodies of rock or metal that move through the solar system.

meter (m) The SI unit for measuring length or distance.

microclimate The climate in a small area.

Mid-Ocean Ridge The continuous chain of mountains on the floor of the major oceans.

Milky Way galaxy The galaxy that is the home of our solar system.

mineral A solid element or compound that has a specific crystal structure.

mineral deposits Rocks that contain an unusually large amount of a mineral.

mixture A combination of different substances that can be separated by physical means.

model A representation of the properties of an object.

Moho The boundary between the earth's mantle and crust.

Mohs scale A number scale for determining the hardness of minerals.

mold A fossil that is a hollow space left in a rock by an object that has dissolved.

moraine A ridge of till that was dropped when the edge of a large glacier melted.

mudflow A moving mass of mud.

Nansen bottle A special device used to collect and measure samples of seawater.

natural gas A gas made up mostly of methane.

natural resource Any material that can be used from the earth.

natural selection The idea that those life forms that are best adapted to an environment will survive.

neap tides Tides that are lower than usual.

nebular (NEHB yuh luhr) **hypothesis** The idea that the sun and the planets formed from a spinning dust cloud, or nebula.

nekton (NEHK tahn) Living things that swim through the water.

Neptune The eighth planet from the sun.

neritic (nih RIHT ihk) **zone** The area that extends from the low-tide line to the edge of the continental shelf.

neutron A subatomic particle that has no charge.

nonclastic rocks Sedimentary rocks that are formed from dissolved minerals in water or from the remains of past life.

nonfoliated rocks Metamorphic rocks that do not have bands of minerals or layers.

nonrenewable resource A natural resource that cannot be replaced.

nonsilicate minerals Minerals that do not consist of silicon and oxygen.

nuclear energy Energy produced from changes in the nucleus of the atom.

nucleus The center of an atom, made up of protons and neutrons.

observation An examination of some part of nature.

occluded (uh KLOO dihd) **front** A front that forms when a cold front catches up to a warm front.

ocean basin A deep depression that holds a large amount of the surface waters of the earth.

oceanic zone The ocean area beyond the continental shelves.

oceanography The study of oceans.

ooze Sediment formed by the remains of ocean animals and plants.

ore A mineral deposit in the earth that contains materials which can be mined for profit.

organic rocks Sedimentary rocks made up of the remains of living things.

organic sediments Sediments made up of the remains of living things.

oscillating (AHS uh layt ihng) **universe theory** The idea that the universe starts with a big bang, but then collapses back together.

outer core The outer layer of the core of the earth.

outer planets The planets beyond the asteroid belt: Jupiter, Saturn, Uranus, Neptune, and Pluto.

outwash Rock material deposited by water produced from the melting of a glacier.

oxidation A process in which oxygen combines with other substances.

paleontologists (pay lee ahn TAHL uh jihsts) Scientists who study life on the earth in past geologic time.

Paleozoic Era The era in which life forms first appeared in abundance.

Pangaea (pan JEE uh) A large land mass that broke apart, forming the continents.

parallax (PAR uh lahks) An apparent shift in the position of an object when it is viewed from different places.

parent rock The rock from which soil is formed.

period A geologic time interval into which eras are divided.

permeability The ability of a material to transmit water.

petroleum A mixture of many liquid hydrocarbons.

phases The different shapes of the moon in the sky.

photosphere The visible surface of the sun.

physical property A characteristic of matter that can be observed without changing the material.

plankton (PLANGK tuhn) Microscopic plants and animals that float near the surface of water.

plate boundaries The areas where the earth's plates meet.

Plates Rigid blocks of the earth's outer crust.

Pluto The ninth planet from the sun.

polar climate A zone where the average temperature stays below 10°C during the year.

polar easterlies Wind belts formed from air moving away from the North Pole.

polar front A front formed where warm air from near the equator meets cold air from a pole.

pollution The adding of harmful substances to the environment.

pond A small, shallow depression that fills with water.

porosity A measure of the number of pores in a material compared with the volume of the material.

porphyry (PAWR fuh ree) An igneous rock with both large and small mineral crystals.

Precambrian Era The oldest and longest era on the geologic time scale.

precipitation (prih sihp uh TAY shuhn) A process by which dissolved materials in water settle out of solution. Water that returns to the earth as rain, snow, sleet, or hail.

pressure belt An area of constant high or low pressure that encircles the earth.

prevailing westerlies Westerly winds found between latitudes 30° and 60° north and south of the equator.

primary (P) waves The first earthquake waves to be recorded by a seismograph.

principle of uniformitarianism (yoo nuh fawr muh-TAIR ee uh nihz uhm) The idea that the processes at work today are the same processes that have been at work throughout earth's history.

prominence A loop of plasma that shoots from the photosphere but is held in the corona by a magnetic field.

property A characteristic that describes a material.

proton A subatomic particle with a positive electrical charge.

protoplanet A collection of condensed gas and dust particles that is thought to form a planet.

protostars Pockets of matter that are the beginnings of stars.

psychrometer (sī KRAHM uh tuhr) An instrument that measures relative humidity.

pulsar (PUHL sahr) A collapsed star that produces rapid bursts of radio waves that repeat many times per second.

quasars (KWAY sahrs) Galaxies that are powerful sources of radio waves.

radiant energy Energy, including gamma rays, X rays, ultraviolet rays, infrared rays, radio waves, and visible light, that travels as waves.

radiation A process in which heat energy travels in the form of waves.

radiation zone The thickest layer of the sun.

radio telescope An instrument that gathers and focuses radio waves.

radioactive decay A process in which atomic nuclei break down, giving off particles and energy.

radioactive element An element that breaks down, or decays, to form other kinds of elements.

radiometric dating A way of measuring geologic time by measuring the decay of radioactive elements that rocks contain.

rain Liquid water that falls to the earth.

rain gauge An instrument that measures the amount of rainfall.

recycling A process in which wastes are reused or changed into reusable products.

red giant A cool red star that is very bright because it is so large.

reference map A map that shows the location of features.

reflecting telescope An optical telescope that uses a curved mirror to gather light rays and produce an image.

refracting telescope An optical telescope that uses a lens to gather light and produce an image.

regional metamorphism The process by which wide areas of rock are changed by great heat and pressure.

relative age The age of something compared with the age of something else.

relative humidity The amount of water vapor in the air compared with the maximum amount of water vapor that air is able to hold at that temperature.

relief map A map that shows mountains, valleys, plains, and their elevations.

renewable resource A natural resource that can be renewed or replaced.

residual soil Soil that remains on top of its parent rock.

revolution The movement of an object along an orbit or path, around another body.

Richter (RIHK tuhr) **scale** A scale of numbers from 1 to 10 that is used to measure the amount of energy released by an earthquake.

rift valley A deep, narrow valley.

river One main flowing body of water formed when all the streams in an area join.

river system A river and all the tributary streams that flow into it.

rock cycle The process of change that shows how the different types of rock are related and how rock material is used and reused.

rotation The turning of an object on its axis.

runoff Water that moves over land.

salinity (suh LIHN uh tee) The number of grams of dissolved salt in a kilogram of seawater.

sand A type of soil that is made up of particles that are larger than those in clay or loam.

satellite Any object that revolves around another object.

Saturn The sixth planet from the sun.

scale A calibrated line that shows a relationship between distances on the earth and distances on a map.

science A way of obtaining knowledge about nature.

scientific method The way scientists gather information and test ideas about nature.

seamounts Underwater volcanic mountains on the abyssal plains.

secondary waves The earthquake waves recorded by a seismograph after the primary waves.

sedimentary (sehd uh MEHNT uh ree) **rocks** Rocks formed from sediment.

sedimentation The process in which materials carried by air, water, or ice are deposited as sediments.

seismic waves The waves produced in an earthquake.

seismograph An instrument that records vibrations in the earth.

shield cone A volcanic cone that has a gentle slope and a broad base.

shore zone The area between the high-tide line and the low-tide line.

shoreline The boundary between the land and sea.

silicate minerals The group of minerals that contain oxygen and silicon.

sill A structure of hardened magma between horizontal rock layers.

sinkhole A huge circular hole caused by the collapse of the roof of a cavern.

sleet Freezing rain, which forms when raindrops freeze while falling to the earth.

slump The sudden movement of a large block of material in a single mass down a slope.

smog A type of air pollution that forms when certain gases given off by automobiles react in the presence of sunlight.

snow The solid form of precipitation that occurs when snowflakes do not melt as they fall.

soil The loose material on the earth's surface in which plants can grow.

soil texture A characteristic of soil that is determined by the diameters of the particles that make up the soil.

solar eclipse A phenomenon that occurs when the earth passes through the moon's shadow.

solar energy Energy from the sun.

solar flare A sudden, violent eruption of plasma from the chromosphere lasting for a short time.

solar system The sun and the objects that move around it.

solar wind A steady stream of electrically charged particles given off by the sun.

space probes Spacecraft sent to study the moon and other planets.

special-purpose map A map that shows a particular feature of an area, such as rainfall, natural resources, or weather.

specific gravity A property that is determined by comparing the mass of a substance with the mass of an equal volume of water.

spectroscope An instrument that separates light into very fine bands of color.

spring tides Tides that are higher than usual.

squall line A line of rising air that forms ahead of a cold front.

stalactite A formation of calcite that extends downward from the roof of a cave.

stalagmite A calcite structure that extends upward from the floor of a cave.

stationary front A front that does not move for a time.

steady state theory The idea that as the galaxies spread, new galaxies form in the space between them.

stratosphere (STRAT uh sfihr) The second layer of the atmosphere.

stratus (STRA tuhs) **clouds** Clouds that spread out in a layer as a large body of air is slowly lifted into the atmosphere.

streak The color of the powder mark made by a mineral as it is rubbed against a piece of porcelain.

stream A relatively small, naturally flowing body of water.

subduction The process by which one plate is pushed below another because of a plate collision.

subduction zone The area where a plate is pushed below another plate.

sublimation (suhb luh MAY shuhn) The process in which vapor changes directly to a solid or a solid changes directly to vapor.

submarine canyons Deep canyons cut into the surfaces of the continental slopes.

subsoil The layer below topsoil.

summer solstice (SAHL stihs) A point in the sky through which the sun passes on the first day of summer in the Northern Hemisphere.

sun-centered model A model of the universe in which the earth and the other planets revolve around the sun.

sunspots Dark areas on the sun.

supernova The violent explosion of a star near the end of its life.

surface waves The slowest and last earthquake waves to reach a seismograph.

surplus A condition that occurs when the amount of precipitation is greater than the amount of evaporation in an area.

technology (tehk NAHL uh jee) The use of knowledge from science in an attempt to improve the quality of human life.

temperate climate A zone where the average summer temperature is above 18°C and the average winter temperature is below 10°C.

temperature A measure of the energy of motion of the molecules in a material.

theory (THEE uh ree) A hypothesis that has been tested many times and that is supported by evidence.

theory of continental drift The idea that the continents were once together and then broke apart and moved to their present positions.

theory of plate tectonics The idea that the earth's lithosphere is broken into moving plates.

theory of sea-floor spreading The idea that the Mid-Ocean Ridge is a crack in the earth's crust through which molten rock rises and spreads as new sea floor.

thermometer An instrument used to measure temperature.

thermosphere (THER muh sfihr) The fourth layer of the atmosphere.

thunder The loud crash that accompanies a flash of lightning.

thunderstorm A violent weather system that produces tall cumulus clouds, strong winds, heavy rain, lightning, thunder, and sometimes, hail and tornadoes.

tidal energy Energy produced by the rise and fall of water due to the tides.

till Rock material deposited directly by a glacier when it melts.

time zones The 24 equal segments of the earth used to standardize time measurements.

topographic (tahp uh GRAF ihk) **map** A map that shows the shapes and heights of the land by using lines that connect points that have the same elevations.

topsoil Soil that contains humus and the weathered minerals that plants need to grow.

tornado A small funnel-shaped whirlwind that spins in a counterclockwise direction around an area of very low pressure.

trade winds Steady easterly winds between the doldrums and the horse latitudes.

transform fault A boundry where plates slide past each other.

transpiration (tran spuh RAY shuhn) The process by which plants release water vapor into the atmosphere through their leaves.

trench A deep valley feature on the sea floor that is produced next to a subduction zone.

tributaries (TRIHB yuh tehr eez) Streams that flow into larger streams or into a river.

tropical climate A zone where the average temperature during the year stays above 18°C.

troposphere (TROH puh sfihr) The first layer of the atmosphere.

turbidity currents Powerful currents formed by underwater landslides.

unconformity (uhn kuhn FAWR muh tee) Any buried surface that represents a break in the rock record.

upwelling A process in which wind can cause deep ocean water to rise.

Uranus The seventh planet from the sun.

valley glaciers Glaciers that form in mountain regions.

Van Allen belts Two doughnut-shaped regions of the magnetosphere in which charged particles are concentrated.

vent The channel that connects the source of magma to the opening of a volcano.

Venus The second planet from the sun.

vernal equinox (VER nuhl EE kwuh nahks) A point in the sky through which the sun passes on the first day of spring in the Northern Hemisphere.

vertebrate An animal with a bony skeleton.

volcano A structure made of materials from within the earth that build up around an opening on the earth's surface.

volume A measure of how much space something takes up.

warm air mass An air mass in which the temperature of the air is warm.

warm front A front that forms when a warm air mass replaces a cooler air mass.

water budget A record of the amount of precipitation and evaporation for an area.

water cycle The continuous movement of water between the earth and the air.

water table The boundary between the zone of aeration and the zone of saturation.

watershed The area that supplies water for a river.

waterspout A tornado that forms over a body of water.

wave height The distance between the bottom part of a wave and the top part of a wave.

wavelength The distance from one crest of a wave to the next crest.

weather maps Maps that provide an overall picture of weather activity across the earth.

weathering The breakup and change of rocks and minerals, mainly from the action of air, water, and frost.

white dwarfs Hot stars that are not bright because they are very small.

wind Moving air.

wind energy Energy produced by the wind.

wind vane An instrument that shows the direction of the wind.

winter solstice (SAHL stihs) A point in the sky through which the sun passes on the first day of winter in the Northern Hemisphere.

zone of saturation The area below the earth's surface that is filled with water.

Index

CREDITS

Cover: Harald Sund, NASA, Tom Powers

Maps: JAK

Skills Handbook Maps: Jim Harvin

Activities: Philip Jones

Contributing artists: Michael Adams: 497, 498, 502, 535; Mark Hannon: 96, 98, 100, 103, 106, 107, 153, 156, 395, 401, 411, 476; Seward Hung: 13, 14, 74, 83, 88, 108, 110, 121, 124, 230, 333, 400, 405, 426, 449, 469, 556; Susan Johnston: 14, 27, 50, 51, 52, 53, 54, 55, 56, 59, 60, 61, 62, 65, 67, 75, 76, 78, 79, 81, 90, 224, 228, 265, 288; George Kelvin: 301, 302, 310, 497, 520, 521, 523; Peter Krempaski: 229; 233, 551; Joseph Lemonnier: 44, 145, 177, 248, 276, 282, 283, 284, 285, 306, 308, 309, 311, 326, 347, 353, 354, 357, 358, 387, 487, 501, 525, 526, 529, 544, 567; Davis Meltzer: 120, 121, 129, 132, 133, 135, 137, 138, 150, 151, 157, 158, 321, 323, 328, 331, 335, 339, 405, 426, 431, 436; Alex Pieterson: 45, 123, 144, 388; Philip Jones: 445, 447, 450, 459; Tom Powers: 24, 124, 127, 136, 174, 215, 407, 413, 433, 474, 478, 496, 537; Taylor Oughten: 143, 367, 371, 373, 374, 375, 376, 377, 379, 380; Stacy Rogers: 86, 125, 222, 230, 422, 423, 494, 495; Delores Santoliquido: 548, 549

i: Harald Sund

iii: reading from left to right. Jet Propulsion Laboratory; The Granger Collection; Tom Till; © T. Dickenson/Photo Researchers, Inc.; NASA; Al Huelga/Neptune Films, Ltd.

Unit One viii: *t*. E.R. Degginger; *b.l*. Ernst Haas/Magnum; © *b.r*. Fernando Scianna/Magnum. 1: *t*. The Granger Collection; *b.l*. NASA; *m., b.r*. The Granger Collection.

Chapter 1 2: Jet Propulsion Laboratory. 4: *t.r*. R. Hoblitt/West Light; *m*. NOAA; *t.l*. J.D. Griggs/USGS; *b*. William Gentile/Picture Group. 5: NASA. 6: *t.l*. © Carl Frank/Photo Researchers, Inc.; *t.r*. © Herb Levart/Photo Researchers, Inc.; *b*. © Hank Morgan/Photo Researchers, Inc. 7: Mark Sherman/Bruce Coleman. 8, 9: Silver Burdett. 10: *l*. R.L. Christiansen/USGS; *r*. Phil Degginger. 14, 15: Silver Burdett. 16: *l., m*. E.R. Degginger; *r*. Grant Heilman Photography; *b*. © James Bill/Science Source/Photo Researchers, Inc. 17: Courtesy of Cray Research, Inc. 18: Owen Franken/Picture Group; *inset* Lamont Doherty Geological Observatory. 19: © Hank Morgan/Photo Researchers, Inc.

Chapter 2 22: The Granger Collection. 24, 27: Silver Burdett. 29: Courtesy of *U.S.A. Today*. 31: NOAA. 34: William Haxby, Lamont Doherty Geological Observatory. 37: NASA. 38: General Electric. 42: *t*. Keith Gunnar/Bruce Coleman; *m*. Aronson Photo/Stock Boston.

Unit Two 46: *t*. Jet Propulsion Laboratory; *b*. Courtesy of Vassar College. 47: *t.l*. Library of Congress; *t.r*. Dennis Milon; *m*. The Granger Collection; *b*. NASA.

Chapter 3 48: © Georg Gerster/Photo Researchers, Inc. 55: Eric Carle/Shostal Associates. 61, 62: NASA. 64: Colour Library International (USA) Ltd. 66: *l*. Lick Observatory; *r*. Dennis Milon. 68: *l*. Tersch Enterprises; *r*. Steve Traudt/Tom Stack & Associates.

Chapter 4 72: NASA. 74: Dennis Milon. 75: David Malin/Anglo Australian Telescope Board. 77: Dennis di Cicco. 80: NASA. 82: *t*. Big Bear Solar Observatory; *m*. Dennis Milon; *b*. Los Alamos National Laboratory. 85: National Optical Astronomy Observatories. 90: E.R. Degginger.

Chapter 5 94: John W. Briggs; *inset* Sovfoto. 99, 100: NASA. 101: *t*. Dennis Milon; *b*. NASA. 104: NASA. 105: *t*. Dennis Milon; *m*. NASA. 106: NASA. 107: Lowell Observatory. 108: NASA. 109: Randa Bishop/After Image. 110: Goddard Space Center. 112: Jet Propulsion Laboratory. 113, 114: NASA.

Chapter 6 118: B. Louise Turtle/Anglo Australian Telescope Board. 122: © Hencoup Enterprises/Science Photo Library/Photo Researchers, Inc. 127: © Robin Scagell/Science Photo Library/Photo Researchers, Inc. 128: Dennis di Cicco. 131: David Malin/Anglo Australian Telescope Board. 132: © Science Source/Photo Researchers, Inc. 135: U.S. Naval Observatory. 142: *t*. RCA; *m*. Tom Pantages.

Unit Three 146: *t*. David Denning/Earth Images; *b.l*. USGS; *b.r*. Michael Sullivan/TexaStock. 147: *t*. The Granger Collection; *b*. Tom Till.

Chapter 7 148: NASA. 155: Runk/Schoenberger/Grant Heilman Photography. 156: NASA. 158: Silver Burdett. 160: *l*. Grant Heilman Photography; *t.r*. E.R. Degginger; *b.r*. William Felger/Grant Heilman Photography. 161: Michal Heron. 164: G.T.E. Laboratories, Inc. 165: NCIC/USGS.

Chapter 8 170: G.D. Plage/Bruce Coleman Ltd. 172: *t*. Mark Newman/Earth Images; *b*. Silver Burdett. 173: *l*. Larry Hamill; *r*. Eagle Picher Industries, Inc. 175: Silver Burdett. 176: *t.l*. John Pawlaski/Tom Stack & Associates; *t.r., b.r*. Breck Kent; *b.l*. Brian Parker/Tom Stack & Associates. 178: *t*. Breck Kent; *b*. Silver Burdett. 179: Smithsonian Institution. 180: Breck Kent. 181: *t*. Grant Heilman Photography; *m*. E.R. Degginger; *b.l*. Breck Kent; *b.r*. Silver Burdett. 183: E.R. Degginger. 185: *l*. Runk/Schoenberger/Grant Heilman Photography; *m*. Tom Stack & Associates; *r*. Breck Kent. 186: Runk/Schoenberger/Grant Heilman Photography. 187: E.R. Degginger. 188: © Reagan Bradshaw 1985.

Chapter 9 192: G.R. Roberts. 194: *All* Silver Burdett *except b.r*. E.R. Degginger; *m.l*. Breck Kent. 196: *r*. Richard Grigg/University of Hawaii; *l*. W. Stoy/Bruce Coleman. 197: *t.l*. © Sandra Grant/Photo Researchers, Inc.; *t.r., b.r*. Silver Burdett; *m*. E.R. Degginger. 198: Silver Burdett. 199: IMAGERY. 200: Silver Burdett. 203: *t*. E.R. Degginger; *b*. Eric Carle/Shostal Associates. 204: *l*. Bill Everitt/Tom Stack & Associates; *r*. S. Summerhays/Biofotos. 205: *t*. Alan Pitcairn/Grant Heilman Photography; *b*. Tom Bean. 206: Silver Burdett. 207: *t.l., t.m*. Breck Kent; *t.r*. Silver Burdett; *b.l*. E.R. Degginger; *b.r*. Grant Heilman Photography. 208: *t.l., m.r*. Silver Burdett; *m.l*. Heather Angel/Biofotos. 209: Kim Steele/Wheeler Pictures. 210: John & Sue Brownlie/Bruce Coleman

Ltd. 212: *l.* Budd Titlow/Tom Stack & Associates; *r.* William Felger/ Grant Heilman Photography. 213: *t.r.* E.R. Degginger; *m.r.* Silver Burdett; *b.l., b.m.* Grant Heilman Photography; *b.r.* E.R. Degginger. 216: Courtesy of Professor H. Wiedemier, Dept. of Chemistry, Rensselaer Polytechnic Institute.

Chapter 10 220: Erik Svensson/After Image. 223: Grant Heilman Photography. 224: *l.* Alan Pitcairn/Grant Heilman Photography; *r.* Library of Congress. 225: *l.* Grant Heilman Photography; *r.* Larry Lefever/Grant Heilman Photography. 226: Craig Aurness/West Light. 227: *t.* Runk/Schoenberger/Grant Heilman Photography; *b.* Breck Kent. 230: *t.* Silver Burdett; *b.l.* Breck Kent; *b.r.* E.R. Degginger. 231: Jim McNee/Tom Stack & Associates. 232: *t.* Barry Runk/Grant Heilman Photography; *b.* Leland Marchant, Western Research Institute. 233: *l.* Steve Allen/Peter Arnold, Inc.; *r.* © M. Hyman/Photo Researchers, Inc. 234: *t.* © Harald Sund; *b.* Breck Kent. 235, 236: © Harald Sund. 237: Dan McCoy/Rainbow. 238: Charles Rotkin/PFI. 240: Larry Lefever/ Grant Heilman Photography. 241: *t.* Jack Dermid/Bruce Coleman; *b.* Adrienne Gibson/Tom Stack & Associates. 246: *l.* Hank Morgan/Rainbow; *r.* Peter Britton.

Unit Four 250: *t.* The Granger Collection; *b.* © T. Dickenson/Photo Researchers, Inc. 251: *t.* Library of Congress; *m.* E.R. Degginger; *l.* Jet Propulsion Laboratory.

Chapter 11 252: © Elt Davis/National Geographic Society. 254: E.R. Degginger. 255: *t.l.* Kurt Scholz/Shostal Associates; *t.r.* Runk/ Schoenberger/Grant Heilman Photography; *b.* Don & Pat Valenti/Tom Stack & Associates. 256: *l.* Dale Jorgenson/Tom Stack & Associates; *r.* Breck Kent. 257: E.R. Degginger. 258: *l.* Tom Till; *r.* M. Timothy O'Keefe/Tom Stack & Associates. 259: Phil Degginger. 261: Tom Till. 262: *t.l.* Steve McCutcheon/Alaska Pictorial Service; *t.r.* Becky & Gary Vestal/Earth Images; *b.* USGS. 264: © Georg Gerster/Photo Researchers, Inc. 265: G.R. Roberts. 266: Allen E. Morton/Dennis Milon. 267: *l., m.* E.R. Degginger; *r.* Grant Heilman Photography.

Chapter 12 272: Tom Till. 274: *l.* Mark Glass/Monkmeyer Press; *r.* E.R. Degginger. 275: *l.* Stephenie S. Ferguson © William E. Ferguson. 277: *l.* NASA; *r.* G.R. Roberts. 278: *l.* Grant Heilman Photography; *r.* Phil Degginger. 279: Knudsens Fotosenter. 280: Breck Kent. 281: *l.* E.R. Degginger; *r.* Grant Heilman Photography. 282: *t.* Bill Evans; *b.* William Felger/Grant Heilman Photography. 284: *t.* Breck Kent; *b.* G.R. Roberts. 285: Allyn Baum/Monkmeyer Press. 287: *t.* Tom Till; *b.* Breck Kent. 288: *l.* R. Hamilton Smith; *m., r.* E.R. Degginger. 290: G.R. Roberts.

Chapter 13 294: Icelandic Photo & Press Service. 297: *l.* Breck Kent; *r.* Smithsonian Institution. 298: The Granger Collection. 300: Woods Hole Oceanographic Institution. 306: Soames Summerhays/ Biofotos. 308: E. Mickleburgh/Ardea, London. 311: *l.* Transworld Features, Holland B.V.; *r.* Icelandic Photo & Press Service. 312: Virginia Polytechnic.

Chapter 14 318: E.R. Degginger. 322: *l.* Gary Rosenquist/Earth Images; *r.* Soames Summerhays/Biofotos. 324: *l.* E.R. Degginger; *r.* Breck Kent. 325: *t.l.* Bill Thompson/Earth Images; *t.r., b.l.* E.R. Degginger; *b.r.* Becky & Gary Vestal/Earth Images. 327: *t.l.* E. Streichan/ Shostal Associates; *t.r.* Breck Kent; *b.* © Harald Sund. 328: Breck Kent. 329: William E. Ferguson. 332: Richard W. Tolbert/After Image. 333: Eric Kroll/Taurus. 337: Jon Hacking/Earth Images. 338: Terraphotographics/BPS. 340: USGS.

Chapter 15 344: University of Nebraska State Museum; photo by James Amos, © National Geographic Society, 1985. 346: William E. Ferguson. 347: E.R. Degginger. 348: *l.* © Georg Gerster/Photo Researchers, Inc.; *m.* Breck Kent; *r.* E.R. Degginger. 349: *l.* Tom Stack & Associates; *m.* Breck Kent; *r.* E.R. Degginger. 350: *t.* Smithsonian Institution; *b.l.* *Tass* from Sovfoto; *b.r.* E.R. Degginger. 352: Breck Kent. 355: J. Westgate, Dept. of Geology, University of Texas. 356: Dave Davidson/Tom Stack & Associates. 359: Courtesy of California Institute of Technology. 362: Breck Kent.

Chapter 16 366: Earl Roberge. 374, 375: Breck Kent. 377: National Park Service. 381: *l.* Gary Zahm/Bruce Coleman; *r.* Nick Decker. 386: *t.* Dan McCoy/Rainbow; *m.* Peter Menzel/Stock Boston.

Unit Five 390: *t.* NOAA; *m.* Daedalus Enterprises, Inc.; *b.* NASA. 391: *t.l.* Library of Congress; *t.r.* The Granger Collection; *b.* Phil Degginger.

Chapter 17 392–397: IMAGERY. 398–405: Silver Burdett. 409: Holt Confer/Grant Heilman Photography. 410: IMAGERY. 412: Jo-Ann Ordano. 414: Erik Simonsen/Black Star.

Chapter 18 418: © David Parker/Science Photo Library/Photo Researchers, Inc. 421: *l.* E.R. Degginger; *m.* Tom Stack & Associates; *r.* Terraphotographics/BPS. 424: Silver Burdett. 427: S.J. Krassemann/ Peter Arnold, Inc. 428: *l.* R. Hamilton Smith; *r.* G.R. Roberts. 429: John Shaw/Tom Stack & Associates. 430: *l.* R. Hamilton Smith; *r.* IMAGERY. 434: *t.* Silver Burdett; *b.* © Southern Living/Photo Researchers, Inc. 435: Dr. William L. Harrison, Sno Mech; *b.* John Shaw/Tom Stack & Associates.

Chapter 19 440: © Howie Bluestein/Photo Researchers, Inc. 445: Alistair B. Fraser. 448: R. Hamilton Smith. 451: © J.P. Vuillomenet/ Photo Researchers, Inc. 452: E.R. Degginger. 454: NOAA. 455: E.R. Degginger. 457: © Margaret Durrance/Photo Researchers, Inc. 459: NOAA. 460: Colour Library International (USA) Ltd.

Chapter 20 464: © Harald Sund. 466: *l.* E.R. Degginger; *r.* Phil Degginger. 472: *l.* NOAA; *r.* NESDIS/NOAA. 478: E.R. Degginger. 479: Breck Kent. 481: © Georg Gerster/Photo Researchers, Inc. 482: E.R. Degginger. 486: *l.* © Photo Researchers, Inc.; *r.* IMAGERY.

Unit Six 490: *t.* J. Frederick Grassle/Woods Hole Oceanographic Institution; *b.* Al Huelga/Neptune Films, Ltd. 491: *t.l.* Library of Congress; *t.r.* The Granger Collection; *b.* E.R. Degginger.

Chapter 21 492: © Michael Nichols/Magnum. 494: Alan Pitcairn/ Grant Heilman Photography. 495: E. Manewal/Shostal Associates. 499: *t.* Robert & Linda Mitchell; *b.* Alan Nelson/Earth Scenes. 501: Phil Degginger. 503: *t.* State of Indiana, Dept. of Commerce; *b.* Richard Kolar/Earth Scenes. 505: Ray Manley/Shostal Associates. 507: Breck Kent/Earth Scenes. 509: E.R. Degginger. 510: Runk/Schoenberger/ Grant Heilman Photography. 511: Click, Chicago.

Chapter 22 516: G.R. Roberts. 522, 523: Les Fields/Neptune Films, Ltd. 524: Woods Hole Oceanographic Institution. 525: © Van Bucher/Photo Researchers, Inc. 527: E.R. Degginger. 528: *t.l.* Mark Sherman/Bruce Coleman; *t.r., b.* © Harald Sund. 529: Southern Stock. 530: E.R. Degginger. 531: *t.* Alan Pitcairn/Grant Heilman Photography; *b.* © Harald Sund. 532: Grant Heilman Photography. 534: Richard Legeckis. 536: Peter Britton. 538: E. Streichan/Shostal Associates. 539: IMAGERY.

Chapter 23 542: Lewis Trusty/Animals, Animals/Earth Scenes. 544: E.R. Degginger. 545: David Overcash/Bruce Coleman. 547: *l., m.* E.R. Degginger; *r.* © George Whitely/Photo Researchers, Inc. 549: © Tom McHugh/Photo Researchers, Inc. 550: *l.* Alan Pitcairn/Grant Heilman Photography. *r.* Holt Confer/Grant Heilman Photography. 551: *t.* E.R. Degginger; *b.* A. Rakoczy/Shostal Associates. 552: Robert D. Ballard/Woods Hole Oceanographic Institution. 554: *l.* W.T. Allen/ Deepsea Ventures; *r.* Woods Hole Oceanographic Institution. 555: The Granger Collection. 556: Susan Kadar/Woods Hole Oceanographic Institution. 558: *t.l.* © J. Fields/Photo Researchers, Inc.; *b.l.* © Bill Curtsinger/Photo Researchers, Inc. *r.* Rod Catanack/Woods Hole Oceanographic Institution. 559: *t.* Dudley Foster/Woods Hole Oceanographic Institution; *b.* Klein Associates. 560: *t.* Deep Sea Drilling Project; *b.* Al Driscoll/Woods Hole Oceanographic Institution. 564: *l.* Bob Evans/Peter Arnold, Inc.; *r.* Tom Pantages.

1 2 3 4 5 6 7 8 9 10—RRD—95 94 93 92 91 90 89 88 87 86